Chassis Design
Principles and Analysis

**Based on previously unpublished
technical notes by
Maurice Olley**

To Bill Milliken
Maurice Olley
Feb 15/65

Chassis Design
Principles and Analysis

**Based on previously unpublished
technical notes by
Maurice Olley**

William F. Milliken

Douglas L. Milliken

Society of Automotive Engineers, Inc.
Warrendale, PA

Library of Congress Cataloging-in-Publication Data

Milliken, William F., 1911-
    Chassis design : principles and analysis / William F. Milliken,
Douglas L. Milliken.
      p. cm.
"Based on previously unpublished technical notes by Maurice Olley."
Includes bibliographical references (p.) and indexes.
    ISBN 0-7680-0826-3
    1. Automobiles—Chassis—Design and construction. 2. Olley,
Maurice, 1889-1972. I. Milliken, Douglas L., 1954- II. Olley,
Maurice, 1889-1972. III. Society of Automotive Engineers. IV. Title.

TL255.M47 2002
629.2'4—dc21

2001057782

Published by: Society of Automotive Engineers, Inc.
                 400 Commonwealth Drive
                 Warrendale, PA 15096-0001 U.S.A.
                 Phone: (724)776-4841
                 Fax: (724)776-5760
                 E-mail: publications@sae.org
                 http://www.sae.org

ISBN 0-7680-0826-3

SAE Order No. R-206

Foreword

From the USA:

Maurice Olley was a really nice guy and the most respected engineer I have ever known. I valued the time I was fortunate to have spent with him.

I don't know what else he was but he was an engineer. He had a walloping background and experience in engineering. He was key in the development of the early automobile. He was also the key to the development of the [*Packard*] Rolls Royce Merlin V-12 engine that powered our WWII P-51 fighter.

He was articulate and funny. He was a quiet and attentive listener. He spoke and drew pictures. His perspectives of parts and assemblies, of about anything—that did or might move—were unmatched. His skills with words and pencil made him easy to understand.

The thing that most accounted for his effectiveness was his skill as a communicator. He was neither arrogant nor humble. He spoke and drew pictures. In any company, his question/answer ratio was about one. It was invariably an informative and pleasant experience for all, including Maurice.

The most rewarding for me was to have been a part of two or more guys leaving the table with an idea that nobody had brought to it.

I was fortunate to have inherited the tools and the craftsmen that Maurice had assembled in the process of setting up Chevrolet's first Research and Development operation.

When he retired, at his asking, I kept his files in the little conference room, off my office. Periodically he would stop by to paw around—not for me or anybody else—but for himself. He often came out to show me something: something old and funny, interesting, informative.

I liked Maurice Olley. He was one of my all-time favorite guys. I learned a lot from him—and he learned a lot from the sum of all of us.

Frank Winchell
September 12, 1998

We wish to point out that Frank Winchell welcomed Olley back to Chevrolet R&D when he returned after retirement. Frank broke all the rules and gave Olley a desk and secretary, which enabled Olley to write the technical notes that are the substance of this book.

From England:

This review of the work and achievements of Maurice Olley is timely—indeed, overdue. He himself was the very reverse of a self-publicist, and it is only right that his name and his many attainments should be recorded high in the list of those who laid the foundations of automobile design and engineering.

He was gifted with unusual clarity, breadth and depth of thinking, but, unlike some of his contemporaries, he was never dogmatic. Indeed, he always displayed a rare degree of mental flexibility, as exemplified by a comment he made during a technical discussion in 1945, "I do not agree with some of the author's statements, but then I cannot imagine any paper written by anybody, including myself, with which I could agree for very long."

At the end of the 20th century, a relatively few international companies dominated the global automobile industry, a state of affairs vastly different from that which existed during Olley's working life, when vehicle design developments were generally carried on by dozens of individual companies working, metaphorically speaking, behind high walls. His personal philosophy, however, was one of openness, particularly where questions of safety were concerned, and his published papers bear witness to this.

Apart from his engineering talent, Maurice Olley was a master of a somewhat different art—the ability to illustrate his argument with a sometimes gentle, sometimes sharp, but always apt aphorism. It is a matter for regret that those bon mots cannot now be collected in a book! Lacking his ability in aphorism, we can only venture a serious and sincere equivalent:

It is high time that we placed on record the great debt that we owe to Maurice Olley.

Reginald Main
Ian Milburn
David Crolla
England, 1998

Many of Olley's aphorisms, referred to in the USA as Olleyisms, have been used as chapter quotes in this book and in Race Car Vehicle Dynamics.

Authors' Preface

"Maurice Olley is a natural phenomenon that Britain has shared somewhat reluctantly with the USA."

Reg Main
IMechE, London

This book stems from our firsthand knowledge of Maurice Olley's accomplishments and his method of working. Maurice Olley was an automobile designer all his life, but unlike many other well-known designers, he was equally experimental **and** analytical. As he approached the various aspects of design during his long career, his objective was always to develop an analytical model and experimentally validate it. With that done, he proceeded to methodically document the results for future use. He worked at a fundamental level and, since the same handling problems constantly recur, the principles he developed are **as valid today as when first developed**.

Almost single-handedly, Maurice Olley developed the concepts and techniques that underlie the engineering approach to vehicle dynamics that we know today. Early on, he focused on the problems of ride, absorbed the analytical work by Rowell and Guest (see Chapter 5), and constructed his "k^2 rig," which enabled him to subjectively evaluate the ride modes and different frequencies of the front and rear suspension. This experimental work led directly to the flat ride concept and the need for a softer suspension on the front. This in turn led to the independent front suspension, which he pioneered at Cadillac in 1932.[1] In order to understand suspension systems he promoted the first force and moment tire tests by Cap Evans at Goodyear and Dr. A.W. Bull at Uniroyal, which ultimately led to the development of comprehensive testing machines at Cornell Aeronautical Laboratory (CAL, now Calspan) and General Motors. Armed with tire data, he was able to tackle the problems of directional stability and control, and suspension design, in conjunction with his early circular skid pad tests. This led to the concept of over and understeer and the significance of slip and steer angles which have dominated our view of car control ever since. His analysis of suspension geometry, the distribution of the roll couple, use of anti-roll bars to control the directional response, the effect of anti-dive and squat, brake distribution, and so forth, followed. In every one of these areas, including the various dynamic oscillations of the unsprung mass, he made critical contributions. Finally, he was responsible for the initiation of the long-term handling research at CAL which led to the equations of motion and an understanding of the transient response.

Olley's technical notes form the basis for this book; these cover his analytical developments, underlying experiments and design experience.

---

[1] See Appendix E for more historical detail.

Vehicle dynamics, as related to the automobile, has been under development for more than 70 years. Because it is a multi-disciplinary subject it has seldom been included in the curriculum of engineering colleges, although courses have appeared in specialized automotive schools. The teaching of vehicle dynamics has been further hampered by lack of adequate textbooks.

In our earlier book, *Race Car Vehicle Dynamics* (RCVD), we presented a summary of vehicle dynamics technology as a consistent way of looking at the vehicle portion of the driver-vehicle handling problem. In RCVD we tried to follow a path between a theoretical textbook and a more popular book on handling. Thus the mathematics was kept to a modest level while focusing on physical understanding.

We were somewhat surprised, but gratified, when a number of engineering colleges adopted our book as the basic text for an introductory undergraduate course. In several cases this resulted from student interest and involvement in Formula SAE race car development. To further this interest, we were requested by SAE to produce the problems in the RCVD Workbook[2] along with the answers. RCVD has also been used as the text for several professional development seminars in vehicle dynamics.

The first part of RCVD deals with fundamental concepts, while the second part is devoted to specific problem areas that are encountered in vehicle handling design. For the student or practicing engineer who wishes to become a competent professional vehicle dynamicist and designer, more extensive study of the subjects covered in the second part of RCVD is required. To meet this need, we now offer the present volume, *Chassis Design: Principles and Analysis*, based on the technical notes of Maurice Olley. We believe this material will be useful to engineers in industry and racing who are involved with handling analysis and design, and also as an advanced text for graduate-level study in universities.

As vehicle dynamicists, we feel a great deal of gratitude toward Maurice Olley and are immensely pleased to be able to publish this first major technical book on his accomplishments. The details involved in making this material available to a wider audience are covered in a separate section, **Origins and Objectives**.

Bill Milliken
Doug Milliken

---

[2] Metz, Daniel L., W. F. Milliken, and D. L. Milliken, *Race Car Vehicle Dynamics Workbook*, R-212, Society of Automotive Engineers, Warrendale, Pa., 1998.

Origins and Objectives

"Today's work is a wonderful thing, its absence is the curse of retirement."

Maurice Olley
c. 1955

Maurice Olley is generally recognized as the most outstanding pioneer and innovator in the ride and handling area. Thus it is an astounding fact that the most comprehensive technical account of his accomplishments as written by Olley himself has remained under wraps for nearly 40 years. The present volume is the result of our continued efforts to make this material available to the practicing engineer, to members of the racing fraternity and the automotive enthusiast.

The story began when Maurice Olley was officially retired in 1955 at the age of 66 from his position as head of Chevrolet Research and Development. Following a career that paralleled the development of the automobile on two continents, the idea of retirement was completely repugnant to him, and after a few years of travel and consulting he returned to Motor City and reappeared at his old location in Chevrolet. Frank Winchell, his successor at R&D, was never one to stand on ceremony or convention, and since he viewed Olley as "the most knowledgeable automotive engineer he had ever known," welcomed him back on an informal basis, setting him up with a desk and secretarial help as well as moving in Olley's old technical files.

At first, Maurice would appear at R&D on a sporadic basis, "browse through his old stuff," and enliven Frank with interesting and amusing things that occurred in the development of the automobile and the airplane. Later he became more focused and by the early 1960s had begun the preparation of a series of monograph reports (ultimately totaling four volumes of over 500 typed pages with some 300 graphs and sketches) encompassing his entire chassis design experience. These monographs are titled:

- Notes on Suspensions—August 1961
- Steady State Steering—September 1961
- Notes on Vehicle Handling—February 1962
- Suspension Notes II—May 1962

Olley completed a final monograph, "Brake Theory," in July 1962. In 120 pages and 40-odd figures, it covers fundamentals of drum brakes, disk brakes and related topics such as brake heating. Brake design and analysis has become a highly specialized discipline, which now includes metallurgy as well as the geometric fundamentals that Olley treats, and we have chosen to exclude this material.

Restricted Publication—A limited number of these monographs were published internally by General Motors carrying the classification, "GM Restricted, Corporation Use Only." Because of Olley's fame, rumors of the existence of these reports circulated within the industry. Over time, some copies reached interested individuals in other companies where they were highly prized and provided the knowledge base for a number of burgeoning chassis engineers. But the monographs were never officially released for general publication and distribution.

I (Bill Milliken) met Maurice Olley in 1952, when we started a long-term handling research program at Cornell Aeronautical Laboratory, under the sponsorship of General Motors. This association continued at a professional and personal level to the time of Olley's death in 1972. During that period, Maurice gave us a complete set of the Chevrolet monographs plus copies of other early technical material on ride and handling. In addition, a lively correspondence devoted to car control and stability flourished throughout those years.

First Publication Attempt—Our first attempt to place this Olley material in the open literature occurred in 1968 when the Research Laboratory Division of General Motors, with the full support of Edward N. Cole, President, gave a contract to the Vehicle Research Department of Cornell Aeronautical Laboratory (CAL) to produce a technical biography of Olley which would include the Chevrolet monographs. Olley was genuinely pleased with this recognition and offered his full support. Our staff, including King D. Bird, David W. Whitcomb and Fred Dell'Amico, enthusiastically pursued the project, contacted many former associates of Olley for their input, and by mid-1968 had an initial draft in hand. Among Olley's associates was William (Bill) Lichty. Beginning in 1957, Olley had lectured on suspension and handling at the General Motors Institute where he met Lichty, then the director of Research and Graduate Studies. In the 1958–1962 period, Lichty had begun work on a biography of Olley, which would have included Olley's "Reminiscences," and his technical notes and papers. This was discontinued and Lichty graciously offered to share the results of his efforts with the Cornell project.

As the draft was readied for submission (1969), the contract was summarily canceled by GM Legal. In the period 1963–1968, GM had been heavily involved in the Corvair litigation and with some justification believed that anything published on handling, however fundamental and factual, could be misconstrued and used against them. Olley, who was to die only a few years later, was immensely saddened by this action.

Present Publication—After writing *Race Car Vehicle Dynamics* (RCVD), it occurred to us that these long-suppressed reports would make a natural companion piece. This was reinforced when Terry Satchell (a contributor to RCVD) asked us to reproduce Olley's original monographs for distribution to some of his co-workers at Pontiac and other parts of General Motors. Olley's material would be complementary in the sense that RCVD lays emphasis on basic handling theory and analysis, while Olley approaches vehicle dynamics with a strong orientation toward design and application. In fact, the analytical developments in RCVD rest on the ideas and concepts developed earlier by Olley and his associates. As a designer he was first interested in acquiring a physical understanding of handling behavior through experiments, after which he developed procedures useful for chassis design and layout.

Thanks to Olley's erudition, his natural ability as a teacher and the fundamental nature of the material, the monographs are as valuable and useful today as when they were written. **For those who wish to understand the fundamentals of chassis design and analysis, this is the place to start.** In addition, we find them inspiring from an historical standpoint. They show how untiring curiosity and the dedicated application of simple experimentation, sound engineering judgment and clear thinking—to an immensely complex problem—can accomplish much. The Olley approach has a great deal in common with that of the Wright Brothers.

Permission and Copyright—Thirty years after publication of the first book was aborted we reopened the project. To obtain a release from General Motors, we first contacted Frank Winchell, now retired from his position as Vice President, GM Engineering Staff. Winchell had recently received the Chairman Award from General Motors, the first and only recipient of this prestigious honor for his outstanding technical contributions. Frank in turn approached Thomas Gottschalk, GM's chief general counsel, who initiated the release through the intellectual property section of the legal staff. In due time, we were "granted permission to re-publish these works without any compensation to General Motors," the only requirement being that the publication, "state that the reports are reprinted with the permission of General Motors." Armed with this release, we approached the Society of Automotive Engineers (SAE International) who agreed to publish the Olley book under an identical arrangement and to an even better level of quality than RCVD.

Approach and Philosophy—In the four reports Olley frequently covers the same aspect of design but in different contexts. As they stand the monographs are not an ideal reference, although they may be chronologically correct in terms of their original development. Furthermore, there is some duplication in the four volumes. We have integrated the four monographs into one book, eliminated duplication and consolidated related material, including the integration of additional Olley material from his other publications and correspondence. In this task we have been exceptionally careful to faithfully reproduce Olley's writings. *Departures and comments are in italics and/or in square brackets* [ ]. For legibility and consistency, the figures and equations have been redone. Olley was a great sketcher and our artist has faithfully copied Olley's sketches as printed in the original monographs. Some inconsistencies in mathematical notation occur in the four volumes; we have attempted to eliminate these and make the notation similar to that of RCVD. Detailed derivations have been added wherever it seemed it would improve the understanding of Olley's mathematical developments. The monographs are Olley's technical testament and in making changes we have always asked ourselves, "Would Maurice have approved?"

It is well to remember when reading this book that it is not only a classical review of the state of the art of handling design but that the greater part of the technology upon which it rests was developed by Olley and his associates in the Cadillac Group at the General Motors Proving Ground. They appear to have been directly responsible for most of the ride and handling concepts developed in this book. Olley was personally responsible for the introduction of the independent front suspension in the USA and the idea of the "flat ride." His foresight enabled the extension of his work into transient analysis in the Cornell Aeronautical Laboratory (CAL) program.

Broader recognition of Maurice Olley is long overdue. His career demonstrates that one creative and inspired individual can influence an industry, for it can truthfully be said that his work has had a positive effect on the ride and handling of every car on the road. It is a privilege to publish this first major book on this portion of Olley's work.

Bill Milliken
Doug Milliken
March 2001

Acknowledgements

We wish to acknowledge the help we received from Frank J. Winchell (retired, GM Vice-President, Engineering Staff), Thomas A. Gottschalk (at the time, Director, GM Legal Staff), Kenneth D. Enborg (Intellectual Property Section, GM Legal Staff), and Barbara Kunkel (GM Librarian). As a result of their efforts, in July 1996 we were granted permission to republish the work of Maurice Olley "without any compensation to General Motors." GM requested "that the SAE publication state that the reports are reprinted with permission of General Motors."

Working with SAE is always a pleasure. We wish to thank the SAE publishing staff and in particular Judy Wieber, our editor, Terry Wilson, the book designer, Robert Richardson, for the index, and Ann Moats, publicity. Also, Peggy Holleran Greb and Jeff Worsinger for their contributions.

A project of this size required a team effort by Milliken Research Associates:

As with *Race Car Vehicle Dynamics* (RCVD), Robb Ramsey, working under a contract with SAE, produced all of the figures. Robb scanned Olley's original figures, traced them on the computer to give a consistent appearance, updated the terminology, and as usual, cheerfully agreed to many revisions. Robb also produced numerous drafts of the cover art.

Also under a contract with SAE, our MRA Associate, Edward M. Kasprzak, took on the daunting task of typesetting Olley's original math, at the same time reworking it to use updated symbols corresponding to RCVD. As part of this effort, he derived the "missing steps" in a number of Olley's mathematical developments, a first-order detective job. Finally, Edward proofread all the chapters and made many useful suggestions.

R. Thomas Bundorf was a member of the original vehicle dynamics group in the Engineering Mechanics Department, GM Research Laboratories, in the 1950s and '60s, under Joseph Bidwell. Tom found out about our Olley project at the first SAE Automotive Dynamics & Stability Conference in the spring of 2000. At that time, he volunteered to review the drafts of two critical chapters—"Ride" (Chapter 5) and "Linkages" (Chapter 7). His very thorough review led to several important revisions as well as a number of smaller corrections.

David J. Segal, a longtime MRA Associate, was helpful in a number of cases where Olley "stumped" us with some of his more difficult derivations. Up until the time of his sudden death, Hugo S. Radt contributed to Olley's tire modeling section and his work is the basis of Appendix B.

Our good friend, Dr. A. E. Moulton, of Moulton Developments and Alex Moulton Bicycles, Ltd. was kind enough to review Olley's Chronology (in Chapter 1) and provide a number of comments based on his experience and his research at Rolls-Royce Heritage Trust, of which he is a member.

We wish to thank all the above members of the MRA team.

Frank J. Winchell wrote the USA Foreword in his usual direct and forceful style, based on his close association with Maurice Olley. Winchell was Olley's successor as Director of Chevrolet Research and Development. The Foreword from England was generously contributed by Reginald Main, IMechE Automobile Division (retired); Ian Milburn, Deputy Managing Director, Nissan European Technology Centre; and David A. Crolla, Professor of Automotive Engineering, University of Leeds.

Photos were contributed by:

William Holleran, Archivist, Kettering/GMI Alumni Foundation
Thomas C. Clarke, independent Rolls-Royce historian
Michael H. Evans, Chairman, Rolls-Royce Heritage Trust
L. Kirk Walters, a devoted Olley enthusiast and historian

We were assisted in finding copies of some of Olley's technical papers and correspondence by Anne Etherington, IMechE; Rosemary E. Grimes, Professional Engineering Publishers, Publishers to the IMechE; and Jeff Worsinger, SAE.

An earlier attempt to publish a technical biography of Maurice Olley was initiated by Joseph Bidwell, GM, in a contract to Cornell Aeronautical Laboratory (CAL) in the 1960s. Some preliminary work was completed before the project was canceled. We have been able to take advantage of this material and wish to acknowledge Joe Bidwell and the original authors at CAL—King D. Bird, David W. Whitcomb, and Fred Dell'Amico.

William (Bill) Lichty, formerly at General Motors Technical Institute, arranged for Maurice Olley to lecture to his students in 1956–1958, after Olley's retirement. Bill has been prominent in preserving the Olley heritage and was a major force in locating the Olley diaries and other material for the GMI/Kettering University Archives. Bill made available to us his extensive correspondence with Olley and has been a source of continuing support throughout this project.

Dr. Charles W. McCutcheon, formerly of the National Institutes of Health, carried on an extensive correspondence with Olley in his later years, and gave us copies of his Olley file.

As with *Race Car Vehicle Dynamics*, Barbara A. Milliken was a great support throughout this project.

William F. Milliken
Douglas L. Milliken
March 2001

Contents

In this book, plain text is by Olley, *italic text was added by the authors.*

Plates

Figures

Tables

CHAPTER 1

Maurice Olley–
His Life and Times

"The entire history of mechanical engineering is of learning from failure. The prima donna type of mind is useless in engineering."

Maurice Olley
c. 1955

1.1 Reminiscences

In the area of automobile ride and handling, Maurice Olley produced more "history" than almost anyone else. Nevertheless, he was extremely conscious of what had gone on before. He viewed his career and accomplishments on a "continuum" of historical events that went back to the evolution of roads, to horse-drawn wagons, steam-powered self-propelled vehicles, the internal combustion engine and other technological developments that preceded his own work.

Maurice Olley never wrote a book-length autobiography but he did produce a brief story of his life in "Reminiscences," which is reproduced here exactly as he wrote it, hand printed in the usual format of his correspondence. This was written in 1957 when he was 68 years old. These "Reminiscences" were written for a presentation to the General Motors Institute faculty at the request of Bill Lichty.

Following Olley's "Reminiscences," we present some other autobiographical material. In 1958 he prepared a chronological summary of his career in sufficient detail that one can follow his engineering activities and his associates as he moved back and forth across the Atlantic for Rolls Royce and later General Motors.

In his "Reminiscences" Olley mentions that he was practically raised on the Holyhead Road, "a great historic road on the island (Great Britain), up which the Roman military supplies came to Chester and The Wall." Since this road and its use by the early horseless carriages so prominently influenced the direction of Olley's career, Bill Milliken once asked Olley to expound on the history of the road and the events that followed. The answer is so characteristic of the sweep and breadth of Olley's approach to his life's work that we include it here.

Following the Holyhead Road story, is a note on Olley's associates, based on a letter to Bill Milliken. This chapter ends with some introductory and historical material taken from the four monographs.

Maurice Olley, c.1914, on the eve of WWI while working as a draftsman/designer at LeCanadel for Sir Henry Royce. Photo credit Kettering/GMI Alumni Foundation, Collection of Industrial History.

<u>Reminiscences</u>   Feb 16/57

I recall a talk given by Kettering in 1944 to SAE students on the unusual theme, for Ket, of "Don't underestimate the Past — Don't overestimate the future". As always, it was a masterpiece of clear thinking, delivered in homely language which only thinly disguised the erudition behind it.

I feel that in this country we do tend to fall into both these errors, and it gives us the unhappy sensation of travelling in a brief bright interval between a foggy past and an equally foggy future. In Britain, on the other hand, though the future may seem even more obscure (and there is less conviction of a "bright new world") there is in general a better sense of direction, from knowledge of what has gone before. The presentation before British technical societies of papers of reminiscences is not intended merely to rouse a nostalgic interest. These papers convey a sense of direction.

I still recall my first arrival in this country in July of 1917, after 12 days spent in dodging submarines across the Atlantic. I had the impression then of a break in the continuity, of being the Sleeper in H. G. Wells' "The Sleeper Wakes", and of being transported 100 years into the future. So one must think of Britain in 1900 as being part of a world of 150, rather than just 50 years ago.

Yet, strangely enough, it was also a world in which many things we regard as new today, were already old, and some of them half forgotten.

For example, the turnpike road had been a feature of the British scene throughout the 18th century, until an exasperated public had burned the toll-gates. And that is why Britain, has no turnpike roads today.

Almost every literate Britain of the Napoleonic period appears to have kept a diary, and some of these note the balloons drifting over the British countryside and speculate how long it will be before the seaports are closed and the entire island becomes a landing field for aircraft.

And the steam-driven coach had run on the highroads up till about 1835 in competition with the new railways, until a Parliament which had railway stocks in its pockets had legislated them out of existence.

One can understand therefore the typical British attitude toward any new development, that it was tried years ago, and didn't work.

At the start of the 20th century (which, of course was 1901, and not 1900 - I still remember the arguments in press and parlor) we liked to believe that the world had reached a condition of equilibrium. It is true there were some dissentiant voices, but they came mostly from poor and ignorant people, or from weak and backward nations. So we paid no attention to them.

We admired the gay mid-century cynicism of Gilbert & Sullivan, but we read Rudyard Kipling, and believed in Imperial Destiny and the White Man's Burden. Also we considered ourselves far in advance economically of the rest of the world, because we had achieved Free Trade in combination with Prosperity, and were the one large nation with negligible tariff-barriers. It was true that our imports were than our exports, but this was nothing to worry about, since the "unfavorable" balance merely represented the effect of our enormous invest. ments in every country of the world.

In the past century the essentially British recip- rocating steam engine, fed with steam from British boilers, and fed largely with British steam-coal, had pushed its way over the entire land & water surface of the globe, and had exploited the world to our immense profit.

Our own island was dominated by the steam rail- ways to the almost complete extinction of every other form of transportation. The magnificent highway and canal systems lay silent and dead, pa- thetic examples of the folly of the 18th century, which had not had the foresight to wait for steam

I was born in Yorkshire, but removed at 4 years old to North Wales, and was raised practically on the Holyhead Road. This is the highway from London along which the Royal Mail coaches had travelled with the Irish mail, before the railways came. It is one of the great historic roads of the island, meeting up on the English plain with the great Roman road sys- tem, up which the military supplies came to Chester and The Wall, the very frontier of civilization.

And this highway lay white and silent, grass-grown along the edges, and almost empty of life. It serv- ed as a convenient playground, and cycle track, a connecting road for farmers, and useful for driv- ing sheep and cattle to market.

But at the turn of the century the Holyhead road began to show signs of reviving life. What young boy would not have been interested in these strange new vehicles, conducted by people wearing goggles & overalls, usually very dirty? The contraptions were obviously unreliable.   They frequently stood at the roadside, regarded skeptically by their owners. Then, after furious effort with a starting handle, which looked like winding up an oversize clockwork toy, would burst into heaving life, and explode themselves away out of sight.

Frequently also they suffered a complete break-down, and then their component parts became scattered around them in the dust.

For, amongst other objectionable features, the pneumatic tires on the cars were tearing our roads to pieces.   These roads, surfaced in the 1780s with a beautiful mosaic of finely graded granite to the appearance of a bathroom floor, were bonded by nothing but the dampness of the climate. Yet the hooves of horses and steel tires of carts had done no damage to them for a century.   The pneumatic tires of a few motor cars ground them to dust in five years.

So then came the tarring of the roads, and our beautiful white highways turned a dirty grey. More objections from a public already incensed against "scorchers" and "road hogs"!

Basic objections also from experienced engineers, risen in defense of the manifest destiny of the reciprocating steam engine.   I think that, in Britain at least, around 1900, steam would have been voted "most likely to succeed."

What engineer with even the rudiments of technical knowledge would see any future in a revival of the humble gas engine?   How could one expect reliable power from a prime mover in which one lit a fire inside a smoothly machined and lubricated cylinder? In which also you got only one working stroke out of four?   In which the piston itself was expected

to work as the crosshead? In which one
cooled the walls of the furnace-cylinder, thus
throwing away the heat and promoting condensa-
tion?

The characteristics of such an abortion were that
it was not even self-starting, but had to be furious-
ly hand turned until it chose to take life. And its
lugging power was entirely lacking, so that a box
behind the engine contained gears which had to
be thrown sideways into and out of engagement at
speed.

There was certainly room for skepticism. And actually the early steam cars were a dream of quiet
power by comparison. Strange that in Britain, after
over a century of experience we never learned to
make a reliable boiler!

The predicted short life of the gasoline engine
did not come true. Races on the Continent, in
Ireland, and the Isle of Man, and reliability trials
up to 15000 miles in Britain, gradually showed the
engineering experts they were wrong. And I think
the thing that really clinched it was the incredible
performance of the airplanes in World War I, which
frequently flew home 100 miles with radiators shot
through and bullets through the crankcase. Obviously real power could be produced for long periods
with unequalled reliability at a weight per horsepower
never approached before. And finally in 1918 the
Atlantic was crossed in a non-stop flight from New-
foundland to Ireland.

In these years I had hammered through the Senior
Central Welsh Board examinations in mathematics,
languages, analytical chemistry, etc, and in a year at

the University of Manchester had acquired an attack of influenza which invalided me out and sent me to farming for a year to recuperate.

Then to Birmingham, a vastly more likeable city, for the apprenticeship which in those days (1907) was the indispensable training for an engineer. (H. W. Ward & Co. machine tool builders, Birmingham)

These were the days of Edward VII (I saw him in Birmingham when he came to "open" the new Cadbury chocolate factory and model village. Six cream colored horses with postilions in medieval costumes, and himself in field marshall's plumes)

Victoria had just seen the old century out, and the Victorian Era had died with her, to be replaced by the Edwardian, essentially similar in its self-complacency, but more lushly exotic in its decorations, and more openly non-rigid in its morals.

And strangely we, the people, were being led away from our century old fear of France, to a fear and distrust of Germany in the form of "the Kaiser".

In several family visits to northern France & Belgium I had become well acquainted with these good people.   It still seemed extraordinarily clever of quite young children to talk fluent French to each other, and, when we shyly tried our own version of the language, extremely clever and polite of them to understand us. Before long it was strange to find oneself thinking in French.

There seemed little the matter with the French

except that a lot of them were extremely poor, and that none of them appeared to have the respectful attitude toward their own government that we had toward ours. But evidently this was due to living in a republic!

Also they had never heard of our historic victories over them, and showed us battle paintings of their victories over us, which our history books had forgotten to mention. It was all quite strange. Apparently there was a national viewpoint which changed completely when one just made the 20 mile trip across the Channel.

In Belgium and Holland we visited the beautiful small Dutch town of Sluys, now some miles inland, but the scene of Edward III's naval victory over the French fleet. Not only does national viewpoint change, but the very land changes. The farm where I recuperated from college is now eaten away by the sea.

The long five years of apprenticeship in Birmingham was over at last. I thought I had learned to work at school, always a 6 day week and in the last few years nearly always a day which lasted till 10 at night. But at Birmingham it was 6.30 in the morning, breakfast at 8, work till 6, and then evening classes! No 8 hour day then, and no 5 day week!

Somewhat surprisingly in November of 1912, I found myself at work in the drawing office of Rolls Royce Ltd at Derby, being groomed for a possible job with Royce himself at his place in the south of France.

On the advice of a distant relative, a manufacturer of ammunition, I had been apprenticed, not -

Gents in baggy trousers—Albert G. Elliot (E), left, and Maurice Olley (Oy), right, outside the house at which they were lodging, "Buena Vista," St. Margaret's Bay, Kent, 1914. At the time Henry Royce had moved to St. Margaret's Bay after parting from his wife and was in rented accommodations before owning a house in the village. When the blackout occurred in September 1914, Oy and E were the two senior designers resident with Royce and helped him design his first aero engine, the V-12 Eagle.

Elliot rose to become chief engineer of Rolls-Royce after Sir Henry died in 1933. In 1937 when Ernest Hives became director and general manager he made E the chief engineer of the Aero Division and asked Maurice Olley if he would return to Rolls-Royce as Chief Engineer, Chassis Division. Olley felt committed to General Motors and declined. Photo credit Rolls-Royce Heritage Trust.

in the automobile trade at which I was aiming, but in the manufacture of machine tools. As it proved, this was a good step. It was based on the idea that before one can design anything one has to know how it will be made.

Consequently I went to Royce in April 1913 as a tool designer. And one of the first jobs was to design a milling fixture for the machining all over of automobile connecting rods! (An indication, this, of why RRLtd gravitated naturally into the manufacture of aircraft engines.)

I still recall that journey south through Paris, and the "blue train" to Toulon, where the harbor was still obstructed by the hulk of the battleship which had spontaneously exploded at anchor the year before.

Then the long slow trip along the coast by the metre-gauge coastal train with the Mediterranean creaming below the yellow cliffs. Everything amazingly blue and gold, and a quality of sunshine never before dreamed of.

Working for Royce was a training in engineering, in manufacturing method, and in design. Modern engineers seldom draw. Royce drew and sketched constantly, took a drawing board to bed with him to put down an idea as soon as it waked him up.

Overall vehicle design, or "styling" never appealed to him. His concern was with the chassis. If the coach builder couldn't put a decent body on it, try another coach builder.

But engine details, transmission design, axles and steering, and the design of tools to make every part, flowed from his sketches continually. In 1918 he gave me an exact description of detonation in a combustion chamber, a thing that was never <u>seen</u> till ultra high speed movies were taken 25 years later. In 1914 he described exactly the faults of self-energised brake design, the extreme sensitivity to changes in coefficient - a thing which is not fully appreciated after 40 years.

All the electrical parts of the car were designed by Royce and made by RRLtd, except the spark plugs and magneto. And presently we were designing generators, and electric starters with planetary reduction gears.

Later in 1913 we were driving north through France on the way home. One of the machined con rods broke and came out through the side of the crankcase. We were rescued by two French motorists in an incredibly noisy touring car, and one realised that French drivers like to hear things happening. Finished the journey by train, and the car limped home to Derby on five pistons and a blanked-off cylinder.

By November I was back on the Riviera, designing electrical fittings, camshaft grinding machines, new installations for the buildings on the estate, drawing office furniture for local manufacture. There were rumblings of war which the French took very philosoph-ically. To them it was just "more of the same".

Drove back again in July 1914. This time successfully except for nine tire blowouts in one afternoon.

Then came WWI and the trips to sunny France were over. Royce had settled near Dover, and we saw the French fleet going out before Britain had declared, and the embark-ation of the first British troops to cross the channel.

There was a confused period when we young draftsmen were trying to get jobs as despatch riders, or in the artillery. Many valuable men were lost to the armed forces. Then we were told to wait, and the demand came for reliable engines to fly either in airplanes or in dirig-ibles. There was no aircraft engine made in Britain, and part of the job was up to RR Ltd.

Late nights and seven day weeks in Royce's villa where a drawing office of sorts had been produced with the aid of gasoline lamps in a few hours. Drafting boards prop-ped up on books and filing cabinets made from cartons. Zeppelin's came over and dropped bombs on open fields and 200 year old graveyards. Then a retired butcher invented a bullet which would strike like a match on the skin of a Zeppelin, and the dirigible was seen once or twice as a fall-ing torch and then no more.

Torpedoings occurred almost daily out in the Channel, and drifting mines, and destroyer fights at night. Broken ships were beached below the headlands, the beaches were barred off with wire, and black with oil, cluttered with wreckage.

And we went on designing engine details and now also planetary reduction gears for tractor airscrews.

We saw our first engines flying across the channel. One of the first pilots lost his way and landed at Lille when he was heading for St. Omer, with only a description of the ancient fortifications to go by. He found himself cordially entertained by the Luftwaffe, and shortly after we read in the German press the most appreciative description of the Rolls Royce aircraft engine!

(But of course our designs still remained on the "classified" list.)

There came the news that the Americans wanted to make our engines. Mr. Johnson of RR Ltd was in the States and had negotiated a contract. One of my chief desires had been to get to the States, even in my Birmingham apprenticeship days. And my first five year contract with RR Ltd, signed in 1913, had stated that I should spend 3 months of each year in the USA.

Actually in July 1914 tickets were bought for the first trip, which was to be first to Stuttgart to see magneto manufacture at Robert Bosch, and then from Marseilles to New York. The war cancelled that, but here was my chance! Royce agreed "for 8 months only". 1917

The 6000 ton Andania out of Liverpool late in June, on a grey evening. 50 passengers aboard. Only two women. Strict instructions not to go to bed, preferably to stay awake with lifebells on

When I woke up after an excellent night's sleep we were at anchor, and I found we were back at the gate of the very dock we had started from. It gradually came out that the ship immediately ahead, a liner for the Far East, had been torpedoed and sunk off the Welsh coast, and we had run for it For three days we lay in Liverpool harbor with nothing to do but look at the waterfront.

On the fourth night we started again, and this time we made it, all the way across, without camouflage or convoy, in just less than two weeks. There were all sorts of close shaves, patrol boats warning us off certain channels north of Ireland, a sub. taking a look at us off the Irish coast, and deciding not to risk it, as there were destroyers around a sub. operating off Nantucket, and finally the boom closed at New York so we had to anchor all night in the open sea off Coney Island. Nearly 120 ships were torpedoed while we were crossing, and the Andania was sunk off Ireland in the next year.

Finally we arrived in New York on the hottest day of a hot summer and had to rush to buy some light clothing, in order to stay alive.

And the contract for RR aircraft engines had been cancelled! The USA was going to build nothing but Liberty engines, which,

miraculously designed in a session
of ten days and ten nights in an upper-
room by a committee of American engineers, was so immeasurably superior to
all others that there was just no chance for
argument!

I first met Henry Crane at the Crane Simplex
plant in New Brunswick. He was building
the French Hispano Suiza engine, but had
completely redesigned the con. rods; and as
a result had got the thing to run very well.

On the subject of the Liberty engine he was unconvinced.

It was October before I   saw the Liberty
engine, the first one, at the Bureau of Standards
in Washington. Major Vincent, in uniform, admitted
to severe damage to water pump drive and to the
ignition generator. I said he had a torsional
vibration. He thought he didn't. I said we had
one on the Eagle engine which had a better-
looking crankshaft, and one of my last jobs in
England had been listening to it with a stetho-
scope under the belly of the engine, and that
we had a damper that would cure it. He was
unconvinced.

The huge Liberty engine program got under
way. But there were corners left open, for us and
we were permitted to fill some of them. The
Franklin Co. in Syracuse made our planetary
reduction gears, FB Stearns in Cleveland
our engines, and a host of other contract-
ors made detail parts. After thousands
of Liberty engine parts had been made the

Chassis test of early Rolls-Royce, 1920, Olley at the wheel. Photo credit Kettering/GMI Alumni Foundation, Collection of Industrial History.

crankshafts broke and had to be redesigned. (No Liberty engine flew in France)
    Our chief office was in Cleveland, and I also had
an office in N. York. In Cleveland I met my
wife.
    But all over the Eastern States parts were
being made. Crankshaft forgings at Worcester
Mass. water pumps in Rhode Island. There was
no final assembly here. All the sub assemblies
went by sea to England, and, strangely, very
few were lost.
    In March 1918 it looked as though the
Germans might win. In November they lost.
And everything collapsed.
    Christmas was spent on the Atlantic on
the way home, prostrated with sea sickness.
By March I was back in New York, and during
the rest of 1919 that year was all over the East,
looking at vacant manufacturing plants. It
had been decided to build the cars in the
States.
    By November it was decided to buy the
wire wheel plant in Springfield Mass, and I
was married, and before Christmas we were
back in Britain, crossing on the captured
German "Imperator" (later the Berengaria) &
close to foundering in a 12 day passage.
    There followed ten years of a fruitless
struggle to make a success of a business
over-financed and wrongly conducted. It
became painfully evident that wealthy
Americans would put up with the incon-
veniences of an imported article, but had no

toleration for a domestic one. After ten years the handwriting was on the wall, and we were in Detroit (Nov. 1930)

Now came the most interesting period. For the past 25 years the engineers had ruled the roost. The uncertain contraption of 1905 had become the "classic" design of automobile, an almost perfectly reliable mechanism, built by engineers to please themselves, and with little or no regard for the passengers.

There had been sporadic attempts to make the vehicle ride decently, but little had been done. The rear passengers still functioned as ballast, stuck out behind the rear wheels. Steering was frequently unstable and the front axle with front brakes made shimmy almost inevitable. The engineers had made all the parts function excellently, but when put together the whole was seldom satisfactory.

So, from here onwards, there was a continual struggle to improve the vehicle as a whole. The history of this period has been written elsewhere.

In 1936 this took us back to England, for six months during which the 25 hp Vauxhall with indep. front suspension was launched. Britain looked good to us and especially London, the city which manages to be at the same time beautiful and comfortable.

On return, Detroit, with it's constant

fretting about yearly models, its strikes, and its climate, seemed the reverse of comfortable. And in the summer of 1937 we returned to Britain to get the new small car started. We sailed on the Empress of Britain from Quebec in a snowstorm in June, and out through Belle Isle Straits on a clear bright evening, into masses of fog. That evening the ship made a terrific swerve, and out of the fog to starboard there emerged the huge black stern of a freighter out of Liverpool. So we missed her. But three years later the beautiful Empress was at the bottom of the Atlantic with thousands of others.

If we had stayed in London we should undoubtedly have enjoyed Britain again. But we got a house in the northern suburbs, more convenient to Vauxhall, and that was a sad mistake. British suburban life, we concluded, is not a thing we appreciate.

Even Detroit looked good on our summer visit in 1938. At last, after nearly 9 years it seemed to be working its way back to something like prosperity. But the news from Europe was horrible and we were kept looking over our shoulder. Finally we cancelled our bookings on the Normandie, which sailed back empty in any case. We were three of only 50 passengers on the Nieue Amsterdam, the flagship of the Holland America Line. Halfway across it was decided to turn the ship around. But then came the news of Munich, and all was rejoicing. A Frenchman who was returning from an American pres-

entation of the Legion of Honor, was a
school teacher in Versailles and a reserve
pilot in the French Air Force. He confessed
his relief. He would have been called upon
to fly WWI biplanes with WWI engines, and
would not have had a chance. His opinion
of French military progress since 1919, and of
the wretched dependence on the Maginot Line,
was a revelation of how France had slipped,

Here was the old furious and sardonic con-
tempt of their own government, which I had
seen in France as a boy.

I had been to the German Opel plant in
1936 and again in 1938. In 1936 western Germany was prosperous, easy & comfortable. The trains were very clean & the
meals were excellent. By 1938 the whole
feeling had changed. Scurrilous anti-American
and anti-Roosevelt posters were everywhere.
Men were disappearing from the shops without
record and without trace. No one looked you
in the eye, and on every hand, on Rhine
steamers and in school courtyards, small
children were being put through military drills.
So I had no belief in Munich. And when we
landed off the Nieuve Amsterdam, and found
the trustful British actually believing in
"Peace in our Time", we could scarcely contain our annoyance.

Yet we must have caught the bug. In
spite of alarms in the papers, and night
maneuvers with searchlights and high flying

planes over London, we seem to have sunk into the universal fool's paradise. When we came over on our regular summer visit in 1939 there was no anxiety that I can remember. We brought just our summer clothes

Almost as soon as we landed Russia joined up with Germany, and the prospect of such an unholy alliance made Roosevelt cancel all American passports. We were trapped!

Followed a week or two of some confusion. Then Rolls Royce Ltd. found I was in the USA and cabled to ask whether I would do for them in WWII what I had done in WWI. I was generally considered a fool for saying yes. Oh, in WWI Wilson had broken his word, after promising to keep America out he had plunged America into it. But F.D.R. wasn't that sort of man at all. We were out, and he was going to keep us out, and business was going to be good. Well - if you insist - go to it - we will give you leave of absence.

There were 6 months of "phony war". During this time I bought small tools and machine tools for RR Ltd. out of my own pocket, till finally the British Treasury saved me from bankruptcy. I had to incorporate myself to avoid becoming a "foreign agent". I had to contend with the Zeiss people in New York who were buying up all Zeiss instruments to prevent the allies getting any of them. For months I felt like an international spy.

The phony war came to a sudden end and RRLtd, to preserve their records, filled an engine case with prints of all their drawings and sent them to Halifax N.S. consigned to me. Previously I had had only a few prints of the Merlin engine, obtained principally from the Cincinnati Milling M/c Co, and from these had been trying to persuade various American manufacturers to undertake parts-production. Now the scene was changing and there was discussion of manufacturing the complete engine in the U.S.A.   On the strength of these discussions the U.S. Treasury Dept. seized my case of drawings in Halifax and held it "somewhere in Washington" under military guard, thus completely stalling all constructive action for several weeks.   During this period Paris was being entered by the Germans & France had collapsed. England was to stand alone for the next 6 months facing Hitler with all Western Europe behind him.   Under these circumstances the delay appeared disastrous.

After a period of purgatory however it was decided that Ford would build the Merlin engine. All my activities were transferred to Dearborn for the next 2 months. The Merlin drawings, which had mysteriously appeared at Dayton, were released, and transferred to 'Gate 4'.

(The remainder of RRLtd's drawings were not released until months later)

At the end of two months, everything was

in the air again. Ford had refused the Merlin contract, and it was transferred to Packard, my office was moved back to the GM Bldg. and we started over again. Luckily Packard were well acquainted with the engine, having been approached as early as October 1939 to make parts, notably crankshafts.

Followed a period during which Packard got started on redrawing all engine details, extending the plant for new engine testcells finishing contract negotiations, and deciding some of the vital details of any such contract, such as "What precisely is a complete Merlin engine?", "Are American threads to be used?", "What ignition system, carburation system, bearing materials, etc. are to be used?"

Three RRLtd engineers arrived with their families and took over the job, and I could get back to my parts supply business, which had now almost standardised itself. To such an extent indeed that I could leave it in good hands and transfer to Washington, where the British Supply Mission, under Michael Dewar, was struggling with problems of supply of tanks, tracked vehicles, gun mounts, ammunition, etc. Here Ford came on the scene again, making their version of the British "Universal Carrier" in Dearborn, and another slightly different type across the river in Windsor.

And suddenly one December evening in Washington D.C. the news of the Japanese attack on Pearl Harbor brought the whole confused picture into focus. From then onwards there was the sense of being one small member of a huge team all pushing one way. Instead of having to struggle across the current all that was needed was a push here and there where it would do the most good.

My office moved back to Detroit and I functioned more as a consulting engineer to the British Tracked Vehicle section.

It was a relief.

By July of 1945 I was out, and in September on the Queen Elizabeth, still in her wartime trim, going back to England for work with Vauxhall. There were a crowd of British troops on board, released prisoners returning from Japanese prison camps, all suffering more or less from beri-beri, and with widely differing accounts of their treatment by the Japs. One young officer loaded with gifts from the owner of the quarry in Honshu where he had worked ever since the fall of Singapore. Others crying nothing but vengeance for unspeakable cruelties.

The work in England, with yearly visits back to the States was pleasant, interesting, and not too arduous. I think it made possible a slow recovery of sanity after the war years.

Then, in May of 1952, after a visit to the USA, extending from January, came a call from Ed. Cole, newly ch. engineer of Chevrolet, to ask me to head up their new Research & Development Section. Vauxhall agreed and it was done.

And the rest is in the records.

Maurice Olley

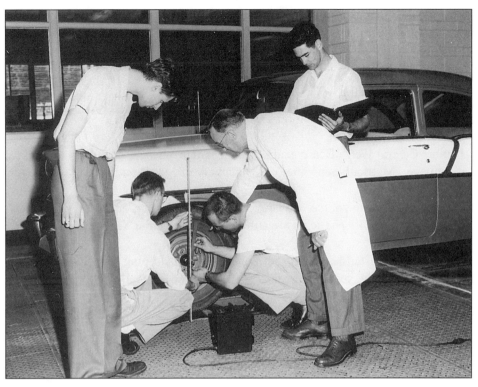

Maurice Olley with students at General Motors Institute, a few years after he wrote his "Reminiscences" in the 1960s. Photo credit Kettering/GMI Alumni Foundation, Collection of Industrial History.

1.2 Chronology–Maurice Olley, Written February 3, 1958[3]

1889: Born Scarboro, England, June 12. Father, Henry R. Olley (Norfolk & Essex ancestry. Escaped Huguenots). Mother, Adeline (nee Todd, London ancestry).

1894: To Llangollen, N. Wales. Father appointed headmaster of Llangollen County School, under new secondary education scheme for Wales.

1905: Honors Central Welsh Board exam. Mathematics, physics, chemistry (analytical), modern language. Matriculation: Victoria University of Manchester.

1906: Honors engineering course, via University of Manchester, one year only, followed by "influenza" (so called). The scars are still in my lungs, so the X-ray experts say.

1907: On a farm at Caister near Great Yarmouth living & sleeping entirely in the open trying to recover from the year in Manchester (have never felt really cold since).

1908–11: Apprentice to H. W. Ward, Lionel Street Birmingham (now, Selly Oak). Sole distinction: their only apprentice to put their big planar table on the floor twice running.

1911–12: H. W. Ward, designer, tooling for special jobs [*first job*].

November 1912: Rolls-Royce Ltd., draftsman on plant layouts under Thomas Nadin.

April 1913: To LeCanadel, nominally as tool & jig designer for Frederick Henry Royce [*later Sir Henry Royce*]. Designing milling fixtures for machining connecting rods all over. Graduated to design for original Rolls-Royce starter and generator. Associated with A. G. Elliott [*a great designer*], Bernard Day and J. A. Moon. Returned to Derby July 1913.

July–October 1913: Design work at Derby.

October 1913–July 1914: At LeCanadel with Sir Frederick Henry Royce. Design work and some estate work (since had enough French). Early adventures with Elliott driving single-cylinder Zenith car. Finally Elliott and I got French driving licenses on Silver Ghost.

July 1914: Return to Derby. Rumors of war. First five-year agreement with Rolls-Royce Ltd. had specified three months each year in USA to study tooling practice. Thomas Nadin and I were to visit Robert Bosch at Stuttgart in September for magneto manufacturing methods [*Rolls-Royce determined to learn foreign manufacturing methods*], and proceed via Marseilles to New York for scheduled visit. WWI started just in time to prevent our internment in Germany.

---

[3] The original manuscript was provided by William Lichty. Comments in italics were mostly provided by Alex Moulton.

Maurice Olley as a young man in England.
Photo credit Rolls-Royce Heritage via
Diane Mazzeo (daughter).

August 1914–December 1914: St. Margaret's-at-Cliffe with Sir Frederick Henry Royce and Elliott.

September 1914: Saw the French Channel Fleet going north past Calais. No one knew where British Fleet was. It was supposed still to be "on review" at Spithead. Britain had not yet declared war. But that night Dover was full of troops embarking on cross-channel steamers. Then we were "at war"—whatever that might mean.

First the time of panic when Rolls-Royce Ltd. was supposed to close its doors. Elliott and I trying to get into dispatch riders at War Office, or into artillery at Maidstone. Then told we were "reserved."

October–November 1914: Afternoon at St. Margaret's with Sir Frederick Henry Royce and James Radley, Alpine trials driver, watching British dirigible struggle back from Dunkirk against a light westerly breeze. Radley responsible for the dirigibles, begging Royce to let him have some Silver Ghost engines, to cut down and lighten for his dirigibles. Britain had **no** aircraft engines of any sort which would really run.

Royce refuses to do a cobbling job in the face of the enemy, but we visit Marvyn O'Gorman at [R.A.E.] Farnboro. O'Gorman's ideas restricted to existing Renault V8 of about 80 hp or RAF V8 of about 90 hp, both air-cooled, and the latter an abominable design for manufacture.

If as much as 150–175 hp, RAF would have to mount engine transversely across fuselage, drive from both ends of crankshaft to two large pusher props, through bevel gearing. O'Gorman determined that air cooling is essential. Royce replies best German engine (Mercedes) is water-cooled and Rolls-Royce does not know how to make air-cooled engines, but is good at water cooling.

Question: What does the Navy think? Where is the Navy's air service?

Visit to Russell Hotel, London to see Lt. C. W. Briggs, who appears to be the Navy's air service engineer, though without an office or an appropriation. Briggs tells Royce he will take as much as 230 hp on a single propeller if he can have a reduction gear for 1100 rpm propeller speed. (Also commits himself to Rolls-Royce manager Claude Johnson on his own responsibility.)

November–December 1914: At St. Margaret's, Royce and Elliott making first Eagle designs. I take care of bits and pieces, the timing gears, camshaft drives and reduction gear. [*Typically the lesser parts would be designed by a selected junior assigned to work with the great men to their approval.*]

December 1914–April 1915: At Bognor, using a rented conservatory as a drawing office, working on planetary reduction gear. Elliott at Derby. Ernest Hives [*Rolls-Royce development genius, later Lord Hives (1950), the superb boss of Rolls-Royce in WWII who drove the Merlin through and later picked up Whittle's jet engine. Truly the founder of Rolls-Royce as a world-class aero-engine firm. He started as a test driver for Rolls cars!*] gets first Eagle running. It burns its (cast iron) piston heads. Elliott at Bognor— the Zephyr aluminum pistons.

April 1915–June 1917: At St. Margaret's. The Eagle and the Hawk (for dirigibles). By [*Robert Harvey Bailey*] scales down the Eagle on a linear 90% basis to make the Falcon. The first Eagle-engined pusher biplane lands behind Dover Castle with engine trouble, leading to dry-sump design with double oil pump. Elliott alternates between St. Margaret's and Derby designing modifications and getting them made. (Remarkably short lag those days between design and production.)

Summer 1916: At St. Margaret's with a mix. At Hendon stealing rides on Handley Page and an experimental DH4 test flight with B. C. Hucks. Crash land near Waltham Abbey. Reprimanded by Claude Johnson.

Elliott and I, more stolen rides in Handley Page over Ramsgate, immediately after a raid by German "Taubes."

Spring 1917: With Hives, investigating torsional vibration on Eagle crankshaft and designing slipper [*probably a friction damper*] for Eagle reduction gear.

June 1917: Claude Johnson in USA to increase production of Falcon or Eagle. Nadin in USA. I point out opportunity for me to catch up on scheduled USA visits, released by Royce "for eight months," to visit USA.

July 1917: Trip to USA from Liverpool on Andania took two weeks, with one false start when P & O boat just ahead of us was torpedoed off Llandudno. No convoys, no camouflage, and losses running 68 a week. U boats operating off Ireland and off Nantucket. Up north, very cold, and in Gulf Stream very hot. Ran away from a whale off the New Jersey coast. New York in mid-July in middle of a heat wave. Rushed by Caswell to a N.Y. store to get some American clothing.

July 1917–November 1918: U.S. government had backed up on a contract to build Falcon engine. Concentrating on Liberty, plus a few American Hispano-Suiza, built by Crane Simplex.

October 1917: Saw first Liberty prototype at Bureau of Standards, Washington, and realized it was at about same stage as Eagle had been 18 months before. Suffering torsional vibrations, although its "experts" wouldn't admit it. No reduction gear, Claude Johnson permitted me to help design reduction gear (planetary) for Liberty engine. Also damped drive for accessories.

Maurice Olley in the 1920s. Photo credit Kettering/GMI Alumni
Foundation, Collection of Industrial History.

Ballyhoo for Liberty made Eagle or Falcon project impossible, but Claude Johnson cleverly wangled permission to place contracts for Eagle sub-assemblies.

This was done in Cleveland, Syracuse and New England. Offices Cleveland, Syracuse, New York. Concentration on Liberty engine spoiled U.S. war effort in the air and made Rolls-Royce job difficult because of supplies. No Liberty engine flew in action. Torsional vibration in early engines led to redesign after thousands had been built. Several efforts to revive production of Eagle, notably by Pierce-Arrow in 1918. Came too late.

November 1918: Armistice and cancellation of British contracts, mostly in New York office.

Christmas 1918: On Atlantic returning to England, to Derby. Claude Johnson proposal to manufacture cars in USA.

March 1919: Return to New York. The year was taken up first with Kenneth K. Mackenzie in N.Y., interviewing people who might back Rolls-Royce car venture. J. B. Duke (tobacco "king") in Charlotte, North Carolina, turned us down because of the anticipated post-war depression. J. E. Aldred of N.Y. accepted the Rolls-Royce proposal.

I spent second half of 1919 looking over possible plant sites all over the East, but avoiding Detroit area. American Wire Wheel plant at Springfield, Mass., was available and was bought.

November 18, 1919: Married in Cleveland—Norma Marie Hruby [*from Ohio*].

December 1919–January 1920: In England, Derby. Arrangements for car manufacture. Preparations at Springfield plant already under way.

1920–1930: Ten years of struggle at Springfield. [*Olley was chief engineer of the Rolls-Royce factory in Springfield, Massachusetts.*[4]] We had the wrong backers. No one could "turn a quick buck" out of the Rolls-Royce job. American buyers would not buy a chassis and wait for a body to fit it. Nor would they accept right hand drive in a **domestic** product. Attempts to build own bodies and supply complete cars finally led to purchase of Brewsters in Long Island City (at great additional cost).

The financial crash of October 1929, mixed with the Aldred fiasco which lost them control of their Gillette business in Boston put Aldred and Rolls-Royce of America on the skids. The axe fell, for John Southern and me, when we were both in Derby in summer of 1930, trying to work out a new program for 20 hp Rolls-Royce cars, in consultation with Evernden.

September 1930: Talk in Detroit with Seaholm, chief engineer of Cadillac, about joining Cadillac as chassis engineer. General Motors had completed speed loop at Milford Proving

---

[4] See Soutter, Arthur W., *The American Rolls-Royce*, Mowbray Company, Providence, R.I., 1976, for a detailed history.

Royce's home in winter months—Villa Mimosa, LeCanadel (near St. Tropez, France). Photograph taken by Maurice Olley in 1924. Left to right, Mrs. Olley, nurse and companion Ethel Aubin, Sir Henry Royce. Supplied by Rolls-Royce Heritage Trust.

Ground in 1928. Sustained speed had run out big ends on every GM car. Only car which could maintain 80 mph indefinitely was a Rolls-Royce Phantom supplied originally for Sam McLaughlin of Canadian Buick. Hence Rolls-Royce cars had very high standing with GM (and have maintained it ever since).

October 1930: Finish up in Springfield. Drive to Detroit.

November 1, 1930: Start work officially with Cadillac. First project was suspension and ride.

For several years with Rolls-Royce America, we had been busy with ride. There is a basic difference between European and American road surfaces, which applies even to railroads, and is probably due to severe climate changes in USA. American road roughness tends to have a longer wave and causes more severe ride disturbance.

Rolls-Royce cars brought to USA from Europe by their owners were frequently suspected of having had the springs changed by Rolls-Royce Ltd. before loading on ship. This because of much worse ride on American roads.

Tests showed need for much softer front springs. These tests received enthusiastic support from Hives and Robotham at Derby. But the occurrence of "oversteer" with softened front springs was difficult to overcome.

Introduced Rolls-Royce type bump-rig at Cadillac (first in USA) and used it to study ride motions.

1931–1932: "k^2 rig" at Cadillac. A 12-cylinder seven-passenger limousine equipped with outriggers and weights, whereby the spring deflections and moment of inertia could be changed at will. Robert Burton from Rolls-Royce had now joined me at Cadillac. Henry Crane, known from WWI days, who was now consultant to Mr. Sloan (GM Chairman), was also interested in basic ride and handling and supported our program.

The k^2 rig gave us two basic principles, i.e., front deflection greater than rear for "flat" ride, and "understeer," produced in this case by loading the front tires heavier than the rear.

1932–1933: The "SLA" [*short-long arm suspension*] with parallel independent suspension both ends. Two had wishbone suspension, the other had our version of Dubonnet suspension (later used by Chevrolet). All had radius arm rear suspension.

Immense forward step in ride and handling.

In March 1933 when SLA cars were demonstrated to General Motors management there was not a bank open in the USA. We were at the lowest point of the Depression. Half-salaries only were being paid in cash. City employees were paid in depreciated city script, etc.

Yet GM management decides to have IFS [*independent front suspension*] on **all** GM cars, in time for 1934 models in November. (Chrysler gets hold of our designs, and duplicates them for their 1934 models.)

1934: Transferred from Cadillac to General Motors staff though still working at Cadillac. Developing improved suspension designs for various divisions including Vauxhall. Torsion rod front suspension for Chevrolet. "Torsion-toggle" suspension for Chevrolet, and later for Vauxhall. Independent rear suspension for Cadillac, etc.

1936: Six months in England introducing torsion-toggle suspension on large Vauxhall.

1937: In June to Vauxhall as passenger car engineer, torsion-toggle suspension on the smaller cars.

1939: In August to N.Y. and Detroit for regular summer visit. WWII starts, all American passports canceled. In Detroit, promote a concentrated drive to save body weight on passenger cars both by design and by control of metal thicknesses to closer tolerances. Also through the physical testing of body stiffnesses. The program is adopted, but I don't get it. Hives discovers me in Detroit, and on receipt of his cable I beg off the GM program and receive "leave of absence."

October 1939: Work for Rolls-Royce in Detroit complicated by lack of funds, and by fact that under Michigan law, if I do business in Detroit for Rolls-Royce I become a "foreign agent." American enthusiasm to "stay out of the war" makes this dangerous. McManus incorporates a Michigan company as a legal safeguard.

Acquire m/c tools [*probably special purpose machine tools, of which the U.S. were superior manufacturers*] and small tools, and ship to Rolls-Royce Ltd. assisted by British staffs in N.Y. and Washington.

Try to persuade Packard to manufacture sub-assemblies of Merlin engine, on same principle as used in WWI. They won't do this without contracting for complete engines, and no one will find the money for this.

Get Wyman Gordon in Chicago making Merlin crankshaft forgings, including special steel from Republic Steel Co. Get Bower Roller Bearing Co. to work on all Merlin bearings.

June 1940 [*the Battle of Britain, Merlins so important*]: The famous shipment of Rolls-Royce print records. Purloined by U.S. Treasury Dept., handed to U.S. Air Force and landed under guard at Wright Field, with a three cornered fight between U.S. Customs, Treasury and Air Force. Washington decides that Ford shall make Merlin in USA.

Nearly a week spent in Dayton, Ohio, awaiting release of Rolls-Royce prints (hot weather, Paris falling and tangle of red tape getting thicker by the minute).

First Corvette, driver is Diane Olley (daughter), early 1950s. Photo credit Kettering/GMI Alumni Foundation, Collection of Industrial History.

Olley's retirement party 1957. Photo credit Kettering/GMI Alumni Foundation, Collection of Industrial History.

Release of prints refused and we are returned to Detroit. Arrive at Ford to learn that Merlin prints **only** are released. Drive back to Wright Field, recover prints and return to Ford by 3 a.m. Performance of the Ford people defies description. Merlin prints are like autumn leaves, being duplicated, retraced, microfilmed. Within two weeks Merlin crankshafts are in existence in correct material but **cast** instead of forged. An engine design appears and is built in extremely short time, and on dynamometer. It is dimensionally the Merlin, but without a single Merlin detail. With fuel injection, cast crank, aluminum block with dry sleeves, etc. (Eight cylinders of it, with a carburetor, later become the Ford tank engine.)

Meanwhile the negotiations between Washington and Ford reach complete stalemate, and instructions come from Washington to transfer all Merlin prints to Packard. Ford opposes this, claiming they will make the engine. Finally prints are retrieved and brought to Packard, who take their time, use their heads, and eventually, with assistance of engineers from Derby, do an excellent job.

1941: By the summer of 1941, Russia had come in on our side, the American attitude was becoming more cooperative. Rolls-Royce work in Detroit, now largely supply of bearings, crank forgings, small tools was proceeding and increasing. But extreme complications with McManus in New York led me to resign and join British mission under

Michael Dewar in Washington, on ammunition and ordinance supplies, and eventually on tanks and armored vehicles. In December came news of Pearl Harbor, USA was in the war. This shifted the control of many Lend-Lease supplies and caused increased delays and complication for some months.

Spring 1942: Return to Detroit, Ford producing separate versions of Universal Carrier in Detroit and Windsor. Ford tank engines for Sherman tanks, Chrysler tanks with 30-cylinder water-cooled engine. Supplies of springs for Churchill tank and for British Universal Carrier, etc. This phase continued three years.

Summer 1945: Back with Vauxhall and to Luton as consultant [*possibly for Maurice Platt*], visiting Detroit each year for talks.

Spring 1952: In Detroit, taken over by Chevrolet as director of Research and Development starting June 1, 1952.

Developing 1955 Chevrolet, Corvette and basic work on air springing, etc.

December 31, 1955: Retired from Chevrolet (1-1/2 years overage). Continued with consulting work for Paramount Engineering Co. attached to Chevrolet Engineering Department until end of June 1957, when retired at age 68.

1.3 Holyhead Road

This section starts off with "The Wall."

This doesn't refer to the walls of Chester, but to the Roman Wall, between Carlisle and Newcastle. This is Hadrian's Wall, and was the second attempt of the Romans to contain the Picts and Scots. In the 2nd, 3rd, and 4th centuries this was literally the frontier of civilization. In its small way it ranks with the Great Wall of China (or the Maginot Line!). Portions of it are still standing, and just after the last war a Temple of Mithras was uncovered and photographed, and then covered up again, "to preserve it for posterity."

Supplies for the Wall were landed at Chichester, at the extreme east end of what is now Portsmouth Harbor, and were carried north from there to the Watling Street, and thence northwest to Chester. And so by sea to Morecambe Bay, and by packhorse and lake barge through the Lake District to the western end of the wall at Carlisle. In southern England, almost next door to Stonehenge, all this Roman stuff rates almost as "modern history." The "ancient" works are a couple of thousand years older, like Stonehenge. And in Bedfordshire, north of London, there are bronze foundries, recently unearthed, which made tools and weapons from bronze bars brought from Cornwall by sea and packhorse. They probably date 1000 years before even Julius made his unsuccessful attempt on Britain, and another hundred before Claudius made a permanent colony. The interest is that the British (or "Welsh") were not blue-pointed savages, and the Romans never claimed they were. This was a lying rumor spread by teutonically minded "historians" in

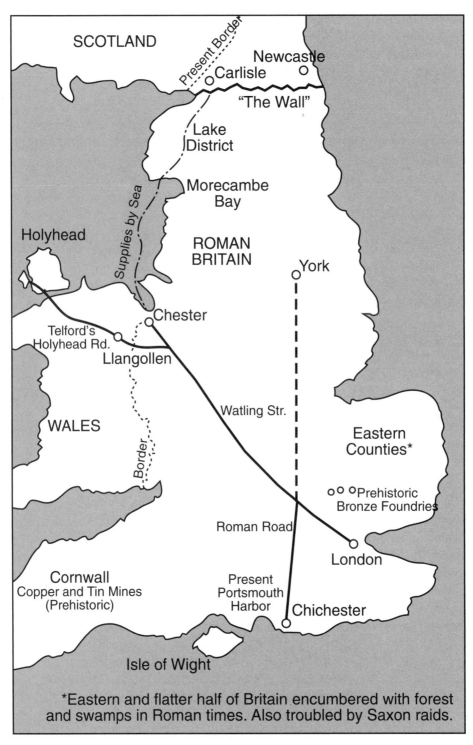

Roman Britain showing the Holyhead Road and Llangollen, Olley's birthplace.
Source: Sketch by Maurice Olley.

Victoria's reign, to disguise the horrible truth that after 450 A.D., with the Romans gone, the whole island was at the mercy of the "northmen" who wrecked that and reduced it to desolation and savagery within a century. Some of the Welsh or Scottish, still regard the "Saxons" ("Saesneq"—Welsh or "Sassenach"—Scottish) as half-civilized.

The importance of the Romans to the present discussion is that they knew about wheeled vehicles and roads to carry them. They knew about cambering the roads for surface drainage and about cutting and filling to limit the grades, so that horses could pull loads on wheels (even without the horse collar, a later invention probably Chinese). They probably knew more than we give 'em credit for because of the devastation wrought by the savages who came after them and gave us the thousand years of the "Dark Ages." For example, at Bath you can still see the Roman lead pipes (wrapped from lead sheet, with a lap joint), which are still feeding water into the great bath. The lead came from the place in North Wales still known as "Minera." And Geraldus Cambrensis in 1180, on a recruiting drive for the Third Crusade, notes that the Roman villas still remaining at Carlton had central heating! He wonders how long it will be before the English adopt this good idea! He'd have had a long wait.

England seems to have clung to the Middle Ages longer than almost anyone else. Samuel Pepys, on his "tours" in the eastern countries in the 1660s uses the same means as Geraldus, or Chaucer's Canterbury pilgrims. They all go "a-foot" or "a-horse." But Pepys does indicate a reviving interest in his "glass coach," and in a friend's "spring cart," which he says rides "mighty well," though not as well as the inventor thinks! (The Pepys coach presumably used rawhide straps for springs.)

The revival of "modern" road building in England seems to have waited till the 18th century, when after a gap of some **thirteen hundred years,** the Roman construction methods were reintroduced by MacAdam and by Telford.

Telford was quite a name in Llangollen history. He had built the Shropshire Union Canal which sprang from the Dee some miles above the town, flowed along a terrace cut on the hillside above the town, and then, a few miles below the town, crossed the valley by the spectacular Pont Cysyllte Aqueduct, and wound its ways into the mysteries of England.

Telford's "new" Holyhead Road was less spectacular, but was an equally notable achievement. You could see that it was "new" by the way it cut through town and country, leaving looped remnants of the old road on either side. Also by its careful and uniform construction and its uniform and moderate grades, designed for four horses to a loaded mail coach.

In the 1890s both road and canal were regarded as "museum pieces," ranking with the dinosaurs. The railway had reached Llangollen some 40 years before and **really** put the town on the map. The train was much faster and cheaper. The road stood empty, except perhaps for a doctor's horse trap. The canal was almost empty, except for a few barge loads of coal or bricks.

Color photo (scanned to black & white) of Holyhead Road in 1997.
Photo credit L. Kirk Walters.

Color photo (scanned to black & white) of Holyhead Road, Llangollen, Wales
(now the A5), looking west from High Street, 1997. Photo credit L. Kirk Walters.

Then—it must have been in 1897—someone threw gravel after midnight at a bedroom window in our early schoolhouse building which stood beside the Holyhead Road in Llangollen. Proved to be a schoolmaster acquaintance of my father's, with a friend, trying to drive from Chester to Holyhead for an adventurous vacation. He claimed they had thought the schoolhouse was an inn. But I think they were too exhausted to care, having covered the 21 miles from Chester in four hours, on a De Dion "quad." We took them in, and they popped away after breakfast. I never did hear if they ever reached Holyhead.

But it seems to me that from that day on that road steadily came to life again. I still recall the jingling of drive chains and whine of gears typical of early cars. And the passionate behavior of two-cylinder car engines when first hand-cranked into life. And then how they quieted down like a good carriage-horse, as the car moved away.

England had steam-driven coaches operating from London to Birmingham as early as the 1830s. The new railways are generally credited with killing road transportation. Actually, the lack of rubber tires was probably responsible. But the ensuing legislation on the use of the highways effectively blocked the development of the motorcar in Britain until some ten years after the USA or the Continent. Motorcars came with a rush just after the turn of the century.

After their triumphs of the 19th century, British engineers were extremely "steam minded." I have heard well-established engineers wax eloquent about "these young fools who think they can get reliable power by lighting a fire in a machined cylinder." The characteristics of the i/c engine were all wrong. It had to drive through a cluster of change gears. It could not even start itself. It got only one working stroke out of four. Worst of all it had to mess about with a lot of electric gadgets, which were bound to fail in wet weather (of which there's plenty!).

So the British put steam engines in their "lorries," and did surprisingly well with them right up to and through WWII. In England it was always well to drive with caution near the bottom of a grade in case there might be a parked lorry drinking water from a stream. But British engineers did nothing with steam for "pleasure cars," comparable with Serpollet in France or Locomobile or White in the USA. They seem to have decided that rich young men with more money than brains might just as well play with their petrol engines.

You can read today in the Proceedings of the I.A.E. the arguments in 1906 of a young iconoclast like Fred Lanchester in his attempts to convince the "respectable" committee of the Institution that the petrol engine was to be taken seriously. He even proved by straight dimensional theory as early as 1906 that a minimum weight i/c engine would have a stroke-bore ratio of about 0.80!, when current practice was close to 1.50.

Of course, by 1907 the argument as to powerplant was almost over. But in Britain it was really not until WWI that the i/c engine established itself in the public mind as a completely reliable mechanism. Its performance on the land, and in the air, in submarines and patrol boats, in tanks, etc., put all questions about internal combustion out of court.

And Royce's effort from his first cars onward had been to show that the i/c engine in a car could be made smooth, silent, and completely reliable. His early cars were two-cylinder, then three-cylinder, then four-cylinder. There was some hesitation then, before the "final" step to the line-six. There was even a Vee 8, started as early as 1905, with special coachwork seating the driver above the engine and intended "to supercede the electric brougham." The line-six engine of 1906 had its initial disappointments, due to torsional vibration, but these were quickly mastered, and Rolls-Royce stayed faithful to the six-cylinder engine for about 50 years.

1.4 Olley's Associates

Note on Olley's associates at General Motors, taken from a letter to Bill Milliken, July 27, 1956.

1. *Robert (Bob) Schilling was Olley's successor at GM (1937). They shared the same enthusiasm for car stability and control and remained close friends until Olley's death.*

2. *Henry Fuchs started to work for Olley in late 1934 or early 1935.*

3. *Von D. Polhemus was a "promising" apprentice under Olley, who later became responsible for suspension development in a staff position at GM.*

4. *In the independent suspension (IFS) work of 1931–1933, Olley was assisted by R. B. Burton (they had worked together at Rolls-Royce), Nat Wyeth and Phil Pretz (later at Ford). The follow-on work after 1934 was done by Fuchs, von Polhemus and finally by Schilling.*

5. *Tire work at Goodyear started in 1931 under Cap Evans.*

6. *Ken Stonex and Bob Schilling were equally responsible for "tackling the transient state."*

1.5 Introduction to the Monographs

In this section we have collected introductory material from Olley's monographs that did not fit into the technical chapters. It is presented as a summary of historical highlights in the evolution of the automobile and its behavior on the road.

Long before the days of the skid pad test or any studies of tire characteristics and steady-state steering, it was realized that the handling of a car, as contrasted for example with the steering of a boat, was a very tricky business.

In fact with the earliest "road locomotives" of the 1800s, disasters to the steering seem to have ended most of the experiments. In the history of the automobile, rear steering has frequently been tried, and always failed. In the early automobiles, tiller steering was used, and was a failure. Yet Lanchester's reversed tiller steering was a notable success.

The problems of steering and handling were discussed in the technical literature, particularly in France, prior to 1930. Most of this work was valueless because it was done with no knowledge of actual **tire characteristics**. The general assumption was that the car steered in the way that Ackermann said it did.

Actually it does so at extremely low speeds, as when turning in a yard or driveway. Which is why we still need to use some approach to Ackermann geometry in steering linkages.

The first approach to a real understanding of tire characteristics, known to the writer [*Olley*], came from the observations of front wheel shimmy made by Rolls-Royce in 1925.

Here it was found, by producing shimmy on smooth steel drums, that each wheel on an axle met the drum toed-in, and that it was swerved outward very rapidly by its contact with the drum. It went up toed-out, so that its opposite descending wheel was toed-in, ready to repeat the cycle.

In other words the tracks on the road were—

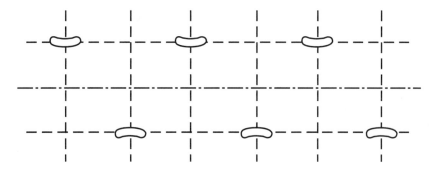

Tire skid marks left on the road by severe axle shimmy.

This was the opposite of the popular theoretical conception of shimmy and showed that the forced precession of the tires in the ground contact caused the gyroscopic couple which fed energy into the tramp. (This is the reason why aligning torque was originally called "precession torque.") [*See Chapter 6 for more detail.*]

Wetting even one drum stopped the shimmy, however strongly excited by unbalance weights, low tire pressure, or exaggerated caster. **The presence of side forces and aligning torques varying with angle, wheel load, and inflation were immediately suspected**.

The published work of Becker, Fromm & Maruhn in Germany about 1929 marked the beginning of the study of tire forces and moments, and led, by 1931, to an increasing understanding of hitherto unexplained peculiarities of car steering and of overall handling.

Steering gears generally had fairly low forward efficiency, and in many cases were nearly irreversible. This was done in an attempt to discourage wheelfight and shimmy, though **it was realized that the loss of road feel was undesirable**. It was also known that car loading had an immense effect on handling. Cars carried trunk racks, with attached trunks. And, when these were loaded, some cars became almost unmanageable.

Steering characteristics were not confined to geometrical "roll-steer" effects such as might result from the misplacing of the steering drag link relative to the front leaf springs, or the slope of the rear springs on a Hotchkiss drive rear axle, but were enormously affected by fore and aft load distribution, or by the relative inflation of front and rear tires.

The effect of the distribution of the roll couple between the front and rear wheels was also observed. For example, attempts to obtain a "flat ride" by using extremely soft leaf springs on the conventional front axles of the day were a failure, partly because the driver lost all "feel of the road" at the steering wheel. The front springs were so close together, (less than 30″ apart) that when they were softened the roll stability of the front end became almost zero, and very little roll couple was transmitted to the front tires. Consequently there was little increase of aligning torque when the car rolled. And in addition the car "oversteered." Front roll stabilizers were used even on conventional front axles. They improved the handling some, but could not save the front axle once the need for soft front springs was fully appreciated, since steering inaccuracies, the constant threat of the shimmy cycle, and reversal of caster angle during braking were still present.

Independent front suspension (IFS) appeared the simplest solution. With this the geometry of the steering system could be accurately controlled however soft the springing, while the shimmy cycle was suppressed by interposing the mass of the car itself in the suspension structure between the two front wheels.

With IFS came a change in steering gears. In front axle suspensions an almost irreversible steering gear was frequently preferred as giving some insulation from the ever-present shimmy tendency. With IFS the steering was found to be heavier even when caster angles were reduced almost to zero. A more efficient steering gear was essential, and the cam-and-roller steering came in to replace the worm and sector, giving an increase from about 45% to 65% in forward efficiency and from almost zero to at least 40% in reverse efficiency. With this reverse efficiency **the driver could for the first time get a real "feel of the road."**

With the introduction of IFS even on large and heavy cars in the USA and with the first tire tests on smooth drums, by Goodyear in 1931 and by U.S. Rubber soon after, the real study of the steering and handling of cars began. The facts on cornering force, aligning torque, camber thrust, and the way these were affected by angle, load, inflation, etc., began to be understood. Soon afterward the first skid pad was built at GM Proving Ground, and it became possible to measure some of the important factors in steady-state steering. However when attempts were made to predict skid pad performance from the tire characteristics obtained on drum tests, it was apparent that there was still a lot to learn. Amongst other things it was evident that flat-road tests of tire characteristics were going to be necessary, since the curvature of the drum caused a reduction in the readings.

A feature that assisted the flat tests is that, within a wide range of speed, the tire characteristics are independent of speed. And a further feature is that tire angles in the two planes, (the horizontal, i.e., slip angles, and the transverse vertical, i.e., camber angles), produce forces and couples, which, within the ranges commonly used, are independent of each other. Even so the variations between individual tires, the variations with tire mileage and the changes caused by load, inflation, traction, and differences in tire construction and shape, have made tire-testing an immensely complicated program. Several attempts have been made to explain tire characteristics mathematically from analogous mechanical structures, but actual flat bed testing remains the most reliable course.

From flat bed testing of tires and steady-state testing of cars on the skid pad some of the observed facts of car steering could be explained, but a great many could not.

For example there was the observed fact that in entering or leaving a curve the moment of inertia of the car in the horizontal plane had an important effect. Also that flexibility in the steering linkage and friction in the kingpins or elsewhere in the steering system, as well as the steering ratio, made enormous differences in the actual handling. None of these things showed up in skid pad tests. So it was necessary to examine transient conditions in steering.

And finally it was evident that the car and its steering, with its roll frequency, and the inertia of the car, of the front wheels, and of the steering wheel itself, formed an oscillating system, the characteristics of which would inevitably affect the handling.

The "checkerboard" tests of 1939 were undertaken in an attempt to obtain answers to some of the questions about transient steering effects. The handling tests on the Pennsylvania Turnpike in 1940 gave some further answers. And the work of the Cornell Aeronautical Laboratory Vehicle Dynamics Department has gone a long way to clearing up the question of the oscillation characteristics.

A great many questions remain unanswered, amongst which is whether an internally more complex steering system, equipped with "power" and with "sensing devices," is either necessary or desirable. In the writer's [*Olley's*] opinion power steering, even in its present form, has introduced more than enough complication, and to go even further would be undesirable.

Today, nearly 40 years after Olley wrote the above, we have failed to produce a power steering system which gives as good a subjective feel and feedback as reliable as a non-powered system. In such a system—for example, a stiff, low friction rack and pinion—the driver's steering force is due to the tire aligning torques, a measure of what is actually happening at the tire contact with the road. On-center feel, so important for comfortable steering on freeways, remains a problem when power steering is required to reduce parking forces.

Regarding the future, Olley continues:

I don't believe the most important developments will be along the lines of "gadgetry" but rather in doing those things which are required and necessary as well for the body as for the soul. For example, increasing yaw damping by some form of non-spin differential and by aerodynamic improvements of a not-too-unsightly type and perhaps most of all avoiding excessive understeer. The techniques and solution of "free" [*or force*] control is most important.

1.6 Suspension (General Discussion)

It may be wondered why we speak of this as a "suspension."

The word is a survival from early horse-drawn carriages, in which the chassis or "perch," which was originally unsprung, carried posts at each end, from which the body was literally suspended by long straps of leather or rawhide, which served both as springs and dampers.

In the 17th century, substitution of leaf springs for the leather straps was the first forward step in suspension practice.

In the conventional leaf spring front axle of 1920, the attempts to get accurate geometry, by making the arc swept by the drag link end fit exactly the arc of the third arm ball as controlled by the front spring, gave in many cases disappointing results.

The desirable simplicity of the "Hotchkiss" control of the rear axle was condemned by many automobile makers on account of unstable handling. Torque tubes, torque arms, and other devices were used to secure axle control.

There may be better things than springs to put between the body and wheels, but for the moment at least we still mount the automobiles on springs of some sort, and damp the ride motion with shock absorbers.

It may be well to point out that the motion of the vehicle does not in any sense reproduce the shape of the road surface over which it travels. This is because of the enveloping-ability of the tires which makes them "swallow" the smaller road irregularities, and because the traveling speed of the vehicle causes the road waves to act principally as excitation of the characteristic resonances of the car suspension. Only the major contour changes of the road, such as the start of an upgrade or downgrade, act slowly enough to produce a closely matching movement of the vehicle as a whole.

An interesting effect of this is the preference for soft suspension in American cars, in contrast to European. American roads are not rougher than those of Europe, but, because of climatic conditions, and probably because American roads are in general much younger than European, their surface irregularities are different from the European, tending to longer wavelengths. This leads to an unending mutual criticism, the Americans finding the European cars too stiffly sprung, and the Europeans considering the American cars too soft.

With the growing knowledge of tire characteristics and the use of the skid pad, it was possible to explain a few of these experiences, but many were still unexplained. So we come to the study of "handling," noting that just as steady-state steering depends chiefly on tires, so handling depends largely on geometry.

CHAPTER 2

Tires and Steady-State Cornering–Slip Angle Effects (Primary)

"Don't let anyone persuade you that the skid pad tests don't mean any-thing. They mean pretty much nearly everything if we will just take the trouble to interpret them. I am bedeviling Bob Schilling and Henry Fuchs on their interpretation."

Maurice Olley,
in a note to a colleague at Vauxhall

2.1 Introduction

In his efforts to understand automobile handling, it was logical for Maurice Olley to ini-tially focus on steady-state cornering. In the 1931–32 period, Olley and associates in the Cadillac group at the General Motors Proving Ground first conceived the circular skid pad test and then developed it into a reliable tool for assessing this aspect of handling. It is still in common use today.

*In his monographs Olley devotes considerable space to his analysis and prediction of skid pad tests, noting a **primary** effect associated with slip angles and a **secondary** effect involving steers. In our reorganization of his monographs we have attempted, insofar as practical, to follow this distinction. Thus Chapter 2 is devoted to steady-state **primary** effects and Chapter 3 to the **secondary** effects. The following paragraphs aim at clarifying the concepts involved.*

In this book, plain text is by Maurice Olley, *italic text is by the authors.*

In the skid pad test, the components of the lateral tire forces in the direction of the turning center must equalize the centrifugal force. In a simple vehicle (say, the nonrolling "bicycle" model of Figure 2.22), slip angles are required at the front and rear wheels to produce these lateral forces. In turn, the slip angles produce steer effects ("slip angle steers") since the wheels are now moving at angles to their planes. Since in the skid pad test the vehicle is required to follow a constant radius path, a compensating adjustment is made in the steering angle (δ) of the front wheels. The governing equation is simply:

$$\delta = \left(\ell/R \right) + \alpha_F - \alpha_R \tag{2.1}$$

where ℓ/R is the wheelbase divided by the turn radius. This is the Ackermann angle, the steer angle required at low speed for the vehicle to track a circle. α_F and α_R are the front and rear slip angles, positive (in Olley's system) when the wheel is yawed to the right. A detailed discussion of Olley's system and SAE's system for measuring slip angles is provided in Appendix A.

Noting that slip angles are a function of lateral acceleration, A_Y, we differentiate to obtain

$$\frac{d\delta}{dA_Y} = \frac{d\left(\alpha_F - \alpha_R \right)}{dA_Y} = \frac{d\alpha_F}{dA_Y} - \frac{d\alpha_R}{dA_Y} \tag{2.2}$$

*This equation defines the fundamental notion of over/understeer as developed by the Olley group. It says that when the rate of change of the front slip angle steer with lateral acceleration is greater than that of the rear, in a constant radius test where the lateral acceleration is varied by speed change, the vehicle is **understeer** (US). When the opposite is true it is **oversteer** (OS), and when the rates of change are equal it is **neutral steer** (NS). US, OS and NS are pure steer properties due to changes in the slip angle steers.*

The under/over steer concept (UO) can be extended to more complex vehicle representations wherein lateral forces result from not only slip angle changes, but also camber and wheel load changes due to lateral and longitudinal load transfers. These effects can be conveniently handled in "effective" slip angle changes, i.e., the forces involved can be explained by changes in the front and rear slip angles, which now become α_{Fe} and α_{Re}. These will affect the δ required to stay on the circle via the individual slopes $d\alpha_{Fe}/dA_Y$ and $d\alpha_{Re}/dA_Y$. They also change $d\delta/dA_Y$.

Another important aspect of the circular skid pad test is that of vehicle attitude to the path. With the simple model it is clear that the only way to develop a rear slip angle is to rotate the vehicle on the path through an angle β. If the center of gravity is mid-wheelbase and the front and rear tires are identical, then the rotation of the vehicle due to α_R creates an equal α_F. No change in δ is required to stay on the circle and the vehicle is NS, i.e., $d\delta/dA_Y$ is zero and the steer angle is equal to the Ackermann angle.

The attitude (β) change discussed above is inherent in the development of slip angles and hence lateral forces in the skid pad test. There are other attitude changes which affect the required steer angle but are not associated with changes in the slip angles and the force balance. For example, suppose some geometric rear steer (relative to the chassis), such as a roll steer or compliance steer, is introduced. This will affect the attitude angle of the vehicle and hence the steer angle, but it will not change the effective slip angles required for force balance.

*Olley makes a strong distinction between changes that affect the front and rear slip angles, which he calls **primary** effects, and those that result in attitude and steer changes without changing the slip angles. The latter are called **secondary** effects. **Primary** steer deals with the basic chassis UO properties and is significant in limit behavior, tire wear, etc.; it is involved with the tire slip angles. **Secondary** steer deals with suspension geometry and roll and compliance steers and plays a strong part in how the car feels to the driver in normal driving.*

Since Olley's objective in this chapter is to analyze the primary effects, he starts by developing a tire model.

Part A: Simplified Tire Models

2.2 Tires

We have to start with tires. And first clear up some confusion of terms.

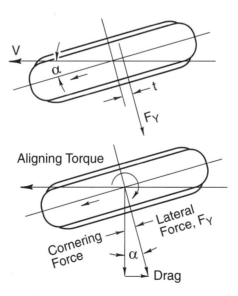

Figure 2.1 *Lateral force and aligning torque.*

When a tire rolls at a slip angle α it produces a lateral force F_Y, in the ground plane, normal to the wheel plane [*see Appendix A for slip angle sign conventions*]. This force actually occurs back of the wheel center at a small and variable distance t, known as the "pneumatic trail." It is usual to assume that F_Y occurs at the wheel center, and to call the turning moment $F_Y t = M_Z$ the "aligning torque" of the tire.

In earlier usage, F_Y was called the "cornering force" of the tire. Bergman and Freeman, in recent SAE papers [*c. 1960*] have used what seems to be a better term, which I feel sure should be adopted. Thus F_Y is called "lateral force." Then $F_Y \cos \alpha$, normal to the path of travel, is called "cornering force," and $F_Y \sin \alpha$, along the path of travel, is called "drag [*see Figure 2.1*]." Except where small angles make it unnecessary it is well to follow this practice.

In approximate solutions of handling problems, where angles are usually small, the cosine is considered equal to unity and cornering and lateral forces are regarded as identical.

The rate of change of cornering force with slip angle was earlier called "cornering power." This has been criticized as being unscientific, and Cornell [*Cornell Aeronautical Laboratory (CAL), now Calspan Corporation*] uses "cornering stiffness," since adopted by SAE [*c. 1956*]. However, "cornering power" has been so widely used and is so well understood that it will be used occasionally in these notes. The values are usually expressed in pounds per degree, though sometimes in pounds per radian.

The term "cornering coefficient," C', is the cornering stiffness per pound of vertical load on the tire. The units are therefore pounds per degree per pound or 1/degree. The value of cornering coefficient on a flat, dry road is ordinarily about 1/6, meaning that, at small slip angles and under normal loads, the cornering force per degree of slip angle is 16 to 17 percent of the load on the tire [*these "rules of thumb" apply to the bias-ply tires of the day*].

When a tire rolls at a camber angle as shown in Figure 2.2, it produces a "camber thrust" F_{Yc} in the ground plane, which actually occurs at a small distance [*camber trail*] t_c **ahead** of wheel center, producing a "camber torque" $F_{Yc} t_c = M_{Zc}$. This is small and generally ignored. The camber thrust is important, however, and cannot be disregarded. In a parallel independent front suspension the camber thrust pushes outwardly as the car rolls laterally on a turn, and therefore demands an increased lateral force and increased slip angle on the front wheels.

The camber thrust is commonly about 0.0175 [*for the tires of Olley's time*] of the vertical load per degree of camber angle. In other words the resultant of the vertical load and the camber thrust is $W/\cos \phi$, and it passes up through the plane of the wheel. It is this fact which permits bicycles to turn corners by "banking," without employing any appreciable slip angle.

As used above, ϕ, the angle of the wheel plane relative to the road, has been renamed "inclination angle," γ. For inclination angles, lean to the right is positive. Camber, ϕ, is positive when the top of the tire leans away from the vehicle.

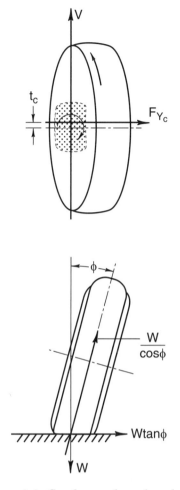

Figure 2.2 *Camber and camber thrust.*

A fortunate fact in attacking steering problems is that the effects of slip angle and camber can be considered separately, since, for the angles usually encountered, the two effects are independent [*not true at the limit of adhesion/onset of sliding; see, for example, RCVD, Section 2.5*].

All four effects—lateral force, aligning torque, camber thrust, and camber torque—are affected by angle, vertical load, inflation, tire construction, rim widths, and road surface, but **are virtually unaffected by speed.**

An important consideration is that, whereas slip angles above very small values cause severe tire wear, the direct effect of camber on tire wear is negligible.

Figure 2.3 shows roughly the changes in the four quantities due to angle and load changes. As to inflation, an increased inflation **increases** lateral force and **decreases** aligning torque. Camber thrust is less affected by inflation but tends also to increase with inflation, while the camber torque probably decreases.

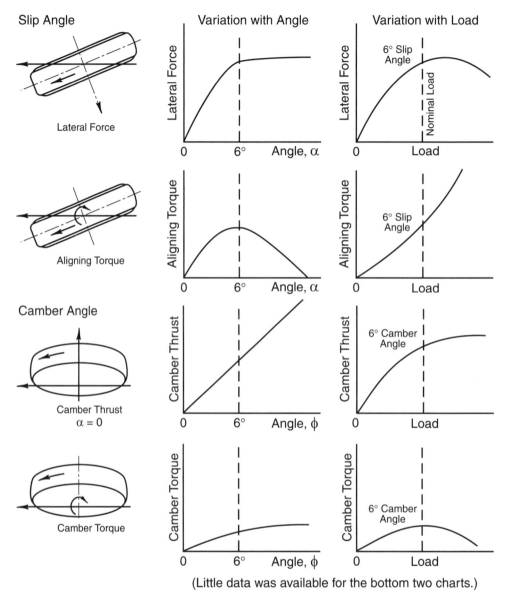

(Little data was available for the bottom two charts.)

Figure 2.3 *Summary of tire forces and moments.*

As to the effects of bias-ply tire construction, decreased cord angle (i.e., a longer cord) tends to increase cornering force by increasing the lateral rigidity of the tire, and is therefore used on racing tires. A flat tread, giving a "square" contact patch, decreases aligning torque. Thus, as the tread wears, particularly at the edges, the aligning torque, and therefore the "feel" at the steering wheel, increases greatly. The aligning torque may readily double in the first few thousand miles of tire life.

The effect of load on lateral force at a given slip angle is of fundamental importance in problems of handling.

When a car is cornering, the load on the outer wheel increases, and on the inner wheel decreases, by an equal amount.

The fact that the curve of lateral force against load is convex upward, Figure 2.4, means that the lateral force of a **pair** of wheels is decreased by the roll moment carried by the tires. This decrease is evidently not linear, but is of this form [*shown on right-hand side of figure*].

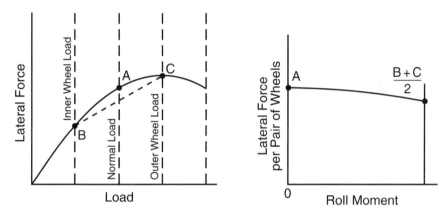

Figure 2.4 *Lateral force vs. load, single tire (left) and a pair of tires (right).*

The scale of the roughly parabolic curve of lateral force versus load varies with the size and construction of the tire. The more "adequate" the tire for the load it carries, the flatter is the curve, and therefore the less is the deterioration of the lateral force of a pair of tires due to lateral weight transfer on a corner [*due to roll moment*].

Hence we can say right away that, to avoid effects of roll moments and load variations in the handling of a car, one method is to use oversize tires for the load.

In contrast to the variation of lateral force with load, the corresponding aligning torque curve is concave upward, showing that the aligning torque for a pair of tires increases with the roll moment; see Figure 2.5.

This doesn't show the whole truth since, on a curve, the decreased lateral force of a front wheel pair calls for an increased slip angle, and hence for an increase in aligning torque. Thus the increase in the torque reaction at the steering wheel as the roll moment carried by the front wheels is increased, for example by an increase in diameter of a front roll stabilizer, can be very marked. But it is obtained at the cost of an increase in front slip angles, and possible increase in front tire wear. If the front tire roll moment is increased too far there is also a marked loss of definition in the handling.

This outline of tire variations shows that to deal with the steering characteristics of cars mathematically and obtain realistic results is, if not impossible, at least extremely difficult.

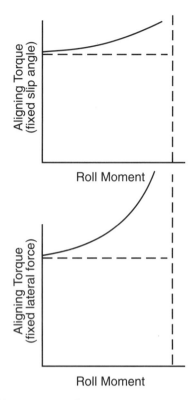

Figure 2.5 Variation in aligning torque on a pair of wheels.

When one considers that the actual handling involves consideration of the driver reaction, suspension design, flexibility and friction in the steering mechanism, moment of inertia of the car, and its wheelbase, etc., it appears that the best one can do is to solve certain portions of the problem by deliberately simplifying it, and then try out the conclusions by road tests.

The curve of lateral force against load, which is convex upward, is described by Walter Bergman [*of Ford*][5] by comparing the tire to three sets of coil springs mounted mutually at right angles to each other. Loading any one of the springs will produce a toggle effect in those at right angles, and will therefore show a decrease of rate. The fact that the vertical rate of a loaded tire is nearly constant, despite the increase of the contact area as the load increases, is sufficient proof that individual radial slices of the tire must have a decreasing rate. Thus lateral loading of the tire decreases the vertical rate, and vertical loading tends to decrease the lateral rate.

The decrease of vertical rate under lateral loads is important because it means that the tire rates which we assume in making the standard roll rate tests on a complete car are

---

[5] See, for example: Bergman, Walter, "The Basic Nature of Vehicle Understeer-Oversteer," International Automotive Engineering Congress, Detroit, Mich., January 11-15, 1965, Society of Automotive Engineers, Paper 957B, 1965.

considerably higher than the actual tire rates which occur under lateral forces on the road. **The axle, the front wheels, and hence the whole vehicle rolls more on a corner than our static tests would indicate.**

The combination in a tire of an increasing length of contact, with a decreasing lateral stiffness for each radial slice of the tire, as the vertical load increases, results in a curve of lateral force versus load, which, at least at the lower slip angles, is roughly parabolic. The apex [*line of peaks*, F_{Ymax}] of each curve moves to the right, i.e., occurs at a higher load, as the slip angle increases, Figure 2.6.

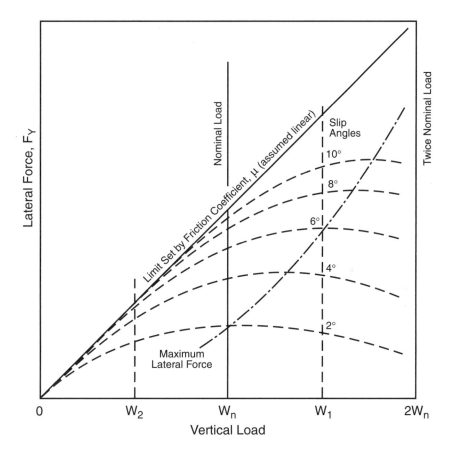

Figure 2.6 *Lateral force vs. vertical load, showing line of peaks at different slip angles.*

The load for maximum lateral force at a given slip angle depends on:

Tire size
Cord angle of tire
Inflation pressure
Rim width, etc.
[*and many other tire design factors*]

In general, an increase of tire size or rim width or decrease of cord angle tend to flatten these curves, and thus make the handling qualities of the car less sensitive to roll moment distribution. This conclusion is amply borne out in practice by the improvement in handling which almost invariably occurs with increase in tire size or rim width.

The roll moment increases the load on the outer tire and decreases the load on the inner tire by a like amount, as at points W_1 and W_2 in Figure 2.6. Because of the convex upward shape of the curve, the increase of lateral force on the outer does not balance the decrease on the inner, and there is a loss of cornering stiffness on the pair.

Effect of Slip Angle on Lateral Force

Each section, as at W_1 or W_2 of Figure 2.6, represents a curve of lateral force versus slip angle, and can be cross-plotted to give such curves. For example, the curves of Figure 2.6 would give us curves against slip angle like those in Figure 2.7. The initial tangent lines, as C_{Wn}, C_{W1}, and C_{W2}, indicate by their slopes the values of initial cornering stiffness or $\dot{F}_Y$ at $\alpha = 0$. The variations of these slopes with changes of load await further tire data. The whole problem can perhaps best be illustrated by a three-dimensional chart, Figure 2.8.

The inclined upper surface in Figure 2.8 represents the limit set by the coefficient of friction of the tread rubber with the road surface. This varies with temperature, moisture, road surface and load. Flat bed [*plank*] tests indicate that $\mu = 1.20$ to 1.25 [*for tires of the 1950s*]. For average road use on a dry surface and for skid pad tests a lower value of μ has sometimes been used. However it is increasingly apparent that the friction coefficient of a tire on a dry road surface of average composition is actually greater than unity.

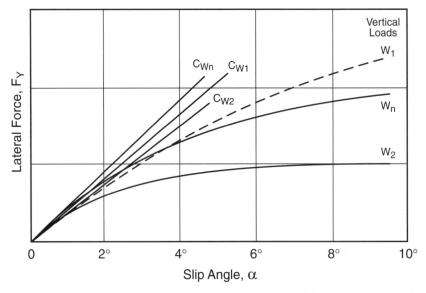

Figure 2.7 *Lateral force vs. slip angle, cross-plot of data from Figure 2.6.*

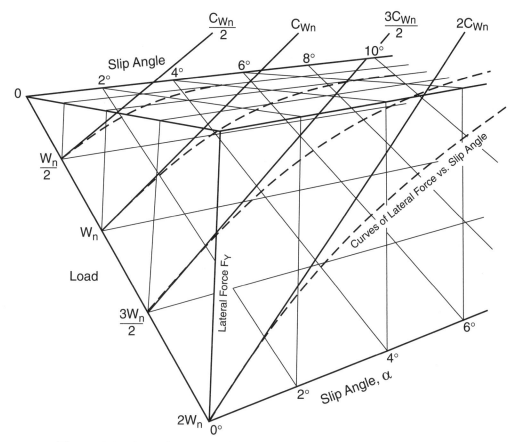

Figure 2.8 *Three-dimensional plot showing relationships between load, slip angle and lateral force.*

[*With current compounds (developed after Olley wrote the above), we now know that the friction coefficient can be much higher, especially for racing tires*].

Mathematical Representation of Lateral Force vs. Slip Angle

Hugo S. Radt[1] of Cornell Aeronautical Laboratory (CAL) accepts a curve, based on the work of Fiala[2] who assumes a parabolic pressure distribution [*this is a nondimensional scheme further described in Appendix B*].

[1] Radt, H. S. and W. F. Milliken, "Motions of Skidding Automobiles," SAE Summer Meeting, Chicago, June 5–10, 1960.

[2] Fiala, E., "Lateral Forces on Rolling Pneumatic Tires," Zeitschrift, *Vereins Deutscher Ingenieure (V.D.I.) 96*, No. 29, pp. 973–979, October 11, 1954.

This may be written:

$$F_Y = C\alpha\left(1 - \frac{1}{3}\left|\frac{C\alpha}{F_{Ymax}}\right| + \frac{1}{27}\left(\frac{C\alpha}{F_{Ymax}}\right)^2\right)$$

(2.3)

Here C is the **initial** cornering stiffness (or cornering power) as described earlier on Figures 2.7 and 2.8, and F_{Ymax} is the maximum value of the lateral force which is set by the vertical load and the friction coefficient.

When $C\alpha = 3F_{Ymax}$ the value of $F_Y = C\alpha/3$, and this is assumed to be the maximum value of F_Y, after which it remains constant.

So we can write $F_{Ymax} = C\alpha_{max}/3$, and Equation 2.3 then is simplified to

$$F_Y = C\alpha\left(1 - \frac{\alpha}{\alpha_{max}} + \frac{1}{3}\left(\frac{\alpha}{\alpha_{max}}\right)^2\right)$$

(2.4)

A further simplification is to say:

$$\frac{F_Y}{F_{Ymax}} = \frac{3\alpha}{\alpha_{max}}\left(1 - \frac{\alpha}{\alpha_{max}} + \frac{1}{3}\left(\frac{\alpha}{\alpha_{max}}\right)^2\right)$$

(2.5)

If we differentiate Equation 2.4 we get

$$\frac{dF_Y}{d\alpha} = C\left(1 - \frac{\alpha}{\alpha_{max}}\right)^2$$

(2.6)

or

$$\frac{\dot{F}_Y}{C} = \left(1 - \frac{\alpha}{\alpha_{max}}\right)^2 = \frac{\text{cornering slope}}{\text{initial cornering slope}}$$

(2.7)

Equations 2.5 and 2.7 are plotted in Figure 2.9.

It may be noted that in Equation 2.5 when the slip angle α is **half** the slip angle for maximum lateral force, α_{max}, the lateral force $F_Y = (7/8)F_{Ymax}$.

Another possibility actually suggested in the Cornell Report[1] is that, assuming constant pressure distribution, a parabolic curve rather than the cubic curve of Equation 2.5 might satisfy the requirements well enough for practical purposes [*the parabolic representation may not work as well with radial tire data*].

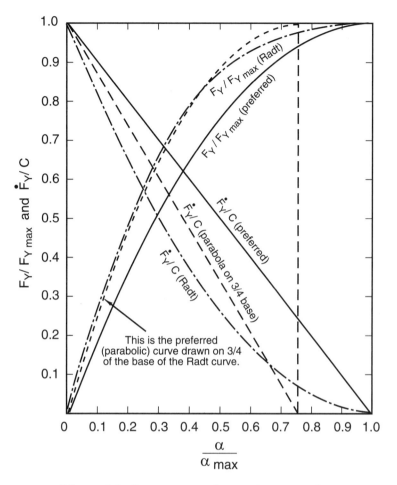

Figure 2.9 *Comparison of curve fits to tire data.*

This would be of the form

$$F_Y = C\alpha\left(1 - \frac{C\alpha}{4F_{Y\,max}}\right) \tag{2.8}$$

and

$$F_{Ymax} = \frac{C\alpha_{max}}{2} \tag{2.9}$$

so the equation becomes

$$F_Y = C\alpha\left(1 - \frac{\alpha}{2\alpha_{max}}\right) \tag{2.10}$$

or
$$\frac{F_Y}{F_{Y\max}} = \frac{\alpha}{\alpha_{\max}}\left(2 - \frac{\alpha}{\alpha_{\max}}\right) \tag{2.11}$$

also
$$\frac{\dot{F}_Y}{C} = 1 - \frac{\alpha}{\alpha_{\max}} \tag{2.12}$$

Equations 2.11 and 2.12 are also plotted on Figure 2.9, and are preferred because they are very much easier to work with.

The difference between curve (2.11) and the earlier curve (2.5) is that in the parabolic curve of (2.11) when $\alpha = \alpha_{\max}/2$, $F_Y = (3/4)\,F_{Y\max}$.

To make a proper comparison however, it is desirable to make the two curves coincide as closely as possible. This is done by drawing the parabola on 3/4 of the base scale of the Radt curve, as shown in Figure 2.9. It is clear from this curve that, except for a certain "over optimism" at the higher slip angles, the parabola is a sufficiently close approach for all practical purposes.

Now, however, we have to find whether either curve will provide an adequate approach to actual tire test curves. Figure 2.10 represents a flat bed test of Corvair 6.50-13 tires at 26 psi inflation.

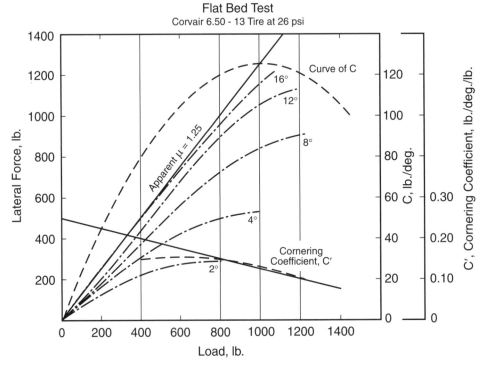

Figure 2.10 Lateral force vs. load and other tire characteristics, 6.50-13 tire.

These may be cross-plotted as in Figure 2.11 to show lateral force versus slip angle at 400, 800, 1000, and 1200 pounds load. Figure 2.10 indicates a friction coefficient of 1.25, which is slightly higher than we think we get on the road or skid pad. However we'll work with it for the moment and conclude that F_{Ymax} will be 500, 1000, 1250, and 1500 pounds, respectively. Then "Radt" curves [*starting with Equation 2.3*] may be drawn through the (7/8) F_{Ymax} points corresponding to $\alpha = \alpha_{max}/2$.

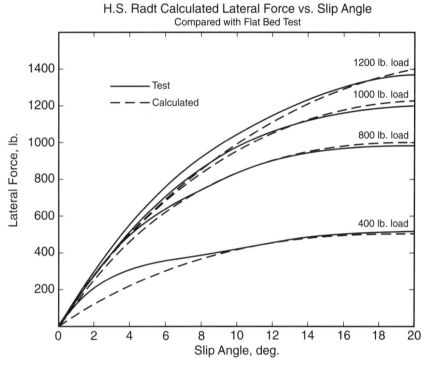

Figure 2.11 *Lateral force vs. slip angle calculated.*

On the 400 lb. curve F_{Ymax} will be 500 lb., 0.875 of this (435.5 lb.) is reached at 11.5°. So α_{max} should be 23°.

The Radt curve is given by:

$\dfrac{\alpha}{\alpha_{max}}$	0.1	0.2	0.3	0.4	0.5	0.6	0.7	0.8	0.9	1.0
$\dfrac{F_Y}{F_{Ymax}}$	0.271	0.488	0.657	0.784	0.875	0.936	0.973	0.992	0.999	1.0

This is drawn as shown in Figure 2.11. Except at the low angles it is a good fit to the test curve. The calculated initial cornering stiffness:

Cornering stiffness $C = \dfrac{3F_{Ymax}}{\alpha_{max}} = \dfrac{1500}{23} = 65.25$ lb./deg.

Cornering coefficient $C' = \dfrac{C}{W} = \dfrac{65.25}{400} = 0.163$

On the 800 lb. curve $F_{Ymax} = 1000$ lb. and from the diagram:

$$\frac{1}{2}\alpha_{max} = 11.2°, \; \alpha_{max} = 22.4°$$

The Radt curve shows an even better agreement with the test curve.

$$C = \frac{3F_{Ymax}}{\alpha_{max}} = \frac{3000}{22.4} = 134 \text{ lb./deg.}$$

$$C' = \frac{C}{W} = \frac{134}{800} = 0.1675$$

On the 1000 lb. curve $F_{Ymax} = 1250$ lb. and 7/8 of this (1094 lb.) occurs at 13.2°, so $\alpha_{max} = 26.4°$.

The curve shows fairly close agreement with test.

$$C = \frac{3F_{Ymax}}{\alpha_{max}} = \frac{3750}{26.4} = 142 \text{ lb./deg.}$$

$$C' = \frac{C}{W} = 0.142$$

On the 1200 lb. curve, $F_{Ymax} = 1500$ lb. and 7/8 of this or 1312 lb. occurs at 16.5°. So $\alpha_{max} = 33°$.

The calculated curve is still in fair agreement with test.

$$C = \frac{3F_{Ymax}}{\alpha_{max}} = \frac{4500}{33} = 136.3 \text{ lb./deg.}$$

$$C' = \frac{C}{W} = 0.1135$$

The next step is to find whether parabolas will serve to replace the Cornell cubic curves. Both are plotted in Figure 2.12 the parabolas being based on 3/4 of the horizontal scale of the Cornell curves. The result is as follows:

W (lb.)	400	800	1000	1200
F_{Ymax} (lb.)	500	1000	1250	1500
α_{max} (parabola)	17.25°	16.8°	19.8°	24.75°
$C = \dfrac{2F_{Ymax}}{\alpha_{max}}$ lb./deg.	58	119	126.3	121.25
$C'\left(\dfrac{\text{lb./deg.}}{\text{lb.}}\right)$	0.1450	0.1488	0.1263	0.1010

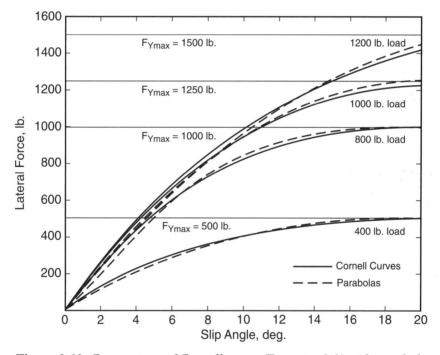

Figure 2.12 *Comparison of Cornell curve (Equation 2.3) with parabola.*

Although it seems unlikely that calculated skid pad curves will ever accurately reproduce an actual skid pad test, **it appears that the parabolic curves will serve our purpose, which is to show the effects of roll moment distribution, camber steer, swing axle, etc**. [*Using comprehensive vehicle models and nonlinear tire data, skid pad curves can now be predicted quite accurately.*]

There are certain unexplained variations in curves of lateral force vs. slip angle. For instance earlier tire tests have shown the lateral force to increase to a maximum as at A, at, say, 12° slip angle, and then to decrease slowly; see Figure 2.13, right panel.

Such a curve is shown in Figure 58 of the Cornell IME report of 1956.[8] This was also occasionally shown when testing on steel drums. More recent tests [*c. 1960*] on flat beds appear to show a tendency for the lateral force to drift upward slowly at the higher slip angles as in the left graph, Figure 2.13. And at light loads for a few degrees of slip angle, the cornering stiffness appears almost as great as at normal load. Probably this is an effect of tread shape. It evidently makes it very difficult to represent any lateral force vs. slip angle mathematically. [*Modern tires tested on a flat, dry surface normally reach a peak in lateral force and stay there.*]

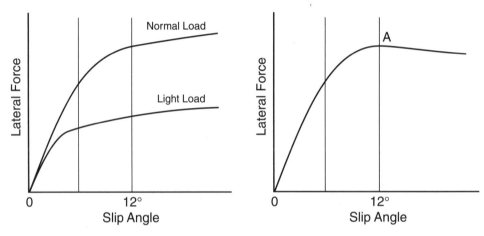

Figure 2.13 *Shape of the lateral force curve.*

Further Study of Parabola

The basic parabola is given by:

$\dfrac{\alpha}{\alpha_{max}}$	0.1	0.2	0.3	0.4	0.5	0.6	0.7	0.8	0.9	1.0
$\dfrac{F_Y}{F_{Ymax}}$	0.19	0.36	0.51	0.64	0.75	0.84	0.91	0.96	0.99	1.0

It was noted previously that the **cornering coefficients** indicated by the parabolic curves are:

$C' = 0.1450$ for 400 lb. load

$C' = 0.1488$ for 800 lb. load

[8] Fonda, A. G., "Tire Tests and Interpretation of Experimental Data," from "Research in Automobile Stability and Control and in Tire Performance," special reprint by Institute of Mechanical Engineers, Automobile Division, 1956.

$C' = 0.1263$ for 1000 lb. load

$C' = 0.1010$ for 1200 lb. load

This decrease of cornering coefficient C' with increased load is invariably found, though the points derived from tests generally show some scatter, particularly at light loads.

In the absence of more detailed information it appears permissible to assume a **linear** decrease of C' with increasing load (shown in Figure 2.10). This implies another parabolic curve for initial cornering stiffness, C, which is also marked on Figure 2.10.

Hence we get the assumption of probable values as follows:

W (lb.)	200	400	600	800	1000	1200	1400
F_{Ymax} (lb.)	250	500	750	1000	1250	1500	1750
$C' \left(\dfrac{lb./deg.}{lb.} \right)$	0.225	0.200	0.175	0.150	0.125	0.100	0.075
C (lb./deg.)	45	80	105	120	125	120	105
α_{max} (deg.)	11.1°	12.5°	14.3°	16.67°	20°	25°	33.3°

The corresponding curves of lateral force versus slip angle are drawn in Figure 2.14, and lateral force versus load in Figure 2.15.

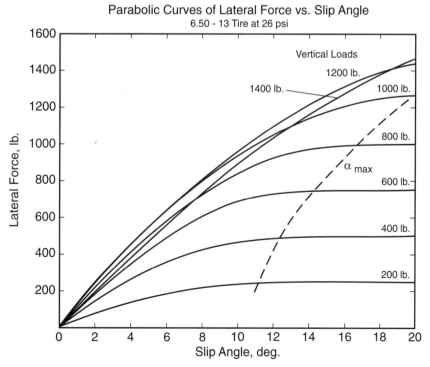

Parabolic Curves of Lateral Force vs. Slip Angle
6.50 - 13 Tire at 26 psi

Figure 2.14 Parabolic approximation, lateral force vs. slip angle.

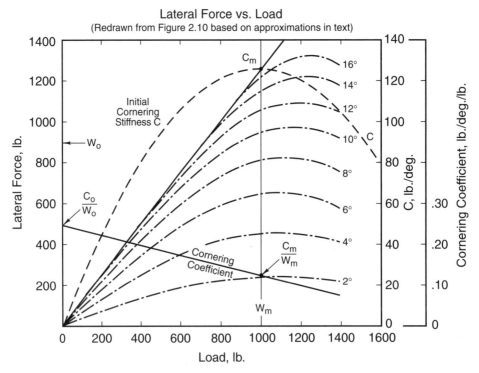

Figure 2.15 *Parabolic approximation, lateral force vs. load.*

Comparing Figure 2.15 and Figure 2.10, **the differences are not such as to cause any significant error in the type of skid pad curves it is proposed to construct.** The assumptions made are illustrated in Figure 2.16.

Then, if W is any load and C is the corresponding initial cornering stiffness, the relationship is:

$$C = C_m \left(1 - \left(\frac{W_m - W}{W_m} \right)^2 \right) = W \frac{C_m}{W_m} \left(2 - \frac{W}{W_m} \right) \qquad (2.13)$$

or

$$C' = \frac{C}{W} = \frac{C_m}{W_m} \left(2 - \frac{W}{W_m} \right) \qquad (2.14)$$

At zero load:

$$\frac{C_0}{W_0} = 2 \frac{C_m}{W_m} \qquad (2.15)$$

In Figure 2.16 the maximum initial cornering stiffness is drawn as occurring at 25% above nominal load. This relationship is not fixed and depends on a lot of variable tire characteristics. For instance, the rated load for the tire shown in Figure 2.15 is 880 lb. and the

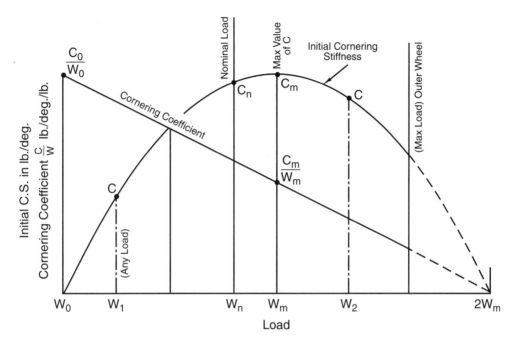

Figure 2.16 *Cornering stiffness and cornering coefficient vs. load.*

maximum value of C occurs at 1000 lb., which is only 13.5% above rated load. Other tires studied have indicated maximum C occurring even somewhat below the rated load.

However it seems safe to assume that, for a tire to be adequate for its job, W_m should be at least 10% greater than the nominal load and this figure of $W_m = 1.10W_n$ will be assumed in subsequent figuring.

It will also be necessary to decide on a probable friction coefficient. Flat bed tire tests invariably indicate friction coefficients greater than 1.0 (from 1.10 to 1.25) and tests on "banking" vehicles such as motorcycles show μ up to 1.2. Other investigators find 1.18. As a matter of convenience 1.20 will be used in subsequent figuring.

Notes on the Olley Tire Model

In this chapter, Olley performs skid pad calculations for various tire/vehicle configu-rations, to illustrate changes in steady-state cornering behavior, with reference to the "primary effects" of slip angle. If he could have had comprehensive flat belt test data on tire families, showing the variations in lateral forces with slip and camber angles, trac-tive effort, etc., for tire design variables, it would have been unnecessary to develop a tire model. In actual fact, comprehensive tests of tire families are still not available because of the tire's complex structure. Dependence is placed on tests of particular tire designs and some theory for extrapolation of performance.

Olley placed great emphasis on the importance of tire characteristics and he remained abreast of developments in tire testing and theory throughout his career. He was aware of the slip angle or yawed-rolling concept (which goes back to Broulheit[9], 1925—also see Appendix A) when he was still at Rolls-Royce working on steering system dynamics. As he notes in a letter of July 27, 1956 to the senior author, the

> "original Becker, Fromm and Maruhn (German) text was in 1929 and read by me [*Olley*] before coming to Detroit in November 1930. But this was of interest to me because it checked out with the Hives-Robotham memo (Rolls-Royce) of September 18, 1925 on High Speed Steering Wobbles and our own shimmy tests of 1926 and 1927."

The Becker, Fromm and Maruhn results were formally published in 1931. By that time Olley (then at General Motors) had requested tire force and moment tests of Goodyear (R. D. "Cap" Evans) which were performed on an 84 inch drum during 1932–33. They were the first force and moment tests on tires in the United States. Olley also requested tire data from U.S. Rubber (Dr. A. W. Bull) which followed the Goodyear work, but which were not published until 1939. The latter tests were run on a much smaller diameter drum and led to Olley's questioning of tests on curved surfaces. Theoretical and experimental work on tires by such investigators as Fromm, von Schlippe and Dietrick, Gough, Joy and Hartley, and Hadekel's monumental summary continued into the 1950s. The next major advance was the Air Force/Cornell Lab on-road tester designed in 1952 and commissioned in 1954. This was the first machine with a six-component strain gage balance, large slip and camber angle capability (±30°) with a constant-force loading system. This machine was used to measure data on actual roads at speeds up to 45 mph and really was an offshoot of the long-term research program in automotive stability and control that General Motors sponsored at the Cornell Lab Vehicle Dynamics Department starting in 1952. Maurice Olley's enthusiasm and support was a major contributor to this program.

Ernst Fiala published a comprehensive theory of the "Lateral Forces on Rolling Pneumatic Tires" in 1954 (in German). A translation was done at CAL in 1957 and the theory was used in "The Motions of Skidding Automobiles" by Radt and Milliken, 1960.

Although he had retired six years before he wrote the monograph on "Steady-State Cornering" in 1961, Olley was up to date on the status of tire testing and theory. Thus he utilized the Fiala-Radt formulation but concluded that a second-order representation (as opposed to third-order) was adequate for his purposes. He refers to data taken on the Air Force-Cornell machine by Fonda and he utilizes data in the literature and from the Evans and Bull tests to establish the general character of tire force and moment data. The source of the Corvair 6.50-13 tire data is puzzling but it must be remembered that he was writing his monographs at Chevrolet R&D at the time when Frank Winchell (head of Chevrolet R&D) was involved in the defense of the 1961 Corvair. If anyone had force

---

[9] Broulheit, G., "The Suspension of the Automobile Steering Mechanism: Shimmy and Tramp," Société des Ingénieurs Civils de France, 1925.

and moment data on Corvair tires, it was certainly Winchell who had available drum data, data deduced from vehicle tests and also from his on-road tire test machine developed for Chaparral. Incidentally, the GM Research Laboratory Flat-Plank machine (manufactured in the 1960–63 period) had probably not come on line yet.

Although we now have the Calspan high-speed flat belt Tire Research Facility (TIRF) (commissioned in 1973 and still in full-time operation) and its low-speed copies by MTS and Japanese companies, the Olley model still appears adequate for the purpose of exploring steady-state cornering of passenger cars.

Note on Wheel and Tire

It will be found in the literature that the wheel and tire combination is regarded in different ways, none of which is "accurate," but each of which has proved satisfactory for each particular case.

For example, sometimes the wheel and tire is regarded as a rigid disk and we are concerned with forces in, or normal to, the plane of the disc, such as F_X, F_Y and F_Z in Figure 2.17.

At other times the wheel is regarded as a slab cut out of the middle of a sphere. Thus the lifting of a car due to an inclined kingpin is due to the rotation of the wheel center O in the inclined plane A-A, and is not appreciably affected by the change in angle of the wheel plane B-B to the vertical.

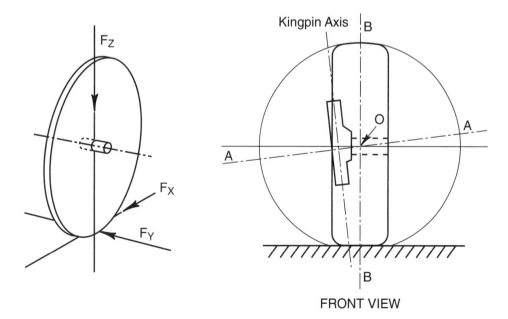

Figure 2.17 Wheel and tire modeled as a disk (left), and as a slab cut from a sphere (right).

When a wheel and tire "rolls" transversely relative to the ground so as to change its camber angle, R. B. Burton,[10] in his report, "The Coil Spring Wishbone Suspension" of March 1949, finds that the vertical reaction force to the load on the wheel passes approximately through a point in the center plane of the wheel at the height of the tire-base. This is the "rim point" P on Figure 2.18 which was also quoted in an early version of Ride and Vibration Terminology in the SAE Handbook.

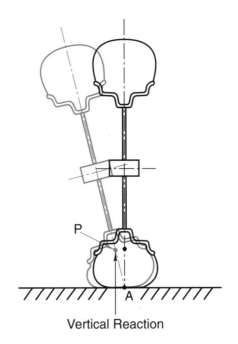

Vertical Reaction

Figure 2.18 *Motion of vertical reaction with inclination angle change.*

However, the plot taken from Burton's results (Figure 2.19) shows that this rim point approaches the ground as the camber angle (and therefore the lateral force on the tire) increases. So we are undoubtedly close enough to the truth if we take the ground contact center A as the point of application of lateral forces.

As camber angle increases the center of reaction force moves closer to the ground, Figure 2.19. It is probable that even at angles of 22° (representing a lateral acceleration of almost 0.4g) the center of [*reaction*] force is still two inches or so above the ground. But, in its final effect on the calculations the difference does not seem worth bothering about.

---

[10] Olley and R. B. Burton worked together at Rolls-Royce of America, Springfield, Mass. Olley was Chief Engineer and Burton was Chief Draftsman. See p. 13 in Soutter, Arthur W., *The American Rolls-Royce*, Mowbray Company, Providence, R.I., 1976.

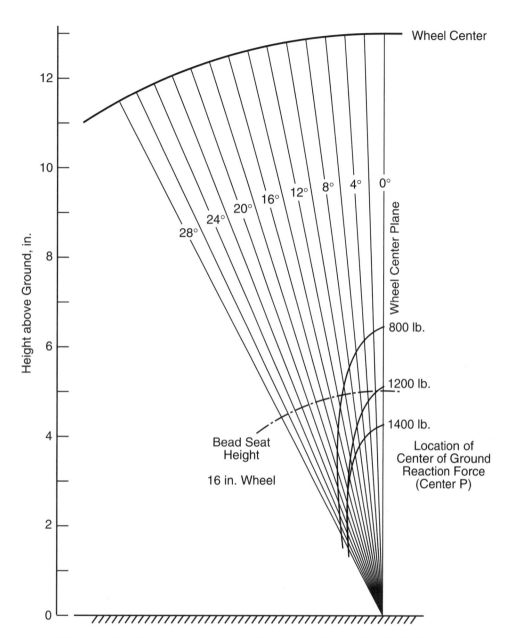

Figure 2.19 *Variation in height of "rim point" found by R. B. Burton.*

Part B: Bicycle Model Examples

2.3 Steady-State Turns (General Discussion)

Introduction

In this section, Olley uses the "bicycle model" to develop steady-state cornering equations which apply to skid pad testing. By using the "bicycle model" he can postpone the introduction of lateral weight transfer (roll moment effects) until Section 2.5. He does, however, include roll steer effects which change the steering angle and attitude angle, although any resulting oversteer or understeer as measured by the steering angle has no effect on the slip angles at the tires. See Appendix C for an early reference to understeer and oversteer. Other geometric and compliance steers are covered in Chapter 3.

Steady-State Turns

A vehicle turning a corner at constant speed and radius has two simultaneous motions. It revolves around the center of turn, O, and rotates about its own center of gravity (CG), both at constant angular velocity r, Figure 2.20.

The centrifugal force is WV^2/gR or WVr/g and this must be balanced by the centripetal force produced by the effective slip angles of the four tires.

Only at extremely low speeds with negligible centrifugal force does a car turn a corner in the "Ackermann" position, with the rear axle in line with the center of turn. At any appreciable speed the car is "nosed-in" at an "attitude angle," and has slip angles such as α_F, at the two front wheels.

If the rear axle stays in a plane normal to the median plane of the car α_R is the rear slip angle, and also the attitude angle. When a "roll steer" effect occurs at the rear axle, the symbol α_R is retained for the slip angle and the attitude angle is figured from this.

A great deal of simplification can now be done by considering that the wheel tread [*track width*] is almost always less than a twentieth of the turning radius R, and the angle δ (the steering angle), and α_F and α_R (the slip angles), are seldom more than 10 degrees. So we can with sufficient accuracy forget the tread, and draw the car as though it were a bicycle, Figure 2.21 [*and with centrifugal force, Figure 2.22*].

All angles are in radians.

> δ is the steering angle
> α_F is the front slip angle
> α_R is the rear slip angle

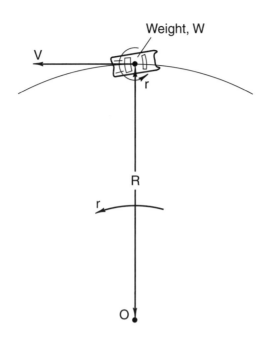

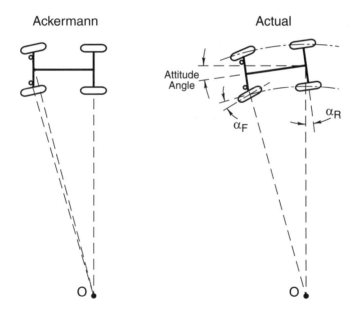

Figure 2.20 *Simplified cornering definitions, top; low speed, left; higher speed, right.*

With sufficient accuracy, ℓ/R is the Ackermann angle, δ_{Acker}. And the angles are so small that we can forget trigonometry and say that: **Steering angle exceeds Ackermann angle by the difference between front slip angle and attitude angle**, or, if there are no roll steer effects either front or rear:

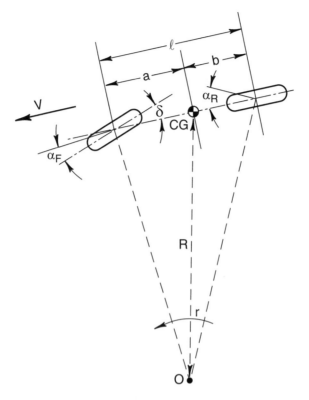

Figure 2.21 *Bicycle model.*

$$\delta = \frac{\ell}{R} + \left(\alpha_F - \alpha_R\right) \tag{2.16}$$

[Olley's sign convention for slip angles is opposite to the SAE convention in J670e. His signs are for yawed tires, positive when the wheel is yawed to the right. See Appendix A for further discussion.]

A great deal of mathematical treatment has been based on these assumptions. But this is an oversimplification, since the front wheel position is almost invariably affected by the lateral roll of the car and the rear axle rarely stays square with the centerline when the car rolls. In other words there is "roll steer" at both ends of the car.

The camber change of the front wheels relative to the ground in an independent front suspension is also a roll steer effect, but, for clarity, it appears better to distinguish it as "camber steer."

When these changes in the front wheels are such as to call for additional turning of the steering wheel as the car rolls on the turn, we call them "understeering" effects.

Camber-Steer–In a Parallel Independent Front Suspension (IFS)

In an independent front suspension with parallel links the roll angle of the vehicle and the tire inclination angle (camber angles) are identical. This simplifies Olley's calculations.

Fortunately, all the roll steer angles are proportional to roll angle, which can be assumed to be proportional to the lateral acceleration $a_y = V^2/R = Vr$ where $a_y/g = A_Y$.

If we define the roll gradient, ϕ/A_Y, of the car by saying that it would roll to an angle of ϕ radians under a lateral acceleration of A_Y in g-units, then in any steady-state condition on a corner the roll angle will be $\phi = (Vr/g)(\phi/A_Y)$.

Since the camber thrust is 0.0175 [*tan 1°*] of the vertical load per degree of camber, it is equal to:

$$\text{Camber thrust} = (\text{load carried}) \times (\text{camber angle in radians})$$

i.e., $$\text{Camber thrust} = W_F\,\phi = W_F\left(\frac{Vr}{g}\,\frac{\phi}{A_Y}\right) \tag{2.17}$$

where W_F = total weight on front tires.

The centrifugal force is evidently:

$$\frac{W_F + W_R}{g}\,Vr = \frac{W}{g}\,Vr \tag{2.18}$$

Roll Steer

Now we can put in symbols for the front and rear "roll steer." These are commonly expressed as percentages. For instance 5% front roll understeer means that, for each degree of roll angle, the mean angle of the front wheels turns 0.05° **toward** the direction of the roll, and 5% rear roll understeer means that for each degree of roll the rear axle turns 0.05° **away from** the direction of roll.

So if we call E_F the proportion of front roll understeer, and E_R of rear roll understeer, we have:

$$\text{Change in steering angle} = +E_F(Vr/g)(\phi/A_Y) \tag{2.19}$$

$$\text{Change in attitude angle} = -E_R(Vr/g)(\phi/A_Y) \tag{2.20}$$

For simplicity we assume that the front wheels stay parallel to the median plane of the car [*i.e., the front wheels lean the same amount as the car leans*] and that the rear wheels remain vertical.

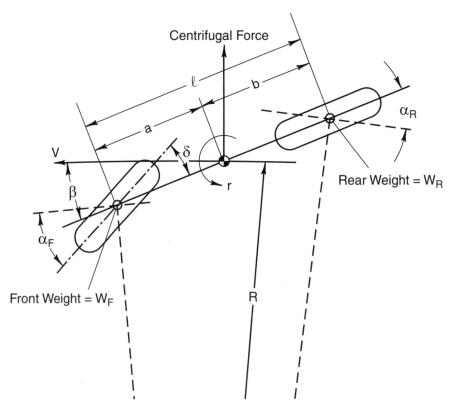

Figure 2.22 *Bicycle model with centrifugal force.*

The total cornering force required from the front tires is now $\dfrac{W_F V r}{g}\left(1+\dfrac{\phi}{A_Y}\right)$ and from the rear tires, it is $(W_R V r)/g$ [*no camber on a solid rear axle*].

Changes in Steer Angle at the Front Wheels

The next assumption we know to be wrong, but we make it for the sake of simplicity. This is to assume a **constant** cornering stiffness C_F (in pounds per radian) for the front wheel pair and C_R for the rear wheels. Then,

$$\alpha_F = \frac{W_F V r}{C_F g}\left(1+\frac{\phi}{A_Y}\right) \tag{2.21}$$

$$\alpha_R = \frac{W_R V r}{C_R g} \tag{2.22}$$

We can also rewrite the Ackermann angle $\delta_{Acker} = \dfrac{\ell}{R}$ as $\dfrac{\ell r}{V}$.

Then we can rewrite Equation 2.16 to give

(Steering angle) – (Ackermann angle) = (front slip angle) – (attitude angle)

$$\left(\delta - E_F \frac{Vr}{g} \frac{\phi}{A_Y} \right) - \frac{\ell r}{V} = \frac{W_F Vr}{C_F g} \left(1 + \frac{\phi}{A_Y} \right) - \left(\frac{W_R Vr}{C_R g} - E_R \frac{Vr}{g} \frac{\phi}{A_Y} \right) \tag{2.23}$$

or $\qquad \delta = \frac{\ell r}{V} + \frac{Vr}{g} \left[\left(\frac{W_F}{C_F} \left(1 + \frac{\phi}{A_Y} \right) - \frac{W_R}{C_R} \right) + \frac{\phi}{A_Y} (E_F + E_R) \right]$ $\qquad$ (2.24)

The whole of the expression in the square brackets is a constant and can be called $\overline{K}$, the "index of understeer" (it is dimensionless) [*all angles in radians*].

The term ϕ/A_Y is called the roll gradient. It is constant and has units rad./g or deg./g.

Olley defines the index of understeer as

$$\overline{K} = \left(\frac{W_F}{C_F} \left(1 + \frac{\phi}{A_Y} \right) - \frac{W_R}{C_R} \right) + \frac{\phi}{A_Y} (E_F + E_R) \tag{2.25}$$

As such, $\overline{K}$ is a dimensionless quantity. This should not be confused, however, with the commonly used definition of stability factor K:[11]

$$K = \frac{1}{g\ell} \left(\frac{W_F}{C_F} - \frac{W_R}{C_R} \right) \tag{2.26}$$

The units for K from Equation 2.26 are sec.^{2}/ft.^{2}. The two definitions are similar, the only differences being Olley's concern over roll steer and camber thrust (ϕ terms) and his choice to exclude $1/g\ell$ (constant for a given vehicle) as part of the index of understeer. Note also that the definition of stability factor changes as the mathematical model of the vehicle increases in complexity. For example, in models with aerodynamic downforce the index of understeer is likely to acquire a velocity dependence.

So we get $\qquad\qquad\qquad \delta = r \left(\frac{\ell}{V} + \frac{\overline{K}V}{g} \right)$ $\qquad$ (2.27)

---

[11] Whitcomb, D. W. and W. F. Milliken, "Design Implications of a General Theory of Automobile Stability and Control," p. 85, Eq. 89c from "Research in Automobile Stability and Control and in Tire Performance," IMechE, London, 1956.

or
$$\frac{r}{\delta} = \frac{V}{\ell + \dfrac{\bar{K}V^2}{g}}$$

(2.28)

And curvature of path for a given steering angle is given by:

$$\frac{1/R}{\delta} = \frac{1}{\ell + \dfrac{\bar{K}V^2}{g}}$$

(2.29)

The chief fault in regarding $\bar{K}$ as a constant is that we are assuming constant cornering stiffnesses for the front and rear wheel pairs, whereas we know that these are reduced by the roll moment and also by the fact that cornering force does not increase linearly with slip angle above 4 or 5 degrees.

But we are also ignoring the effect of traction in reducing the cornering stiffness of the rear tires. We are ignoring the inward radial component of the tractive force, which is appreciable on rear drive cars at high attitude angles (and on front drive cars is even greater and includes a turning moment in the direction of yaw). We omit the greater rolling resistance of the heavily loaded outside tires. We are ignoring the effect of the aligning torque on all four wheels. And finally we are assuming that the steering wheel is rigidly held and rigidly connected to the front wheels, which is certainly not true.

So that, even for steady-state cornering, our figures will not be true. However, as a "useful caricature" of actual road experience, they are considered true enough to be interesting. One reason for this is that, in most conditions of **highroad handling** [*high speed driving*] the angles dealt with in the above equations are quite small, five degrees or less.

Looking again at $\bar{K}$, we see that its value depends largely on the relative size of W_F/C_F and W_R/C_R, not therefore on the actual weights on front and rear wheels, but on the ratios of these weights to the corresponding cornering stiffness. This accounts for the stable handling of "Scenicruisers" and heavy trucks with weight distributions front/rear of 30/70 or so.

We can see also that W_R/C_R can easily be greater than W_F/C_F, and that, if the other corrective factors are small, the value of $\bar{K}$ may be **negative**. This is the definition of an **oversteering car**. And, at a certain **"critical speed"** [12] defined by $V_{crit} = \sqrt{g\ell/-\bar{K}}$ the value of r/δ, the yaw velocity for a given steering angle, becomes infinite. That is, at or above this speed a steady-state turn is impossible, and maintaining a straight course is a matter of "tight-rope walking" [*the difficulty depends on the amount of oversteer*].

---

[12] We believe the concept of a "critical speed" was first put forth by Olley in an internal General Motors memorandum of 1934, "Stable and Unstable Steering"; see Appendix C. Here he examines path behavior of an oversteering car to lateral force disturbance at increasing speed.

When $\bar{K}$ is zero $r/\delta = V/\ell$, i.e., $\delta = \ell/R$. The steering angle is equal to Ackermann at all speeds. The car has "neutral steering."

When $\bar{K}$ is positive (i.e., understeer) the yaw velocity in response to steering angle increases to a maximum value when $V_{char} = \sqrt{g\ell/\bar{K}}$ and decreases at higher speeds. The speed of maximum yaw velocity has been called (by GM Research Lab) the "characteristic speed" of understeer. But actually it is only a rather flat peak on the curve of yaw velocity.

Equation 2.29 shows that the curvature of path produced by a given steering angle decreases continuously on an understeering car as the speed increases, whereas the opposite is true on an oversteering car. [*Thus in theory*] the driver can be aware of any oversteer or understeer tendency at quite moderate speeds.

The dimension of the denominator in Equations 2.28 and 2.29 above is a length. In fact one can regard the understeering car as one in which the **effective wheelbase** $\ell + \left(\bar{K}V^2/g\right)$ increases as the speed increases. In the oversteering car, with $\bar{K}$ negative, the reverse is true, and when $V^2 = -g\ell/\bar{K}$ **the effective wheelbase is zero**, and the car is not easily steerable. [*These effects come from the change in yaw damping with speed.*]

Now we have to distinguish two different steering effects:

- Those which change the slip angles of the wheels in steady-state cornering. These could be called "primary" steering effects.

    For example:

    > The W_F/C_F and W_R/C_R ratios
    > Camber steer
    > Effects of roll moment distribution
    > Traction effects
    > Changes in toe-in, front or rear
    > Cambered wheels, front or rear.

- Those which change the angles of the wheels relative to the car centerline.

    Because these do not change the slip angles in steady-state cornering they might be called "secondary" steering effects. The rear end secondary effects show up on the skid pad as a change in the attitude and steering angles, understeer causing a lesser attitude and correspondingly greater steering angle. While if, as is usual, the steering angle is measured directly at the front wheel spindles, **the front end secondary effects do not show up at all**.

    These secondary effects are:

    > Front and rear roll steering
    > Steering due to lateral deflections in front and rear suspensions.

Consider for example the roll steer represented by $(Vr/g)(\phi/A_Y)E_F$ in Equation 2.24 for the front wheels, and $(Vr/g)(\phi/A_Y)E_R$ for the rear.

The front roll understeer simply reduces the effective steering angle as the car rolls. When running on a straight, wavy road surface, it makes the car turn slightly to the right when it rolls to the right, etc., like [*the static lean-steering of*] a bicycle. (For this reason roll understeer was originally called "bicycle stability.")

To maintain a given radius of turn, front roll understeer simply demands additional turning of the steering wheel, of which the driver is barely conscious, since he judges the turn largely by the torque reaction at the steering wheel rather than its position.

In independent front suspension (IFS), front roll understeer, which consists of toeing the wheels out as they rise, was introduced principally to reduce wheelfight. Yet it does have an effect on handling, particularly if it is **negative** (i.e., a roll oversteer) since this calls for reversing the direction of turn of the steering wheel as the car rolls (an awkward operation with a flexible steering linkage, a large reduction ratio, and heavy steering wheel). And furthermore because roll oversteer is regenerative, the steer causes the roll and the roll, in turn, causes increased steer, etc.

In general, front roll steer, either over- or under-, must be used only in small amounts. On straight, wavy roads, changes in road camber and roll angle occur too rapidly to permit compensation by turning the steering wheel, which can therefore be regarded as fixed. [*In a calculation of steady-state steering on a circle, Equation 2.24 can be used including the term $(Vr/g)(\phi/A_Y)E_F$, on the assumption of position control and rigid steering linkage.*]

However for the steady-state steering represented by Equation 2.24 we have to agree that it was unfair to regard the steering wheel as fixed and the steering linkage as rigid and thus to insert the term $(Vr/g)(\phi/A_Y)E_F$. [*In this paragraph, Olley takes exception to the "position control assumption" for ordinary highway driving. That is, the driver accommodates for small amounts of front roll steer without being aware of it. Later he avoids the issue of roll steer by using the front wheel steer angle.*]

The rear roll understeer represented by $(Vr/g)(\phi/A_Y)E_R$ also calls for additional turning of the steering wheel, and is also an example of "bicycle stability." However it is not quite comparable with front roll steer. As already stated it does show up in skid pad tests. In ordinary straight road handling the effect of rear roll steer is more pronounced than front roll steer. Rear roll understeer feels very much like increased caster in giving more positive reaction at the steering wheel, both on straight roads and on turns.

On a Hotchkiss [*solid*] rear axle the limitations of rear roll understeer are set by the increase in axle tramp and brake dive as the understeer is increased.

With regard to roll **oversteer** effects it might be well to point out that these become more objectionable and more difficult to handle the greater the flexibility and/or friction in the steering mechanism, and the larger the reduction ratio in the steering.

2.4 Calculating Steady-State Steering Characteristics (Bicycle Model)

Introduction

The calculations in this section, and the other sections in this chapter, are summarized at the end of the chapter.

In this section, Olley first discusses the three types of steady-state steering tests in terms of the equations for the "bicycle model." These are the constant radius, fixed speed, and fixed steer tests.

*He then calculates three examples using the **third** type of test, the fixed steering angle test, and draws some practical conclusions on the effects of cornering stiffness distribution (front to rear) and roll steer.*

Example 1	*Equal front and rear tire loadings*
	Zero roll and camber steers
	Front cornering stiffness = 225 lb./deg.
	Rear cornering stiffness = 250 lb./deg.
Example 2	*Equal front and rear tire loadings*
	Zero roll and camber steers
	Front cornering stiffness = 250 lb./deg.
	Rear cornering stiffness = 225 lb./deg.
Example 3	*Bicycle model with roll angle (requires four-wheel model)*
	Equal front and rear tire loadings, tires from Example 1
	Front roll camber =\ 5.73°/0.5g (understeer)
	Rear axle roll steer = 3% (understeer)

The conventional skid pad test is for constant radius (variable speed) as opposed to the fixed steering wheel test. He discusses the constant radius test next followed by the "infinite" skid pad (constant speed) test. There is also further discussion of the fixed steering angle test.

Measuring Steering Characteristics

If we rewrite Equation 2.24 (which introduced $\bar{K}$) as

$$\delta = \frac{\ell}{R} + \bar{K}\frac{V^2}{gR}$$

(2.30)

it is evident that we can measure the steady-state steering in three ways:

1. **Skid Pad Method** [*Constant Radius Test*]

   Keep R constant, vary V, and measure δ.
   Then the Ackermann angle ℓ/R is constant, and (if $\bar{K}$ were constant) δ would vary linearly with V^2, or with the lateral acceleration V^2/R.

2. **Skid Pad at Fixed Speeds**

   Given a sufficiently large flat area, and a marker pole for a center, we can keep V constant, for a series of tests, vary R, measure δ.

   Then, since

   $$\delta = \frac{V^2}{gR}\left(\bar{K} + \frac{g\ell}{V^2}\right) = \text{(lateral acceleration)} \times \text{(constant)} \qquad (2.31)$$

   δ will again vary linearly with lateral acceleration.

3. **Fixed Steering Angle**

   Given adequate instrumentation and area, δ can be fixed and locked, and the car driven at varying speeds with the curvature of the path and slip angles, etc., measured.

   Since curvature of path

   $$\frac{1}{R} = \frac{\delta}{\ell} - \frac{\bar{K}}{\ell}\frac{V^2}{gR} = \frac{\delta}{\ell} - \text{(constant)} \times \frac{\text{(lateral acceleration)}}{g} \qquad (2.32)$$

   the path curvature will vary linearly with lateral acceleration.

The linearity of the results in the three cases above depends, however, on the assumed constant cornering stiffnesses C_F and C_R. In actual fact these are not constant because of roll moments, etc. However, it has proved useful to plot the results of tests against lateral acceleration (g-units) because departures from a straight line on such plots give a clear indication of the effects of roll moments, etc.

Examples

It seems best at this stage to show some simple examples, on the basis of tests with a fixed steering angle δ.

Example 1: [*Fixed or Constant Steer Angle Input, the third test type*]

Consider the simple case of Equations 2.16, 2.21 and 2.22 for $\phi = 0$.

$$\delta = \frac{\ell}{R} + \left(\alpha_F - \alpha_R\right) = \frac{\ell r}{V} + \frac{Vr}{g}\left(\frac{W_F}{C_F} - \frac{W_R}{C_R}\right) \tag{2.33}$$

No allowance is made for roll or camber steer, so $\overline{K} = \left(\dfrac{W_F}{C_F} - \dfrac{W_R}{C_R}\right)$.

Then
$$\frac{r}{\delta} = \frac{V}{\ell + \dfrac{\overline{K}V^2}{g}} \qquad \text{(repeat of 2.28)}$$

and
$$\frac{1/R}{\delta} = \frac{1}{\ell + \dfrac{\overline{K}V^2}{g}} \qquad \text{(repeat of 2.29)}$$

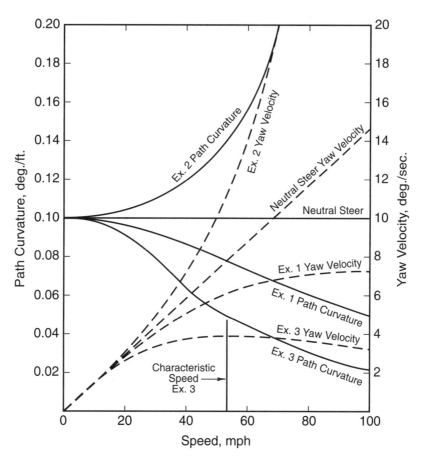

Figure 2.23 *Constant steer angle, $\delta = 1°$; test results plotted vs. speed.*

Let: W_F = 2000 lb.
W_R = 2000 lb.
ℓ = 10 ft.
C_F per wheel pair = 225 lb./deg. = 12900 lb./rad.
C_R per wheel pair = 250 lb./deg. = 14300 lb./rad.
$$\frac{W_F}{C_F} = 0.155, \quad \frac{W_R}{C_R} = 0.140, \quad \overline{K} = 0.015$$
"Characteristic speed" of understeer:

$$V = \sqrt{\frac{g\ell}{\overline{K}}} = \sqrt{\frac{322}{0.015}} = 146.5 \text{ ft./sec. or 100 mph} \tag{2.34}$$

Assuming a steering angle δ of 1 deg. (0.01745 rad.) the curvature of path and yaw velocity are plotted in Figure 2.23 against speed, and in Figure 2.24 against **lateral acceleration**.

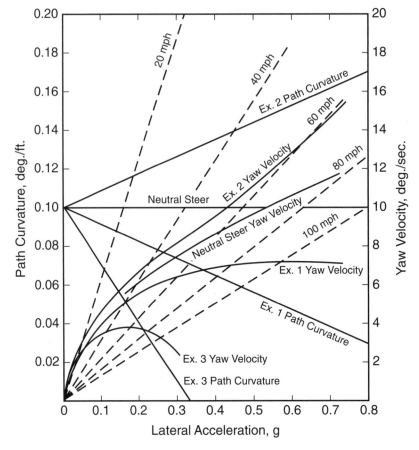

Figure 2.24 *Constant steer angle,* $\delta = 1°$*; test results plotted vs. lateral acceleration.*

The purpose of plotting against speed in Figure 2.23 is simply to show the very flat maximum of the yaw velocity at 100 mph and the continuous decrease of path curvature at increasing speed. At 100 mph, the path curvature has halved [*path radius doubled*], or in other words, the "effective wheelbase" has doubled [*effective wheelbase is another way to describe the effect of oversteer and understeer—this is an understeer effect*].

In Figure 2.24 it is shown that the lines of path curvature are straight, as stated above, and radial lines representing speed may be drawn through the yaw velocity curves.

Example 2

Starting with the simple case of **Example 1**, we just reverse the inflation of the front and rear tires so as to make the front cornering stiffness 250 lb./deg. and the rear 225 lb./deg. The entire handling characteristic changes drastically to oversteer. The critical speed of oversteer is now 100 mph at which speed the response to steering angle both in path curvature and yaw velocity becomes infinite. The response to steering angle, as compared with the low speed response, has **doubled** at 71 mph [*for this case*].

This sensitivity to comparatively small changes in differential tire pressure is certainly in agreement with practical road tests, and accounts for the fact that we seek to produce a greater margin of understeer.

Example 3

In this example, keeping the cornering stiffness of the front and rear tires as in **Example 1**, we add some practical features of a conventional car with IFS and a rear axle.

Suppose we say that the front wheels roll with the sprung mass of the car through 5.73° (0.10 rad.) for a lateral acceleration of 0.5 g.

Then ϕ/A_Y in Equation 2.24 above $= (0.10/0.50) = 0.20$ rad./g.

It has been suggested above that, for a steady-state test, the front roll understeer, assuming a rigidly held steering wheel and a rigid linkage, doesn't really mean anything. So we neglect any front roll steer effects, and assume that δ, the fixed steering angle of one degree, is fixed **at the front wheel spindles**.

Then Equation 2.24 above becomes:

$$\delta = \frac{\ell r}{V} + \frac{Vr}{g}\left[\left(\frac{W_F}{C_F}\left(1 + \frac{\phi}{A_Y}\right) - \frac{W_R}{C_R}\right) + \frac{\phi}{A_Y}E_R\right] \tag{2.35}$$

$$\frac{W_F}{C_F}\left(1 + \frac{\phi}{A_Y}\right) = 0.155 \times 1.2 = 0.186$$

We assume a 3% rear roll understeer, i.e., $E_R = 0.03$,

then
$$\frac{\phi}{A_Y} E_R = 0.20 \times 0.03 = 0.006$$

and
$$\overline{K} = 0.052$$

Characteristic speed of understeer:

$$V = \sqrt{g\ell/K} = 78.7 \text{ ft./sec. or } 53.7 \text{ mph}$$

The path curvature and yaw velocity (in deg./ft. and deg./sec.) are entered with the simple understeer case of **Example 1**, the oversteer case of **Example 2**, and neutral steer, on the charts, Figures 2.23 and 2.24, plotted against speed and against lateral acceleration.

As can be seen, the additional understeer, contributed mostly by the camber steer of the IFS and a little by the rear understeer, amounts to a drastic change in handling characteristics.

This also is in agreement with practical road tests.

Figure 2.24 particularly shows the marked reduction in yaw velocity in **Example 3** as compared with **Example 1**.

The above three examples have all referred to tests of Type 3 [*described at the beginning of Section 2.4*] **in which the effective steering angle is fixed**.

Now we should probably consider the conventional skid pad test of Type 1 [*constant radius, as described in the next paragraph*].

Conventional Constant Radius/Variable Speed Skid Pad Test

In this test, the vehicle is driven around a circle of fixed radius, at various speeds. The normal procedure is to start at a very low speed, to determine the Ackermann steer angle (wheelbase angle). Then the vehicle is accelerated to a higher speed and the steering is adjusted to follow the circle. Once a steady-state condition is reached, another data point is taken, and so on, for each new speed.

Turn indicators are fitted directly to the front wheel spindles, so that the **effective** steering angle is measured, and front roll steer is disregarded.

The attitude angle is also measured, and the roll angle.

Sometimes the steering wheel angle is measured, but, because of the flexibility in the steering mechanism, the difference between the angle reading from the steering wheel and the front wheels serves chiefly as a measure of the **steering effort**, rather than the roll steer geometry.

The front slip angle is not measured directly, but is derived from the equation:

$$(Front\ slip) = (effective\ steering\ angle) - (Ackermann) + (attitude)$$

If desired the rear slip angle can also be derived from the relationship:

$$(Rear\ slip) = (attitude) + E_R\ (roll\ angle)$$

In some cases the "yaw" of the rear axle relative to centerline of the car is measured directly by an indicator. This is the better method when there is lateral flexibility in the axle mounting.

The applied steering angle (δ) can be obtained from:

$$(Applied\ steering\ angle) = (effective\ steering\ angle) + E_F\ (roll\ angle)$$

From the equation:

$$\delta = \frac{1}{R}\left(\ell + \frac{\bar{K}V^2}{g}\right) \qquad \text{(repeat of 2.30)}$$

one can see that on the assumption of constant values for C_F and C_R, the plots of the various angles against lateral acceleration will all be straight lines, as in Figure 2.25.

But probably the most important fact in handling problems is that front and rear slip angle curves are **not** actually straight lines, when plotted against lateral acceleration. This is seen next.

The "Infinite Skid Pad" (Testing at Constant Speed)

With the availability of large, flat concrete surfaces, such as airport aprons, it becomes increasingly possible to conduct a series of skid pad tests around a fixed center, each series being made at constant speed, varying the lateral acceleration by varying the radius.

The results might be very informative, since the restricted radius and varying speed of present skid pads introduce some doubtful features. Thus an understeering car with a "correct" roll moment distribution [*to give a reasonable amount of understeer*] might give steering diagrams at, say, 30 and 60 mph as shown in Figure 2.26.

By doubling the speed the Ackermann angle for a given lateral acceleration is reduced to one quarter. But the difference between actual steering angle and Ackermann is unaffected, i.e., $\delta - \beta$ is the same at 30 and 60 mph.

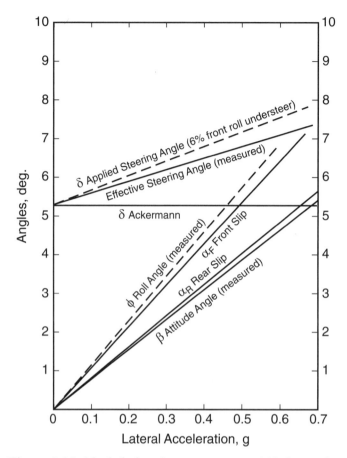

Figure 2.25 *Ideal skid pad curve, constant 108 foot radius,
for **Example 3** (6% front and 3% rear, roll understeer).*

So, although at the higher speed the steering is evidently more sensitive, there is still a comfortable margin for accurate handling at the higher speed. In other words a specific steering angle accurately defines a certain lateral acceleration and therefore a certain curvature of path.

Now compare this with Figure 2.27 of a car with too much roll moment carried on the rear tires.

Here the slope of the 30 mph steering angle curve indicates good definition of steering up to about 0.4g. But the 60 mph curve shows little definition above about 0.2g, and a definite oversteer slope from 0.3g upward.

Hence we can say that, on a normally understeering car, carrying too much roll moment on the rear tires causes a steering angle curve which, particularly at the higher speeds, starts upward in a normal understeer direction, but then, at some moderate lateral acceleration, such as 0.25g, bends downward in an oversteer direction. Above 0.25g, it requires **less** steering angle for **more** path curvature.

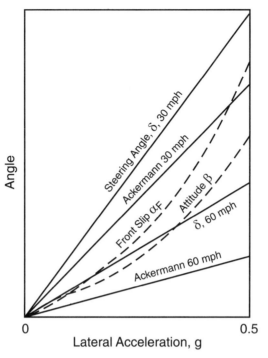

Figure 2.26 *Constant speed test results at two speeds.*

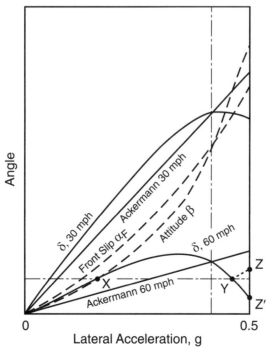

Figure 2.27 *Constant speed test, excessive rear roll moment.*

Under such conditions the same steering angle, such as points X and Y, can account for two widely different path curvatures.

Such a steering characteristic evidently provides no adequate definition of path curvature from the **position** of the steering wheel. It is just as well, therefore, that the torque reaction at the steering wheel gives the driver at least a rough idea of the front slip angle and ensures the return of the steering toward the zero position, when the wheel is released.

However, when the condition is one of definite oversteer, as at point Y above, the only way to make the car turn faster is to momentarily increase the steering angle, as at Z, and then bring it back sharply as at Z′ to catch the turn in the steady-state condition. In fact, in the case of a vehicle with consistent oversteer [*beyond the critical speed*] it is observed that normal turns are actually made in a series of jerks, the steering wheel being used to "excite" the turn, and then immediately backed off to hold the steady-state condition.

The use of very large skid pads allowing the driver to hold V constant and vary R and δ for a complete test undoubtedly offers improved results over the restricted skid pad.

Fixed Steering Angle

The first test method held R constant and varied V and δ. The second held V constant and varied R and δ. Both methods permit running about a fixed center, which is used to measure the attitude angle and sometimes the roll angle also.

In these tests V is always measured from the known radius and the time for a circuit, since speedometer readings are unreliable under conditions of lateral acceleration.

Given a sufficient area of flat surface it would seem that a better method of testing, already tried by Cornell Aeronautical Laboratory, is now available. This is to fix either the applied steering angle δ, or the "effective" steering angle (at the front wheel spindles) and thus reproduce from actual tests not only the actual slip angles α_F and α_R, but the path curvature and yaw velocity curves of Figures 2.23 and 2.24.

Yaw velocity can be indicated by a gyroscopic rate-of-turn indicator. And Schilling some years ago designed a double "fifth wheel," counterbalanced against centrifugal force, which can simultaneously record:

1. The speed, V
2. The attitude angle, $\beta = \alpha_R - (Vr/g)(\phi/A_Y)E_R$, and
3. The roll angle, $\phi = (Vr/g)(\phi/A_Y)$

and can thus be a direct check on the theoretical quantities of Figures 2.23 and 2.24. Direct measurement of rear slip angle also appears in the C.A. Freeman report [*the authors do not have this reference, possibly an internal GM report*]—this would be a worthwhile project and does not appear difficult to do.

Part C: Four-Wheel Model Examples

2.5 Lateral Weight Transfer Effect (Wheel Pair)

Introduction

The calculations in this section, and the other sections in this chapter, are summarized at the end of the chapter.

In this section, Olley first points out the importance of the distribution of the total roll moment (on the tires) between the front and rear wheel pairs. He then notes that it is this distribution which produces nonlinearities in the front and rear slip angle curves plotted against lateral acceleration from a skid pad test.

After that he develops the method for calculating the distribution of the roll moment. He considers two examples (not to be confused with Examples 1 and 2 of Section 2.4):

1. *Assumes finite roll center heights at front and rear but does not consider the roll of a rear axle on its tires.*

2. *Considers a case typical of passenger car suspensions of the 1960 era, where the front roll center is on the ground (or approximately so) and there is roll of the solid rear axle on its tires.*

In the second case, he calculates two examples of lateral weight (load) transfer distributions (LLTD):

Case A   Equal weight transfer front and rear.

Case B   50% more weight transfer on rear than on front.

To avoid confusion we reiterate:

- *The total roll moment (or couple) about the roll axis (due to centrifugal force acting above the roll axis and the sprung weight moment, $W\phi$) is distributed in proportion to the front and rear suspension roll rates.*

- *The total roll moment on the front or rear pair of tires includes the roll rate plus the moment due to the height of the roll axis above the ground.*

- *Thus the roll moment distribution on the tires (or lateral load transfer distribution) is generally different from the suspension roll rate distribution due to the ride springs and the anti-roll bar (if fitted).*

Olley, along with many other designers, uses the roll axis concept for visualization and simple calculations. In reality the roll axis is rarely stationary or in the center of the car. Therefore, more accurate models resolve the forces in the suspension linkages directly.

Distribution of the Roll Moment (about the Ground)

One of the most important factors in the handling of a vehicle is the distribution of the roll moment, or, in other words, the relationship of the lateral load transfer from the inner to the outer tire, which occurs on corners as between the front and the rear wheel pairs.

But probably the most important fact in handling problems is that front and rear slip angle curves are **not** actually straight lines when plotted against lateral acceleration. The extent of departure from the straight line shows graphically the effect of the distribution of the roll moment on the front and rear wheel pairs.

The two skid pad charts in Figure 2.28 illustrate the roll moment effect.

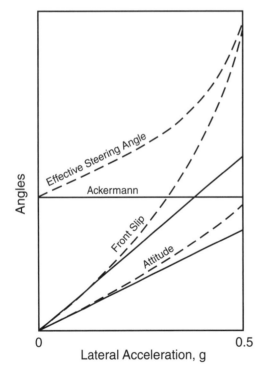
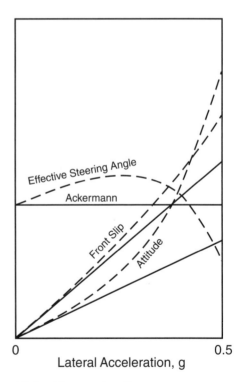

Left - Too much roll moment on front tires - excessive front slip angle at 0.5 g. Excessive understeer.

Right - Too much roll moment on rear tires - excessive attitude angle at 0.5 g. Initial understeer reverses suddenly into oversteer at high lateral acceleration.

Figure 2.28 Effect of changes in roll moment distribution.

Roll Moment Effects

Distribution of the roll moment (roll couple) between front and rear wheel pairs can be arrived at with **sufficient accuracy** with an analysis based on the geometry of Figure 2.29:

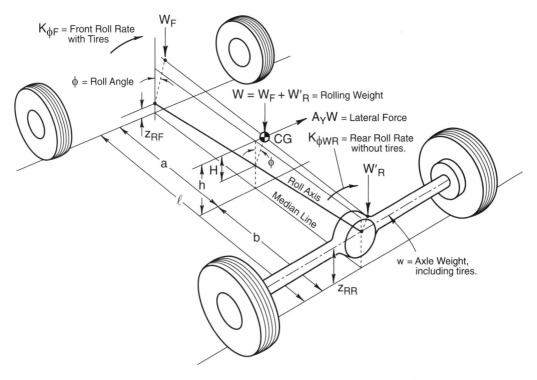

Figure 2.29 *Basic geometry of the roll axis model (ignoring roll of rear axle on tires).*

The total load on the rear tires: $W_R = W'_R + w$.

The total moment about the roll axis is $WH(A_Y + \phi)$.

[*Here, the first term is the moment due to lateral acceleration while the second term accounts for the lateral displacement of the CG from the vehicle centerline.*]

Let:

A_Y = lateral acceleration (in g-units)
A_{YF} = lateral acceleration at front axle (in g-units)
A'_{YR} = lateral acceleration at rear axle (in g-units)
$K_{\phi F}$ = front roll rate **with** tires (lb.-ft./rad.)
$K_{\phi R}$ = rear roll rate **with** tires (lb.-ft./rad.)
$K_{\phi WR}$ = rear roll rate **without** tires (lb.-ft./rad.)
$K_{\phi TR}$ = axle roll rate on its tires (lb.-ft./rad.)

ϕ = roll angle of vehicle relative to ground (rad.)

ϕ_{uR} = roll angle of axle relative to ground (rad.)

h = total height of CG of rolling mass above ground (ft.)

H = height of the CG above the roll axis (ft.)

z_{RR} = height of CG of axle (assumed same as height of rear roll center) (ft.)

z_{RF} = height of front roll axis (ft.)

t_F = front wheel track $\Big\}$ Assume equal, $t = t_F = t_R$ (ft.)
t_R = rear wheel track

W_F = front rolling weight (lb.)

W'_R = rear rolling weight (lb.)

w = weight of rear unsprung [*rear axle assembly, including tires*] (lb.)

W_R = total rear weight: $W_R = W'_R + w$ (lb.)

ΔW_F = front weight transfer (lb.)

ΔW_R = rear weight transfer (lb.)

M_c = rolling moment constant (lb.-ft.) (see page 454)

Note: It is considered desirable in general to allow for the roll of the axle, and resulting camber thrust of the rear tires. [*But Olley is about to ignore this.*]

Drawing a horizontal line through the CG to the front and rear, one sees that the moment can be divided into $W_F(h - z_{RF})(A_Y + \phi)$ at the front and $W'_R(h - z_{RR})(A_Y + \phi)$ at the rear. Then, if we ignore the slight roll of the axle on the tires:

$$\left(K_{\phi F} + K_{\phi WR}\right)\phi = \left(A_Y + \phi\right)\left[W_F(h - z_{RF}) + W'_R(h - z_{RR})\right] \qquad (2.36)$$

or

$$\phi = \frac{A_Y\left[W_F(h - z_{RF}) + W'_R(h - z_{RR})\right]}{K_{\phi F} + K_{\phi WR} - \left[W_F(h - z_{RF}) + W'_R(h - z_{RR})\right]} \qquad (2.37)$$

$$\text{Roll moment on front tires} = K_{\phi F}\phi + W_F z_{RF} A_Y \qquad (2.38)$$

$$\text{Roll moment on rear tires} = K_{\phi WR}\phi + W_R z_{RR} A_Y \qquad (2.39)$$

Since z_{RF} is frequently zero with IFS, and z_{RR} may be 12 inches or so, it is evident that the roll **moments** on the tires are not proportional to the roll **rates**.

Roughly speaking, on most conventional passenger cars as now made the roll moments carried by the front and rear tires are approximately equal when the front roll rate is **twice** the rear roll rate, both rates **including** the tires. It is inadvisable to carry an excessive proportion of the total roll moment at either end of the car, as there is danger of lifting the inside wheel on a sharp turn. This is particularly true on the driving wheels, whether front or rear, since as the vertical load is reduced, the total adhesion of such a tire may be required for traction, leaving it without cornering force capability.

It has been usual practice to conduct skid pad tests in development work, with means, such as roll-stabilizers, for varying stiffness to alter the distribution of the roll moment. The aim is to avoid the extremes of the two sketches on Figure 2.28, and produce similar upward curvature in the front slip and attitude curves, resulting in a steering angle curve which approximates a straight line, as in Figure 2.25.

The important thing is that the distribution of the roll moment on the tires is **not** the same as the distribution of the roll **rates** [*measured about the roll axis*]. For instance, on a conventional passenger car it is perfectly possible to have equal roll moment distribution front and rear when the front roll rate is double the rear.

Roll Moment Effects–Analysis Based on the Layout of Figure 2.30 and Notation of Figure 2.29

The basic equations are:

$$K_{\phi F}\phi + K_{\phi WR}\left(\phi - \phi_{uR}\right) = \left(A_Y + \phi\right)\left[W_F h + W_R'\left(h - z_{RR}\right)\right] \qquad (2.40)$$

$$K_{\phi TR}\phi_{uR} = K_{\phi WR}\left(\phi - \phi_{uR}\right) + W_R z_{RR}\left(A_Y + \phi_{uR}\right) \qquad (2.41)$$

The term $W_F h + W_R'\left(h - z_{RR}\right)$ is the rolling moment constant for the car and may be called M_c.

Then
$$K_{\phi F}\phi + K_{\phi WR}\left(\phi - \phi_{uR}\right) = M_c\left(A_Y + \phi\right) \qquad (2.42)$$

Whence
$$M_c\left(A_Y + \phi\right) - K_{\phi F}\phi = K_{\phi TR}\phi_{uR} - W_R z_{RR}\left(A_Y + \phi_{uR}\right) \qquad (2.43)$$

or
$$\phi = \frac{A_Y M_c + K_{\phi WR}\phi_{uR}}{K_{\phi F} + K_{\phi WR} - M_c} \qquad (2.44)$$

and
$$\phi_{uR} = \frac{M_c\left(A_Y + \phi\right) + W_R z_{RR} A_Y - K_{\phi F}\phi}{K_{\phi TR} - W_R z_{RR}} \qquad (2.45)$$

Also
$$\Delta W_F = \frac{K_{\phi F}\phi}{t} \quad \text{and} \quad \Delta W_R = \frac{K_{\phi TR}\phi_{uR}}{t} \qquad (2.46)$$

Now we have to assume a certain proportion between the front and rear weight transfers. This proportion is described by $\Delta W_F / \Delta W_R$.

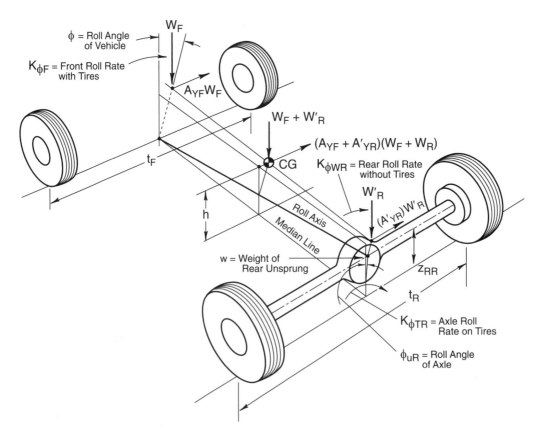

Figure 2.30 *Roll axis geometry—front roll center at ground and rear axle roll on tires.*

Then if front and rear wheel tracks are equal: $K_{\phi F}\phi = \dfrac{\Delta W_F}{\Delta W_R} K_{\phi TR}\phi_{uR}$

Then from Equation 2.45

$$\phi_{uR} = \frac{M_c\left(A_Y + \phi\right) + W_R z_{RR}}{K_{\phi TR}\left(1 + \left(\Delta W_F/\Delta W_R\right)\right) - W_R z_{RR}} \tag{2.47}$$

and

$$K_{\phi F} = \frac{\left(\Delta W_F/\Delta W_R\right) K_{\phi TR}\phi_{uR}}{\phi} \tag{2.48}$$

and $$K_{\phi WR} = \frac{M_c\left(A_Y + \phi\right) - K_{\phi F}\phi}{\phi - \phi_{uR}} = \frac{K_{\phi TR}\phi_{uR} - W_R z_{RR}\left(A_Y + \phi_{uR}\right)}{\phi - \phi_{uR}} \tag{2.49}$$

Examples

Let: $A_Y = 1g$
       $W_F = 2000$ lb.
       $W_R' = 1700$ lb.   (rear rolling weight)
       $w = 300$ lb.   (rear unsprung weight)
       $h = 2$ ft.
       $z_{RR} = 1$ ft.   (height of rear roll axis)
       $\phi = 0.20$ rad.   (5.73° roll angle at 0.5g lateral)
       $t = 5$ ft.
       $\ell = 10$ ft.
       $R = 108$ ft. [*a standard-sized test circle at GM Proving Grounds*]

Then: $M_c = W_F h + W_R' \left(h - z_{RR} \right) = 5700$ lb.-ft.

and $M_c \left(A_Y + \phi \right) = 6840$ lb.-ft.

       $W_R z_{RR} = 2000$ lb.-ft.

For the tire rate it has been usual to use a static rate of about 1000 lb./in., but this makes no allowance for the decrease of vertical rate which occurs in the presence of lateral forces. It seems reasonable to assume a vertical tire rate of 833 lb./in. or 10000 lb./ft.

Then $K_{\phi TR} = 125000$ lb.-ft./rad. (2180 lb.-ft./deg.)

Now consider two simple variations in roll moment distribution [*based on Example 3, Sections 2.4. and 2.5*]:

<u>**Case A**</u> Equal weight transfer front and rear

   $\Delta W_F = \Delta W_R \ \ \left(\text{i.e., } \Delta W_F / \Delta W_R = 1 \right)$

Then from Equation 2.47

$$\phi_{uR} = \frac{M_c \left(A_Y + \phi \right) + W_R z_{RR}}{2K_{\phi TR} - W_R z_{RR}} = \frac{8840}{248000} = \begin{cases} 0.0356 \text{ rad.} \\ 2.04 \text{ deg.} \end{cases} \text{(at } A_Y = 1)} \tag{2.50}$$

From Equation 2.48

$$K_{\phi F} = \frac{K_{\phi TR} \phi_{uR}}{\phi} = \frac{125000 \times 0.0356}{0.20} = \begin{cases} 22250 \text{ lb.-ft./rad.} \\ 388 \text{ lb.-ft./deg.} \end{cases} \tag{2.51}$$

$$K_{\phi WR} = \frac{M_c(A_Y + \phi) - K_{\phi F}\phi}{\phi - \phi_{uR}} = \frac{6840 - 4450}{0.1644} = \begin{cases} 14538 \text{ lb.-ft./rad.} \\ 254 \text{ lb.-ft./deg.} \end{cases} \tag{2.52}$$

$$\Delta W_F = \frac{K_{\phi F}\phi}{t} = \frac{4450}{5} = 890 \text{ lb.} \tag{2.53}$$

$$\Delta W_R = \frac{K_{\phi TR}\phi_{uR}}{t} = 890 \text{ lb.} \tag{2.54}$$

Note that if tires are included in the rear roll rate, this will be:

$$K_{\phi R} = \frac{14550 \times 125000}{139550} = 13033 \text{ lb.-ft./rad.} \tag{2.55}$$

which is only 58.6% of the front roll rate.

Case B 50% more weight transfer on rear than front or $\Delta W_F = 0.667\Delta W_R$.

Then,

$$\phi_{uR} = \frac{M_c(A_Y + \phi) + W_R z_{RR}}{1.667 K_{\phi TR} - W_R z_{RR}} = \frac{8840}{206333} = \begin{cases} 0.0428 \text{ rad.} \\ 2.45 \text{ deg.} \end{cases} \tag{2.56}$$

$$K_{\phi F} = \frac{0.667 K_{\phi TR}\phi_{uR}}{\phi} = \begin{cases} 17842 \text{ lb.-ft./rad.} \\ 311 \text{ lb.-ft./deg.} \end{cases} \tag{2.57}$$

$$K_{\phi WR} = \frac{M_c(A_Y + \phi) - K_{\phi F}\phi}{\phi - \phi_{uR}} = \frac{6840 - 3560}{0.1572} = \begin{cases} 20850 \text{ lb.-ft./rad.} \\ 364 \text{ lb.-ft./deg.} \end{cases} \tag{2.58}$$

$$\Delta W_F = \frac{K_{\phi F}\phi}{t} = \frac{3560}{5} = 712 \text{ lb.} \tag{2.59}$$

$$\Delta W_R = \frac{K_{\phi TR}\phi_{uR}}{t} = \frac{5350}{5} = 1070 \text{ lb.} \tag{2.60}$$

Note that, if tires are included in the rear roll rate, this will be:

$$K_{\phi R} = \frac{20850 \times 125000}{145850} = \begin{cases} 17900 \text{ lb.-ft./rad.} \\ 312 \text{ lb.-ft./deg.} \end{cases} \qquad (2.61)$$

i.e., virtually the same as the front roll rate. **In other words equal roll rates front and rear put about 50% more roll moment on the rear than on the front tires.**

2.6   Calculating Steady-State Steering Characteristics with Lateral Load Transfer Distribution (LLTD)

Introduction

The calculations in this section, and the other sections in this chapter, are summarized at the end of the chapter.

Having determined the load (or weight) transfer for two cases, **Cases A** *and* **B** *at the end of the previous section, Olley now calculates the steady-state constant radius skid pad curves, utilizing his previously developed tire model. He first summarizes the applicable formulas and then tabulates the calculations, presents plots and discusses the results of* **Cases A** *and* **B***.*

In these examples traction effects are **not** *included, neither are roll steers. Also, the examples are for equal front and rear static weights, same tire characteristics front and rear, and same roll gradient (body roll angle per g). The handling differences between the first two examples are solely due to roll moment (LLTD) distribution and camber thrust variations on the front and rear. As anticipated, the front and rear slip angles vs. lateral acceleration are nonlinear.*

In the section entitled "Some Variations," he considers some variations on the first two examples. These are:

    a. Increased weight transfer on front tires
    b. Increased weight on front axle
    c. Decreased inflation on front tires

Olley also considers a third case, **Case C***, in which the vehicle CG is lowered. He starts with* **Case A** *(equal weight transfer front and rear) and reduces the CG height from 24 in. to 18 in., other parameters remaining the same. Figure 2.35 gives the results to be compared to Figure 2.31.*

The result of **Case C** *suggests an examination of the lateral forces on left and right hand tires. Calculations and plots for* **Cases A***,* **B** *and* **C** *follow in the section entitled "Tire Lateral Forces."*

Tires

The assumptions made on the tires (see Figure 2.16) are:

Normal load [*static*]: 1000 lb.
Load at maximum initial cornering stiffness (W_m) = 1100 lb.
Cornering stiffness at this load (C_m) = 150 lb./deg.

Hence $\qquad \dfrac{C_m}{W_m} = 0.150$

and $\qquad \dfrac{C_0}{W_0} = 0.300$

Hence cornering coefficient:

$$C' = \frac{C}{W} = \frac{C_m}{W_m}\left(2 - \frac{W}{W_m}\right) = 0.150\left(2 - \frac{W}{1100}\right) = 0.300 - 0.0001364W$$

Friction coefficient: $\mu = 1.20$

Thus $\alpha_{max} = \dfrac{2F_{Y\,max}}{C} = \dfrac{2.4W}{C}$

[*for a parabola based on 3/4 horizontal scale of CAL curves; see Figure 2.9*]

Summary of Steady-State Equations

We can now apply the following equations to the prediction of skid pad (or steady-state) cornering.

Subscript o is used to designate the **outer** tire.
Subscript i is used to designate the **inner** tire.

1. Roll moment distribution (weight transfer)

    If A_Y = Lateral acceleration in g-units
    Front tires: $\Delta W_F = A_Y K_{\phi F}\phi/t$
    Rear tires: $\Delta W_R = A_Y K_{\phi TR}\phi/t$

2. Effect of vertical load on initial cornering coefficient

$$C' = \frac{C}{W} = \frac{C_m}{W_m}\left(2 - \frac{W}{W_m}\right) \tag{2.62}$$

3. Lateral force vs. slip angle (single wheel)

$$F_Y = C\alpha\left(1 - \frac{\alpha}{2\alpha_{max}}\right)$$ (2.63)

where $$\alpha_{max} = \frac{2F_{Ymax}}{C} = \frac{2\mu W}{C}$$ (2.64)

At slip angles **above** α_{max}, $F_Y = \mu W$ (2.65)

4. Total lateral force

   Let F_{Yo} = lateral force on **outer** tire
         F_{Yi} = lateral force on **inner** tire

   Then for **total lateral force**:

   On parallel independent wheels: $F_{Yo} + F_{Yi} = (A_Y + \phi)W_F$ (2.66)

   On rear axle tires: $F_{Yo} + F_{Yi} = (A_Y + \phi_{uR})W_R$

   This is because camber thrust is approximately:

   (Camber thrust) $\approx$ (vertical load)(camber angle in radians)

5. Solution for slip angle (without traction) [*see 3. above*]:

$$\left[\left(\frac{C}{2\alpha_{max}}\right)_o + \left(\frac{C}{2\alpha_{max}}\right)_i\right]\alpha^2 - (C_o + C_i)\alpha + (\text{total lateral force}) = 0$$ (2.67)

Hence, we can find the slip angle α for any lateral acceleration, A_Y.

Also, having found α, we can apply this to the formula for lateral force for a single wheel (above) to find the lateral force which each tire is producing.

In making these calculations we assume that the slip angle is the same on the two tires of a pair, that the tires have zero camber initially and that in the front independent suspension the two wheels move in planes parallel to the median plane of the car. Roll steer at front or rear is not included in the calculations.

The two Cases A and B have equal weights front and rear, and assume equal tire characteristics front and rear. It is also assumed that the roll gradient of the car is the same in both cases, namely a roll angle of 5.73° for a lateral acceleration of 0.5g. **Therefore the only things which contribute to the differences in handling are the roll moment distribution and the variations in camber thrust on the front and rear tires.**

Case A $\Delta W_F = \Delta W_R = 890 A_Y$

Table 2.1   Case A, Front and Rear

A_Y (g)	0.0	0.2	0.4	0.5	0.55	0.6	0.7
W_o (lb.)	1000	1178	1356	1445	1489.5	1534	1623
W_i (lb.)	1000	822	644	555	510.5	466	377
$(C/W)_o$ (1/deg.)	0.1636	0.1392	0.1150	0.1030	0.097	0.091	0.0785
$(C/W)_i$ (1/deg.)	0.1636	0.188	0.2122	0.2244	0.2305	0.2365	0.2485
C_o (lb./deg.)	163.6	164	156	149	144.5	139.5	127.5
C_i (lb./deg.)	163.6	154.5	137	124.5	117.5	110.5	93.7
$C_o + C_i$ (lb./deg.)	327.2	318.5	293	273.5	262	250	221.2
$(\alpha_{max})_o$ (deg.)	14.65	17.25	20.9	23.3	24.7	26.4	30.6
$(\alpha_{max})_i$ (deg.)	14.65	12.75	11.3	10.7	10.42	10.12	9.65
$(C/2\alpha_{max})_o$	5.58	4.75	3.74	3.20	2.93	2.64	2.08
$(C/2\alpha_{max})_i$	5.58	6.05	6.05	5.82	5.63	5.45	4.85
$(C/2\alpha_{max})_o +$ $(C/2\alpha_{max})_i$	11.16	10.80	9.79	9.02	8.56	8.09	6.93
Front lateral force $1.2\,W_F A_Y$ (lb.)	0.0	480	960	1200	1320	1440	1680
Rear lateral force $1.0356\,W_R A_Y$ (lb.)	0.0	414	828	1036	1140	1243	1450
From above we find:							
α_F (deg.)	0.0	1.60	3.73	5.325	6.35	7.65	12.0
α_R (deg.)	0.0	1.365	3.15	4.44	5.25	6.24	9.165
$\alpha_F - \alpha_R$ (deg.)	0.0	0.235	0.58	0.885	1.10	1.41	2.835
Steer angle δ (deg.)	0.0	5.535	5.88	6.185	6.40	6.71	8.135

Note: The rear axle roll gradient is $\phi_{uR}/A_Y = 0.0356$ rad./g.

Discussion of Case A—These values are plotted in Figure 2.31 and show a normal and desirable amount of understeer, which is entirely due to the roll of the car and the camber thrust of the parallel independent front wheels.

Even a comparatively small change in the front wheel static camber will have a marked effect on steady-state steering. Figure 2.31 has dotted lines representing the calculated effect of 2° positive wheel camber on α_F and δ, which shows an appreciable increase in front slip angle and understeer.

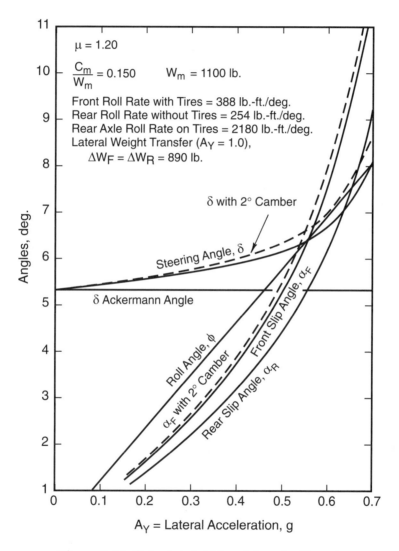

Figure 2.31 *Calculated skid pad data for Case A.*

A particular warning in connection with all these calculated curves concerns the roll angle. This is shown as increasing directly with A_Y up to 0.7g. This probably represents more than the allowed bump clearance, and bump or rebound stops (or both) will engage before any such lateral acceleration is reached.

For example, front roll rate is 388 lb.-ft./deg. and of this 2180 lb.-ft./deg. is in the tires. So the front roll rate of springs alone is:

$$\frac{388 \times 2180}{1792} = 472 \text{ lb.-ft./deg. [springs in series]}$$

The assumed wheel track is 60 in., and the roll angle is 0.10 rad. at 0.5g. Thus the total deflection at the two wheels is ±3 in., and of this approximately 2-1/2 in. will occur in the suspension and 1/2 in. in the tire. Thus even 0.5g lateral will come close to engaging the bump stops, the effect of which is similar to a greatly increased front stabilizer bar. When either stop is engaged the roll rate is nearly doubled, and when both are engaged the roll rate is that of the tires alone, or 2180 lb.-ft./deg. The rear axle is much less likely to hit its bump stops, because their spacing is so much narrower than the wheel track.

Consequently, above 0.5g, with the assumed amount of roll, we could expect a much more severe upward bend of the steering angle curve than is shown in Figure 2.31.

Case B $\Delta W_F = 712 A_Y$, $\Delta W_R = 1070 A_Y$ [$\Delta W_R / \Delta W_F = 1.5$]

Table 2.2 Case B, Front

A_Y (g)	0.0	0.2	0.4	0.5	0.55	0.6	0.7
W_o (lb.)	1000	1142.4	1284.8	1356	1391.6	1427.2	1498
W_i (lb.)	1000	857.6	715.2	644	608.4	572.8	502
$(C/W)_o$ (1/deg.)	0.1636	0.144	0.125	0.115	0.110	0.1055	0.0955
$(C/W)_i$ (1/deg.)	0.1636	0.183	0.2025	0.2122	0.2170	0.222	0.2315
C_o (lb./deg.)	163.6	164.5	160.5	156	153	150	143
C_i (lb./deg.)	163.6	157	145	137	132	127	116
$C_o + C_i$ (lb./deg.)	327.2	321.5	305.5	293	285	277	259
$(\alpha_{max})_o$ (deg.)	14.65	16.7	19.25	20.9	21.8	22.8	25.1
$(\alpha_{max})_i$ (deg.)	14.65	13.1	11.85	11.25	11.07	10.82	10.38
$(C/2\alpha_{max})_o$	5.58	4.92	4.17	3.73	3.51	3.29	2.85
$(C/2\alpha_{max})_i$	5.58	6.00	6.10	6.09	5.96	5.87	5.59
$(C/2\alpha_{max})_o +$ $(C/2\alpha_{max})_i$	11.16	10.92	10.27	9.82	9.47	9.16	8.44
Front lateral force $1.2 W_F A_Y$ (lb.)	0.0	480	960	1200	1320	1440	1680
Thus: α_F (deg.)	0.0	1.58	3.58	4.915	5.725	6.675	9.30

Table 2.3 Case B, Rear

A_Y (g)	0.0	0.2	0.4	0.5	0.55	0.6	0.7
W_o (lb.)	1000	1214	1428	1535	1588.5	1642	1749
W_i (lb.)	1000	786	572	465	411.5	358	251
$(C/W)_o$ (1/deg.)	0.1636	0.134	0.105	0.0905	0.0835	0.076	0.0615
$(C/W)_i$ (1/deg.)	0.1636	0.193	0.222	0.2365	0.2438	0.2511	0.2658
C_o (lb./deg.)		162.8	150	138.5	132.5	125	107.5
C_i (lb./deg.)		151.5	127	110	100.2	90	66.75
$C_o + C_i$ (lb./deg.)		314.3	277	248.5	232.7	215	174.25
$(\alpha_{max})_o$ (deg.)	$\dfrac{2.4W_o}{C_o}$	17.9	22.85	26.6	28.8	31.5	39.0
$(\alpha_{max})_i$ (deg.)	$\dfrac{2.4W_i}{C_i}$	12.45	10.80	10.15	9.88	9.55	9.02
$(C/2\alpha_{max})_o$		4.55	3.28	2.60	2.30	1.985	1.38
$(C/2\alpha_{max})_i$		6.10	5.88	5.43	5.08	4.71	3.70
$(C/2\alpha_{max})_o +$ $(C/2\alpha_{max})_i$		10.65	9.16	8.03	7.38	6.695	5.08
Rear lateral force $1.0428\,W_R A_Y$ (lb.)		417	835	1043	1147	1250	1460
Thus: α_R (deg.)		1.4	3.4	5.0	6.12	7.625	12.90
See Figure 2.32						At this point the inner wheel has reached its max. lat. force, 301 lb.	
Steer angle δ (deg.)		5.48	5.48	5.215	4.905	4.35	1.70

The front wheels are assumed to have zero design camber and to move up and down parallel to the median plane of the car.

Discussion of Case B—The very marked sudden oversteer is evident from Figure 2.32. Our assumption as to tire characteristics cannot be too far wrong, since Figure 2.32 shows the steering quality which is typical of a car carrying too much roll moment on the rear tires. The steering is virtually "neutral" up to 0.4g, and the sudden oversteer shows up only when the car is pushed exceptionally hard on a corner.

We prefer as a rule to draw skid pads against lateral acceleration rather than miles per hour, because such curves show graphically any departure from linearity in the response to lateral acceleration.

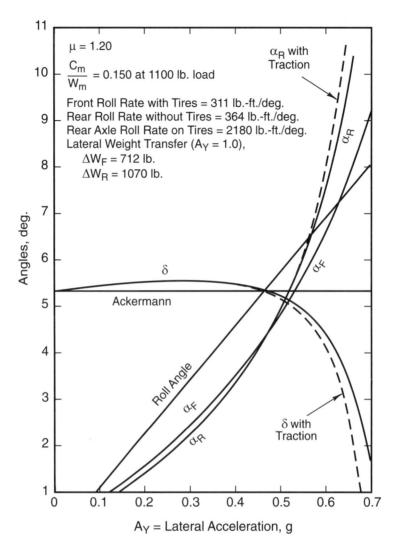

The figure displays calculated skid pad data with the following annotations:

μ = 1.20

$\dfrac{C_m}{W_m}$ = 0.150 at 1100 lb. load

Front Roll Rate with Tires = 311 lb.-ft./deg.
Rear Roll Rate without Tires = 364 lb.-ft./deg.
Rear Axle Roll Rate on Tires = 2180 lb.-ft./deg.
Lateral Weight Transfer (A_Y = 1.0),
ΔW_F = 712 lb.
ΔW_R = 1070 lb.

α_R with Traction

α_R

α_F

δ

Ackermann

Roll Angle

α_F

α_R

δ with Traction

Angles, deg.

A_Y = Lateral Acceleration, g

Figure 2.32 *Calculated skid pad data for Case B.*

However, in Case B it seems desirable, as an example of how suddenly the oversteer actually occurs, to redraw Figure 2.32 on a base of miles per hour. Figure 2.33 shows that, on the flat surface and the 108 foot radius the car is reasonably under control up to 27 mph, but from this speed upward it is virtually out of control. [*Note: The curves with traction are discussed later.*]

Some Variations

It is possible to figure the effect of all sorts of variations on the two basic Cases A and B. The effect of front wheel design camber has already been indicated in Case A, the result being an appreciable increase in understeer.

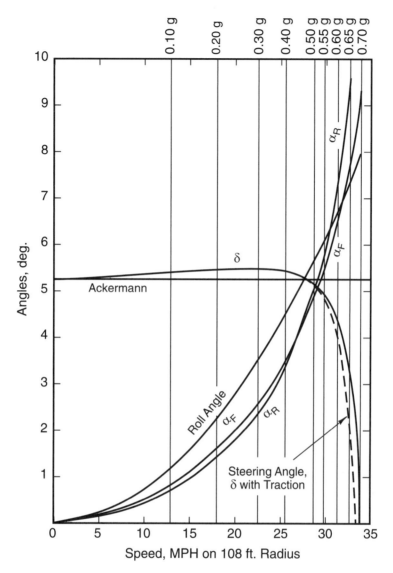

Figure 2.33 *Case B data replotted against speed.*

a. Increased **weight transfer** on front tires:

$\Delta W_F = 1070$ lb. at $A_Y = 1g$

$\Delta W_R = 712$ lb. at $A_Y = 1g$

This results in increased understeer, particularly at lateral accelerations above 0.4g.

A notable advantage is that the effect of traction in dissipating the cornering power of the rear tires, and thus causing oversteer, is greatly reduced as the rear weight transfer is reduced.

However, a notable disadvantage is that, as weight transfer on the front tires is increased, the handling of the car becomes "heavier," because of increased aligning torque.

b. Increased **weight** on front tires:

$$
\left.\begin{array}{l}
W_F = 2200 \text{ lb.} \\
W_R = 1800 \text{ lb.}
\end{array}\right\} \; 55/45 \text{ weight distribution}
$$

This results in a general increase in understeer even at low lateral accelerations. It also results in increased roll angle (since the CG has moved 6 in. forward and the roll axis is inclined). With the same roll rates as in Case A the front weight transfer is increased and the rear decreased.

$\Delta W_F \; (A_Y = 1g)$ becomes 925 lb.

$\Delta W_R \; (A_Y = 1g)$ becomes 875 lb.

Because of the lighter load on the rear, the effect of traction in increasing α_R at accelerations above 0.5g, becomes more marked.

c. Decreased **inflation** in front tires:

It is rather difficult to ascertain any general rule for the variation of cornering stiffness with inflation. A typical curve, for tires of rather low initial cornering stiffness, is given in Figure 62 of the CAL-Institute of Mechanical Engineers report, and is reproduced in Figure 2.34. This applies to 5.00-16, 6.00-16, and 7.00-16 tires.

The variation is not in direct proportion to inflation. But a reduction of inflation from 24 to 16 psi (or 33%) reduces C from 114 to 84 lb./deg., or 26%.

The effect of reducing front tire inflation is very similar to increasing front load, i.e., general increase in understeer (together with heavier handling).

It is not worthwhile to reproduce the curves and figures for all these possible variations, since the general trend is obvious, and any particular case is readily worked out.

Case C—Reduced CG height—A more important variation, which requires some attention, is the effect of lowering the CG.

To try this out, I have taken Case A above and have reduced h, the height of the CG, from 24 in. to 18 in., changing nothing else. The result is instructive as a strong argument for building low cars.

The roll of the car at 0.5g is reduced from 5.73° to 3.7°.
The roll of the axle on its tires, from 1.02° to 0.80°.

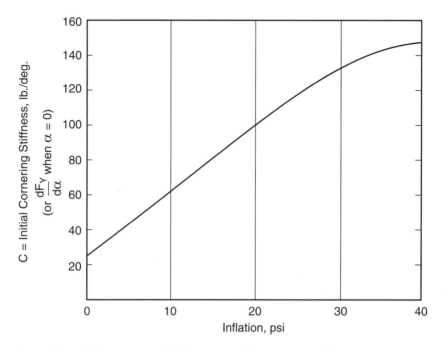

Figure 2.34 *Cornell Aeronautical Lab curve of cornering stiffness vs. inflation pressure.*

ΔW_F at 0.5g is reduced from 445 lb. to **288** lb.
ΔW_R at 0.5g is reduced from 445 lb. to **352** lb.
Total transfer at 0.5g is reduced from 890 lb. to **640** lb.

Other quantities are:

A_Y (g)	0.20	0.40	0.50	0.55	0.60	0.70
α_F (deg.)	1.47	3.245	4.34	4.975	5.68	7.42
α_R (deg.)	1.345	3.03	4.055	4.67	5.38	7.24
δ (deg.)	5.425	5.545	5.585	5.605	5.60	5.48

See Figure 2.35, Case C.

The overall result has been to reduce the understeer of Case A to almost neutral steering. If more understeer and more "steering feel" were desired, it could readily be obtained by a slight increase in front stabilizer.

However the greatest improvement in handling is due to the reduction in the difference of the lateral forces on the outside and inside tires.

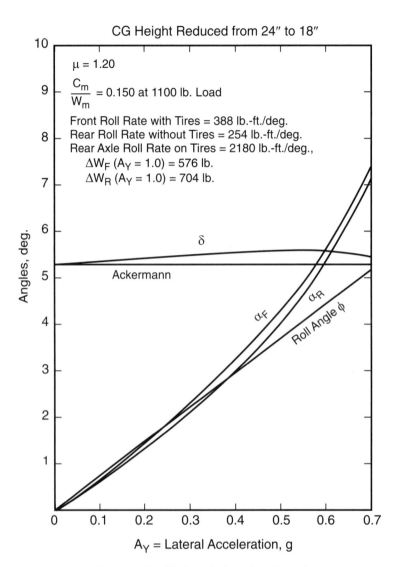

Figure 2.35 *Skid pad plots for Case C.*

Tire Lateral Forces

The different lateral forces on the outside and inside tires are readily obtained as indicated in the following tabulation. And incidentally, the necessary calculation gives a useful check on the accuracy of the previous figuring.

The calculation follows from Equation 2.67,

$$\text{Total lateral force on outer tire} = F_{YFo} = C_o\alpha_F - \left(\frac{C}{\alpha_{max}}\right)_o \alpha_F^2 \tag{2.68}$$

$$\text{Total lateral force on inner tire} = F_{YFi} = C_i\alpha_F - \left(\frac{C}{\alpha_{max}}\right)_i \alpha_F^2 \qquad (2.69)$$

Adding these two gives total lateral force at front, and similarly for the rear tires.

The calculation and results for the three cases, A, B and C follow along with some discussion.

Table 2.4 Case A, Front and Rear Summary

A_Y (g)	0.2	0.4	0.5	0.55	0.6	0.7
Front						
α_F (deg.)	1.6	3.73	5.325	6.35	7.65	12.0
$C_o\alpha_F$ (lb.)	262.5	581	792	918	1068	1530
$\left(\dfrac{C}{2\alpha_{max}}\right)_o \alpha_F^2$ (lb.)	12.2	52	90.5	118	154.5	300
F_{YFo} (lb.)	250.3	529	701.5	800	913.5	1230
$C_i\alpha_F$ (lb.)	247	510	662	746	845	Beyond $(\alpha_{max})_i$
$\left(\dfrac{C}{2\alpha_{max}}\right)_i \alpha_F^2$ (lb.)	15.5	84	165	227	319	
F_{YFi} (lb.)	231.5	426	497	519	526	452.5
Front lat. force (lb.)	481.8	955	1198.5	1319	1439.5	1682.5
Rear						
α_R (deg.)	1.365	3.15	4.44	5.25	6.24	9.165
$C_o\alpha_R$ (lb.)	224	492	661	758	870	1170
$\left(\dfrac{C}{2\alpha_{max}}\right)_o \alpha_R^2$ (lb.)	8.84	37.1	63	81	102.5	175
F_{YRo} (lb.)	215.16	454.9	598	677	767.5	995
$C_i\alpha_R$ (lb.)	210.5	432	552	617	690	860
$\left(\dfrac{C}{2\alpha_{max}}\right)_i \alpha_R^2$ (lb.)	11.25	60	114.5	155	212	408
F_{YRi} (lb.)	199.25	372	437.5	462	478	452
Rear lat. force (lb.)	414.41	826.9	1035.5	1139	1245.5	1447

Figure 2.36 shows the comparison between front and rear tires. Similar investigations of Case B, and Case C (with low CG), are shown in Table 2.5.

Table 2.5 Cases B and C, Front and Rear Summary

A_Y (g)	0.2	0.4	0.5	0.55	0.6	0.7
Case B	**Front** See Figure 2.37					
F_{YFo} (lb.)	247	520	675	760	854	1083
F_{YFi} (lb.)	233	440	525	560	586	596
	Rear					
F_{YRo} (lb.)	217	472	628	724	838	1155
F_{YRi} (lb.)	200	363	415	423	412	301
Case C	**Front** See Figure 2.38					
F_{YFo} (lb.)	232	481.5	617.5	691.5	768	941
F_{YFi} (lb.)	220	422.5	512.5	551.5	588	642
	Rear					
F_{YRo} (lb.)	211	442	572	642	716.5	891
F_{YRi} (lb.)	200	380	456	488	516.5	552

The three figures—2.36, 2.37, and 2.38—plot lateral force per wheel against lateral acceleration. The mean lateral force required is also shown.

They illustrate several useful facts. For instance,

1. They show why a car cannot develop the lateral acceleration on corners of a motorcycle. We have assumed a "maximum" dry road friction coefficient of 1.2, which is justified by tire tests. Yet it is evident that in Figure 2.36 the vehicle is not going to get much higher than $A_Y = 0.70$ because of the rapid collapse of lateral force on the inside **front** tire.

    And similarly in Figure 2.37, showing the collapse of lateral force on the inside **rear** tire.

2. The progressive separation of the lateral forces on the two tires of a pair is directly due to roll moment. And the reduced separation in Figure 2.38 is an indication of how sensitive this separation is to the height of the CG and why it is important to keep the CG low on sports cars and race cars. It appears that maximum lateral forces on the inside wheels will not be reduced in Figure 2.38 even at $A_Y = 0.7$.

3. The increased slope of the "mean line" on front tires [*compared with the rear tires*] in all three figures illustrates the increased demand for lateral force on the front tires, to balance the camber thrust of the parallel independent front wheels.

4. In Figure 2.37 the mean lateral force on the front tires is the same as in Figure 2.36. But the separation between outer and inner lateral forces is greater in Figure 2.36

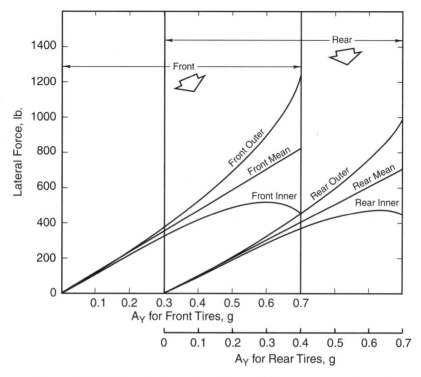

Figure 2.36 *Distribution of total lateral force on tires, Case A.*

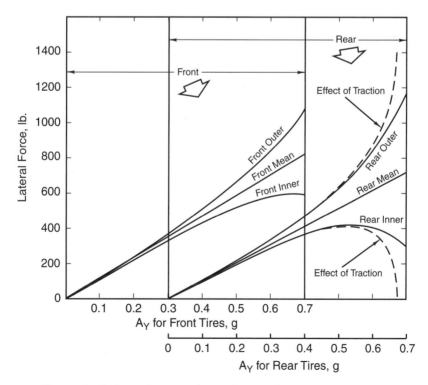

Figure 2.37 *Distribution of total lateral force on tires, Case B.*

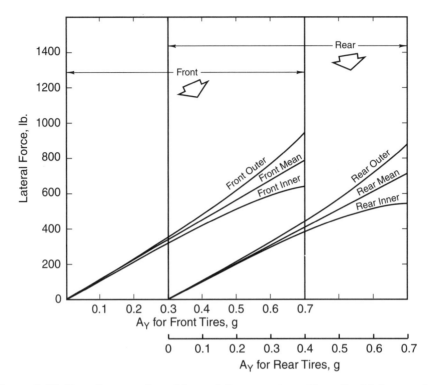

Figure 2.38 *Distribution of total lateral force on tires, Case C with lowered CG.*

because of the greater weight transfer in Case A. From the nature of the aligning torque with vertical load, shown in Figure 2.3, it follows that Case A will have more "steering feel" or will have heavier handling than Case B. Figure 2.38, with the reduced CG height, has both a lower mean lateral force and less separation than the other two, and will therefore have definitely lighter handling.

2.7 Traction Effects

Introduction

The calculations in this section, and the other sections in this chapter, are summarized at the end of the chapter.

Evidently the thing which has been missing so far from the calculations is the effect on the steering of the tractive force necessary to drive the vehicle through the turn. We shall have to find approximately what these tractive forces are on the 108 foot radius of the standard skid pad. And we will need to make an "educated" guess as to what such tractive forces may do to the cornering stiffness of the driving tires. [*In the early 1960s when Olley wrote this section, tire data under tractive conditions was sparse and unreliable.*]

Earlier, the car was represented as a two-wheeled vehicle. But since we shall be concerned with roll moments [*LLTD*] and different effects on the outside and inside wheels, it is more logical to represent the car as shown in Figure 2.39.

α_F = front slip angle
α_R = rear slip angle
β = vehicle slip angle at CG
δ = steering angle
F_{YF} = lateral force, front wheel pair
F_{YR} = lateral force, rear wheel pair
A_Y = lateral acceleration (in g-units)

F_{YF} and F_{YR} are external lateral forces exclusive of lateral forces needed to balance camber thrust. Because of the small angles actually involved we have been assuming in all calculations that $F_{YF} = A_Y W_F$ and $F_{YR} = A_Y W_R$.

The justification for this can be seen from the force polygon in Figure 2.40 representing Case A, Section 2.6, at 0.65g lateral acceleration.

Here CA represents centrifugal force at the CG, $A_Y(W_F + W_R)$.

Angle BAD $= \alpha_F + a/R = \beta + \delta = 12.065°$ or 0.21 rad.

Angle FDE $= \beta = \alpha_R - b/R = 4.8°$ or 0.0838 rad.

CE is drawn at right angles to DE, and represents the direction of the tractive force.

Then
$$AD = F_{YF} \approx A_Y W_F$$
$$DE = F_{YR} \approx A_Y W_R$$

And if F_R is the rolling resistance of the four tires,

$$CE = (\text{tractive force}) - F_R = 2F_X - F_R \tag{2.70}$$

Also: $CE \cong AB \times (BAD) + BC \times (FDE)$ with angles in radians, or

$$2F_X - F_R \approx A_Y W_F (\alpha_F + a/R) + A_Y W_R (\alpha_R - b/R) \tag{2.71}$$

but
$$W_F(a/R) = W_R(b/R) \tag{2.72}$$

so
$$2F_X - F_R \approx A_Y(W_F \alpha_F + W_R \alpha_R) \tag{2.73}$$

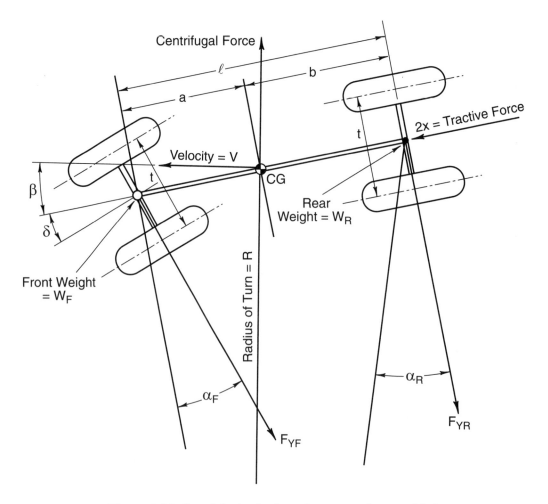

Figure 2.39 *Simplified vehicle with tractive forces added.*

Or, with $W_F = W_R$ and $W = W_F + W_R$ (total car weight)

then
$$2F_X - F_R \approx \frac{A_Y W}{2}(\alpha_F + \alpha_R) \tag{2.74}$$

From the above equation we can estimate the tractive force needed to maintain the car at constant speed on the curve.

From the polygon diagram, we can see that the effective tractive force is actually the component at right angles to AC. But the angle β is so small that $(1/2)A_Y W(\alpha_F + \alpha_R)$ will effectively represent total traction, less rolling resistance.

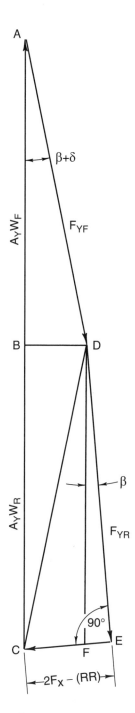

Figure 2.40 *Force polygon representing Case A (Section 2.6).*
$$A_Y = 0.65g$$

By using this force polygon approach and defining the effective tractive force as the com-
ponent at right angles to the centrifugal force, Olley comes up with a "tractive force less
a rolling resistance." He is then confronted with estimating the rolling resistance in the
presence of a driven wheel, i.e., one with a driving torque or force at the roadway. The
following discussion is interesting in light of the problem that still exists when attempting
to separate rolling resistance and tractive effort tests on a modern tire tester.

Rolling Resistance

It is a matter of doubt whether to include the rolling resistance of all four wheels or of the
front wheels only. The argument for including all four wheels is that all four rolling resistances assist in retarding the car when the tractive effort is removed.

One question is to what extent the traction forces at the rear tires cause a weight transfer
from front to rear. It is frequently assumed that all rear traction forces cause such a
weight transfer. But obviously this is not so. The transfer depends on the height of application of the **resisting** forces.

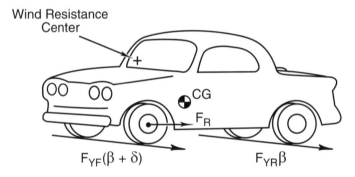

Figure 2.41 *Location of resistances.*

On the skid pad the speed is low enough for wind resistance not to be serious. And since
the speed is constant there is no appreciable transfer of weight rearward from forces at
the CG.

The front wheel rolling resistance occurs at the height of the wheel spindles (since
these are free-rolling wheels). But the front to rear weight transfer from this cause is
only 3 or 4 pounds, and is negligible.

**The chief resistances to be overcome on the skid pad are the rearward components
of the tire lateral forces**, and these occur at ground level, as does the traction force, so
that fore and aft equilibrium is not disturbed.

Hence it appears we can ignore such weight transfer.

Combined Longitudinal and Lateral Tire Force

On Figure 2.42, let AB represent the center plane of a wheel which is following a path OC, having a slip angle AOC $= \alpha_R$.

It develops a lateral force F_Y, the maximum value of which is represented by OD.

Or OD $= F_{Ymax} = \mu W$.

If a traction force F_X (= OG) is applied through the tire, F_{Ymax} is reduced to OH which is $\sqrt{\mu^2 W^2 - F_X^2}$.

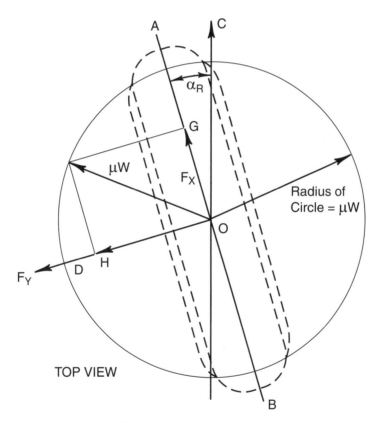

Figure 2.42 *Introduction to tire friction circle.*

This [*the friction circle of Figure 2.42*] is usually accepted as an adequate explanation of the reduction of cornering stiffness under traction. It is probably incomplete in that the presence of tractive forces in the tire contact patch presumably disturbs the cornering ability of the tire in other ways. However it will serve well enough for our purpose.

Then we can regard the presence of traction as simply reducing the effective friction coefficient at the driving tires from μ as previously assumed to

$$\mu' = \mu\sqrt{1 - \left(\frac{F_X}{\mu W}\right)^2} \qquad (2.75)$$

When we use these new values of μ' at the rear tires in the previous calculations, we shall get new and increased values of α_R and β. And these will again give us increased values of F_X, and a "fatter" force polygon, as on Figure 2.40, and so forth. However in most cases which have been tried these additional refinements do not seem worthwhile. It appears sufficient to proceed as follows, in Table 2.6.

The authors have not been able to ascertain how Olley came up with "68 lb." for the rolling resistance (RR) in Table 2.6. Since he uses a constant value over the lateral acceleration range, we assume it is an estimate. The magnitude appears reasonable. Note that Olley uses the same rolling resistance value for Case B.

These results are added to Figure 2.31 and reproduced as Figure 2.43. They show the progressive increase in α_R due to traction and the fact that at high slip angles traction may cause the δ curve to "hook over," indicating a possible breakaway of the rear tires.

The results are also entered in Figure 2.44 (a revision of Figure 2.36), where they show clearly the effect of traction in reducing the cornering ability of the **inside rear tire**. At 0.70g the calculations indicate that the inside tire has passed beyond the apex of its assumed curve of lateral force vs. slip angle, and can produce only a lateral force limited to the vertical load multiplied by the diminished friction coefficient μ'.

It appears from the calculations that the more heavily loaded outside tire does not suffer a great reduction in cornering stiffness. This is because of the small value of $\left(F_X/\mu W\right)^2$, in Equation 2.75. The thing that makes the lateral force on the outer tire grow, and which increases α_R, is the rapidly decreasing cornering stiffness of the **inside** tire.

These calculations assume a frictionless differential, i.e., that the tractive effort $2F_X$ is divided equally between the two rear wheels. A high friction differential [*limited slip*] or "free-wheel" type [*like the Detroit Locker*] will evidently improve the situation by reducing the tractive force on the inside wheel and give better cornering at high values of A_Y.

The next thing to consider is the effect of rear wheel traction in Case B with 50% higher weight transfer on the rear than on the front tires. Because of its importance, these calculations will also be given in full, Table 2.7.

[Rather than reproduce Figures 2.32, 2.33, and 2.37 here, Olley goes back and overplots the traction effects on these earlier figures.]

Table 2.6 Case A (Rear) with Traction Effects Included

A_Y (g)	0.5	0.55	0.6	0.65	0.7
$\alpha_F + \alpha_R$ (deg.)	9.765	11.60	13.89	16.865	21.165
$\alpha_F + \alpha_R$ (rad.)	0.1705	0.2025	0.2425	0.2942	0.3690
$A_Y W/2$ (lb.)	1000	1100	1200	1300	1400
$2F_X - RR$ (lb.)	170.5	222.75	291	382.5	516
$2F_X$ (Add 68 lb.)	238.5	290.75	359	450.5	584
Outer μW (lb.)	1734	1787	1841	1894	1950
$(F_X/\mu W)^2$	0.00474	0.00662	0.0095	0.01415	0.0224
$\mu' W$ (lb.)	1730	1781	1832	1880.5	1928
C_o (lb./deg.)	149	144.5	139.5	134	127.5
$(\alpha_{max})_o = \dfrac{2\mu' W}{C_o}$ (deg.)	23.2	24.65	26.25	28.1	30.2
$C_o/2(\alpha_{max})_o$	3.215	2.93	2.66	2.385	2.11
Inner μW (lb.)	666	612.6	559.2	505.8	452.4
$(F_X/\mu W)^2$	0.032	0.0555	0.1035	0.202	0.416
$\mu' W$ (lb.)	655	595	529	451	345
C_i (lb./deg.)	124.5	117.5	110.5	102.2	93.7
$(\alpha_{max})_i = \dfrac{2\mu' W}{C_i}$ (deg.)	10.5	10.13	9.57	8.825	7.35
$C_i/2(\alpha_{max})_i$	5.93	5.8	5.775	5.8	6.38
$C_o + C_i$ (lb./deg.)	273.5	262	250	236.2	221.2
$\dfrac{C_o}{2(\alpha_{max})_o} + \dfrac{C_i}{2(\alpha_{max})_i}$	9.145	8.73	8.435	8.185	8.49
Whence: α_F (deg.)	5.325	6.35	7.65	9.415	12.0
α_R (deg.)	4.45	5.29	6.30	7.78	10.475
Steer angle δ (deg.)	6.175	6.36	6.65	6.935	6.825

From these [*traction effects*] it is evident that:

1. The sharp and sudden oversteer of Case B is rendered even worse by even the minimum traction required to maintain constant speed on the turn. Any sudden application of power above 0.50g will cause the car to "spin out."

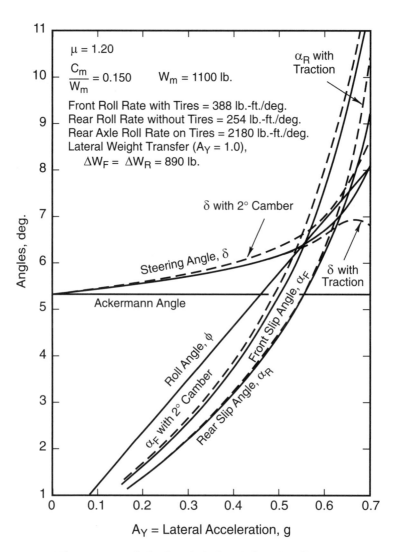

Figure 2.43 *Calculated skid pad data for Case A,*
with traction effects added to Figure 2.31.

2. Car cannot reach 0.70g because of lack of traction on inside rear wheel (unless a high friction differential is fitted).

3. Figure 2.37 shows the greatly increased divergence between lateral forces on the two wheels caused by traction, as compared with Case A.

This can be shown even more clearly if one plots a more extreme condition than Case A. If one considers, for example, a case in which the weight transfer in front is 50% higher than in rear, it is found that the "oversteer" tendency due to normal traction becomes negligible.

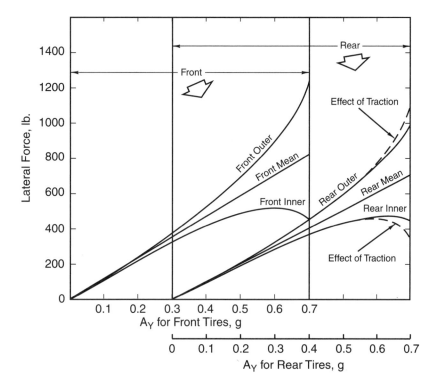

Figure 2.44 *Distribution of total lateral force for Case A.*

Thus, carrying too much roll moment on the rear tires not only makes for sudden oversteer under "coasting" conditions [*dropped-throttle oversteer*], but also greatly increases the tendency of the rear end to break loose due to traction.

(How far one should go in the direction of making a car that will not break loose at the rear due to traction is a matter of driver experience and road conditions. In general, a condition roughly like Case A, which under normal steady traction cannot be made to "spin out" at the rear, is preferred by most drivers.)

4. The significance of these traction effects is that, even under steady-state cornering, traction has an oversteering tendency above 0.50g. Excess traction for acceleration in the turn increases this tendency.

Generally speaking, on releasing the accelerator of a rear drive car with IFS, the traction effect being removed, the yaw velocity will decrease and the car will return to a more controllable condition.

In an extreme case, however, like Case C, with excessive rear roll moment, this desirable result is by no means certain since the car oversteers at high lateral acceleration even without traction.

Table 2.7 Case B with Traction Effects Included

A_Y (g)	0.5	0.55	0.6	0.65	0.7
$\alpha_F + \alpha_R$ (deg.)	9.915	11.845	14.30	17.635	22.2
$\alpha_F + \alpha_R$ (rad.)	0.1730	0.2065	0.2495	0.3075	0.3870
$A_Y W/2$ (lb.)	1000	1100	1200	1300	1400
$2F_X - RR$ (lb.)	173	227.2	299.4	399.7	542
(Add 68 lb.) $2F_X$	241	295	367	468	610
Outer μW (lb.)	1840	1905	1970	2035	2100
$(F_X/\mu W)^2$	0.0043	0.0060	0.00867	0.01322	0.0211
$\mu' W$ (lb.)	1836	1899	1961.5	2021.5	2078
C_o (lb./deg.)	138.5	132.5	125	117	107.5
$(\alpha_{max})_o = \dfrac{2\mu' W}{C_o}$ (deg.)	26.5	28.6	31.35	34.5	38.7
$C_o/2(\alpha_{max})_o$	2.61	2.31	1.99	1.695	1.39
Inner μW (lb.)	558	494	430	366	301.5
$(F_X/\mu W)^2$	0.04675	0.0895	0.182	0.410	*see note below
$\mu' W$ (lb.)	545	471	389	281	
C_i (lb./deg.)	110	100.2	90	79	
$(\alpha_{max})_i = \dfrac{2\mu' W}{C_i}$ (deg.)	9.9	9.4	8.65	7.12	
$C_i/2(\alpha_{max})_i$	5.56	5.45	5.21	5.55	
$C_o + C_i$ (lb./deg.)	248.5	232.7	215	196	
$\dfrac{C_o}{2(\alpha_{max})_o} + \dfrac{C_i}{2(\alpha_{max})_i}$	8.17	7.76	7.20	7.245	
Whence: α_F (deg.)	4.915	5.725	6.675	7.785	
α_R (deg.)	5.035	6.210	7.905	10.925	
Steer angle δ (deg.)	5.180	4.815	4.07	2.16	

*Evidently this cannot produce 305 lb. traction. Wheel will spin before 0.7g is reached.

5. A basic limitation of the four-wheeled vehicle is evidently the great reduction of cornering ability due to lateral weight transfer. Even with an assumed friction coefficient of 1.20 the two Examples 1 and 2 are going to be limited to a lateral acceleration in the neighborhood of 0.70g or less.

At various times "self-banking" vehicles have been proposed. These do nothing to improve the cornering ability so long as the lateral weight transfer is not affected.

The only "banking" which is really effective is that of the bicycle, which steers almost entirely by camber thrust, and in which there is no lateral weight transfer. These can show lateral accelerations greater than 1.0g. However, as shown in Figure 2.38, the cornering of a four-wheeled vehicle can be greatly improved by simply lowering the CG.

Measurements since made at Calspan (in a bicycle research program[13] for the original Schwinn company) indicate that the cornering of conventional bicycles (with low and medium tire pressures) may depend more on slip angle than camber angle.

Studies and experiments by Milliken Research Associates, Inc. indicate that a car with highly negatively cambered motorcycle tires (all wheels leaning inward) can realize higher lateral forces than with the same tires vertical. In this case a pair of negatively cambered wheels, with lateral load transfer, realize a higher lateral force than without load transfer. This is because the inward camber thrust on the heavily loaded outside wheel more than compensates for the camber thrust of the lightly loaded inside wheel. Generally, camber thrust increases almost linearly with load.[14]

Power Required

The power at the rear wheels figured on a basis of the calculated traction forces is shown in Figure 2.45. This is for a 4000 lb. car. It appears to be in general agreement with power measurements on the skid pad when allowance is made for the weight of the vehicle.

2.8 Neutral Steer Point and Static Margin

Introduction

The concept of a neutral steer point (NSP) for automobiles stems from the neutral point for aircraft and appears to have been introduced into the literature by G.E. Lind Walker.[15] The concept of static margin, (SM) again from aircraft practice, follows.

---

[13] Roland, R. D., Bicycle Tire Testing, Phase II, CAL Report No. YA-3063-K-2, 1975.

[14] Milliken, W. F. and Milliken, D. L., *Race Car Vehicle Dynamics*, R-146, Society of Automotive Engineers, Warrendale, Pa., 1995. See pages 290–292 and Figure 7.5.

[15] Walker, G. E. L., "Directional Stability, a Study of Factors Involved in Private Car Design," *Automobile Engineer* (UK) Volume 40, Numbers 530, 533, p. 281, 370, 1950.

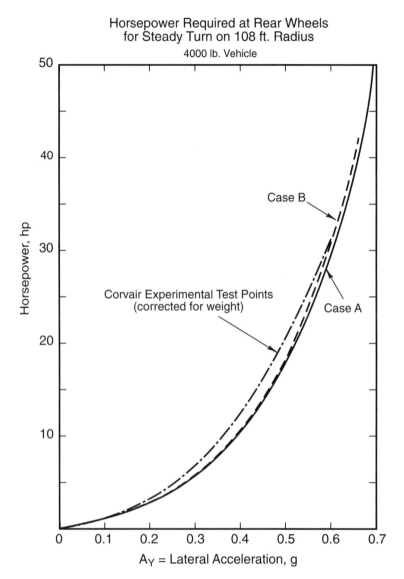

Figure 2.45 *Power required on the skid pad.*

Related concepts such as the Bundorf compliances[16] are not discussed by Olley since they were developed after Olley wrote his monographs.

Neutral Steer Point

The understeer or oversteer of a car can be defined by locating the position of the "neutral steer point." If a line is drawn through the CG parallel to the roll axis, there will be a

---

[16] Bundorf, R. T., "The Effect of Vehicle Design Parameters on Characteristic Speed and Understeer," Paper No. 670078, Society of Automotive Engineers, 1967.

point on this line at which a horizontal lateral force (Y_0) will cause the car to drift sideways but will maintain a straight course. This is the NSP, and the distance this is from the CG divided by the wheelbase, or $(d - a)/\ell$ in Figure 2.46, is the "static margin," which (with some limitations) defines in one dimensionless quantity, the directional stability of the vehicle [*for the fixed control case*].

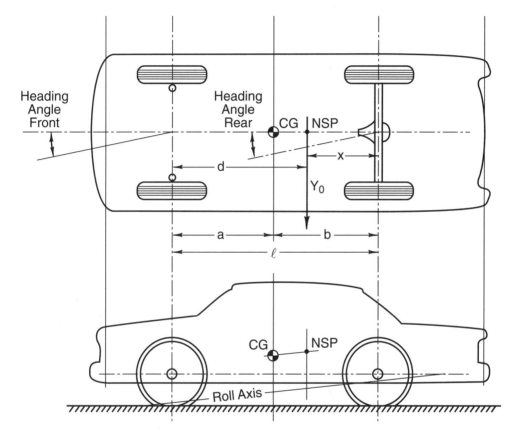

Figure 2.46 *Location of neutral steer point (NSP).*

One has to make several assumptions:

1. It is assumed that the combined cornering stiffnesses of the front and rear wheel pairs (C_F and C_R) are constants.

2. Roll of the rear axle on its tires is ignored, and rear axle weight is added to the rolling (sprung) weight.

3. It is assumed that the steering wheel is rigidly held and that the steering linkage is rigid (so that front roll steer is significant).

4. Front wheels are assumed to roll through same angle as the car [*parallel IFS*].

[An expression for the static margin, SM, is derived as follows:]

If: Y_0 = applied lateral force at NSP
C_F = front cornering stiffness per wheel pair (lb./rad.)
C_R = rear cornering stiffness per wheel pair (lb./rad.)
ϕ/A_Y = roll angle (radians) per 1g lateral acceleration—roll gradient (rad./g)
E_F = front roll understeer (proportion of roll)
E_R = rear roll understeer (proportion of roll)

Then: Force Y_0 rolls the car through angle $= \dfrac{Y_0}{W_F + W_R} \dfrac{\phi}{A_Y}$ (2.76)

Camber thrust on front wheels $= W_F \dfrac{Y_0}{W_F + W_R} \dfrac{\phi}{A_Y}$ (2.77)

Slip angle of front wheels $= \alpha_F = \left(\dfrac{\ell - d}{\ell} + \dfrac{W_F}{W_F + W_R} \dfrac{\phi}{A_Y} \right) \dfrac{Y_0}{C_F}$ (2.78)

[from moments about the rear axle]

But *[due to roll understeer]* the front wheels have turned to the left in Figure 2.46 through an angle

$$\dfrac{Y_0}{W_F + W_R} \dfrac{\phi}{A_Y} E_F$$ (2.79)

So the front "heading angle" will be α_F + (front roll steer):

$$Y_0 \left[\dfrac{\ell - d}{C_F \ell} + \dfrac{1}{W_F + W_R} \dfrac{\phi}{A_Y} \left(\dfrac{W_F}{C_F} + E_F \right) \right]$$ (2.80)

The rear wheels, due to roll understeer, have turned to the right in the figure through an angle

$$\dfrac{Y_0}{W_F + W_R} \dfrac{\phi}{A_Y} E_R$$ (2.81)

So the heading angle at the rear will be α_R + (rear roll steer),

$$Y_0 \left[\dfrac{d}{C_R \ell} - \dfrac{\phi}{A_Y} \dfrac{E_R}{W_F + W_R} \right]$$ (2.82)

If the two headings are equal:

$$\frac{\ell - d}{C_F \ell} + \frac{1}{W_F + W_R} \frac{\phi}{A_Y} \left(\frac{W_F}{C_F} + E_F \right) = \frac{d}{C_R \ell} - \frac{\phi}{A_Y} \frac{E_R}{W_F + W_R} \tag{2.83}$$

$$\frac{\ell - d}{\ell} \left(\frac{1}{C_F} + \frac{1}{C_R} \right) = \frac{1}{C_R} - \frac{1}{W_F + W_R} \frac{\phi}{A_Y} \left(\frac{W_F}{C_F} + E_F + E_R \right) \tag{2.84}$$

At this point Olley leaves out a number of steps. The following was derived by Edward Kasprzak.

Rearranging Equation 2.84 gives the following sequence of formulas:

$$\frac{\ell - d}{\ell} \left(\frac{C_F + C_R}{C_F C_R} \right) = \frac{1}{C_R} - \frac{1}{W_F + W_R} \frac{\phi}{A_Y} \left(\frac{W_F}{C_F} + E_F + E_R \right)$$

$$\frac{\ell - d}{\ell} = \left(\frac{C_F C_R}{C_F + C_R} \right) \left[\frac{1}{C_R} - \frac{1}{W_F + W_R} \frac{\phi}{A_Y} \left(\frac{W_F}{C_F} + E_F + E_R \right) \right]$$

$$\frac{\ell - d}{\ell} = \frac{C_F}{C_F + C_R} - \frac{1}{W_F + W_R} \frac{C_F C_R}{C_F + C_R} \frac{\phi}{A_Y} \left(\frac{W_F}{C_F} + E_F + E_R \right)$$

$$\frac{\ell - d}{\ell} = \frac{C_F}{C_F + C_R} - \frac{W_F}{W_F + W_R} \frac{C_R}{C_F + C_R} \frac{\phi}{A_Y} + \frac{1}{W_F + W_R} \frac{C_F C_R}{C_F + C_R} \frac{\phi}{A_Y} (E_F + E_R)$$

$$\frac{\ell - d}{\ell} = \frac{C_F}{C_F + C_R} - \left[\frac{1}{W_F + W_R} \left(W_F \frac{C_R}{C_F + C_R} \frac{\phi}{A_Y} + \frac{C_F C_R}{C_F + C_R} \frac{\phi}{A_Y} (E_F + E_R) \right) \right]$$

Now, Olley defines the static margin as $SM = (d - a)/\ell$. *That is,*

$$SM = \frac{d - a}{\ell} = \frac{d - (\ell - b)}{\ell} = \frac{d - \ell + b}{\ell} = \frac{b - (\ell - d)}{\ell} = \frac{b}{\ell} - \frac{\ell - d}{\ell}$$

Using the last of these relations, the static margin is calculated from two terms. The first term is $b/\ell = W_F/(W_F + W_R)$. The term $(\ell - d)/\ell$ is derived before. Combining these:

$$SM = \frac{b}{\ell} - \frac{\ell - d}{\ell}$$

$$= \frac{W_F}{W_F + W_R} - \left\{ \frac{C_F}{C_F + C_R} - \left[\frac{1}{W_F + W_R} \left(W_F \frac{C_R}{C_F + C_R} \frac{\phi}{A_Y} + \frac{C_F C_R}{C_F + C_R} \frac{\phi}{A_Y} (E_F + E_R) \right) \right] \right\}$$

$$= -\frac{C_F}{C_F + C_R} + \left[\frac{1}{W_F + W_R} \left(W_F + W_F \frac{C_R}{C_F + C_R} \frac{\phi}{A_Y} + \frac{C_F C_R}{C_F + C_R} \frac{\phi}{A_Y} (E_F + E_R) \right) \right]$$

$$= \frac{1}{W_F + W_R} \left[W_F \left(1 + \frac{C_R}{C_F + C_R} \frac{\phi}{A_Y} \right) + \frac{C_F C_R}{C_F + C_R} \frac{\phi}{A_Y} (E_F + E_R) \right] - \frac{C_F}{C_F + C_R}$$

which is Equation 2.85.

At this point we go back to Olley's original derivation,

$$SM = \frac{d - a}{\ell} = \frac{NSP - CG \text{ location}}{\ell}$$

$$SM = \frac{1}{W_F + W_R} \left[W_F \left(1 + \frac{C_R}{C_F + C_R} \frac{\phi}{A_Y} \right) + \frac{C_F C_R}{C_F + C_R} \frac{\phi}{A_Y} (E_F + E_R) \right] - \frac{C_F}{C_F + C_R} \quad (2.85)$$

With no roll effects $[\phi/A_Y = 0]$,

$$SM = \frac{W_F}{W_F + W_R} - \frac{C_F}{C_F + C_R} = \frac{b}{\ell} - \frac{C_F}{C_F + C_R} \quad (2.86)$$

With front camber thrust only $[E_F + E_R = 0]$:

$$SM = \frac{W_F}{W_F + W_R} \left(1 + \frac{C_R}{C_F + C_R} \frac{\phi}{A_Y} \right) - \frac{C_F}{C_F + C_R} \quad (2.87)$$

$$SM = \frac{b}{\ell} \left(1 + \frac{C_R}{C_F + C_R} \frac{\phi}{A_Y} \right) - \frac{C_F}{C_F + C_R} \quad (2.88)$$

These can be applied to the Examples 1, 2, and 3 from Section 2.4:

Example 1

$$SM = \frac{W_F}{W_F + W_R} - \frac{C_F}{C_F + C_R}$$

$$SM = 0.50 - \frac{12900}{27200} = 0.50 - 0.475 = 0.025 \quad \text{(Understeer)}$$

Example 2

$$SM = 0.50 - \frac{14300}{27200} = 0.50 - 0.525 = -0.025 \quad \text{(Oversteer)}$$

Example 3 (disregarding roll steer)

$$SM = \frac{W_F}{W_F + W_R}\left(1 + \frac{C_R}{C_F + C_R}\frac{\phi}{A_Y}\right) - \frac{C_F}{C_F + C_R}$$

$$SM = 0.50\left(1 + (0.525)(0.20)\right) - 0.475 = 0.0775 \quad [\textit{Understeer}]$$

Example 3 (including 5% front and 3% rear roll understeer)

$$SM = 0.0775 + \frac{1}{W_F + W_R}\frac{C_F C_R}{C_F + C_R}\frac{\phi}{A_Y}\left(E_F + E_R\right)$$

$$SM = 0.0775 + \left(\frac{18447}{40 \times 272} \times 0.20 \times 0.08\right) = 0.1047 \quad [\textit{Understeer}]$$

In this way the amount of understeer contributed by the various features of the suspension and tires, etc., are given clear values in increased static margin.

Mr. Schilling suggests an easy way of estimating SM from the skid pad curves. At the lower values of lateral acceleration:

$$SM = \text{approximately } \frac{\alpha_F - \alpha_R}{2(\alpha_F + \alpha_R)} = \frac{\delta - \ell/R}{2(\alpha_F + \alpha_R)} \qquad (2.89)$$

This can be seen from the above equations, for instance:

Example 1

$$SM = \frac{W_F}{W_F + W_R} - \frac{C_F}{C_F + C_R} \tag{2.90}$$

$$= \frac{\dfrac{W_F}{C_F} - \dfrac{W_R}{C_R}}{\left(W_F + W_R\right)\left(\dfrac{1}{C_F} + \dfrac{1}{C_R}\right)} \tag{2.91}$$

$$= \frac{\alpha_F - \alpha_R}{\left(W_F + W_R\right)\left(\dfrac{1}{C_F} + \dfrac{1}{C_R}\right)} \tag{2.92}$$

$$SM = \frac{\alpha_F - \alpha_R}{\ell\left(\dfrac{\alpha_F}{b} + \dfrac{\alpha_R}{a}\right)} \tag{2.93}$$

Example 2

$$SM = \frac{W_F}{W_F + W_R} - \frac{C_F - \dfrac{W_F}{W_F + W_R} C_R \dfrac{\phi}{A_Y}}{C_F + C_R} \tag{2.94}$$

$$= \frac{\dfrac{W_F}{C_F} - \dfrac{W_R}{C_R} + \dfrac{W_F}{C_F}\dfrac{\phi}{A_Y}}{\left(W_F + W_R\right)\left(\dfrac{1}{C_F} + \dfrac{1}{C_R}\right)} \tag{2.95}$$

$$= \frac{\dfrac{W_F}{C_F}\left(1 + \dfrac{\phi}{A_Y}\right) - \dfrac{W_R}{C_R}}{\left(W_F + W_R\right)\left(\dfrac{1}{C_F} + \dfrac{1}{C_R}\right)} \tag{2.96}$$

$$= \frac{\alpha_F - \alpha_R}{\left(W_F + W_R\right)\left(\dfrac{1}{C_F} + \dfrac{1}{C_R}\right)} \tag{2.97}$$

$$= \frac{\alpha_F - \alpha_R}{\ell\left(\dfrac{\alpha_F}{\left(1 + \phi/A_Y\right)b} + \dfrac{\alpha_R}{a}\right)} \tag{2.98}$$

In both examples

$$\text{Static margin} = \frac{\left(\text{front slip}\right) - \left(\text{rear slip}\right)}{\left(\text{total weight} / C_F\right) + \left(\text{total weight} / C_R\right)} \tag{2.99}$$

which is close to $$SM = \frac{\alpha_F - \alpha_R}{2\left(\alpha_F + \alpha_R\right)} = \frac{\delta - \ell/R}{2\left(\alpha_F + \alpha_R\right)} \qquad \text{(repeat of 2.89)}$$

2.9 Swing Axle

Introduction

The calculations in this section, and the other sections in this chapter, are summarized at the end of the chapter.

It has long been suspected that the basic fault of the swing axle [*shown later in Figure 2.50*] is not its lifting (jacking) effect on corners, its changes of wheel camber, nor even its high roll center, but **simply the fact that it is an independent suspension, so that its "spring base" is equal to the wheel track**.

On a conventional rear axle in a passenger car the spring base [*spring track*] is commonly about 3/4 of the wheel track. So, except for a spring distortion effect in the case of leaf springs, the rear roll rate without tires is only 9/16 of the roll rate of an independent.

However there is nothing to prevent our imagining a rear axle conventional in all respects except that it has a spring base equal to the wheel track. And we can then compare its steering effects with those of a comparable swing axle. **When this is done one finds that, although the swing axle is "worse" in that the slip angles are somewhat greater, the two designs are not far apart in steering qualities**. Also one finds that oversteering effects in the swing axle may be eliminated in exactly the same way as in the conventional axle, i.e., by reducing the roll moment on the rear tires.

If the spring rates required for a flat ride are to be maintained, to reduce the rear roll moment on a swing axle requires some special springing arrangements whereby the full spring rate is developed in ride, but only a partial spring rate is used in roll. [*Some variations are the "swing run-around" (Kieft, 1950s), "camber compensator" (pivoted transverse leaf spring) and the "Z-bar" (anti-roll bar with ends facing opposite directions).*]

Approximate Figuring of Swing Axle

First it is necessary to know the lateral forces on the outer and inner tires in a turn. This has already been done (Figures 2.36, 2.37 and 2.38) for a conventional car.

In figuring the swing axle it has been found best to first consider a rigid axle, having the same roll center height as the swing axle and a spring base equal to the wheel track. From this the distribution of vertical loads and lateral forces on outer and inner tires can be found. This lateral force distribution is then used to find the lift of the rear of the car caused by the swing axle. Then this lift is used to re-figure the steering characteristics of the swing axle. And from this new figures can be obtained for the lateral forces on the inner and outer wheels.

Evidently these new lateral forces can be "played back" into the calculations to see if they make any appreciable difference in the final result. Actually they do not. Hence it is concluded that the approach described above, starting with a rigid axle, is satisfactory.

Another confirmation is that the method described, when applied to the Corvair for example, gives skid pad diagrams that are closely in agreement with actual test results.

1. Because the single-joint swing axle is so much easier to figure than the two-joint, and appears to give realistic results, this is what we use. But we retain the high roll center of the two-joint axle.

2. We also take another liberty by ignoring the roll of the rear wheels on the tires, and simply add the tire deflection to the spring deflection.

3. We ignore the non-rolling [*unsprung*] weight of the swing axle.

4. And the tires are treated as sections through the middle of a sphere. That is, variations in wheel track, and in wheel center height, due to camber changes, are ignored.

Roll Moments

Now, with a slight variation on the nomenclature so far used, we can first consider the case of the rigid axle, Figure 2.47.

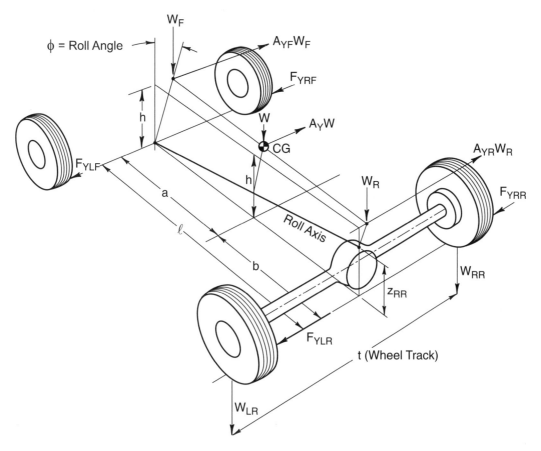

Figure 2.47 *Geometry for rigid rear axle case*
(no axle roll on rear tires, zero front roll center height).

A_Y = lateral acceleration (g-units)
$K_{\phi F}$ = front roll rate (with tires)
$K_{\phi R}$ = rear roll rate (with tires)
ΔW_F = front weight transfer
ΔW_R = rear weight transfer
W = total rolling weight (spring weight)
W_F = rolling weight on front axle
W_R = rolling weight on rear axle
$M_c = W_F h + W_R \left(h - z_{RR} \right)$ (This is the rolling moment coefficient.)

*The next several pages lacked adequate explanation in Olley's original, and the authors
have added numerous short derivations and extra text.*

The rolling moment coefficient M_c (about the roll axis) has two components:

One component is $\left[W_F h + W_R (h - z_{RR}) \right] A_Y$.

The other component is $\left[W_F h + WR(h - z_{RR}) \right] \phi$ (this is a "weight moment" due to lateral offset of the CG after the car has rolled).

Can now write, $\left(K_{\phi F} + K_{\phi R} \right) \phi = \left(A_Y + \phi \right) M_c$

The left side is the total spring moment about the roll axis. The right side is the centrifugal force and weight moment about the roll axis.

or
$$\left(K_{\phi F} + K_{\phi R} \right) = \left(\frac{A_Y + \phi}{\phi} \right) M_c$$

$$= \left(\frac{A_Y + \left(\dfrac{\phi}{A_Y} \right) A_Y}{\left(\dfrac{\phi}{A_Y} \right) A_Y} \right) M_c$$

$$\left(K_{\phi F} + K_{\phi R} \right) = \left(\frac{1 + \dfrac{\phi}{A_Y}}{\dfrac{\phi}{A_Y}} \right) M_c \tag{2.100}$$

Solve for ϕ / A_Y :

$$\frac{\phi}{A_Y} \left(K_{\phi F} + K_{\phi R} - M_c \right) = M_c$$

or
$$\frac{\phi}{A_Y} = \frac{M_c}{K_{\phi F} + K_{\phi R} - M_c} \tag{2.101}$$

Olley now says, forget the lateral forces to balance any camber thrust. With this assumption,

$$WA_Y = F_{YLF} + F_{YRF} + F_{YLR} + F_{YRR}$$

Now,

$$\Delta W_F = \frac{K_{\phi F}\phi}{t} = \frac{K_{\phi F}}{t}\frac{\phi}{A_Y}A_Y \qquad (2.102)$$

$$\Delta W_R = \frac{K_{\phi R}\phi + W_R A_Y z_{RR}}{t} = \frac{K_{\phi R}\dfrac{\phi}{A_Y}A_Y + W_R A_Y z_{RR}}{t}$$

The first term is the moment about the roll axis. The second term is the moment about the ground.

$$\Delta W_R = \frac{A_Y}{t}\left(K_{\phi R}\frac{\phi}{A_Y} + W_R z_{RR}\right) \qquad (2.103)$$

From Equation 2.100, $$K_{\phi F} + K_{\phi R} = \frac{1 + \dfrac{\phi}{A_Y}}{\dfrac{\phi}{A_Y}}M_c \qquad (2.104)$$

Example [*Step 1*]—A 4000 lb. car has equal weight distribution front and rear, **no roll stabilizer** [*anti-roll bar*] and **rear spring separation equal to the wheel track**. CG is 24 in. above the ground; rear roll center 15 in. above ground; wheel track 60 in.; wheelbase is 120 in. as before.

Let W_F = 2000 lb.
W_R = 2000 lb.
h = 2 ft. [*CG height*]
z_{RR} = 1.25 ft.
t = 5 ft.
d_F = effective deflection, front, ft. (spring plus tire)
d_R = effective deflection, rear, ft. (spring plus tire)
ϕ = 0.20 radian (at A_Y = 1g) or $\dfrac{\phi}{A_Y}$ = 0.20 rad./g [*roll gradient*]

$$M_c = W_F h + W_R\left(h - z_{RR}\right) = \left(2000\times 2\right) + \left(2000\times\left(2 - 1.25\right)\right) = 5500 \text{ lb.-ft.}$$

$$K_{\phi F} + K_{\phi R} = \frac{1 + \dfrac{\phi}{A_Y}}{\dfrac{\phi}{A_Y}}M_c = \frac{1 + 0.2}{0.2}\times 5500 = 33000 \text{ lb.-ft./rad.}$$

$$K_{\phi F} = \frac{W_F}{d_F} \times \frac{t^2}{4} = \frac{2000}{d_F} \times \frac{25}{4} = \frac{12500}{d_F} \; ; \; \text{also,} \; K_{\phi R} = \frac{12500}{d_R}$$

Note: This formula is derived as follows,

$$\text{Moment from one wheel} = \frac{W_F}{2} \times \frac{t}{2}$$

$$\text{Moment from two wheels} = W_F \times \frac{t}{2}$$

$$\text{Roll rate} = K_{\phi F}$$

$$\text{Roll moment} = K_{\phi F}\phi_F = K_{\phi F}\frac{d_F}{t/2}$$

$$K_{\phi F}\frac{d_F}{t/2} = W_F \frac{t}{2} \quad \text{and} \quad K_{\phi F} = \frac{W_F}{d_F}\frac{t^2}{4}$$

Suppose we make d_R = 8 in. = 0.667 ft.

Then $\qquad K_{\phi R} = \dfrac{12500}{d_R} = \dfrac{12500}{0.667} = 18741$ lb.-ft./rad.

but [*from above*] $\qquad K_{\phi F} + K_{\phi R} = 33000$ lb.-ft./rad.

therefore $\qquad K_{\phi F} = 33000 - 18471 = 14259$ lb.-ft./rad.

and $\qquad d_F = \dfrac{12500}{K_{\phi F}} = \dfrac{12500}{14259} = 0.877$ ft. = 10.5 in.

(These are about the front and rear effective deflections of spring plus tire that we need for a flat ride.)

From Equation 2.102,

$$\Delta W_F = \frac{A_Y}{t} K_{\phi F} \frac{\phi}{A_Y} = \frac{14259 \times 0.20}{5} A_Y = 570 A_Y \text{ lb.}$$

or 570 lb. for A_Y = 1.0.

From Equation 2.103,

$$\Delta W_R = \frac{A_Y}{t} K_{\phi R} \frac{\phi}{A_Y} + W_R z_{RR} = \frac{18741 \times 0.20 + 2000 \times 1.25}{5} A_Y = 1250 A_Y \text{ lb.}$$

or 1250 lb. for $A_Y = 1.0$.

This is completely unpractical. $\Delta W_R = 1250 A_Y$ means that at $A_Y = 0.7g$ there will be only 125 lb. on the inner rear tire. *Figured as follows,*

$$\Delta W_R = 1250 \times 0.7 = 875 \text{ lb.}$$

The static load on one rear wheel is 1000 lb., 1000 – 875 = 125 lb. load on the inner rear tire at 0.7g.

About the practical limit has already been reached in **Case B** [*Section 2.5, page 100, 50% more weight transfer on rear than on front*], with $\Delta W_F = 712 A_Y$ lb. and $\Delta W_R = 1070 A_Y$ lb., though even this leaves only 251 lb. on the inside rear tire at 0.7g.

> *The static load on one rear wheel = 1000 lb.*
> *1070 × 0.7 = 749 lb., the transfer at 0.7g*
> *1000 – 749 = 251 lb. on the inside rear tire.*
> *This is about a practical limit for transfer on the rear.*

It seems desirable to look at the possibility of achieving the conditions of **Case A** or **Case B, assuming that we may fit a front roll stabilizer to make $K_{\phi F}$ anything we like.** *In other words, Olley re-calculates Case A and Case B (from Section 2.5) with the addition of a front anti-roll bar. Using this data for the present example (swing axle) one can get back to more equal load transfer front and rear.*

Case A [*Step 2*] with Addition of Front Roll Stabilizer [*and equal weight distribution*]

At $A_Y = 1g$, $\Delta W_F = \Delta W_R = 890$ lb. [*Equations 2.53 and 2.54, page 100*]

$$K_{\phi F} \frac{\phi}{A_Y} = \Delta W_F t = 4450 \text{ lb.-ft.}$$

From Equation 2.103, (page 139)

$$\Delta W_R t = 4450 = A_Y \left(K_{\phi R} \frac{\phi}{A_Y} + W_R z_{RR} \right)$$

$$4450 = K_{\phi R} \frac{\phi}{A_Y} + 2500$$

So
$$K_{\phi R}\frac{\phi}{A_Y} = 1950 \text{ lb.-ft.}$$

and
$$\left(K_{\phi F} + K_{\phi R}\right)\frac{\phi}{A_Y} = 4450 + 1950 = 6400$$

From Equation 2.104, (page 139)

$$\left(K_{\phi F} + K_{\phi R}\right)\frac{\phi}{A_Y} = M_c\left(1 + \frac{\phi}{A_Y}\right) = 5500\left(1 + \frac{\phi}{A_Y}\right)$$

$$6400 = 5500\left(1 + \frac{\phi}{A_Y}\right) \implies 900 = 5500\frac{\phi}{A_Y}$$

or
$$\frac{\phi}{A_Y} = \frac{900}{5500} = 0.164 \text{ rad./g} \ (4.7° \text{ roll at } 0.5g)$$

$$\frac{K_{\phi F}\frac{\phi}{A_Y}}{\frac{\phi}{A_Y}} = K_{\phi F} = \frac{4450}{0.164} = 27134 \text{ lb.-ft./rad. } (473.5 \text{ lb.-ft./deg.})$$

$$\frac{K_{\phi R}\frac{\phi}{A_Y}}{\frac{\phi}{A_Y}} = K_{\phi R} = \frac{1950}{0.164} = 11890 \text{ lb.-ft./rad. } (207.5 \text{ lb.-ft./deg.})$$

$$d_R = \frac{12500}{K_{\phi R}} = \frac{12500}{11890} = 1.05 \text{ ft. } (12.6 \text{ in. deflection})$$

$K_{\phi F}$ [*to get equal weight transfer front and rear, namely 890 lb./g*] can be achieved by a stabilizer, but to get a flat ride d_F would have to be at least 15 inches.

Thus, unless we use unconventional rear springing, we should have to use air springing and self-leveling to get a practical result anything like 12 in. of static deflection.

Case B [*Step 3*] with Addition of Front Roll Stabilizer Bar [*and equal weight distribution*]

At $A_Y = 1g$, $\Delta W_F = 712$ lb., $\Delta W_R = 1068$ lb. [*see Equations 2.59 and 2.60*]

$$K_{\phi F} \frac{\phi}{A_Y} A_Y = \Delta W_F t = 712 \times 5 = 3560 \text{ lb.-ft.}$$

From Equation 2.103,

$$\Delta W_R t = 1068 \times 5 = 5340 = A_Y \left(K_{\phi R} \frac{\phi}{A_Y} + W_R z_{RR} \right)$$

$$5340 = \left(K_{\phi R} \frac{\phi}{A_Y} + 2000 \times 1.25 \right)$$

or $\quad K_{\phi R} \dfrac{\phi}{A_Y} = \Delta W_R t - W_R z_{RR} = 5340 - 2500 = 2840 \text{ lb.-ft.}$

$$\left(K_{\phi F} + K_{\phi R} \right) \frac{\phi}{A_Y} = 3560 + 2840 = 6400$$

From Equation 2.100 or 2.104

$$\left(K_{\phi F} + K_{\phi R} \right) \frac{\phi}{A_Y} = \left(1 + \frac{\phi}{A_Y} \right) M_c$$

$$6400 = 5500 \left(1 + \frac{\phi}{A_Y} \right)$$

$$\frac{900}{5500} = \frac{\phi}{A_Y} = 0.164 \text{ rad./g} \quad \left(4.7° \text{ roll at } 0.5g \right)$$

$$\frac{K_{\phi F} \dfrac{\phi}{A_Y}}{\dfrac{\phi}{A_Y}} = K_{\phi F} = \frac{3560}{0.164} = 21707 \text{ lb.-ft./rad. (379 lb.-ft./deg.)}$$

$$\frac{K_{\phi R} \dfrac{\phi}{A_Y}}{\dfrac{\phi}{A_Y}} = K_{\phi R} = \frac{2840}{0.164} = 17317 \text{ lb.-ft./rad. (302 lb.-ft./deg.)}$$

$$d_R = \frac{12500}{K_{\phi R}} = \frac{12500}{17317} = 0.72 \text{ ft. (8.65 in. deflection)}$$

Evidently this is the more practical arrangement [*than the situation without the front anti-roll bar*].

By figuring exactly as before, we get the skid pad chart of Figure 2.48. This is entirely similar to **Case B** in Figure 2.32, but is not the same because of the reduced roll, and because we are now ignoring the roll of the rear axle on its tires.

Figure 2.49 shows the division of the lateral forces for Figure 2.48 (comparable with Figure 2.37). We shall need these (at the rear) to estimate lifting and camber change effects when the rigid axle is replaced by a swing axle.

The **lateral forces** are:

Table 2.8 Tire Lateral Forces for Case B

A_Y (g)	0.20	0.40	0.50	0.55	0.60	0.65	0.70
Front							
F'_{Yo} (lb.)	239.5	503.5	653	734	824	924	1040
F'_{Yi} (lb.)	225.5	426.5	511	546	572	588	590
$F'_{Yo} + F'_{Yi}$ (lb.)	465	930	1164	1280	1396	1512	1630
Rear							
F'_{Yo} (lb.)	209	450	600	688.5	796	933	1096
F'_{Yi} (lb.)	191	350	400	411.5	404	367	304
$F'_{Yo} + F'_{Yi}$ (lb.)	400	800	1000	1100	1200	1300	1400

[*The primed (F'_{Yo}, F'_{Yi}) variables refer to Case B with swing axle, Figure 2.48*]

In the case of the rigid axle of which we are ignoring the roll on the tires, F'_{Yo} and F'_{Yi} at the rear are identical with F_{Yo} and F_{Yi}, respectively.

In the front tires, if the wheels remain parallel to the median plane of the car

$$F'_{Yo} = F_{Yo} + W_o \phi$$
$$F'_{Yi} = F_{Yi} + W_i \phi$$

(2.105)

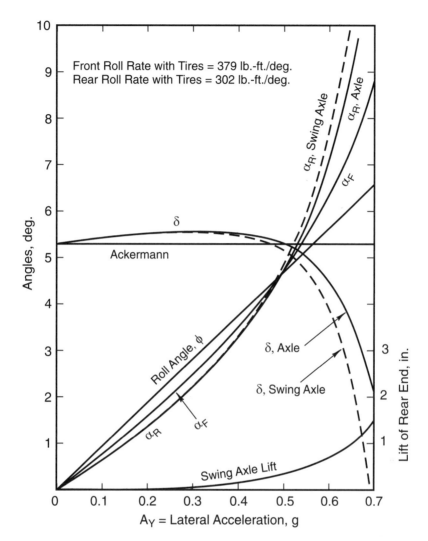

Figure 2.48 *Skid pad plots for* **Case B** *(without and with swing axle) with front roll stabilizer (Step 4).*

Swing Axle

Now consider the modifications that have to be introduced to give a reasonable representation of a swing axle.

The axle is credited with an "equivalent roll center" [*static condition*] which, with the dimensions stated, will be 15 in. above the ground. It is thenceforth treated as a single-joint swing axle.

F_{Yo} and F_{Yi}, the outer and inner lateral forces, are "external." That is, they do **not** include the lateral force necessary to balance camber thrust.

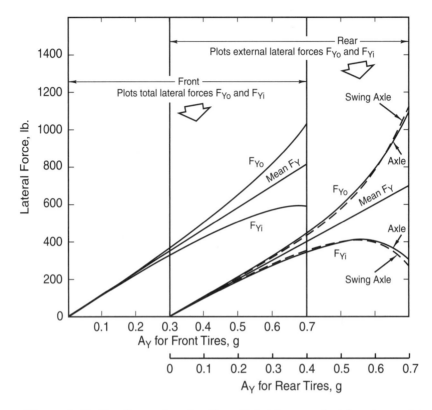

Figure 2.49 *Tire force plots for* **Case B** *(without and with swing axle) with front roll stabilizer.*

Assuming that roll rate $K_{\phi R}$ contains the tire deflection (i.e., ignoring the roll of the suspension on the tires) camber angles γ are equal either side [*only in this unique case*].

Then, since the spring base is assumed to remain horizontal, both the rear springs extend equally when the rear of the car lifts, and thus the roll angle ϕ is not changed by reason of the lift. Under these assumptions (which are only approximately correct, like our other swing axle assumptions), roll angle ϕ remains the same as in the case already studied of the rigid axle [*see previous section*].

The new element introduced by the swing axle is the lift Δz_{RR}, which occurs due to the **difference** between F_{Yo} and F_{Yi}, and which itself increases $W_o - W_i$, and hence $F_{Yo} - F_{Yi}$.

It appears reasonable to assume that the tires act like sections through the middle of a sphere so that we may **ignore variations in wheel track**, t, and in wheel radius.

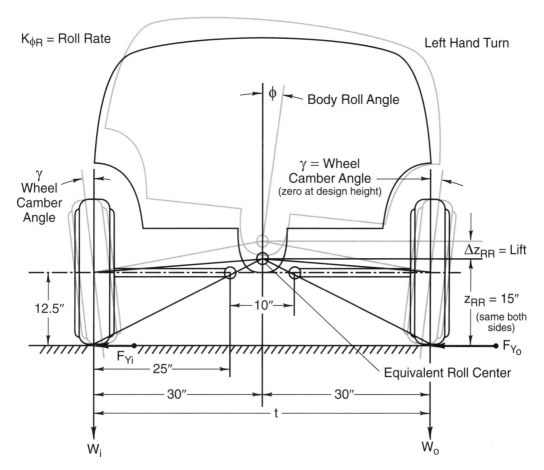

Figure 2.50 *General layout for swing axle, rear view.*

Now, for the swing axle, we need:

> The lift, Δz_{RR} [*approximate, for a non-iterative solution*]
> The camber angle, γ [*inclination angle*]
> The new values of vertical forces W_o and W_i.
> The relationship of total lateral force, F'_{Yo}, to external lateral force, F_{Yo}.

To correctly calculate the effect of jacking and camber change on a swing axle, iteration is required, i.e., the lateral tire forces determine the jacking, which in turn changes the camber, which then changes the lateral tire forces, etc. Olley notes under "Approximate Figuring of Swing Axle," that experience indicates that only one iteration is sufficient for a practical solution.

To start the process, he uses the lateral tire forces which he obtained from his "Approximate Figuring of Swing Axle" (Section 2.9), which "is based on a rigid axle with the roll center height of the swing axle and a spring base (or spring track) equal to the wheel track." This gives a better approximation to the wheel loads on a swing axle.

*He uses **unprimed** lateral force symbols, such as F_Y, which have no camber thrust in them. He refers to these as "external" forces which do not include lateral forces to balance camber thrust. The term "external" may be confusing—it might be better to read this as "initial applied lateral forces before jacking has taken place." The primed variables, F_Y', include the lateral force due to camber; see Equations 2.115 through 2.118.*

The Lift

Lifting force
$$\left(F_{Yo} - F_{Yi}\right)\frac{z_{RR} + \Delta z_{RR}}{t/2} \tag{2.106}$$

Therefore, lift
$$\Delta z_{RR} = \frac{\text{rear lifting force}}{\text{rear ride rate}} = \frac{\left(F_{Yo} - F_{Yi}\right)\left(z_{RR} + \Delta z_{RR}\right)}{\left(W_R / d_R\right)\left(t/2\right)} \tag{2.107}$$

or lift
$$\Delta z_{RR} = \frac{\left(F_{Yo} - F_{Yi}\right)z_{RR}}{\left(W_R / d_R\right)\left(t/2\right) - \left(F_{Yo} - F_{Yi}\right)} \tag{2.108}$$

Camber Angle

$$\gamma = \frac{\Delta z_{RR}}{t/2} \tag{2.109}$$

Vertical Forces

$$\left(W_o - W_i\right)\frac{t}{2} = K_{\phi R}\frac{\phi}{A_Y}A_Y + W_R A_Y\left(z_{RR} + \Delta z_{RR}\right) \tag{2.110}$$

and
$$\left(W_o - W_i\right)\frac{t}{2} = A_Y\left[K_{\phi R}\frac{\phi}{A_Y} + W_R\left(z_{RR} + \Delta z_{RR}\right)\right] \tag{2.111}$$

or
$$\left(W_o - W_i\right) = \frac{2A_Y}{t}\left[K_{\phi R}\frac{\phi}{A_Y} + W_R\left(z_{RR} + \Delta z_{RR}\right)\right] \tag{2.112}$$

and
$$W_o + W_i = W_R = \text{weight on rear tires} \tag{2.113}$$

So
$$W_o = \frac{W_R}{2} + \frac{A_Y}{t}\left[K_{\phi R}\frac{\phi}{A_Y} + W_R\left(z_{RR} + \Delta z_{RR}\right)\right] \tag{2.114}$$

$$W_i = \frac{W_R}{2} - \frac{A_Y}{t}\left[K_{\phi R}\frac{\phi}{A_Y} + W_R\left(z_{RR} + \Delta z_{RR}\right)\right] \tag{2.115}$$

Lateral Forces

$$F'_{Yo} = F_{Yo} + W_o\gamma = \left(C_o\alpha - \frac{C_o}{2(\alpha_{max})_o}\alpha^2\right) + W_o\gamma \tag{2.116}$$

From left to right, these terms are:

F'_{Yo} = *total lateral force on outside wheel*
F_{Yo} = *lateral force without camber thrust, outside wheel*
$W_o\gamma$ = *camber thrust, outside wheel*
$C_o\alpha - \dfrac{C_o}{2(\alpha_{max})_o}\alpha^2$ = *lateral force due to slip angle, Equation 2.10*

$$F'_{Yi} = F_{Yi} - W_i\gamma = \left(C_i\alpha - \frac{C_i}{2(\alpha_{max})_i}\alpha^2\right) - W_i\gamma \tag{2.117}$$

In each case $\alpha_{max} = \dfrac{2F_{Ymax}}{C}$ up to $\alpha = \alpha_{max}$.

And, summing Equations 2.116 and 2.117,

$$(C_o + C_i)\alpha - \left(\frac{C_o}{2(\alpha_{max})_o} + \frac{C_i}{2(\alpha_{max})_i}\right)\alpha^2 = F_{Yo} + F_{Yi} + \left(W_o - W_i\right)\gamma \tag{2.118}$$

$$= A_Y W_R + \left(W_o - W_i\right)\gamma$$

Lift

Accepting the rear lateral force values of the re-figured Case B as representing F_{Yo} and F_{Yi}, we get the following:

$$\Delta z_{RR} = \frac{(F_{Yo} - F_{Yi})z_{RR}}{(W_R/d_R)(t/2) - (F_{Yo} - F_{Yi})} = \frac{1.25(F_{Yo} - F_{Yi})}{6950 - (F_{Yo} - F_{Yi})} \tag{2.119}$$

The lift is plotted in Figure 2.48. **The rapid increase of lift after $A_Y = 0.5g$ looks quite representative of experience with swing axles.**

Table 2.9 Tabulation of Lift Forces for Swing Axle Example

A_Y (g)	0.20	0.40	0.50	0.55	0.60	0.65	0.70
$F_{Yo} - F_{Yi}$ (lb.)	18	100	200	277	392	566	792
$1.25\left(F_{Yo} - F_{Yi}\right)$ (lb.)	22.5	125	250	347	490	708	990
$6950\left(F_{Yo} - F_{Yi}\right)$ (lb.)	6932	6850	6750	6673	6558	6384	6158
Δz_{RR} (ft.)	0.00032	0.0146	0.0296	0.0415	0.0598	0.0887	0.1285
Δz_{RR} (in.)	0.039	0.175	0.356	0.498	0.717	1.064	1.54
γ (rad.)	0.0013	0.0058	0.0118	0.0166	0.0239	0.0355	0.0514
γ (deg.)	0.0745	0.334	0.677	0.95	1.37	2.035	2.94

Vertical Forces

$$W_o = \frac{W_R}{2} + \frac{A_Y}{t}\left[K_{\phi R}\frac{\phi}{A_Y} + W_R\left(z_{RR} + \Delta z_{RR}\right)\right] \qquad (2.120)$$

or $\qquad W_o = 1000 + \frac{A_Y}{5}\left[2840 + 2000\left(1.25 + \Delta z_{RR}\right)\right]$

$$W_o = 1000 + A_Y\left[1068 + 400\Delta z_{RR}\right]$$

and $\qquad W_i = 1000 - A_Y\left[1068 + 400\Delta z_{RR}\right]$

Table 2.10 Tabulation of Vertical Forces for Swing Axle Example

A_Y (g)	0.20	0.40	0.50	0.55	0.60	0.65	0.70
$1068A_Y$ (lb.)	213.6	427.2	534	587.4	640.8	694.2	747.6
$400\Delta z_{RR}A_Y$ (lb.)	0.26	2.34	5.92	9.14	14.35	23.1	36.0
$A_Y\left(1068 + 400\Delta z_{RR}\right)$ (lb.)	213.9	429.5	539.9	596.5	655.2	717.3	783.6
W_o (lb.)	1214	1429.5	1540	1596.5	1655	1717.5	1783.5
W_i (lb.)	786	570.5	460	403.5	345	282.5	216.5

Table 2.11 Tabulation of Tire Operating Conditions for Swing Axle Example

A_Y (g)	0.20	0.40	0.50	0.55	0.60	0.65	0.70
$(C/W)_o$	0.134	0.105	0.090	0.082	0.074	0.066	0.0565
$(C/W)_i$	0.193	0.222	0.237	0.245	0.253	0.261	0.2705
C_o (lb./deg.)	162.8	150	138.6	131	122.5	113.3	100.8
C_i (lb./deg.)	151.5	126.8	109	98.6	87.2	73.7	58.5
$C_o + C_i$ (lb./deg.)	314.3	276.8	247.6	229.6	209.7	187.0	159.3
$(\alpha_{max})_o$ (deg.)	17.9	22.85	26.7	29.25	32.4	36.4	42.5
$(\alpha_{max})_i$ (deg.)	12.45	10.80	10.12	9.80	9.50	9.22*	8.88*
$\dfrac{C_o}{2(\alpha_{max})_o}$	4.55	3.28	2.60	2.24	1.89	1.56	1.185
$\dfrac{C_i}{2(\alpha_{max})_i}$	6.09	5.87	5.38	5.03	4.59	4.0	3.295
$\dfrac{C_o}{2(\alpha_{max})_o} + \dfrac{C_i}{2(\alpha_{max})_i}$	10.64	9.15	7.98	7.27	6.48	5.56	4.48

* In these two cases $\alpha_R > (\alpha_{max})_i$.

Table 2.12 Tabulation of Rear Lateral Forces for Swing Axle Example

A_Y (g)	0.20	0.40	0.50	0.55	0.60	0.65	0.70
$A_Y W_R$ (lb.)	400	800	1000	1100	1200	1300	1400
$W_o - W_i$ (lb.)	428	859	1080	1193	1310	1435	1567
γ (rad.)	0.0013	0.00584	0.01183	0.0166	0.0239	0.0355	0.0514
$A_Y W_R + (W_o - W_i)\gamma$	400.55	805	1012.8	1119.8	1231.3	1351	1480.5

Table 2.13 Tabulation of Slip and Steer Angles for Swing Axle Example

A_Y (g)	0.20	0.40	0.50	0.55	0.60	0.65	0.70
α_R (deg.)	1.33	3.26	4.86	6.02	7.705	10.45	14.65
α_F (deg.)	1.525	3.44	4.725	5.485	6.395	7.45	8.82
$\alpha_F - \alpha_R$ (deg.)	0.195	0.18	−0.135	−0.535	−1.31	−3.0	−5.83
δ (deg.)	5.495	5.48	5.165	4.765	3.99	2.30	−0.53

Table 2.14 Division of the Lateral Forces, and Comparison between the Swing Axle and the Rigid Axle

A_Y (g)	0.20	0.40	0.50	0.55	0.60	0.65	0.70
$C_o\alpha$ (lb./deg.)	216	489	674	788	945	1183	1475
$\dfrac{C_o}{2(\alpha_{max})_o}\alpha^2$	8	34.8	61.4	81.2	112.4	170	254
F'_{Yo} (lb.)	208	454.2	612.6	706.8	832.6	1013	1221
$W_o\gamma$ (lb.)	1.6	8.35	18.2	26.5	39.6	61	91.5
F_{Yo} (lb.)	206.4	445.85	594.4	680.3	793	952	1129.5
$C_i\alpha$ (lb./deg.)	201.5	414	530	594	672.5	Values below are	
$\dfrac{C_i}{2(\alpha_{max})_i}\alpha^2$	10.75	62.4	127	182	273	μW_i since	
F'_{Yi} (lb.)	190.75	351.6	403	412	399.5	$\alpha_R > \alpha_{R\,max}$ 339	260
$W_i\gamma$ (lb.)	1.02	3.35	5.45	6.7	8.25	10.0	11.0
F_{Yi} (lb.)	191.77	354.95	408.45	418.7	407.75	349	271
$F_{Yo} + F_{Yi}$ (lb.)	398.17	800.8	1002.8	1099.0	1200.7	1301	1400.5
Theoretical, from Table 2.8 Rear	400	800	1000	1100	1200	1300	1400
$F_{Yo} - F_{Yi}$ (lb.)	14.63	90.9	185.95	261.6	385.25	603	858.5
For the axle, we found:	18	100	200	277	392	566	792

Evidently the assumed values for $F_{Yo} - F_{Yi}$ were sufficiently close to the new values to make further calculation unnecessary.

The revised values for F_{Yo} and F_{Yi} are entered in Figure 2.49, and it is seen that there is little difference between these external lateral forces on the rigid axle and the swing axle, except for a greater spread at high lateral acceleration in the case of the swing axle.

The values of α_R and δ for the swing axle are shown in Figure 2.48, and this shows that α_R increases more rapidly and therefore δ drops more rapidly above $A_Y = 0.5$g in the case of the swing axle.

Traction

To finish the job one should really include the changes produced by traction, as before. But we know in advance that the effects of traction will be much the same as in Figure 2.32. Perhaps they will be worse, since we do not have enough information on the effect of driving through cambered wheels [*once again Olley is stymied by the lack of good tire data*].

All we do have is that whenever parallel independent wheels are driven, whether in front or rear of a car, severe tire wear occurs. This suggests a considerable reduction of cornering capability on cambered wheels under traction.

"De-Stabilizing" the Swing Axle

Earlier it was shown that the **Case A** condition of $\Delta W_F = \Delta W_R = 890$ lb. was impractical in the case of a swing axle with conventional rear springing. It would require 12.6 in. static rear ride deflection, or effective rear spring rates of approximately 79 lb./in. And to get a flat ride would require 15 in. front deflection, or front springs of approximately 67 lb./in. This could be done with air springing, but there would be problems of brake dive. The front roll rate without stabilizer would be 175 lb.-ft./deg. and 300 lb.-ft./deg. would have to be added to this by a front roll stabilizer [*anti-roll bar*].

But there is another way to get the desired result, namely to de-stabilize the rear suspension. [*In this case, Olley uses "de-stabilize" to describe an arrangement "opposite" to the conventional stabilizer bar (or anti-roll bar). In more recent years this type of pivoted transverse leaf spring has also been called a "camber compensator." Other springing arrangements can be used to give the same effect.*]

Part of the ride rate is supplied by the transverse leaf spring, which, being pivoted in the middle, contributes nothing to the roll rate. The roll rate and part of the ride rate is supplied by the coil springs.

In the case of a low car with a relatively heavy rear end, like the Corvair, it appears permissible to dispense with the coil springs entirely, i.e., have **no** rear roll rate.[17]

---

[17] This was the case of the 500cc Kieft, driven by Stirling Moss 1951–2, which he states was "the biggest step forward which I have ever experienced." (Moss, Stirling and Laurence Pomeroy, *Design and Behaviour of the Racing Car*, William Kimber, London, 1963.) Reducing the roll couple on the driving wheels has generally been beneficial.

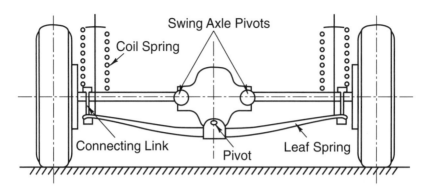

Figure 2.51 *Swing axle with addition of pivoted transverse leaf spring.*

With a higher CG and equal weight distribution this seems undesirable, as it calls for too much weight transfer on the front tires. Some improvement can be made over the reworked **Case B** by letting the car roll a bit more.

For example we could take the old figure of $\dfrac{\phi}{A_Y} = 0.20$, i.e., car rolls 5.73° for $A_Y = 0.50$g.

Then $\Delta W_F = \Delta W_R$

$$K_{\phi F}\frac{\phi}{A_Y}A_Y = K_{\phi R}\frac{\phi}{A_Y}A_Y + W_R A_Y z_{RR}$$

$$K_{\phi F} - K_{\phi R} = \frac{W_R z_{RR}}{\phi/A_Y} = \frac{2500}{0.20} = 12500 \text{ lb.-ft./rad.}$$

But

$$K_{\phi F} + K_{\phi R} = \frac{1+\phi/A_Y}{\phi/A_Y}\left(W_F h + W_R\left(h - z_{RR}\right)\right) = 6 \times 5500 = 33000 \text{ lb.-ft./rad.}$$

So

$$K_{\phi F} = 22750 \text{ lb.-ft./rad.} = 397 \text{ lb.-ft./deg.}$$

$$K_{\phi R} = 10250 \text{ lb.-ft./rad.} = 179 \text{ lb.-ft./deg.}$$

and

$$\Delta W_F = \frac{K_{\phi F}}{t}\frac{\phi}{A_Y} = \frac{22750}{5}\times 0.20 = 910 \text{ lb./g}$$

$$\Delta W_R = \frac{K_{\phi R}\dfrac{\phi}{A_Y} - W_R z_{RR}}{t} = 910 \text{ lb./g}$$

If we use 8 in. deflection at the rear, or (neglecting unsprung mass) 125 lb./in., the normal rear roll rate would be 327 lb.-ft./deg. We should therefore have to put about 57 lb./in. into the balanced leaf spring, leaving 68 lb./in. for the coil springs, which would give the desired ride rate and a rear roll rate of 178 lb.-ft./deg.

If we used 10 in. front deflection, which would give a front roll rate of 262 lb.-ft./deg., we should need a front stabilizer of 135 lb.-ft./deg. to bring $K_{\phi F}$ up to the required figure [*to the total of 397 lb.-ft./deg.*].

We can thus make a car, similar to **Case A**, with reasonable front and rear ride deflections, a reasonable front stabilizer, and a "de-stabilized" rear end. We will tackle this first, as before, by considering a rigid rear axle; Table 2.15.

Table 2.15 Front and Rear Tire Characteristics, Rigid Rear Axle

A_Y (g)	0.2	0.4	0.5	0.6	0.7
W_o (lb.)	1182	1364	1455	1546	1637
W_i (lb.)	818	636	545	454	363
$(C/W)_o$	0.1385	0.1140	0.1015	0.089	0.0767
$(C/W)_i$	0.1885	0.2132	0.2256	0.238	0.2505
C_o (lb./deg.)	164	155.5	147.7	137.5	125.5
C_i (lb./deg.)	154.2	135.8	123	108	91
$C_o + C_i$ (lb./deg.)	318.2	291.3	270.7	245.5	216.5
$(\alpha_{max})_o$ (deg.)	17.3	21.1	23.65	27.0	31.3
$(\alpha_{max})_i$ (deg.)	12.73	11.25	10.63	10.1	9.58
$C_o/2(\alpha_{max})_o$	4.74	3.69	3.12	2.55	2.0
$C_i/2(\alpha_{max})_i$	6.05	6.03	5.79	5.35	4.75
$C_o/2(\alpha_{max})_o$ $+C_i/2(\alpha_{max})_i$	10.79	9.72	8.91	7.90	6.75
Front side load $1.2A_Y W_F$ (lb.)	480	960	1200	1440	1680
Rear side load $A_Y W_R$ (lb.)	400	800	1000	1200	1400
From this we get, with a rigid rear axle:					
α_F (deg.)	1.585	3.765	5.38	7.835	12.375
α_R (deg.)	1.31	3.05	4.30	6.075	8.96
δ (deg.)	5.575	6.015	6.38	7.06	8.715

Figure 2.52 plots these results. Evidentially the "de-stabilizing" of the rear end has permitted an amount of understeer comparable to **Case A**. To translate these values into swing axle figures, we first have to find the external lateral forces F_{Y1} and F_{Y2} on the rear wheels and the total lateral forces F'_{Y1} and F'_{Y2} on the front wheels. These are given in Table 2.16.

Table 2.16 Lateral Forces for De-Stabilized Swing Axle

A_Y (g)	0.2	0.4	0.5	0.6	0.7
Front					
F'_{Yo} (lb.)	250	533	705	920	1245
F'_{Yi} (lb.)	230	427	495	520	435
$F'_{Yo} + F'_{Yi}$ (lb.)	480	960	1200	1440	1680
Rear					
F_{Yo} (lb.)	207.5	440	578	742	965
F_{Yi} (lb.)	192.5	360	422	458	435
$F_{Yo} + F_{Yi}$ (lb.)	400	800	1000	1200	1400
These are shown in Figure 2.53. Using these values, we find the lift of the rear end:					
Δz_{RR} (in.)	0.03	0.164	0.317	0.59	1.14
This is plotted in Figure 2.52. It is substantially less than in Figure 2.49, thanks to the reduced roll moment on the rear end and hence reduced values of $F_{Yo} - F_{Yi}$.					
Using these values for lift, and assuming as before that total lateral force on the rear tires is $A_Y W_R + (W_o - W_i)\gamma$, we get the following revised values for α_R.					
α_R (swing axle) (deg.)	1.31	3.095	4.38	6.315	10.225
Whence δ (deg.)	5.575	5.970	6.300	6.820	7.450
These are entered in Figure 2.52, showing that the change from rigid axle to swing axle reduces the understeer. Finally we obtain the revised values for the rear lateral forces, F_{Yo} and F_{Yi}.					
Rear					
F_{Yo}	207.5	437	573	732	985
F_{Yi}	192.5	363	427	468	415

These are given in Figure 2.53, and it is seen that the change in F_{Yo} and F_{Yi} from the rigid axle is negligible.

Thus the use of de-stabilized rear springing on the swing axle has resulted in a steady-state steering resembling in every way the normal understeer of a conventional car with IFS and conventional rear axle.

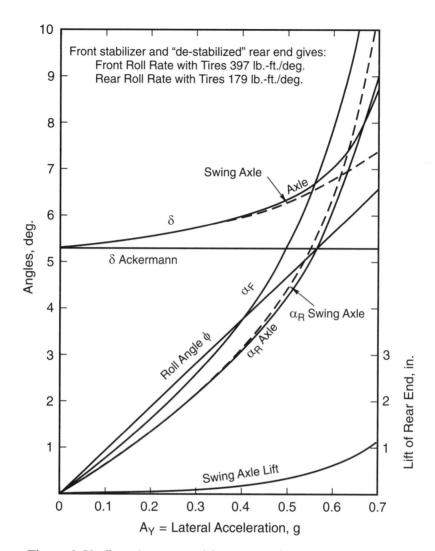

Figure 2.52 Case A *version of the swing axle, skid pad comparison between rigid axle and de-stabilized swing axle (Step 5).*

2.10 Summary of Steady-State Steering (Primary Effects)

This section is Olley's summary of this chapter.

Considerations of steady-state steering do not by any means cover this whole problem of the steering and handling of a car.

Steady-state is chiefly concerned with "primary" steering effects, namely, those which change the actual slip angles.

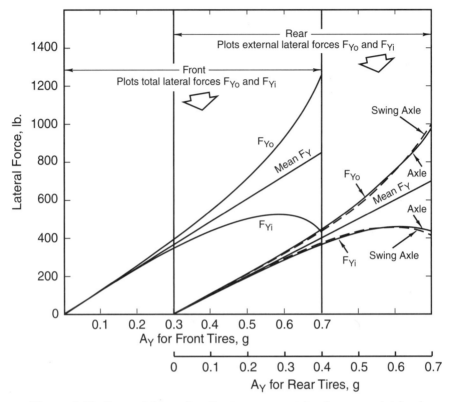

Figure 2.53 *Lateral force distribution comparison between rigid axle and de-stabilized swing axle.*

These effects are sensitive to:

1. Tire characteristics, including the effect of inflation.
2. Fore and aft load distribution, as related to the tire characteristics at either end. That is: W_F/C_F and W_R/C_R.
3. Roll moment distribution, or relative lateral weight transfer between front and rear wheel pairs.
4. Traction forces, but the effect of these is also closely related to the roll moment carried on the driving tires.
5. Height of the CG and height of the roll axis relative to the wheel track.
6. Designed wheel camber and toe-in.

A swing axle offers a particular problem, because:

1. The spring base is equal to the wheel track.
2. Because of the changes of wheel posture with standing height, either the springs must be stiff, or there must be a leveling device.
3. In normal designs the roll center is exceptionally high.

(The above three effects make for a high weight transfer, and consequent oversteer.)

4. Under lateral forces the rear end tends to lift, thus increasing the weight transfer. And this lift occurs "suddenly" at higher lateral accelerations.
5. This lift gives the wheels positive camber, making for oversteer.

Of these, the first three have the major effect. A rigid axle, with the wide spring base, stiff springs and high roll center of a swing axle, normally behaves very much like a swing axle.

"Secondary" steering effects are those which, without actually changing the slip angles (in steady-state steering), change the angles of the wheels relative to the median plane of the car. They are:

Roll steer (front and rear)
Lateral deflection steer

Steady-state steering characteristics are best revealed by **skid pad tests**.

As commonly carried out, with steering angle indicators on the front wheel spindles, the only roll steer characteristic which shows up on the skid pad test is rear roll steer. Rear roll understeer decreases the attitude angle, and therefore increases the steering angle δ. It makes no change, however, in the actual slip angles α_F and α_R.

Oversteer and Understeer (Steady-State)—Steering characteristics are sensitive, not to front and rear weight distribution, but to the relation of the front and rear weights to the front and rear cornering stiffnesses.

Where this ratio is greater in the front than the rear the steering angle δ must increase with increasing lateral acceleration, i.e., the car "understeers."

Where the ratio is greater in the rear, the car "oversteers" and requires less steering angle as lateral acceleration increases. The instability of this situation is obvious, since the only way to make a car turn faster is to give it more steering angle. In an oversteering car this means giving it more steering angle for a moment and then immediately turning the steering wheel back in an attempt to catch the position which will maintain a steady turn at the faster rate.

An oversteering car has the further characteristic that, at or above a certain **critical speed**, the car becomes completely unstable directionally, and can be held to any path, curved or straight, only by constant to and fro movements of the steering wheel which thus becomes the equivalent of the balancing bar of a tightrope walker. [*Oversteer cars are still stable below the critical speed because of the yaw damping.*]

Large and heavy vehicles have been handled with oversteering characteristics deliberately produced and, because of the time lag in steering transitions, have been successfully controlled up to quite high speeds, approaching if not exceeding their **critical speeds**. Smaller cars and shorter wheelbases become increasingly difficult.

Roll Moments—Steering characteristics are also extremely sensitive to the distribution of the roll moment between the front and rear wheel pairs, i.e., the lateral weight transfer front and rear.

In particular, if the weight transfer at the rear is too great, the steering characteristic of a normally understeering car will reverse to oversteer above a certain lateral acceleration.

Traction—Rear wheel traction [*rear drive*] causes a rather sudden decrease in rear cornering capability above a certain lateral acceleration, and therefore tends to produce a reversal in the oversteer direction as described above.

However, this traction effect is itself highly sensitive to lateral weight transfer and becomes critical only when excessive roll moment is carried on the rear tires.

Maximum Lateral Acceleration—Any four-wheeled vehicle is limited in maneuverability at higher lateral accelerations by the weight transfer from the inner to the outer wheels. Thus, even with a friction coefficient of rubber on a dry road as high as 1.20, the maximum lateral acceleration of the car may be 0.70g or less.

This effect is absent on a motorcycle, for example, which can corner up to the limit set by the friction coefficient and still maintain its maneuverability.

Evidently also this limitation of cornering ability is very sensitive to CG height, as shown by **Case C**, and there are great advantages in building cars low and with wide wheel tracks.

The limitation in maximum lateral acceleration on four-wheeled vehicles is largely compensated by the fact that, since they steer by slip angle, and the slip angle produces aligning torque, the roll moment carried by the front tires gives a turning moment at the steering wheel which is the driver's "feel of the road."

If the driver is alert, and if the steering system has reasonable reverse efficiency, the driver should always be aware of the frictional character of the road surface.

Camber Steer—If the car rolls, on springs and tires, as much as 5.73° (0.10 rad.) for 0.5g lateral acceleration, the camber thrust on parallel independent front wheels has the effect of calling for a 20% increase in lateral force from the front tires.

Camber thrust also occurs due to the designed camber of the front wheels. And camber thrust exists at the rear also, due to the roll of the axle on its tires.

Swing Axle—The oversteering effects for which swing axles are commonly blamed, coupled with lifting of the rear end of the vehicle, can be avoided by "de-stabilizing" the rear suspension, so as to reduce the lateral weight transfer on the swing axle to about the same value as would avoid oversteer on a conventional rear axle.

When this is done the swing axle has certain advantages over the conventional axle, including the absence of "tramping" and inherent ride damping.

Roll Steer—*With these last two items (roll steer and lateral deflection steer) Olley gets ahead of himself—these items are discussed in the next chapter.*

Although rear roll steer appears on the skid pad charts, it has been considered desirable to deal with roll steer under "handling" rather than under "steady-state steering."

It may be pointed out that "primary" understeering effects (including camber steer of IFS) definitely sacrifice some of the maneuverability of the car for the sake of directional stability.

But the "secondary" effects sacrifice nothing. They simply, under lateral acceleration, produce changes in the posture of the wheels, relative to the median plane of the car in such ways as are found to improve handling, and independently of conscious action by the driver. They have no effect on maneuverability, but a profound effect on general handling.

But these secondary effects also have their limitations. Chief of these is the fact that, with much roll steer, a car will not run straight on a wavy road surface involving changes in lateral road slope.

Also, when entering a turn, car roll is delayed, and after leaving a turn it persists for a time. So there is a time lag limiting the effectiveness of roll steer.

Finally, certain types of roll steer lead to other undesirable suspension effects such as axle tramp and brake dive.

Lateral Deflection Steer—This has been studied in certain particular cases, but principally along the lines of avoiding troubles, rather than producing positive improvement. At first sight it appears preferable to roll steer, since it avoids the time lag.

Further study of lateral deflection steer is definitely needed. [*About ten years after Olley wrote this, General Motors commissioned the Vehicle Handling Facility (VHF) in the Chevrolet Engineering Center, a specialized machine designed to measure chassis kinematics and compliance, including lateral force compliance steer and aligning torque compliance steer.*[18] *Today, lateral deflection steer is well-known and is used in chassis tuning.*]

---

[18] Nedley, A. L. and W. J. Wilson, "A New Laboratory Facility for Measuring Vehicle Parameters Affecting Understeer and Brake Steer," Paper No. 720473, Society of Automotive Engineers, 1972.

2.11 Summary of Calculations in Sections 2.4 through 2.9

These sections include steady-state calculations of skid pad tests to show "primary", i.e. slip angle, effects for changes in various design (or configuration) variables. Table 2.17 summarizes the various worked examples.

Section 2.4 Calculating Steady-State Steering Characteristics (Bicycle Model)

Objective:	*Calculate the effects of cornering stiffness and roll steer without lateral weight transfer.*
Results:	*Example 1: Equal loads front and rear. Higher cornering stiffness on rear causes understeer.*
	Example 2: Equal loads front and rear. Higher cornering stiffness on front causes oversteer.
	Example 3: Same as Example 1, but with IFS and 3% rear axle roll understeer. Causes drastic understeer.
	Repeat for constant radius/variable speed shows straight line plot for constant cornering stiffness.
	Repeat for two speeds. Steering more sensitive at higher speed.
	Repeat for excessive rear roll stiffness, requires four-wheel model. Understeer at lower accelerations to oversteer at higher accelerations.

Section 2.5 Lateral Weight Transfer Effect (Wheel Pair) (Four-Wheel Model)

Objective:	*Calculate the distribution of roll rates and lateral weight transfers. No skid pad calculations.*
Results:	*The lateral load transfer distribution between front and rear depends on both the respective heights of the front and rear roll centers and the front and rear suspension roll stiffness (about the roll axis).*
	Equal roll rates front and rear do not ensure equal lateral load transfers front and rear.
	Olley shows how excessive front roll stiffness promotes understeer and excessive rear roll stiffness promotes oversteer at higher lateral accelerations. He then calculates (using the base vehicle of Example 3, Section 2.4) the following:

Table 2.17 Summary of Worked Examples in Chapter 2

Part B - Bicycle Model Examples

Page or Figure	Front Weight	Rear Weight	Total C Front lb./deg.	Total C Rear lb./deg.	Front Roll Steer	Rear Roll Steer	Front Roll Camber deg./g	Rear Roll Camber deg./g	Front Roll Stiffness lb.-ft./deg.	Rear Roll Stiffness lb.-ft./deg.	R-R-Stiff w/Tires lb.-ft./deg.

Constant 1 deg. Steer Angle Test

	Page or Figure	Front Weight	Rear Weight	Total C Front	Total C Rear	Front Roll Steer	Rear Roll Steer	Front Roll Camber	Rear Roll Camber
Example 1	84	2000	2000	225	250	0	0	0	0
Example 2	87	2000	2000	250	225	0	0	0	0
Example 3	87	2000	2000	225	250	0	3% US	11.4	0

Constant Radius Test

	Page or Figure	Front Weight	Rear Weight	Total C Front	Total C Rear	Front Roll Steer	Rear Roll Steer	Front Roll Camber	Rear Roll Camber
Example 3	2.25	2000	2000	225	250	0	3% US	11.4	0

Constant Speed Test

	Page or Figure	Notes
	2.26	Data Unknown - reasonable characteristics
	2.27	Data Unknown - excessive rear roll moment (not really a bicycle model)

Part C - Four-Wheel Model Examples - Independent Front and Axle Rear Suspension

	Page or Figure	Front Weight	Rear Weight	Total C Front	Total C Rear	Front Roll Steer	Rear Roll Steer	Front Roll Camber	Rear Roll Camber	Front Roll Stiffness	Rear Roll Stiffness	R-R-Stiff w/Tires	Notes
Case A	99	2000	1700	327	327	0	0	11.4	0	388	254	227	Equal load transfer front and rear
Case B	100	2000	1700	327	327	0	0	11.4	0	311	364	312	50% more load transfer on rear
Case C	110	2000	1700	327	327	0	3% US	11.4	0	388	254	227	CG height reduced from 24 in. to 18 in.
	2.31												As Case A but addition of 2 deg. positive camber on front also included in the plot
	2.43												As Case A but addition of traction

Constant Radius Test

	Page or Figure	Front Weight	Rear Weight	Total C Front	Total C Rear	Front Roll Steer	Rear Roll Steer	Front Roll Camber	Rear Roll Camber	Front Roll Stiffness	Rear Roll Stiffness	R-R-Stiff w/Tires	Notes
Case A	104	2000	1700	327	327	0	0	11.4	0	388	254	227	
Case B	106	2000	1700	327	327	0	0	11.4	0	311	364	312	
	2.32												As Case B but addition of traction also plotted (calculations on page 126)
Case A, variation a	109	2000	1700							no data	no data	no data	As Case A, change in load transfer distribution to give 50% more on front (no plot)
Case A, variation b	110	2200	1800							388	254	227	55/45% weight distribution
Case A, variation c	110	2000	1700	327	(-26%)	327							Discussion of trend with decreased front tire inflation pressure
Case C	2.35												Shows effect of reduced total load transfer

Swing Axle Development

	Page or Figure	Front Weight	Rear Weight	Front Roll Stiffness	Rear Roll Stiffness	Notes
Step 1	139	2000	2000	249	327	Rear axle with rear spring track equal to wheel track - discarded
Step 2	141	2000	2000	473	207	Rear as Step 1 plus addition of front stabilizer bar - discarded
Step 3	143	2000	2000	379	302	Accept increased rear roll stiffness
Step 4 Swing Axle	2.48	2000	2000	379	302	Detailed calculations on Tables 2.9 through 2.14
Step 5 Swing Axle-a	2.52	2000	2000	397	179	Reduced rear roll stiffness with transverse leaf spring

Case A: Equal weight transfer front and rear.

Case B: 50% more weight transfer on rear than front.

No plots are given, but the results are used in Section 2.6.

Section 2.6 Calculating Steady-State Steering Characteristics with Lateral Load Transfer Distribution (LLTD)

Objective: *Calculate constant radius test with lateral load transfer, for comparison with constant radius version of Example 3 (no load transfer) from Section 2.4.*

Results: *Case A: Yields normal (desirable) understeer on constant radius skid pad (largely due to camber thrust from bias ply tires on IFS). Olley also shows considerable increase in US due to adding +2° of static camber on front, Figure 2.31 (page 105).*

Case B: Yields sudden oversteer at higher lateral accelerations, from approximately neutral steer at lower accelerations. Replots these results against speed on skid pad, showing large sensitivity to speed, Figures 2.32 (page 108) and 2.33 (page 109).

Case C: Variation of Case A, in which CG is lowered. Results in marked decrease in understeer to approximately neutral steer. Difference in lateral forces on left and right wheels reduced.

Olley also calculates and plots the front and rear lateral tire forces for Cases A, B and C. These are useful for more detailed understanding of results. Figures 2.36, 2.37 and 2.38.

Section 2.7 Traction Effects

Objective: *Re-calculate the constant radius test with traction on the rear wheels. Calculate the road load power for the constant radius test.*

Results: *Develops a calculation method for introducing traction effects (on driving wheels). Calculates skid pad curves for Case A and B (of Section 2.6). Also tire lateral forces for Case A.*

Case A: Traction effect causes δ curve (steer angle) to "hook over" at high lateral acceleration (Figure 2.43).

Case B: Application of power (traction) at rear wheels causes "spin out." Excessive rear roll couple and traction, found to be very unde-

sirable; the rear tire lateral tire forces fall off rapidly in this case (Figure 2.32, page 108).

Section 2.8 Neutral Steer Point and Static Margin

Objective: *Develop neutral steer point (NSP) and static margin (SM) concepts. No skid pad calculations or plots.*

Model: *Bicycle model.*

Examples: *Variations on Examples 1, 2, and 3 from Section 2.4.*

Results: *Develops method for calculating NSP and static margin*

Calculates SM for Examples 1, 2 and 3 of Section 2.4 with the following results:

Example 1: SM = 0.025 (positive is understeer) page 133
Example 2: SM = − 0.025 (negative is oversteer)
Example 3: SM = 0.1047 (understeer, includes 5% front and 3% rear roll-understeer)
Example 3, disregarding roll steer: SM = 0.0775 (understeer)

Section 2.9 Swing Axle

Olley starts off with the following statement regarding swing axles:

The problem with the swing axle on the rear is found to be mainly due to the spring base equaling the track (as for any independent suspension) and hence has a higher roll moment on the rear tires. A solid axle has a spring base ≈ 3/4 track. If the rear springs are softened on a swing axle, a flat ride cannot be attained. The situation can be improved by a front roll stabilizer bar and a Z-bar or transverse leaf spring (ride spring with zero roll stiffness) on the rear.

*Initial Objective: As an **approximation** of a swing axle (and to confirm that the spring base is a critical element) he considers a rigid axle having the same roll center height as a swing axle but with a spring base equal to the wheel track.*

Results: *Compares results with those of Section 2.5 for solid axle. In particular compares Case B (with and without swing axle) with front roll bar, Figure 2.48 (page 145). The individual tire forces are given on Figure 2.49. He comments on wheel deflections and the achievement of front and rear deflections for "flat ride."*

Second Objective: To modify the approximate representation of a swing axle, discussed above, to obtain a reasonable representation of a swing axle. To do this he must include the swing axle "lift."

Model and Example: Uses the lateral tire forces from the approximate solution (under Initial Objective) to calculate the lift (or jacking) and the camber changes for Case B. He recognizes that these changes produce a "new" lift—that is, a cyclic or iterative process—but demonstrates that one calculation cycle is enough in practice.

He calculates lift, vertical forces, tire characteristics, rear lateral forces, slip and steer angles for this first cycle (Tables 2.9 through 2.14).

Results: The results are given in Figures 2.48 (skid pad results) and 2.49 (lateral tire forces). The lateral tire forces are comparable to those for the rigid axle, which says that no further iteration is necessary. The slip angle rises more rapidly above $A_Y = 0.5g$ for the swing axle and the steer angle drops more rapidly.

Third Objective (Step 5): "De-stabilize" or lower the roll moment on the rear swing axle by use of a Z-bar or camber compensator (pivoted leaf spring), and compare to a conventional solid rear axle.

Model and Example: Case A with front stabilizer and "de-stabilized" rear suspension.

Results: See Figure 2.52 (page 157) comparing rigid rear axle and de-stabilized swing axle. Calculations given in Tables 2.15 and 2.16. They perform nearly the same in a steady-state steering test. Tire forces are given on Figure 2.53 (page 158).

CHAPTER 3

Steady-State Cornering– Steer Effects (Secondary)

"In short, the years 1933–34 saw the beginning of a real engineering approach to suspension development and Maurice Olley was the originator and teacher of this brand of engineering."

Robert Schilling
Research Laboratories
General Motors

3.1 Introduction

The notes on steady-state steering [*Chapter 2*] have dealt chiefly with skid pad results.

With the exception of rear roll steer, the skid pad reveals what I [*Olley*] have called "primary" steering effects, namely, those effects which change the front and rear slip angles, α_F and α_R, and consequently the steering angle δ.

The common skid pad procedure indicates the effect of rear roll steer in that, for example, rear-roll **understeer** will decrease the attitude angle and consequently increase the steering angle δ. In fact it calls for an increased rotation of the steering wheel. But, on the skid pad, this understeer has no effect on the actual slip angles.

Evidently, therefore, there is a whole series of steering characteristics which are important to the **handling** of the car, but which are not shown by skid pad tests.

The skid pad, by indicating α_F and α_R, gives a very good indication of factors affecting tire wear. It also indicates excellently how the car may be expected to behave when pushed to its limit on a corner, particularly whether it will tend to "drift" or "spin."

The driver's impression of the handling of a car, on straight roads and on turns, is only partially affected by its primary steering characteristics. The secondary characteristics, which have to do with geometry rather than with tires, also have a profound effect on handling.

The notes on steady-state steering have already covered the general definitions of understeer and oversteer. One can say that, if a car understeers, then the path curvature [$1/R$] from a given steering angle becomes less as the speed increases, and, if it oversteers, the curvature increases with the speed.

Note on Understeer/Oversteer as Measured in Skid Pad Tests

It is important to have a clear understanding of the concept of understeer/oversteer (UO) in relation to the several types of skid pad tests.

Although Olley doesn't state it explicitly, what he is getting at in his concept of UO is the "yawing" behavior of the vehicle when exposed to a lateral acceleration in steady-state turning maneuvers. In these maneuvers two fundamentally different things occur: (1) effective slip angle changes at the front and rear wheels, and (2) geometric steer changes at the front and rear wheels. The first results from the force and moment balance (tire forces and moments vs. centrifugal force) and the second, from suspension effects due to roll of the body and structural compliances due to centrifugal force. Olley refers to these as "primary" and "secondary" effects, respectively. Both effects produce changes in the front and rear lateral tire forces and hence changes in the yawing moment on the vehicle. But since (by definition) the UO concept is for steady-state and hence zero yawing moment, these yawing moments are equilibrated (yaw moment trim) by a yawing moment due to steering. In short, the unbalanced yawing moments from slip angle and steer changes due to the centrifugal force are being measured in terms of the control moment supplied by the front wheels.

All these steady-state skid pad tests are of the nature of "trim control" tests. Olley and most other investigators prefer to think in "steer" terms, but "yawing moment" terms are equally acceptable.

If we think in steer terms then two choices exist: (1) steer at the front wheels and (2) steer at the steering wheel. If the latter, then steering gear ratio and steering system compliances enter the picture. SAE,[19] concerned with drivers of passenger cars, calls a car understeer "if the ratio of steering wheel angle gradient to the overall steering ratio is greater than the Ackermann steer angle gradient," where the gradients are with respect to steady-state lateral acceleration. The race driver is more concerned with what is happening at the front and rear tires and the resultant yawing moment.

---

[19] Vehicle Dynamics Terminology, SAE J670e, 1976.

A number of tests are used to measure understeer/oversteer characteristics. The follow-ing should be noted relative to the interpretation of these various UO tests:

Constant Radius/Variable Speed—In this test the tractive force at the driving wheels changes with the speed. The slip angle at the driving wheels is therefore changing due to tire friction ellipse effects. The aerodynamic forces on the vehicle are also changing.

Constant Throttle/Variable Steer—In this test an approximation to constant speed is made by use of constant throttle. The test is composed of a number of runs, each with different steer input. Because of the changes in input steer, the speed is generally not quite constant.

Constant Speed/Variable Radius—In this test the path curvature and hence yaw damping is changing.

Constant Steer/Variable Speed—In this test the path curvature is changing and hence the yaw damping. This is also called the "spiral test," for the path that the vehicle traces over the ground.

Constant Speed on a Straight Sloping Road—In this test the normal load on the tires is reduced as the tilt of the road is increased. An understeer car tends to run down the grade (until corrected with steering).

3.2 Roll Effects

The effect of roll steer has already been noted in preliminary figuring, though not in the skid pad charts. However, before going further, a full definition of roll steer seems to be needed.

Consider a wood model such as shown in Figure 3.1.

We found the following discussion of roll steer difficult to follow because the forces caus-ing the roll are not given. It appears that Olley assumes a car with a high yaw inertia and he is examining roll steer entirely due to an inclined roll axis. For unequal roll cen-ter heights front and rear, when the car rolls the median plane yaws relative to the initial path. Since the axles remain perpendicular to the median plane (zero axle roll steer), the axles yaw relative to their initial path and the car crabs sidewise.

After looking at an alternate definition, Olley finally concludes that his original defini-tion of zero roll steer, with the axles moving perpendicular to the ground, is the correct choice, and is the most desirable design for driving on a twisted road.

This is the simplest demonstration of a vehicle with an inclined roll axis and **zero roll steer**. [*When these axles roll, they do not steer relative to the body.*]

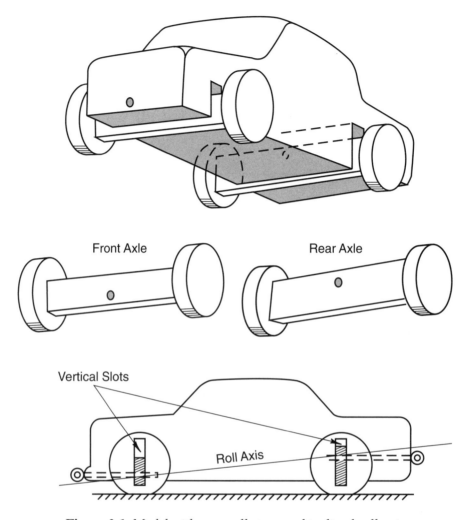

Figure 3.1 *Model with zero roll steer and inclined roll axis.*

Since the slots are normal to the median plane of the car and are **vertical**, it follows that, when the car rolls, the traces on the ground of the four wheels remain parallel to the trace of the median plane.

It is important to note that this does **not** mean that the sprung mass continues to hold to its original path when it rolls.

Thus, consider Figure 3.2, of a car with zero roll steer [*according to Olley's definition above*].

If the slope of the roll axis is θ (rad.) and the roll angle is ϕ (rad.), the yaw angle of the median plane, **and of the four wheels** is

$$\psi \cong \phi\theta \tag{3.1}$$

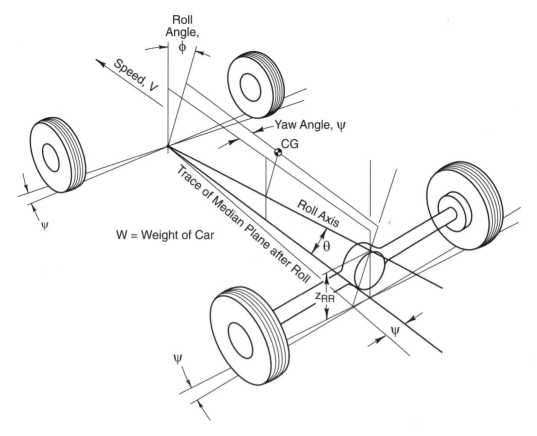

Figure 3.2 *Simplified car with zero roll steer.*

This is not a steering effect: although the course [*path*] has changed [*once the "transient" is over*] the car continues to run in a straight line.

During the "transient" there is a roll damping (and yaw damping) effect. An angular velocity in roll $d\phi/dt$, which we could call $\dot{\phi}$, will evidently cause a rate of change of yaw $d\psi/dt$ which is $\dot{\phi}\theta$.

Hence, if we may assume that, as it rolls, the car follows a new path set by axle steer angles, the yaw velocity $\dot{\phi}\theta$ will cause a centrifugal force at the CG of $WV\dot{\phi}\theta/g$.

This force opposes the roll and is directly proportional to the speed of the car and the angular velocity of roll. It is therefore a "fluid damping" effect on the roll.

Thus consider the car to be traveling at 60 mph and oscillating [*in roll*] through 2 deg. either side of vertical.

> W (rolling weight) = 4000 lb. [*also called sprung weight*]
> V = 88 ft./sec.
> θ = 0.10 rad.

Maximum $\phi = 2° = 0.035$ rad.
Let roll frequency $= 100$ cpm $= 10.47$ rad./sec.
Maximum roll velocity $\left(\dot{\phi}_{max}\right) = 10.47 \times 0.035 = 0.366$ rad./sec.
Maximum damping force at CG: $WV\dot{\phi}\theta/g = 400$ lb.

If the assumption (originally made by de Lavaud[20]) that the direction of car travel follows its tires [*infinite cornering stiffness*] is even approximately correct, the roll damping from the inclined roll axis, at the higher speeds, is considerable.

With real tires, the yawing of the axles produces slip angles at the tires [*and thus this roll/ yaw damping is reduced*].

Inclined Roll Axis

It is sometimes argued that the definition of zero roll steer worked-out above is not satisfactory, and that the definition should rather be based on the roll axis. The argument against this is that, as stated above, the change in yaw with roll is not a steering effect since the path of the car is still a straight line after the roll has occurred.

However, suppose the slots in the wood model, instead of being vertical, were cut normal to the roll axis. If $\theta = 0.10$ rad., as above, this amounts to giving 10 percent roll **under-steer** to the rear axle, and 10 percent roll **oversteer** to the front wheels. The overall result is that, despite the inclined roll axis and the corresponding yaw angle ψ, **the direction of motion of the car is unchanged by the roll.**

This condition can be applied to an actual car, by putting 10 percent understeer in the geometry of the rear suspension and 10 percent oversteer in the front steering linkage. And it is surprising that, within my [*Olley's*] knowledge, this condition has never been deliberately tried.

Possibly one reason is that, with IFS, a roll oversteer implies toeing the wheels **in** as they rise, and this is extremely undesirable for wheelfight [*see Section 6.3, Wheelfight*].

But another and probably more powerful reason is that, in all these questions of roll steer, we are really thinking of two conditions. The first is the roll of the car on a smooth road, and the second is the motions of the wheels relative to the median plane of the car on a wavy road as shown in Figure 3.3.

This may be considered a generalized representation of a wavy road, in which the wavelength λ may be any thing from 3 feet to 100 feet.

---

[20] de Lavaud, S., 1928, *Technique Moderne*, Vol. 20, No. 7, "The Problem of Independent Rear Wheels."

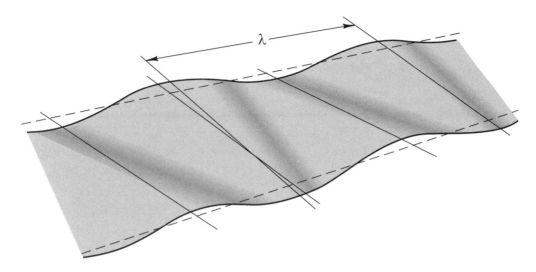

Figure 3.3 *Wavy road.*

Evidently the "zero roll steer" of the original wood model, which maintains its wheel traces on the ground parallel to the median plane, stands the best chance of running straight on such a road surface.

It is therefore concluded that we are right in the definition of zero roll steer. [*Namely, that for zero roll steer, the axles move in planes perpendicular to the road.*]

3.3 Wheel Control (Rear Axle)

Continuing with the subject of secondary steer effects in steady-state cornering, Olley now examines roll steer arising from various suspension types.

The pointing of the front wheels depends on the steering geometry, and of the rear wheels on the geometry of the rear suspension. We have to consider the practical means of controlling the direction of the wheels.

Rear Axle

When the car rolls one wheel rises, relative to the car, and the other falls through an equal distance. So, if the links in Figure 3.4 are initially horizontal, although the axle will advance a little as the car rolls, it will remain in a plane normal to the median plane of the car. If the front steering linkage is also neutral, the direction of the car will change due to the inclined roll axis, just as in the wood model, but the car will continue to run straight. One can think of the **roll axis of the axle**, as a horizontal line through the axle center, as shown.

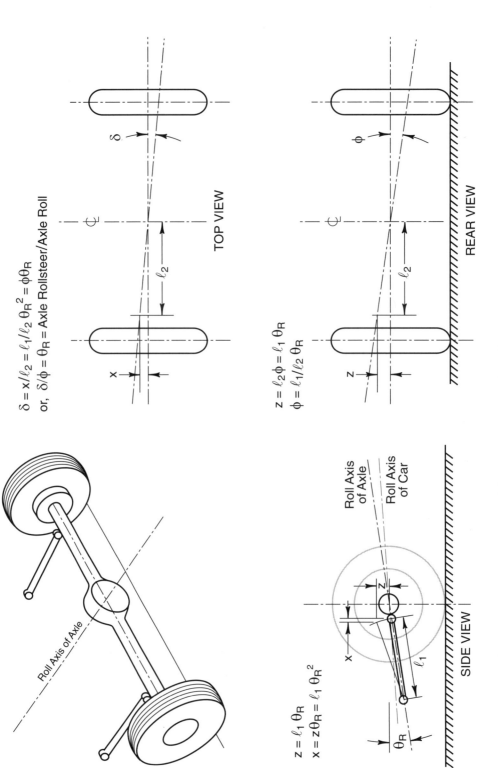

Figure 3.4 Rear axle roll steer.

If the links slope downward toward the front at an angle of θ_R radians to the horizontal, then the roll understeer of the axle is $100\theta_R\%$, regardless of the separation between the links, or their length, as shown in Figures 3.4 and 3.5.

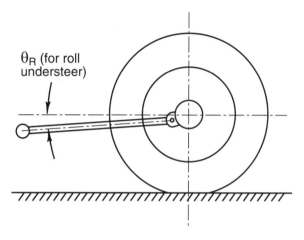

Figure 3.5 Inclined rear-axle roll-axis gives roll understeer.

The length of the links does not affect the percent of roll steer at any given standing height. But their length does affect the **rate of change of roll steer** with variations in standing height.

Consider for example a Hotchkiss-controlled rear axle with 60 in. long rear springs. Suppose it to have neutral rear steer at curb weight, and to depress 2 in. at full load. The effective link length will be about three-eighths of the spring length or 22.5 in. Then at full load it will have $(2 \times 100)/22.5 = 8.9\,\%$ roll understeer [*the percent change in θ_R*].

Hotchkiss Rear Axle

The typical Hotchkiss rear axle of the 1930s was arranged somewhat like that shown in Figure 3.6, with symmetrical rear springs having upturned eyes and considerable positive camber.

The "equivalent link" CD was about three-eighths of the total spring length, the axle radius of action AB was parallel to it, and its slope provided at normal standing height a very marked roll oversteer [θ_R *sloped downward toward the rear*].

This was not done accidentally. The slope of AB caused the wheel center to move backward as it rose over a road bump, and this was considered, quite rightly, to reduce shock and "harshness" on rough roads.

However, the slope of AB might be 0.10 rad. (5.75°) to the horizontal, which meant that if the car rolled 2° to the right, for example, the axle would turn 0.20° to the right in plan

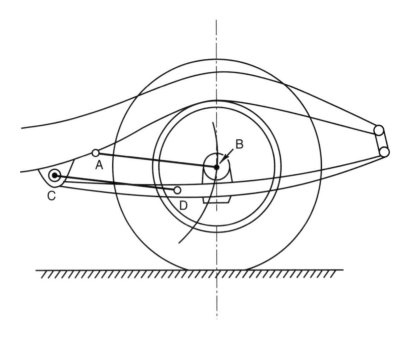

Figure 3.6 *Hotchkiss rear axle with symmetric springs.*

view. At first sight this seems ridiculously small, but it undoubtedly accounted for the reputation of the Hotchkiss drive for directional instability.

The geometry error is in the oversteer direction so that its effect is cumulative. An original roll causes yawing motion of the axle, which causes the car to turn, increasing the roll, and hence the yaw, etc. At higher speeds 10% rear roll oversteer becomes intolerable.

By road-testing cars in which the height of the front spring eye, and therefore the slope of CD, was adjustable on the road, it was possible to make CD (and AB) horizontal or give them both a small downward slope forward.

These tests were made nearly thirty years ago [*c. 1930*], but I still recall the extraordinary impression made by the simple change toward rear roll understeer. **For the first time a Hotchkiss drive car appeared to have a real sense of direction**.

But if the understeer slope of AB became too great, three faults began to show:

- Increase in harshness and shock.
- Increased rear axle tramp and frame cross-shake.
- Increased lift of the rear end in braking and squat in acceleration.

At one stage overslung rear springs were tried (as in Figure 3.7) giving a very pronounced roll understeer. These were not a success. Besides the above three faults, they

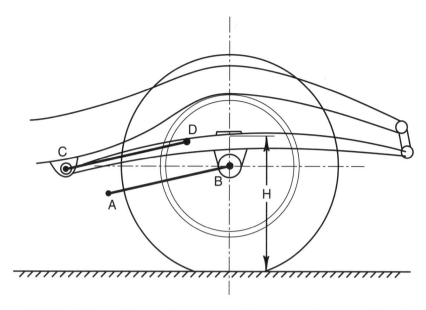

Figure 3.7 *Hotchkiss with overslung rear springs; excessive rear roll understeer.*

had the further disadvantage that the increased height H to the main plate of the spring led to severe power and brake-hop.

The progressive lowering of cars has now led to rear springs which may have a slight roll oversteer at curb weight, becoming as much as 10 percent understeer at full load.

Lighter rear axles have undoubtedly helped to reduce the faults of axle tramp and shake. Better shock absorbers, stiffer body structures, and softer tires have also helped to make understeering rear geometry more acceptable.

Torque Tube Rear Axle (and Panhard Rod)

In Figure 3.8, the roll axis of the **axle**, on which the roll steer depends, is controlled by A, the center of the forward ball-joint, or its equivalent, and B the "control-point" of the Panhard rod. This is the point at which the rod passes through the median plane of the car.

The height of point B varies and, in general, as the car is loaded point B sinks toward the ground more than point A. Thus, although the roll steer geometry varies with load much less than with the Hotchkiss, it generally tends toward the oversteer direction with increased load.

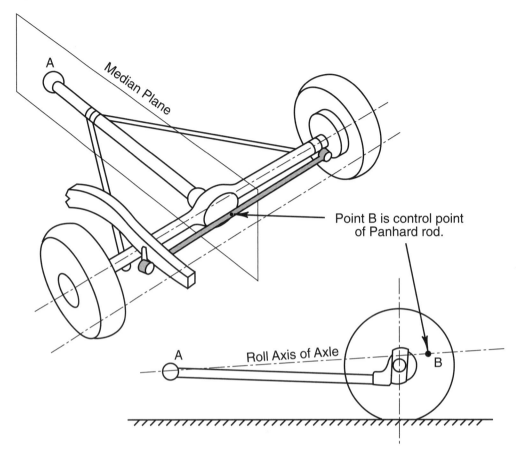

Figure 3.8 *Torque tube and Panhard rod rear axle.*

Four-Link Rear Axle

In Figure 3.9, the transverse line through C, where the **planes** of the upper and lower links meet is the pivot center of the equivalent torque arm. The position of this center varies a lot with axle motion, the torque arm becoming short at maximum bump, and lengthening toward rebound.

The roll geometry is quite different, however. The axle roll axis runs from point A, where the lower links converge, to B, where the upper links converge. If the lower links are parallel in plan view, point A is at infinity, and the axle roll axis is then always parallel to the plane of the lower links. In Figure 3.9 this would give the axle considerable roll oversteer, which would be good for axle tramp but quite bad for handling.

When the lower links converge as shown, the change in the slope of axis AB is quite rapid, so that there is considerable change in roll steer, though in general this is rather less than in the case of a Hotchkiss drive [*rear axle*]. The height of the axis AB above the ground is much greater than usual, and increases at higher loads due to the rising of

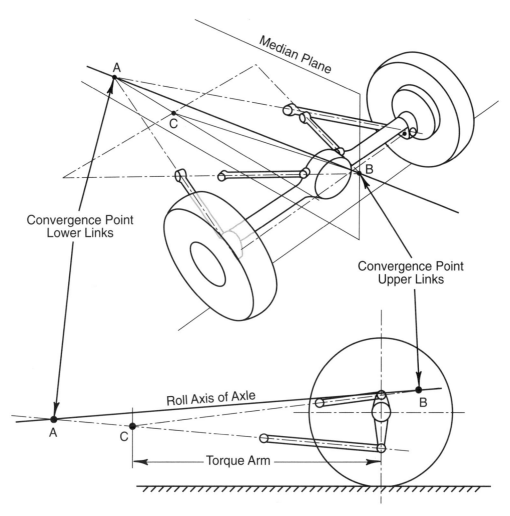

Figure 3.9 *Four-link rear axle.*

point B. The high roll center tends to put an excessive roll couple on the rear tires, as in the case of the swing axle. The high center may be good for restraining axle tramp, or the reverse, depending on stiffness of body and various resonance factors.

Three-Link and Panhard Rod

In Figure 3.10, the torque arm geometry is the same as in the case of the four-link arrangement, except for the fact that the effective torque arm is moved to the right of the median plane. The effect of this is described below.

The rear center of the axle roll axis is now point B where the Panhard rod crosses the median plane. The roll center of the axle is therefore much lower than in the four-link. And the "roll steer" slope of AB remains almost constant with changes of load.

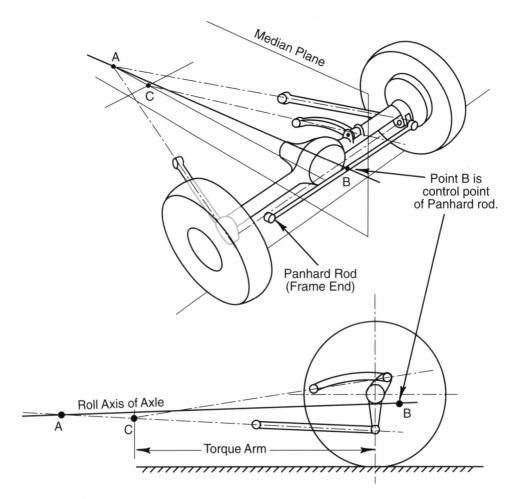

Figure 3.10 *Three-link and Panhard rod.*

This type of rear suspension was successfully used on the Jaguar C-Type race car (1950), developed by Bill Heynes, Bob Knight and Jim Randle and, more recently, analyzed by Norman Smith, formerly of Jaguar. Lacking a limited slip differential, it improved the acceleration by keeping wheel loads equal under acceleration, minimizing wheel slip.

It was later used by the Ramchargers on a drag car (1959), and analyzed by Bill Shope. In the initial trial (without analysis) the geometry overcompensated for the engine torque reaction, bouncing both right wheels off the track! Shope brought this design to the authors' attention and has analyzed the three-link suspension[21] with the additional requirement of 100% anti-squat to maintain static link angles and hence equal wheel loads under acceleration.

---

[21] Smith's and Shope's analyses are the basis for problems in Section 1.17 of *Race Car Vehicle Dynamics Workbook*, R-212, Society of Automotive Engineers, Warrendale, Pa., 1998.

Offset Torque Arm

The effect of the offset torque arm is illustrated in Figure 3.11. Normally the propeller shaft torque T_D transmitted to the axle tends to put extra vertical load on the left rear tire and reduce the load on the right rear.

Since the sprung mass of the car is rolled to the **right** by the torque reaction T_D of the powerplant, the amount of under-loading [*reduction in load*] of the right rear wheel depends on the relative front and rear roll rates.

Now, however, suppose an offset torque arm as shown and **$L/a = G$, the reduction ratio of the axle**.

The upward force from the front of the torque arm $= T_A/L$

and
$$\frac{T_A}{L} = \frac{GT_D}{L} \tag{3.2}$$

So the left hand rolling moment on the body is $GT_D a/L$, which is equal to T_D.

This completely balances the torque reaction of the powerplant, so the body does not roll under engine torque. And at the same time the torques on the axle are balanced, so the vertical loads on the two wheels are equal.

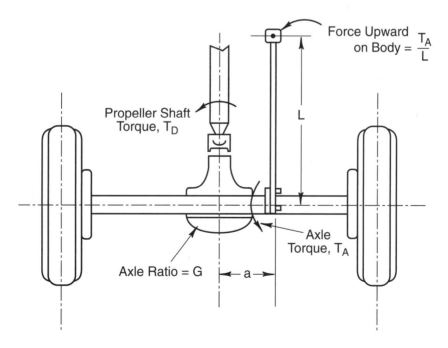

Figure 3.11 *Offset torque arm.*

There is only one drawback, namely, a small tendency for the car to roll to the right when braking.

Swing Axle Geometry

In earlier analysis of swing axles it has been assumed that the pivots are horizontal and parallel to the median plane. This is seldom so. There are generally toe changes as the wheels move up and down.

Understeer Geometry

Suppose the pivots to be parallel to the median plane, Figure 3.12, but inclined downward—forward at an angle θ. Then, for a wheel deflection z, the toe angle is $z\theta/L$ and the corresponding roll angle is $2z/t$ (both in radians).

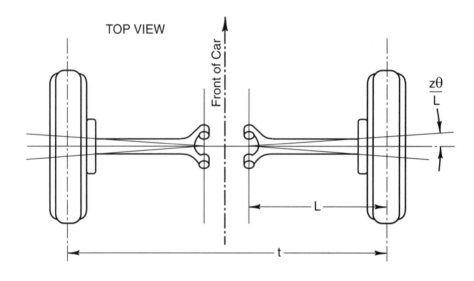

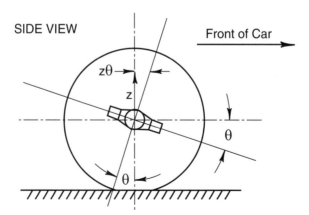

Figure 3.12 Rear swing axle geometry with inclined pivots.

Then, $\dfrac{\text{toe change}}{\text{roll angle}} = \dfrac{z\theta}{L}\dfrac{t}{2z} = \dfrac{t}{2L}\theta$ [*which equals fraction roll steer*]

$t/2L$ may be about 1.2.

Then if $\theta = 5.73°$ (0.10 radian), percent understeer = 12%.

As with IFS, this roll understeer is obtained at the expense of toe change with variation in standing height. And if L is 25 in., for example, the toe change per wheel is 0.004 radian or 0.230° per inch of wheel deflection. This is considerable and, if there is much variation in standing height due to load variation, could lead to running at light loads with toed-out rear wheels, which is undesirable because of oversteer.

Diagonal Pivot

In Figure 3.13, the wheels toe-in both above and below design height [*assuming that the swing arms are level at design height*].

The toe angle, δ, as a function of ride position is [*derived as follows*]:

From top view: $\delta \cong x/L$ (3.3)

From side view, using Olley's parabolic approximation to a circle (see Chapter 7, Linkages):

$$x = \frac{z^2}{2\left(L/\tan\theta\right)} \qquad (3.4)$$

Then,

$$\delta \cong \frac{x}{L} \cong \frac{z^2}{2L/\tan\theta}\frac{1}{L} = \frac{1}{2}\frac{z^2}{L^2}\tan\theta \qquad (3.5)$$

If, as on the Corvair, $L = 23$ in. and $\theta = 37°$ the toe angle $\delta = 0.754\dfrac{z^2}{1058}$ or, in degrees, $\delta = 0.041z^2$.

z (in.)	1	2	3	4
δ (deg.)	0.041	0.164	0.369	0.656

The rate of change of toe near design height is negligible, but it becomes considerable near bump and rebound positions. There is an effective roll understeer when wheels are toed-in [*on the rear*]. In this case it is not great due to small toe change at design height.

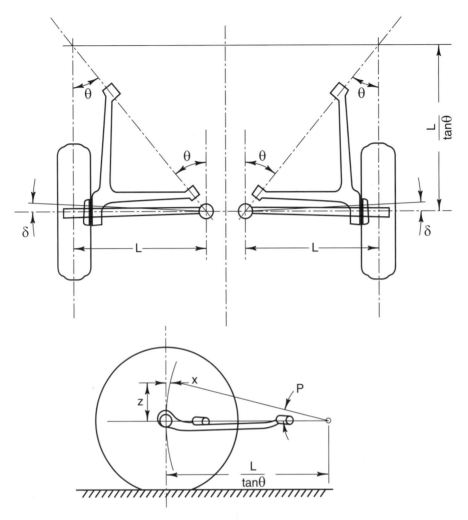

Figure 3.13 *Diagonal pivot swing axle.*

However, on a swing axle it is possible to produce an initial toe-in at design height, and in this case as little as 0.125° designed toe-in can produce a very marked understeer effect and more stable handling.

This function of "permanent" toe-in as a means for handling stability is a form of roll steer, which does slightly change the slip angles. It slightly increases the slip angle on the "outer" or more heavily loaded tire, and reduces slip angle on the inner tire, thus increasing the cornering ability of the pair. (However, it should be noted that toed-in **rear** wheels under heavy traction forces have a pronounced tendency to wear the **inside** of the tire treads.)

The fact that such small changes can have such a marked effect is an indication that the handling of a car involves an extremely delicate balance of the lateral forces on the tires.

Another common method of obtaining increased cornering ability from a swing axle, and therefore more stable handling, is to set the wheels with as much as 1.5° to 3° **negative camber**. [*On some competition cars in the era of bias-ply tires as much as 10 degrees was used successfully.*]

3.4 Wheel Control (Front Suspensions and Steering)

The above notes have covered the roll steer of rear wheels in the case of axles and swing axles. Since the rear tires are the "fulcrum" about which maneuvering of the car takes place, improving the sense of direction of the rear tires is probably the most important step toward improved handling. [*In terms of yawing moment, the rear tires are stabilizing like the tail on an airplane or a weather vane.*]

Roll Steer of Front Wheels

Roll steer of front wheels will be covered chronologically, starting with the conventional leaf spring front axle of the 1920s and '30s.

It should be noted that roll steer of (rigid) rear axles is concerned only with rolling motions of the axle relative to the car's median plane. The **ride** motions of pitch and bounce, which occur in the median plane, have normally no effect on the pointing of the rear wheels.

In the case of a front axle the problem of obtaining a predictable front end geometry is much more difficult, since it depends not only on the motion of the axle but also on the accuracy of the steering linkage. The ride motions of the axle will have a marked steering effect, whereas rolling of the axle will have different steering effects. Application of the brakes may have serious steering effects. Normal front axle steering therefore has to be a compromise.

The difficulties increase with increasing softness of suspension. This was one reason why softer front springs forced the use of independent suspension.

Probably the only way to get complete steering accuracy in a front axle is to mount the steering gear on the axle, as is done in some large coaches. Any desired roll steer can then be obtained, as in rear axles, by the suspension geometry.

It should be noted, however, that the front axle has one advantage over the independent in that roll steer can be produced without varying the toe-in, and therefore with less risk of tire wear.

Front Axle

In the early 1930s, as frames were lowered, the handling of some cars became dangerously unstable. The reason is illustrated in Figure 3.14.

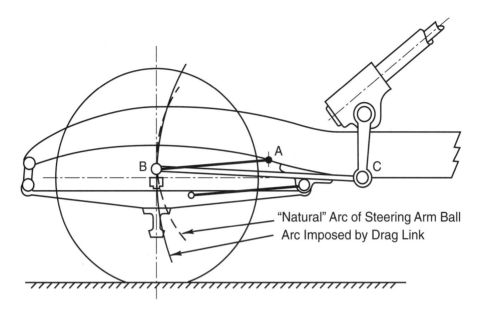

Figure 3.14 *Front axle on lowered frame, looking at left front wheel.*

With the leaf spring shackled at the front, the "natural" arc of travel of the steering ball B, with the wheels pointing straight ahead, would be about center A. But, the arc imposed by the drag link [*BC*] is about center C.

Consequently when the car takes a left hand turn and rolls to the right, the drag link will push the ball forward, and increase the left hand turn. In fact, the car has strong **right hand roll oversteer** [*right roll gives left steer, which is oversteer in a left hand turn*].

Some cars built with this geometry had this fault so strongly that at high speed a left hand highway turn was taken without moving the steering wheel by just stepping on the accelerator. The slight right hand roll caused by engine torque was enough to start the steering action, which was cumulative, since the oversteer caused more roll, which caused more oversteer, etc.

The fault could frequently be cured simply by using a down-turned rear eye on the front springs, Figure 3.15.

Then the left hand turn was practically neutral, while the right hand turn (with left hand roll) produced a left hand wheel motion, i.e., the axle had **left hand roll understeer** [*left roll gives left steer which is understeer in a right hand turn*].

From such experiences a rule-of-thumb method of roll steer test grew up. This was that, if the front of a vehicle was bounced by hand, with the car standing on the floor, the **steering wheel** should turn **right** when the nose moved **down** and/or turn **left** when the nose moved **up**, in order to give stable handling. This, of course, applies only to a vehicle with left hand steering.

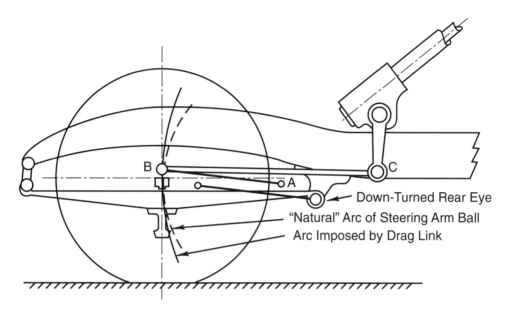

Figure 3.15 *Corrected geometry for axle on lowered frame.*

It should also be noted that the requirement is that the "natural" action radius AB in the design height position should be approached by the drag link **from above**, in the case of the rearward steering shown in Figures 3.14 and 3.15.

Forward Steering

The same considerations apply in the forward steering of a truck, Figure 3.16. But here a down-turned spring eye is undesirable. The drag link CB should approach the natural radius AB from **below**. This results in a fairly neutral steer in right turn roll, with **right hand roll understeer** [*right roll gives right steer which is understeer in a left hand turn*].

Geometry in Roll

It will be seen that the above considerations apply to ride motions of the axle. They do not apply completely to roll motions. And this is where some of the main difficulties of front axle steering come in. Figure 3.17 shows some of these difficulties.

If the front springs are initially flat, and disregarding eye offsets, the principal effect of compressing or extending a spring is to move that part of the axle backward [*assumes shackle at front and eye at rear*]. And since the spring spacing is generally narrow (only about half the wheel track) the axle I-beam, when one spring only is compressed, may be considerably out of square with the car centerline.

Thus, in the upper view of Figure 3.17, if the left hand spring only is compressed, we may assume that the ball B has an accurate linkage layout and follows the spring motion.

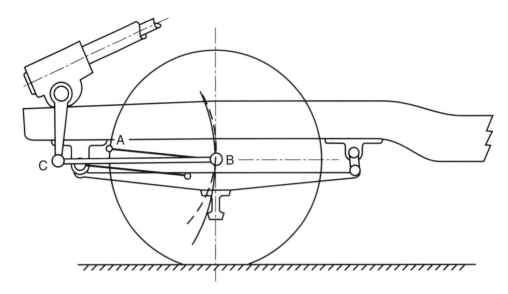

Figure 3.16 Axle with forward steering location as used in trucks.

But the kingpin D moves back further than the ball. So there is an appreciable left hand swerve.

Similarly in the lower view of Figure 3.17, if the right hand spring only is compressed, we can assume that ball B is undisturbed. But the kingpin D now moves forward, and thus produces a right hand swerve. These errors are small, but so is any tolerance for steering error in a vehicle traveling at turnpike speeds.

Leaf Spring Geometry

These problems make one extremely interested in the geometry of the leaf spring, particularly in the radius of action R_M of the load point M, Figure 3.18. This has been very carefully worked out in the SAE Leaf Spring Manual[22] not only for unsymmetrical springs, but also for springs in which one-half is "faked" to resist brake dive.

A convenient formula for an unsymmetrical spring with "perfect" circular bending is that:

$$R_M = \frac{3ab^2}{a^2 + 3b^2} \tag{3.6}$$

However, in most practical cases it is close enough to assume that R_M is three-eighths of the total spring length. [*See further notes on leaf spring geometry in Chapter 10.*]

---

[22] *SAE Spring Design Manual*, AE-11, Society of Automotive Engineers, Warrendale, Pa., 1990 [*obviously Olley was referring to an earlier version*].

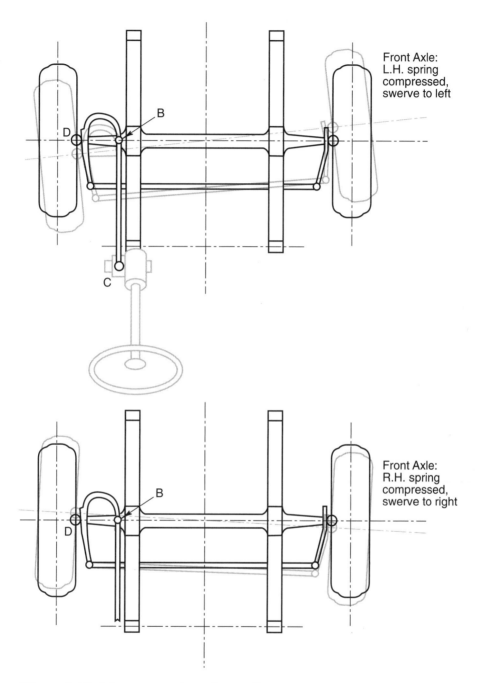

Figure 3.17 *Axle steer resulting from roll motion (or from one wheel bump).*

Front Axle Center Point

The great difficulty in link-steering with a front axle is that no points on the axle, except possibly the load points or center bolts of the two springs, follow a strictly prescribed path. The paths in ride, in roll, and in one wheel bump are all different. Even the center

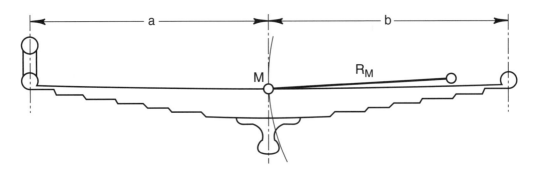

Figure 3.18 *Leaf spring and equivalent link.*

of the axle is not a neutral point, since it follows the vertical arcs of the spring geometry in ride, while in pure roll it moves fore and aft without vertical motion.

The only clear indication from all this is the overwhelming need for **long front springs**. And, added to all the above arguments is the fact that the angular windup when the brakes are applied varies inversely as **the square of the spring length.**[23]

Independent Front Suspension

Two forms of truly parallel IFS are shown in Figure 3.19. The Dubonnet (fixed kingpin), top, has truly parallel wheel motion and "fixed" steering geometry. The Dubonnet will be referred to later as an example of "positive centrifugal caster." The steering linkage on the Dubonnet is stationary, as wheels move up and down, so there is no roll steer.

Volkswagen (Porsche), Figure 3.19, bottom, also has truly parallel wheel motion and "perfect" steering geometry (when running straight) as long as offset D is equal to arm radius R and the plane of the tie rods lies parallel to the wheel arms. The interest in the Porsche design is that, although the steering linkage is unsymmetrical, the steering geometry is "perfect" under the conditions indicated.

Wishbone Suspension

Wishbone suspension, Figure 3.20, is generally (and preferably) built with a steering linkage symmetrical about the car centerline. Hence any geometry "errors" in the linkage will not cause swerving due to ride motions. (The solution of linkage problems is covered in Chapter 7, Linkages.)

In contrast to the [*solid*] front axle, the wheel support can move up and down relative to the car **in only one prescribed path**. Therefore accuracy can be obtained in the

---

[23] Ibid, page 1.73, Figure 6.7. Note that this applies for springs of equal rate.

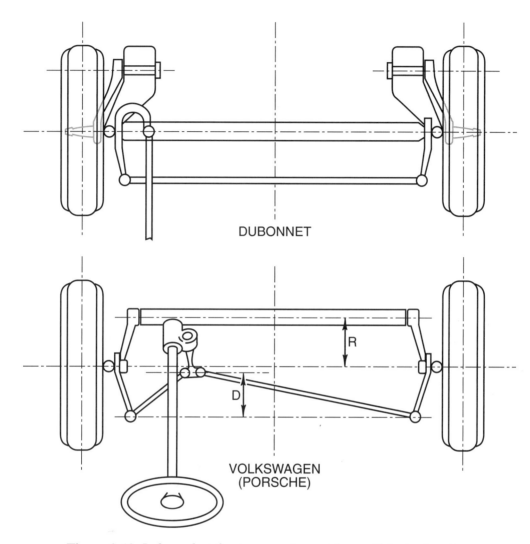

DUBONNET

VOLKSWAGEN
(PORSCHE)

Figure 3.19 Independent front suspensions with parallel wheel motion.

steering linkage, regardless of the softness of the springs, or the amount of wheel motion. Actually, however, complete accuracy is seldom obtained and is often not attempted.

For example, in the case of a steering linkage back of the wheels, the "natural arc" of the steering ball B may be traced by a radius AB in Figure 3.20. But, the tie rods CB may be longer than AB, and the inner ball C may be 1/4 in. to 3/8 in. **lower** than point A.

Rear Steering Linkage

Looking at the left front wheel, Figure 3.21, the result of lowering the inner ball C will be to cause the spindle end to move rearward as it rises, as along line DD. At the same time, the extra **length** of the rod CB, makes the wheel toe-in above and below center.

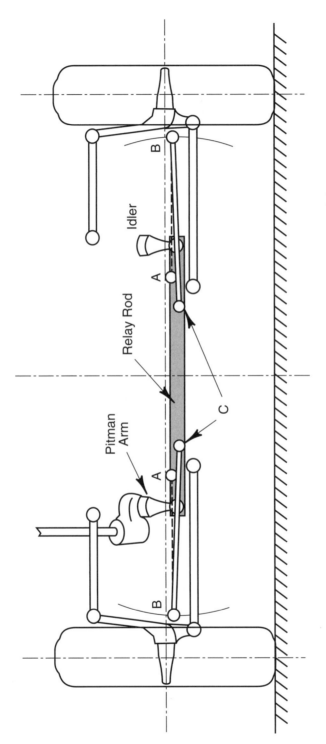

Figure 3.20 Wishbone or short-long arm (SLA) front suspension, viewed from rear.

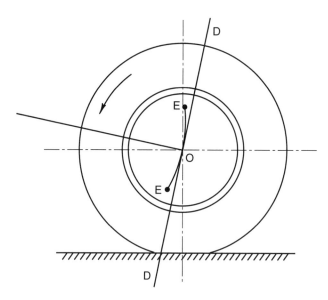

Figure 3.21 Wheel path for rear steering location, left-front suspension.

The combination of the slope and the length of CB, therefore produces an arc like EE. Although this is a steering inaccuracy it is a definite advantage.

Firstly, the "flinching" backward of the wheel center O as the wheel rises, representing a wheel toe-out motion, gives an important reduction in wheelfight. Secondly, when the car rolls on a turn, the outer wheel tends to toe-out while the inner toes-in, which is a roll understeer, tending toward more stable handling. Thirdly, the toe-in changes which occur at some considerable distance above and below center (due to tie rod length), mean that on a hard turn the **slip angle on the lightly loaded inner wheel is reduced, and on the heavily loaded outer wheel increased**, tending toward a modification of extreme understeer and reduction of tire wear. (There are also advantages in the camber angles of the outer wheels on wishbone suspensions, which will be referred to later.)

Since the steering linkage is symmetrical, these "inaccuracies" in steering have the great advantage as compared with a front axle in that they produce no swerve due to ride motions of the vehicle. But they have the serious disadvantage that toe-in varies with standing height. And this affects tire wear, and also affects the "feel" of the car at the steering wheel.

However, this fault can be minimized by making point O in Figure 3.21 represent wheel position at **light** load. Then additional loading will cause little change in toe setting.

Forward Steering Linkage

With forward steering linkage, Figure 3.22, the conditions are reversed. To obtain roll understeer slope DD, the inner tie rod balls must be **raised** above their theoretical position.

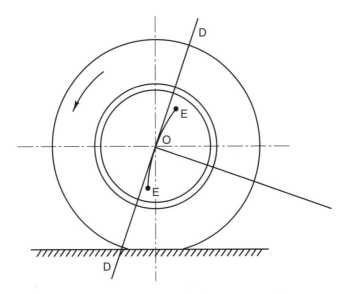

Figure 3.22 Wheel path with front steering location.

And, if the tie rods are "too long for the job," the wheels will **toe-out** above and below center.

On the face of it this looks like a less favorable condition than the first case, since the severe toe change now occurs in the more heavily loaded condition of the wheel. And on a turn the reduction in slip angle occurs on the heavily loaded outer wheel. Undoubtedly it causes a much stronger roll understeer than in the case of the rear steering linkage.

Toe-in variation with standing height may be minimized by arranging that point O in figure shall represent the standing height near **maximum** expected load.

Forward steering linkage has an important advantage when used with **anti-dive suspension geometry**. (This is referred to in Chapter 7.) The radius AB (Figure 3.20) for accurate steering on a suspension with anti-dive increases rapidly ahead of wheel center, and decreases back of wheel center. Thus the possible accuracy of steering geometry improves with a forward linkage [*we interpret this generalization as "longer links" are usually desirable*].

3.5 Understeer and Oversteer Effects, Front and Rear

Roll understeer, whether front or rear, has the characteristic that when the vehicle rolls left it steers left, and vice versa. For this reason it will be found, in some early notes, referred to as "bicycle stability."

A question which frequently arises is whether, for example, a rear axle with roll oversteer can be compensated by an understeering front layout. An example of the reverse effect has already been given, namely that a rear roll understeer compensated by a front over-steer could result in a car which, in spite of an inclined roll axis, would stay on course when it rolled.

I do not think we have enough background to give a positive answer in this latter case. But in the former, i.e., **an oversteering rear end**, I think we can say positively that there is no practical way of compensating for it. This seems to be explained by considering that, whenever a maneuver is started by the front tires, it is the rear tires which have to act as the **fulcrum** about which the maneuver takes place. Anything that makes this ful-crum "firm" contributes strongly to handling stability.

Amongst such desirable factors one can list:

> Rear roll understeer
> Less load on rear tires [*assuming no change in cornering stiffness with load*]
> Less roll-couple on rear tires
> Higher inflation in rear tires
> Toed-in rear wheels
> Negative cambered rear wheels
> Longer wheelbase
> Larger tires [*on rear*]

These effects all move the neutral steer point (NSP) aft, by increasing the stabilizing yaw moment (about the CG) produced by the rear tires.[24]

3.6 Torque Steer

Reference has already been made to some of the practical limitations of roll steering: the effect of wander on wavy roads, the effect of roll due to engine torque on an oversteering front suspension, etc.

Now we have to generalize this statement on torque reaction roll by saying that permis-sible roll steer of a vehicle in either direction (under- or oversteer) is limited by consider-ations of maximum torque reaction on the vehicle.

Consider for example a light sports car with a powerful engine and conventional rear axle. The car rolls to the right in acceleration.

> Roll **oversteer**, either front or rear, will cause extremely unstable handling on left turns, with power, but better stability on right turns. The car will pull left in acceleration.

---

[24] For a further discussion of yaw moment and directional stability, see Milliken, W. F. and D. L. Milliken, *Race Car Vehicle Dynamics*, R-146, Society of Automotive Engineers, Warrendale, Pa., 1995, particularly Chapter 5.

Roll **understeer** will cause the car to pull right in acceleration and left hand turns (under power) will be more stable than right turns.

However, if the car is fitted with independent rear suspension (other than the Mercedes single-joint type), or with a De Dion axle, or with an offset torque arm, as in Section 3.3, it then absorbs the engine torque internally, and ceases to roll under power. Then this limitation of roll steer ceases to apply.

An important advantage of lateral deflection steer (next section) is that it is not affected by engine torque.

3.7 Lateral Deflection Steer

In addition to the changes in the pointing of the wheels (relative to the median plane) due to the roll of the car, there are sometimes appreciable changes due to deflections in the suspension mechanism under lateral forces. These have been less thoroughly studied than roll steer effects, partly because they are more difficult to measure accurately.

Probably the only realistic way of measuring them is by instrumentation on the road. However static shop tests[25] give clear indications that lateral deflection steering effects exist. Their importance became apparent with increasing use of rubber bushings.

The following discussion of the forces in a front wishbone suspension is purely diagrammatic and qualitative, based on Olley's general experience. Without the addition of the numerical value of the centrifugal force, no "static" quantitative analysis of this truss structure is possible.

Figure 3.23 serves to illustrate the variations in forces in the upper and lower arms (assuming spring load on **lower** arm). When standing level there is compression in the upper arm and tension in the lower. The force at the lower knuckle ball is represented by arrow X. At the **outer wheel** on a turn the force at the tire tread may be represented by arrow Y [*the vector combination of vertical and lateral force*].

Then the force diagram ABC shows AB for the force on the lower ball D, and BC for **tension** in the upper arm. There is obviously also a considerable compression in the lower arm.

---

[25] In the early 1970s, a dedicated machine for measuring suspension kinematics and compliances was developed at Chevrolet. This is described in SAE Paper No. 720473, "A New Laboratory Facility for Measuring Vehicle Parameters Affecting Understeer and Brake Steer," Nedley, A. L. and W. J. Watson. There are now [*2001*] several types of machines that can make these measurements, such as the Anthony Best Dynamics Suspension Parameter Measuring Machine (SPMM).

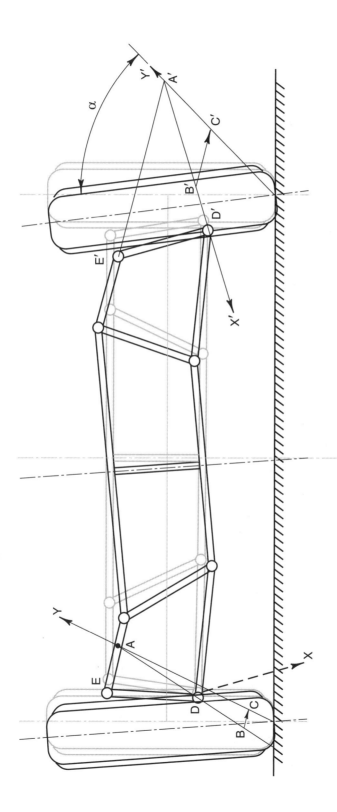

Figure 3.23 Front wishbone suspension. Black lines show position in a turn.

At the **inner wheel** we can assume a friction angle Θ of about 45°. So Y′ is the force at the tire tread. Then A′B′ represents the force at the lower ball D′, and B′C′ a considerable **compression** in the upper arm. There is evidently a high tension in the lower arm.

So, if there is rubber in the pivot joints, we can expect D to move in, and E to move out, while D′ moves out and E′ moves in. This will affect the steering. If the tie rods are low down and rearward of the wheels, both outer and inner wheels will turn slightly to the right, which is the **oversteer** direction.

On the other hand, if the tie rods are low down and **forward** of the wheels, the result is a slight turning of the wheels in the **understeer** direction. If the tie rods are high up near the level of the upper arms these effects are reversed. But high tie rods are normally very difficult to arrange, and they have to be very short to match the geometry of the short upper arms. Hence we can count this as a distinct advantage for forward steering linkage, in addition to the greater accuracy already mentioned in the case of anti-dive.

Evidently at some height between D and E there is a point on the knuckle where there is a minimum amount of lateral deflection. And this would be the best height for the tie rods. One can probably guess that in most cases this point is some three or four inches above D.

In the case of the Dubonnet or Porsche suspension designs there is evidently a steering effect from the lateral deflection of the radius arms. In the Chevrolet Dubonnet it is an understeering effect. In the Porsche design it depends on the height of the tie rods, as in the wishbone [*SLA*] design.

Flexibility of Steering Linkage

In many cases the actual flexibility of the steering linkage, particularly if it contains a bell crank or has a long rocker shaft in the steering gear, may contribute an appreciable lateral deflection **understeer** effect.

Because of the pneumatic trail of the tires and the caster offset, the front wheels tend to yield to any applied lateral force as far as flexibilities in the steering system will permit.

Timing of Lateral Deflection Steer

This brings to mind why lateral deflection steer is so important, and why it should receive more attention than we have been in the habit of giving it. Whereas all roll steer effects take a little time to develop, since they depend on the roll angle of the car, lateral deflection steer appears almost instantly with the application of side force. This applies to all types of lateral deflection steer, whether front or rear.

Rear-Steer Effects

a. **Hotchkiss**

Generally the Hotchkiss rear axle is free from any tendency for the axle to yaw when pushed laterally. This is true if the springs are parallel and if we ignore the roll steer effects. It is not true where the springs converge forward, as shown in Figure 3.24. In this case there is evidently a lateral deflection **oversteer**.

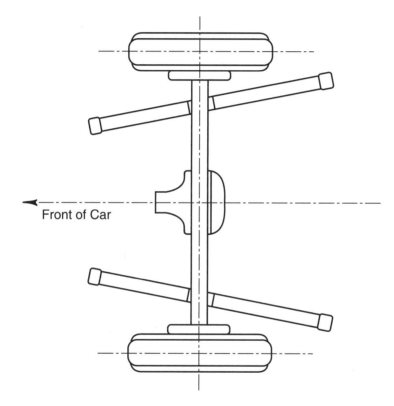

Front of Car

Figure 3.24 *Leaf springs converging forward equals deflection oversteer.*

However, quite apart from an actual steering effect, there is the question of the use of the rear tires as a fulcrum for all maneuvers, referred to earlier.

From time to time, to reduce side shake or for other reasons, rear springs have been tried with main leaves split down the center [*reducing the lateral stiffness*]. In every case this has resulted in vague and "rubbery" handling immediately recognized by the driver.

It appears that the arrangement of a Hotchkiss rear axle with lateral deflection **understeer**, Figure 3.25, has not been adequately studied. It may have serious faults as regards tramp and cross-shake, but it appears to offer handling advantages, particularly wind-handling (see Section 3.11).

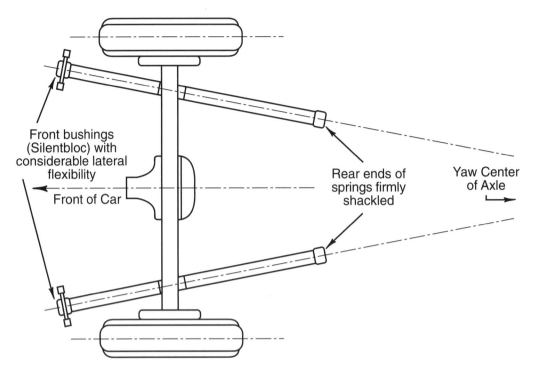

Front bushings (Silentbloc) with considerable lateral flexibility

Front of Car

Rear ends of springs firmly shackled

Yaw Center of Axle

Figure 3.25   Concept—leaf springs converging rearward for deflection understeer.

b. **Torque Tube**

The torque tube shown in Section 3.3 will evidently have lateral deflection oversteer if the Panhard rod is flexibly connected either to the frame or the axle. Yet some flexibility is found to be essential to suppress road noise and harshness. An acceptable compromise can only be found by road tests.

c. **Swing Axle**

The first type of swing axle shown at the end of Section 3.3 is generally free from lateral steer effects, provided the drive casing is suitably mounted. The second type, where rubber bushings are used for the pivots, is quite likely to show lateral deflection oversteer.

Of these diagonal pivot types probably the best for lateral deflection is the simplified type, Figure 3.26, which relies on the drive shaft itself for one arm of the triangle.

3.8 Straight Running

On a car with independent front suspension there is no such thing as a fixed position of the steering wheel for straight running.

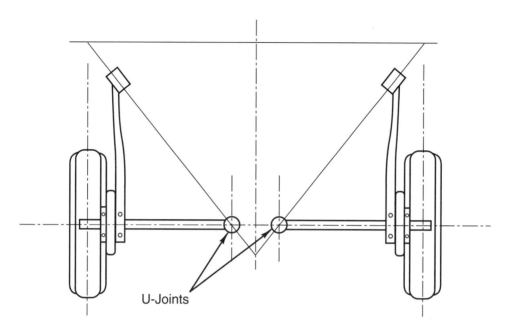

U-Joints

Figure 3.26 Simplified rear swing axle arrangement.

Camber thrust per degree of camber relative to the road surface is about one ninth of the lateral force per degree of slip angle [*this varies with tire design*]. Hence one degree of roll of the car has to be balanced by about 0.11° of change in the direction in which the front wheels are pointing. With an overall steering ratio of 27 to 1, this means about a 3° turn of the steering wheel. [*This slow steering ratio was required for manual steering of a heavy car. Current steering ratios are more in the range of 15:1 or 20:1 (with power assist).*]

If the suspension has enough dry friction to "stick" within a total range of one inch of vertical motion on either side, this means that, on a smooth road, the car may rest within about one degree to right or left of vertical. To continue to run straight this means that the front wheels may have to point anywhere within 0.22° of steering angle. In other words the steering wheel position for straight running may vary within 6 degrees.

This is true **without** any roll steer. If there were a total of 10% roll understeer on the car, this apparent backlash at the steering wheel would be approximately doubled. In actual maneuvering of the car, especially in a gusty wind, the shock absorbers may momentarily have much the same effect as dry friction.

Hence one of the requirements for directional stability in the handling of a vehicle with IFS is a minimum of dry friction in the suspension, front or rear, and avoidance of severe shock absorber action. Fortunately with the soft suspensions habitually used with IFS, hard shock absorber settings are unnecessary. But with such soft suspensions the vertical "sticking range" due to dry friction is increased, so that it becomes more than ever necessary to build friction-free suspensions for the sake of handling.

What has been said above about the "apparent backlash" on a straight, smooth road is a useful picture, but imagines a situation that rarely occurs.

Actually, side forces, whether from relative wind or from road camber, are almost always present and are constantly changing. And the tires can resist such forces only by developing slip angles.

Small movements of the steering wheel are therefore necessary to hold a course even on a straight road. And these have a value in giving the driver a feel of the road surface, through the aligning torque of the tires. When the surface becomes slippery the driver should be aware of it immediately. (On a motorcycle for example, which handles by camber thrust, the rider has no such warning.)

3.9 Suspension Geometry Effects

There are a variety of suspension geometry effects that influence car handling. In this section, Olley relies on a wealth of practical design experience to discuss these effects, which are so important to understanding the compromises of an actual design.

Toe-In and Camber

A change toward toe-out as the wheels rise has been shown as a means of avoiding wheelfight and getting roll understeer in IFS. It has also been mentioned that even quite a small toe-in of the **rear** wheels, such as may be done in a swing axle, or a De Dion axle, has a marked effect in improving handling stability.

In the early days of our understanding of over- and understeer it seemed that, if toed-in **rear** wheels were desirable, then toed-out **front** wheels might be equally desirable. By trial, however, it was quickly proved that the reverse was true. The more the front wheels are **toed-in** at design height, the better the handling stability of the car. The effect can even be seen in skid pad tests, but it is unmistakably so in actual handling. In fact, if tire wear would allow us to toe the front wheels in as much as 1/2 in. per pair (or approximately 0.5° per wheel) the handling could be notably improved.

The conclusion is that, with toed-in wheels, as the car rolls, the more heavily loaded tire, by its aligning torque has a small but appreciable tendency to turn both front wheels "under" the roll, and that the driver feels this "bicycle stability" effect at the steering wheel. Toed-out front wheels reverse this tendency, and in practice give the driver a peculiar "lost" feeling.

The relation of toe-in setting to camber setting is also of interest. Both camber and toe-in are actually legacies from the days of horse carriages, which have come to the automobile as a tradition.

Camber thrust in itself does not produce appreciable tire wear. But a positive camber setting increases understeer, and thus calls for increased front slip angles, and so indirectly increases tire wear.

Positive camber pushes outwardly on the wheel and toe-in pushes inward. Some wheel alignment devices aim to produce a condition where these two forces balance each other so that each individual front wheel tends to run straight. At first sight this seems ideal. But it ignores the fact that a slip angle, however small, produces tire wear, while a camber angle does not. Thus, whatever the camber setting on two front wheels, least tire wear will occur at zero toe setting.

However, there is some slack and flexibility in the linkage system which controls the toe setting, and the tire aligning torques and rolling resistance therefore affect the setting. Hence it is necessary for accuracy to set the toe-in **with the wheels rolling forward**.

With increasing tire cross-sections, low-profile tires, and low inflations, aligning torques have increased considerably in recent years. Also, in the first few thousand miles of running the aligning torque may well double. For example, Cornell Lab on new 7.60×15 tires with 1150 lb. load and 28 psi inflation finds an aligning torque of 255 lb.-in./deg., but at 7000 miles this has increased to 490 lb.-in./deg.

There therefore seems to be less and less need for toe-in, or for caster, and certainly no need whatever for positive camber. [*We believe Olley is referring to sedans without power steering, c. 1960.*]

Camber-Change Variations (Wishbone Suspension)

In the case of IFS with truly parallel wheel motion, such as the Chevrolet Dubonnet or the Porsche, the camber angle of the wheels relative to the ground (if we disregard flexing of the arms) is the same as the roll angle of the car.

This is not true on the wishbone suspension. In this there is considerable negative camber of the wheels in the bump and rebound positions, so that, when the car rolls on a turn the camber angle relative to the ground is decreased on the more heavily loaded outer wheel, and increased on the inner wheel.

The effect of this is to decrease the total camber thrust and the resulting understeer, but a secondary effect is to produce excessive camber angles relative to ground on the inner tire, leading to tire-squeal.

Figure 3.27 shows that, because of the change toward negative camber, and because of the initial angle of the knuckle AB in the design position, for equal up and down movements of the wheel center O the camber change is more severe on the rebound than on the bump side. However these are at extreme bump and rebound positions. Under ordinary hard cornering conditions the up and down motion of the wheel center does not normally

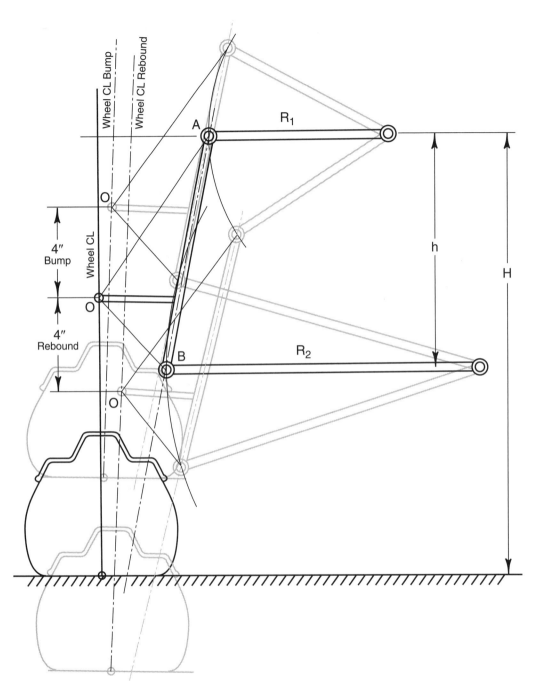

Figure 3.27 *Wishbone linkage construction.*

exceed 2 inches, and, with a normal layout of the arms the change toward negative camber rarely exceeds one degree. This will be deducted from the roll angle to give the camber relative to ground on the outside wheel, and added on the inside wheel. Various modifications are used, based on the position at which the camber change rate becomes zero.

The upper and lower arms are of unequal length. Always at some position of the wheel the arms become parallel, and at this position the camber change rate is zero. The plot of the camber change rate is nearly a straight line, as shown in Figure 3.28.

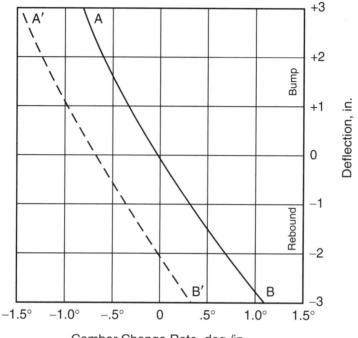

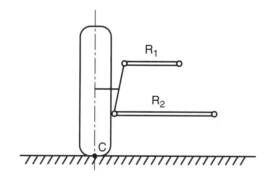

Figure 3.28 Camber change curve, AB.

1. If the arms are both horizontal at design height the camber change rate curve is like AB in Figure 3.28. This might be called the "classical" layout giving the closest approach to parallel wheel motion.

    It was thought originally that this gave the least excitation of wheelfight or shimmy. The roll center is at ground level. And, if the arm lengths are inversely as their height from the ground, the contact point C moves in a vertical straight line, and the roll center remains at ground level in all wheel positions.

2. The next variation was as shown in Figure 3.29. The outer end of the upper arm was raised, the lower arm remaining horizontal. The result is to produce a camber-change center O toward the "inside" of the wheel and a camber-change radius OC. The roll center, z_{RF}, is also raised.

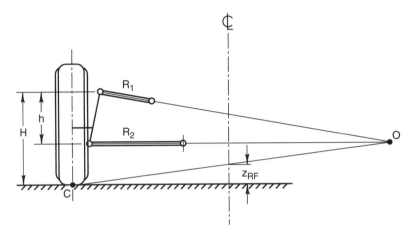

Figure 3.29 Wishbone suspension with angled upper arm.

The camber change rate is like dashed line A′B′ in Figure 3.28.

If the lengths of the two arms are inversely as the heights of their **outer ends** from the ground, the height of the roll center z_{RF}, remains constant at all wheel positions.

This geometry has been much used. It decreases negative camber at rebound, and increases negative camber at bump, thus benefiting the camber relative to ground on both the outside and inside wheel on a turn. It thus reduces extreme understeer, prevents squeal of the inside tire, and reduces tire wear.

Disadvantages are that there is a camber change rate at design height which favors the build-up of the shimmy cycle, thus increasing the wheelfight tendency.

Also the roll center height z_{RF}, if it exceeds one or two inches, frequently causes an amount of uncertainty in handling, not completely understood, but probably due to the lateral motion of the tire tread on the road.

3. The third variation was to use the divergent arms of variation 2 above, but to slope the lower arm as shown in Figure 3.30 so as to bring the camber change center O down to ground level. This brings the roll center to the ground and means that the tire tread moves vertically.

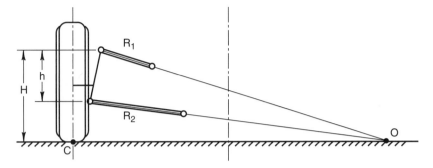

Figure 3.30 *Wishbone suspension both arms angled—Crane geometry.*

If we also satisfy the condition that,

$$R_1H = R_2(H - h)$$ (3.7)

then the roll center O virtually **stays** on the ground, and the tire tread moves vertically at all wheel positions.

With the same slope of the upper arm at design as in Variation 2, the divergence of the two arms is less than in Variation 2. Then the rate of camber change at design is less, and the wheelfight tendency is less. The curve of camber change rate is less severe than A′B′ in Figure 3.28.

As originally proposed by Mr. H. M. Crane this suspension also used an exceptionally long upper arm, so that the camber change rate was remarkably uniform.

This is an extremely good front suspension layout both for handling, and for tire wear and squeal. The disadvantages are:

- Low ground clearance under inner pivot of lower wishbone.
- Some wheelfight tendency.

4. Reversed Swing Arm

This is becoming used as a solution to the wheelfight problem [*see Section 6.3*]. The wheel as it moves up from the design position is changing toward positive camber, as shown by the location of the camber change center "outside" the wheel in Figure 3.31.

The center of roll, as drawn, is on the ground, and, if $R_1H = R_2(H - h)$ it remains on the ground at all wheel positions.

This is extremely favorable for the elimination of wheelfight (because of the camber change). But negative camber at full bump is reduced, and at full rebound is greatly increased.

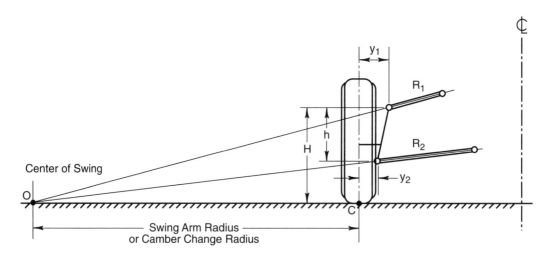

Figure 3.31 Wishbone suspension—reversed swing arm.

Therefore understeer is increased, tire wear increased, and squeal of the inner tire on turns may be increased seriously. This geometry should therefore not be used on a car which rolls much, or has heavily loaded front tires.

Geometry Calculations—The method of figuring the wheel geometry on a wishbone suspension, with allowance for the offsets y_1 and y_2 in Figure 3.31, is fully described under "Linkages" in Chapter 7.

As a matter of interest Figure 3.32 gives a comparison of wheel camber and camber change rate for Variation 1 and Variation 4 above. The dimensions selected are:

	Variation 1	Variation 4
R_1 (in.)	8	8
R_2 (in.)	14	14
H (in.)	19	19
h (in.)	10	10
Drop of upper arm at design (in.)	0	1
Drop of lower arm (in.)	0	0.84
Camber change radius (in.)	∞	150
Upper offset y_1 (in.)	5	5
Lower offset y_2 (in.)	3	3

Figure 3.32 shows clearly the advantage of Variation 4, the reversed swing arm, in maintaining a "positive" camber change rate for some distance above design height. It also shows that on the inside wheel at 6° roll on a turn, which is about 3° rebound position [*also a −3 inch wheel deflection*], the wheel will have 9° negative camber relative to ground, which is bad for tire wear and squeal.

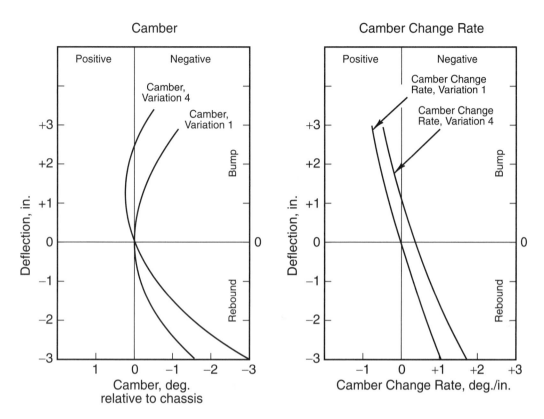

Figure 3.32 *Camber and camber rate for Variations 1 and 4.*

Caster

Positive caster, originally provided to improve road feel [*and spin back*], is also more or less of a tradition. With increased [*tire*] aligning torque and with steering systems having increased reverse efficiency, there seems little need for caster. [*Remember, Olley is writing in the days before power assist steering was common. For spin back with power steering, positive caster is typically used.*]

However on loose gravel surfaces where the aligning torque tends to fail, a small positive caster does still improve the handling.

One thing is clear, namely, that **the need for caster and criticism of handling generally should never be made until tires have run at least 5000 miles** [*this figure may not be true for modern radial tires*].

Kingpin Angle

The kingpin angle ϕ_k, Figure 3.33, is provided to reduce the offset d_1 [*scrub radius*] of the wheel plane from the kingpin centerline. It reduces torque round the kingpin and load on the steering linkage when brakes are applied (or, on front drive cars, when traction is

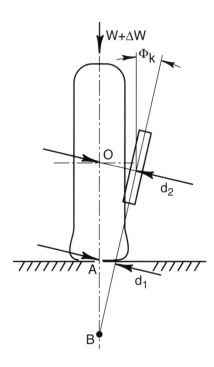

Figure 3.33 *Front view, kingpin geometry.*

applied). However the ground offset d_1 has no effect on the forces delivered to the king-pin by a free-rolling wheel [*with the exception of the rolling resistance which is balanced on a symmetric car*].

When the wheel is rolling over a bumpy road, the standing radius OA is constantly changing [*due to* ΔW] resulting in changes of wheel rotation speed, and consequently in horizontal fore and aft forces delivered to the wheel spindle at the wheel center O. These transient forces may be as much as 300 lb. and, with the large offset d_2, produce large "hammering" couples around the kingpin. The only way to reduce these is to reduce the offset d_2 at the wheel spindle.

The kingpin angle, with the offset d_2, lifts the car as the wheels are steered. The result of this, with the vertical load on the wheels, is to act as a centering spring on the steering system. Suppose the wheel to be turned round the kingpin through a small angle δ (radians). The fore and aft travel of point O is δd_2. The radius (OB in Figure 3.33) of its path in side view is $d_2/\sin\phi_k \cong d_2/\phi_k$.

The slope of the path of O in side view is thus $\dfrac{\delta d_2}{d_2/\phi_k} = \delta\phi_k$.

If W is the vertical load on the wheel, the centering force [*weight moment*] is therefore $W\delta\phi_k$.

The return torque is $W\delta\phi_k d_2$. And the return **rate** is $W\phi_k d_2$ (lb.-in./rad.)

For example, if $\phi_k = 8°$, $W = 1000$ lb. and $d_2 = 4$ inches then

$$\text{Return rate} = \frac{8 \times 4000}{57.3} = 560 \text{ lb.-in./rad.} = 9.75 \text{ lb.-in./deg.}$$

Not very great, but on both wheels, at, say, $10°$ steering angle, it will be 195 lb.-in., and is thus appreciable when turning street corners.

(Note: This effect depends on d_2, not d_1. It is just the same with "center point" steering, i.e., when $d_1 = 0$.)

Wheelfight

It should be noted that what is generally called a **positive** swing arm effect (i.e., a camber change radius toward the "inside" of the wheel) is a motion of the wheel toward **negative** camber as it rises.

The sequence of operations appears to be that, if there is a "positive" swing arm effect, a left front tire, for example, when it is turned outward rapidly by contact with the road, will produce a clockwise torque (from the driver's viewpoint) which will slightly lift the left front wheel, and so depress the opposite wheel, which meets the ground toed-in, thus repeating the cycle. Thus the wheelfight, as observed on the bump-rig rolls [*discussed in Chapter 5*], is a miniature reproduction of the true shimmy cycle.

Hence the benefit derived from the reversed swing arm geometry.

However, these observations do not always hold. On the Corvair, for example, it is observed that the wheelfight is rather like a higher frequency form of caster wobble, with little tramping of the wheels. Yet this car benefits from reversed swing arm geometry.

Also some military trucks with independent suspension have shown a similar "wheel shimmy" which actually appears to be a higher frequency caster wobble, and which, as in all cases of caster wobble, can be eliminated by a moderate increase of kingpin friction.

3.10 Effect of Road Surface

A "generalized" rough road surface may be imagined as something like Figure 3.34, a twisted wave surface. The wavelength λ may be anything from 3 ft. to 100 ft., and with this variation and the variation in speed and wheelbase of the vehicles almost any of the natural frequencies of a vehicle and its suspension may be excited.

The shorter wavelengths will excite wheelfight and shimmy of the front wheels, and axle tramp at the rear. Longer waves will excite the ride motions of pitch and bounce, and transverse rolling motions of the car.

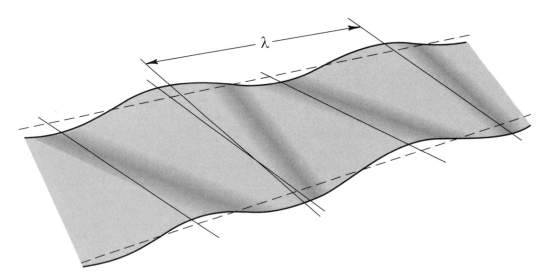

Figure 3.34 Idealized rough road.

To permit a vehicle to maintain anything approaching a straight course on such a road, especially in the presence of long waves (exceeding, say, 25 ft.) it is evident that steering must be reasonably close to neutral as far as roll steer is concerned. It is this consideration more than anything else which prevents overindulgence in any of the "artificial" stabilizing tricks such as roll understeer.

The acceptable limits for any given car have to be found by road tests, the only general rule being that **the longer the wheelbase, the less will be the deviation in the handling of the car**. (It is understood that there are similar conditions in aircraft design, namely, that natural inherent directional stability in an airplane is severely limited by the need for maintaining a straight course in turbulent air.)

3.11 Wind Handling

Introduction

In the early 1960s when Olley wrote this section, he was severely hampered by the lack of wind tunnel data on actual cars. In lieu of measured data, it appears that he looked at data on airfoil and airship shapes and attempted to extrapolate this to automotive shapes—a risky extrapolation at best. In particular, we have deleted Olley's section on the movement of the center of pressure with yaw angle (relative wind direction) because typical bluff automotive shapes do not behave like streamlined airship shapes. Perhaps the only parallel that can be drawn is that the center of pressure is typically toward the front of the body, unless very large tail fins are used.

What is important to know is that a lateral wind force (due to either vehicle slip angle and/or relative wind angle) can be said to act at a "center of pressure." This force, times the distance to the CG, creates a yawing moment. Both the lateral component and the yawing moment of the wind force influence car handling.

When a vehicle running straight at a fair speed runs into a gust of crosswind, the relative angle of the wind to the car may vary between, say, 15 and 45 degrees. This angle of attack of the wind tends to be less at the higher speeds.

As a general rule the yawing moment of the wind gust about the CG of the car increases rapidly with increased speed of the car. At the same time the resistance to yaw, or **yaw damping**, decreases as the speed increases.

To expand on Olley's "general rule" above: The relative wind angle to the car and its magnitude change with car speed. The aerodynamic force changes by the square of the relative wind magnitude. For a constant location of the center of pressure, C.P., the yawing moment increases with speed. However, the C.P. location may change with relative wind angle (aerodynamic yaw angle) for typical automobile shapes.

Yaw Damping Due to the Tires

Consider for example the case of a symmetrical four-wheel trailer, Figure 3.35, with four "fixed" wheels [*and central CG*], proceeding along the road at a speed V (ft./sec.) and yawing slightly with a rotary velocity r (rad./sec.). The small lateral velocity at either end is:

$$v = \frac{r\ell}{2} \qquad (3.8)$$

$$\text{Slip angle due to yaw rate } = \frac{v}{V} = \frac{r\ell}{2V} \qquad (3.9)$$

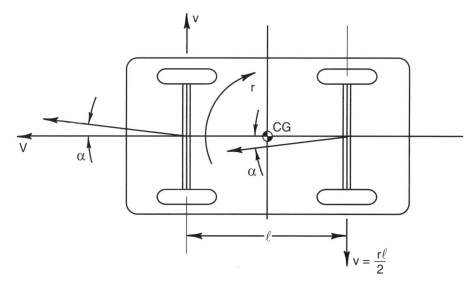

Figure 3.35 *Car with fixed steering—the "trailer" model.*

If the combined cornering stiffness at either end is C lb./rad., the total couple resisting yaw $= C\alpha\ell = Cr\ell^2/2V$ [*where C is independent of speed*].

Hence the resistance to yaw varies directly as the cornering stiffness and yaw velocity, as the square of the wheelbase, and inversely as the road speed.

The aerodynamic yaw damping of the car body is probably negligible compared to the yaw damping generated by the tires, except possibly at very high speeds and/or on vehicles with large stabilizing tail fins.

The tire damping is very high at low speed, Figure 3.36, where it is limited only by the friction coefficient of rubber on the road, but decreasing in a hyperbolic curve. Note that this symmetrical four-wheel trailer has no "sense of direction," i.e., if it yaws there is no moment about the CG tending to straighten it [*only to damp it*].

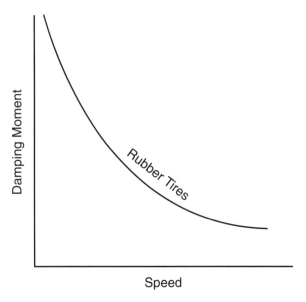

Figure 3.36 Yaw damping vs. speed.

However, if the weight is moved a little forward, while C remains constant at both ends, the vehicle immediately has a "positive static margin." This is equally so if the front inflation is made somewhat less than the rear. And if the front wheels are mounted on kingpins and are held elastically, the directional sense of the vehicle can be greatly increased, since the front slip angles will tend to align the front wheels.

The above remarks on yaw damping are incomplete. It has already been noted that on a vehicle with an inclined roll axis there is a roll-damping and yaw-damping effect that **increases** with speed. There is also the actual roll damping due to shock absorbers and suspension friction, which may be as much as 0.30 of "critical." Thus there seem to be at least two types of yaw damping

> From the tires direct—varying with $1/V$
> From roll damping in the suspension—independent of V.

This may account for the fact that strongly understeering cars as built in this country, even though their wheelbases are shorter than they should be, do not generally exhibit directional oscillations, in still air, of the type described in the Cornell Aeronautical Laboratory papers of 1956,[26] at speeds up to 90 mph or more. On the other hand almost all oversteering cars built in earlier years have shown such oscillations, though these are probably due to subconscious corrective movements by the driver.

Path of Car

The car yaws away from the wind gust. In some cases a wind gust from the left will turn the steering wheel suddenly to the right. In other cases there will be no appreciable reaction at the steering wheel. These are the more difficult cases, since the driver has no feel of the gust.

What seems to happen is that the wind force, Y_W, is more or less in line with the front wheels, Figure 3.37, supplying the necessary centripetal force for the turn, **without** any front slip angle. The necessary rear centripetal force, F_{YR}, is supplied by the rear slip angle α_R.

The center of turn O is more or less in line with the **front** wheels. In a steady turn $Y_W a = F_{YR} b$. This can explain why a vehicle can yaw away from a wind gust with the front wheels pointing straight ahead and feeling no slip angle. But this still does not explain why, in some cases, the gust can throw the car into a sharp turn with no appreciable reaction at the steering wheel. This can only be explained by excessive friction, and probably flexibility in the steering linkage.

It would seem at first sight that wind handling could be improved by changes in the direction of **oversteer**, as for example by raising the front tire pressure. However, this does not work out because, particularly at high speed, it makes recovery from the effects of a gust too difficult. On the contrary **reducing** the front tire inflation generally benefits wind handling.

As a means of opposing the initial impulse of the wind gust, any form of **roll steer** seems out of the question, since the initial roll is generally too small.

---

[26] Milliken, W. F., et al., "Research in Automotive Stability and Control and in Tyre Performance," The Institution of Mechanical Engineers, London, 1956.

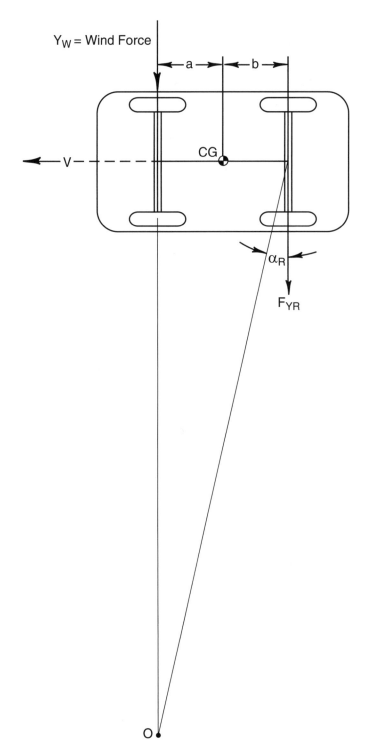

Figure 3.37 *Wind gust, center of pressure (C.P.) assumed at front axle.*

If the center of wind pressure is as shown in Figure 3.38, the gust (from the left) will tend to roll the car to the **right**, and into a right hand turn, which will roll it to the **left**. The initial roll therefore depends on: the shape of the body which controls distance x, on the height of the body which controls distance h, on the wheelbase, the cornering stiffnesses of the tires, etc.

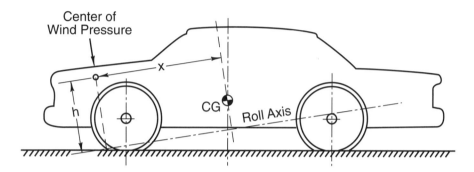

Figure 3.38 *Relative positions of C.P., CG and roll axis.*

In some cases the initial roll, which is small, is **toward** the gust, showing that the effect of yaw slightly overbalances the effect of roll. There are indications that, in recovery after the gust, a reasonable amount of roll understeer is desirable. However, inherent or "primary" understeer, as described earlier, is probably more desirable.

Lateral deflection steer in connection with wind handling appears to offer more promising results than roll steer because of its "immediate" effectiveness. But it seems that only lateral deflection steer at the **rear** is to be recommended. (And this has been least studied.)

At the front of the car the direction of turn of the front wheels required to oppose lateral accelerations are opposite, depending on whether the initial impulse comes from the car or from the tires.

Thus, consider a wind force from the left, Figure 3.39, and the lateral deflections discussed earlier in Section 3.7 and Figure 3.23.

In this case the **rearward** steering linkage, which we found would tend to oversteer [*lateral force oversteer*] in the case of an ordinary steering maneuver, will now tend to turn the front wheels to the left, opposing the gust and reducing the yaw of the vehicle. A forward steering linkage will have an opposite effect and will increase yaw [*lateral force understeer*].

The rear wheels do not play this dual role. Their job in all cases is to resist the lateral forces coming to them from the car. Hence it would appear that a yaw center for the axle to the **rear** of the axle, as described in Figure 3.25, holds great promise for increased directional stability under all handling conditions including wind gusts [*this amounts to*

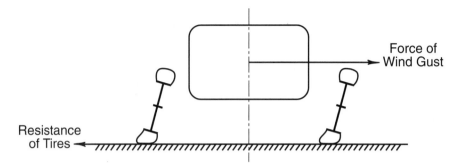

Figure 3.39 *Lateral deflection from wind gust.*

lateral force understeer]. Even under traction on turns this seems to offer an understeering effect similar to that of a high-friction [*limited slip*] differential.

Factors Affecting Wind Handling

Amongst the things that are known to affect wind handling, one can list:

1. Changes in body shape, which shift the center of wind pressure rearward.

    With the adoption of more nearly streamlined body shapes, the center of wind pressure at small angles of attack has moved forward, and cars have become less wind-stable. A streamlined section is highly unstable unless fitted with a tail. A well-known example is the streamline section bracing wires on WWI biplanes which drummed until they broke, and had to be replaced by non-streamlined wires.

    Station wagons (provided the rear tires are not overloaded) are notably more wind-stable than sedans, because of body shape. Cars with low hoods are generally more wind-stable.

    Tail fins have been strongly advocated, by analogy with aircraft. However, their usefulness is limited by the fact that automobiles travel not in the air but on roads, and while fins improve stability in still air at high speed, they may make the handling too sensitive to wind direction.

2. Increased wheelbase is an evident step in the right direction, bearing in mind that the yaw damping from the tires varies with the **square** of the wheelbase.

    In particular, short wheelbase vehicles with much front and rear overhang are difficult for wind handling. This is partly because the k^2/ab ratio is excessive (see Chapter 5). In other words the wheelbase length is not adequate to control the flywheel effect of the body when it yaws.

3.   Scale effects are important. An overall steering characteristic, which would be tolerable on a large truck, might be totally unsafe on a sports car, not from difference of speed but simply because of the quicker responses of the smaller vehicle compared with human reaction times.

4.   Roll understeer (the "bicycle stability") helps wind handling, not when the gust strikes, since the initial roll is small, but later when the driver is attempting to recover from the effects of the gust. However, in practice roll understeer is severely limited by the considerations already mentioned.

5.   Reduction of dry friction or excessive damping in the suspension. The apparent backlash in the steering resulting from suspension friction is referred to earlier. The consequent lack of definition in the straight-ahead position of the steering is confusing in a gusty wind.

6.   Friction in the steering linkage or low reverse efficiency in the steering gear is even more confusing in wind handling. So is a "rubbery" steering [*system*]. For safe handling in a wind the steering system needs to be sensitive and accurate.

7.   **Centrifugal Caster**—A single manufacturer (Lanchester) as early as 1898 solved the handling problem, and incidentally wind-handling, in a way which has seldom been equaled. This was Lanchester's "reversed tiller steering," Figure 3.40. The tiller turns in the same direction as the front wheels.

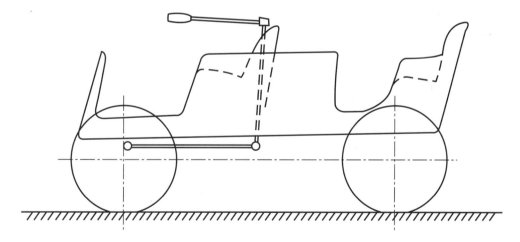

Figure 3.40 Lanchester reversed tiller steering.

It follows that the centrifugal force of the turn, falling on the tiller, the driver's arm, and the driver himself, tends to "wash out" the turn. And Lanchester found that by putting a few pounds of lead in the tiller handle, the directional stability of the car could be immensely improved, in ordinary handling and in a wind.

The Chevrolet Dubonnet has roughly the same characteristics. Here the weight of the suspension boxes ahead of the kingpins, under the centrifugal force of a turn, plus the roll of the car on the turn, acts as a powerful supplement to the aligning torque of the tires for straightening the front wheels. When driving on a cambered road, the weight of the boxes tends to turn the wheels toward the ditch just as mechanical caster does.

In fact the forward weights act just like mechanical caster, except in two important respects.

First: A sudden wind gust has the reverse effect from mechanical caster. Instead of tending to turn the wheels **away from** the wind, the inertia of the boxes, under the sudden lateral acceleration, tends to turn the front wheels **into** the wind. A car with this suspension appeared to be completely insensitive to wind gusts.

Second: Whereas mechanical caster increases the tendency to shimmy, the inertia of the boxes suppresses all tendency to shimmy or wheelfight.

On a wishbone suspension with forward steering linkage the same result could be obtained by loading the relay rod (see Figure 3.20) with a large weight (100 lb. or so), but this weight of idle metal is not considered reasonable.

The same effect has been produced electronically, on the Cornell experimental car,[27] with exactly the same results.

3.12 Summary

The earlier notes on steady-state steering [*Chapter 2*] made some reference to the "secondary" steering effects which did not actually affect the slip angles, but which were just as important in their effect on handling.

This chapter has attempted to summarize most of what might be called the geometry effects. (However, the general discussion of linkages is contained in Chapter 7.)

Roll steer is discussed, and the reason why this is **not** tied up with the roll axis. Then the various types of wheel-control linkages and their effect on roll steer and ride-steer variations are discussed.

Steering effects due to lateral deflections are discussed. These have been relatively neglected in the past, and are probably important because they are more "punctual" than roll steer.

---

[27] Segel, Leonard, "Concept and Design," Paper No. 650658; Bundorf, R. Thomas, "The Use of a Variable-Stability Vehicle in Handling Research," Paper No. 650659. Both papers appear in *The Variable-Stability Automobile*, SP-275, Society of Automotive Engineers, Warrendale, Pa., 1965.

The notes on wind-handling are probably incomplete and unsatisfactory. There is every indication that we do not fully understand the subject. The only "cures" we have to date are: centrifugal caster, body shape, increased wheelbase, and sensitive steering.

There must be a more fundamental cure, and it may be found in lateral deflection steer.

Camber change variations in wishbone suspensions are discussed along with their effect on wheelfight.

CHAPTER 4

Transient Cornering

*"The major part of the control problem, however, comes during states
of transition, when the car is entering or leaving a curve, when it
passes from one curve into a reverse curve, or when the car on the
straightaway is under the influence of crosswinds or varying pavement
slopes. Our control problems are most acute when the side (lateral)
forces are variable in intensity and direction...."*

**Kenneth A. Stonex
General Motors Proving Ground, 1940**

4.1 Introduction

*Transient cornering, i.e., the behavior of a car on turn entry and recovery, was of interest
to automobile engineers from the earliest days, however, its measurement and analysis
was not pursued until the late 1930s. The first substantial effort to measure and record
transient behavior (to the knowledge of the authors) was the "checkerboard" test performed at the General Motors Proving Ground in mid-1938 by Kenneth A. Stonex. This
was reported in a paper to the Detroit Section of SAE, December 1940, and published in
SAE Journal (Transactions), Vol. 48, No. 3. In this test a simple passing maneuver was
recorded by photographing the car on a "giant checkerboard" grid that had been
painted on the tarmac. In addition to determining the path of the car by this means,
other instrumentation simultaneously recorded steering angle, vehicle roll angle, etc.*

*In September 1938, Robert Schilling (also at GM Proving Ground) published a report
entitled "Handling Factors" in which he described in considerable detail, but in **qualitative** terms, what happens during the "transition" or transient phase of cornering. This is
still one of the best physical explanations available.*

*Schilling moved to the GM Research Laboratory Division and in February 1953 presented
a paper at the Industrial Mathematics Society, Detroit, entitled "Directional Control of*

Automobiles," in which he presents a linear analysis of time-based behavior. The result is a fourth-order equation which gives, for typical numerical values, two modes of oscillation and their frequencies and damping. He also suggests that a complete understanding of handling with the driver in the control loop will require a servo-type analysis.

In 1953, General Motors gave the Cornell Aeronautical Laboratory (CAL) a contract to apply analytical and measurement techniques developed for aircraft to the automobile for fully exploring transient or dynamic behavior. The work was performed in CAL's Flight Research Department, which later spun-off the Vehicle Dynamics Department for non-aircraft work. Both Olley and Schilling were responsible for the initiation of this program and Schilling was the GM project leader. Leonard Segel was the project engineer and principal analyst, as well as section head of the group at CAL. In 1956 the results of the first three years of effort were presented in England at the Institution of Mechanical Engineers. A comprehensive linear theory had been developed which enabled the prediction of frequency responses and transient response to control input for a variety of vehicle characteristics and operating conditions. These predictions were substantiated by experimental measurements with an instrumented vehicle. The CAL work placed the analysis and understanding of transient behavior on a firm mathematical basis.

Olley's treatment of transient cornering, in his monograph of 1962, references some of this earlier work and discusses the effect of the k^2/ab ratio in yaw on the transient response. Inasmuch as the monographs are mainly a summary of his own work and experience, he does not discuss the CAL research, assuming it is well documented elsewhere. He was of course familiar with this research and as noted earlier played a prominent role in its initiation.

Because the transient behavior is so important, we have decided to begin this chapter with summaries of the checkerboard test, Schilling's qualitative transient analysis and his linear analysis, along with a brief review of the CAL results. Olley's specific treatment of turn entry follows.

4.2 Checkerboard Test[28] (Stonex)

For a small scale transition test, the case of a car turning out to pass another was selected; that is, the car was driven straight in one traffic lane, then turned to drive a parallel course in the adjacent traffic lane, the various angles being measured continuously. The primary test problem, of course, is the method of measurement, which is complicated greatly as soon as the path is different from a circular arc, partly because the center of reference continuously varies and partly because the variables must be recorded continuously. A completely new recording system has to be substituted for the transit for measuring attitude and roll, and the steering angle must be recorded simultaneously.

---

[28] Stonex K. A., "Car Control Factors and Their Measurement," Society of Automotive Engineers, December 1940.

The method finally selected is photographic. The test course has a giant checkerboard with 2-foot squares painted on it, and a 35-mm movie camera is mounted on the car top, inclined so that the optical axis of the lens intersects the ground about 20 feet in front of the car. The camera used at present has a special shutter, with exposure time decreased to about 1/400 second, and has a crosshair in the aperture plate at the optical axis.

The car is set up with indicator dials measuring the steering angle of each wheel, rear axle steering and steering wheel angle, all mounted on the front of the car in the camera field; these dials are operated by Autosyn motors as in the skid pad test. Figure 4.1 shows the car set-up for the test. Stops are put on the steering wheel, one to the right and one to the left of the straight-ahead position; they are adjusted by trial so that the driver can enter the checkerboard squarely, jerk the steering wheel against the right stop as quickly as possible, back against the left stop as quickly as possible, and come out square with the grid but in the adjacent traffic lane. Stops are used so that the test can be repeated.

The test is run in this manner with the camera operating from before the turn is started until the car is straightened up. The camera therefore makes a simultaneous record of the indicator readings and the aspect of the checkerboard at the rate of 24 frames per second.

The key to this test method lies in the realization that the pictures of a checkerboard pavement can be projected on a checkerboard screen so that the squares coincide only when the angle between the optical axis of the camera lens and the pavement is the same as the angle between the optical axis of the projector lens and the screen, and when the distances along the optical axis between the camera and pavement and between the projector and screen are in the ratio of the sizes of the two sets of squares. In other words, the aspect of the camera lens to the pavement and the projector lens to the screen must be the same. To eliminate possible projection errors, the same lens is used in the camera and projector.

Figure 4.1 *Car set-up for checkerboard test.*

Figure 4.2 shows the apparatus used in reading the film. At the left is a still projector for 35-mm film, mounted on a bar so that it can be moved back and forth. The object at the right is essentially a screen ruled in 2 inch squares and mounted in gimbals so that it can be rotated simultaneously about the three mutually perpendicular axes AA′, BB′ and CC′, and with adjusting screws and circular scales so that it can be moved easily and its angular position determined. Means are also provided for allowing and measuring linear motion of the face along the BB′ and CC′ axes.

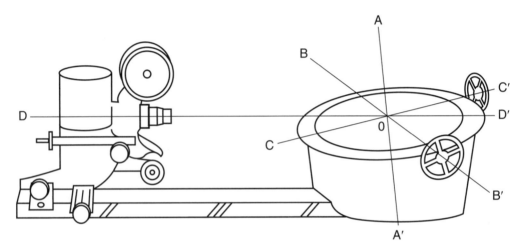

Figure 4.2 *Apparatus used for reading film.*

The line DD′ is the optical axis of the lens and, in the zero position, the crosshair image will fall on the screen at O. The linear movements are then adjusted so that the projected squares somewhat coincide with the rulings on the screen. The projector may have to be moved somewhat to get the size of the squares right; since the ratio of sizes of screen ruling and pavement squares is 1:12, the projector is 1/12 as far from the screen as the camera was from the point of intersection of the optical axis and pavement. The screen is then adjusted about its axes so that the squares coincide with the rulings, and the various angles are read. The car is started parallel to the direction of the squares, so that deviations measured about the AA′ axis are the instantaneous angles between the car axis and the original course; this quantity is called course angle. Roll angle is measured about the CC′ axis and declination plus pitch angle is measured about the BB′ axis. The declination is found statically from the camera height and pitch by subtraction.

Figure 4.3 shows the top of the table used as the screen. Figure 4.4 shows the squares properly adjusted. Figure 4.5 shows roll angle alone out of adjustment; note that the projection of the squares is oblique. Figure 4.6 shows pitch angle out of adjustment; note that the projections are rectangular but of different sizes in the upper and lower parts of the picture. Figure 4.7 shows course angle out of adjustment; the projections are square and parallel but not parallel with the ruling. Figure 4.8 shows both linear positions out of adjustment; the squares do not coincide with the rulings.

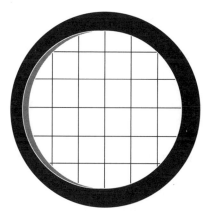 

Figure 4.3 (left) *Top of table used as screen.*
Figure 4.4 (right) *Projected squares properly adjusted on screen.*

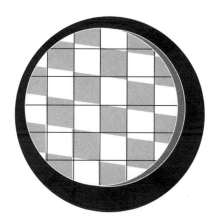 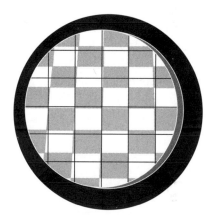

Figure 4.5 (left) *Roll angle alone out of adjustment.*
Figure 4.6 (right) *Pitch angle out of adjustment.*

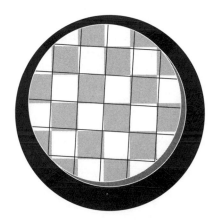 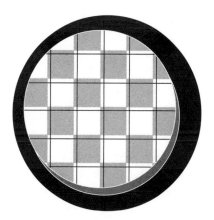

Figure 4.7 (left) *Course angle out of adjustment.*
Figure 4.8 (right) *Both linear positions out of adjustment.*

It is evident that the aspect of the car with respect to the plane of the pavement can be completely determined with good accuracy by this method, and that the distance along the optical axis between the camera and a point on the pavement can also be found. Since the indicators of steering angle, steering wheel angle, and rear axle steering can also be photographed in each frame, it is evident that both the car position with respect to the pavement and the relative motion between any parts of the car can be simultaneously recorded at arbitrary increments of time.

Since we can find the place where the optical axis intersects the pavement and can measure its length and the camera height and have the course angle, we can determine the position of the vertical line through the camera lens and, consequently, can find the position of the front and rear wheels at every frame. For practical purposes it may be assumed that the path of the front and rear wheels is found continuously. If we know the path, we can find the instantaneous direction of travel, and the angle between the direction of travel and the car axis at the rear wheels is by definition the attitude. We have measured the steering angle and can therefore calculate front slip angles. Furthermore, since we know the distance between consecutive points and the tangents at each point, we can, under the assumption of uniform curvature between alternate points, calculate the radius of curvature and the radial acceleration.

Figure 4.9 is an exaggerated diagram of a car on the test course showing the angular relations. For simplicity we ordinarily consider the average of the front wheel angles; for special purposes we sometimes consider the individual wheels.

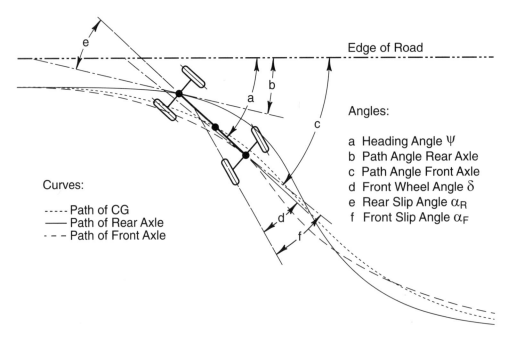

Figure 4.9 Exaggerated diagram of car on test course showing angular relations.

Figure 4.10 shows the form in which the results are presented. The lower part of the sheet shows a scale drawing of the test course with the path of the optical axis and the point below the camera lens indicated. The scale above this is in terms of the frames on the film, one point for each frame, with the values plotted beginning with the first frame in which the optical axis intersects on the checkerboard. This is also a time scale and, if the speed is constant, a distance scale. All the values except path are plotted on it.

The first curves to leave the baseline are the steering wheel and front wheel angles. The steering wheel angle divided by the average steering angle should give the front wheel angle; the difference is due to steering linkage flexibility [*also called compliance*].

The next curve is the theoretical course angle. This is a hypothetical course which would be taken by a car with no slip angle as shown by the front wheel angle, and the comparison of its gradient with that of the actual course angle is a measure of understeer.

This curve is found by accumulating the front wheel angle. The actual course angle is measured about the axis AA′ in Figure 4.2. Understeer can also be measured by comparison of front and rear slip [*actually, slip angle gradients*].

The roll angle curve has an appreciable lag over the front wheel angle and front acceleration and may lag behind the rear acceleration.

The front and rear slip angles are the difference between the path angles and the course angle; the path angles show considerable irregularity, which may be due in a large part to the probable errors in measurement. In order to compute lateral accelerations, a smooth curve is drawn through the path angle points. This probably gives a good approximation of the average lateral acceleration but leaves the peak values undetermined.

Either the skid pad or checkerboard tests can, of course, be extended to a much larger scale to care for higher speeds or longer or different types of transition with no fundamental change in the procedure. The principal errors in both tests as conducted are due to the human factor; in the skid pad test the driver must follow the circular course very accurately for the basis of the calculation of lateral force, and in the checkerboard test the driver must perform the transition in the same manner to obtain comparable results on a series of cars. The accuracy would be improved considerably by increasing the scale so that the path deviations would be of little relative importance. Still greater accuracy would be attained by substituting a mechanical system of steering the car and eliminating the personal factor entirely.

These tests, it should be pointed out again, are tests of car control and not of car handling. The ultimate objectives are to determine quantitatively the attributes of the most precise control and by correlating these with the opinion of a large number of people to determine what characteristics give optimum handling.

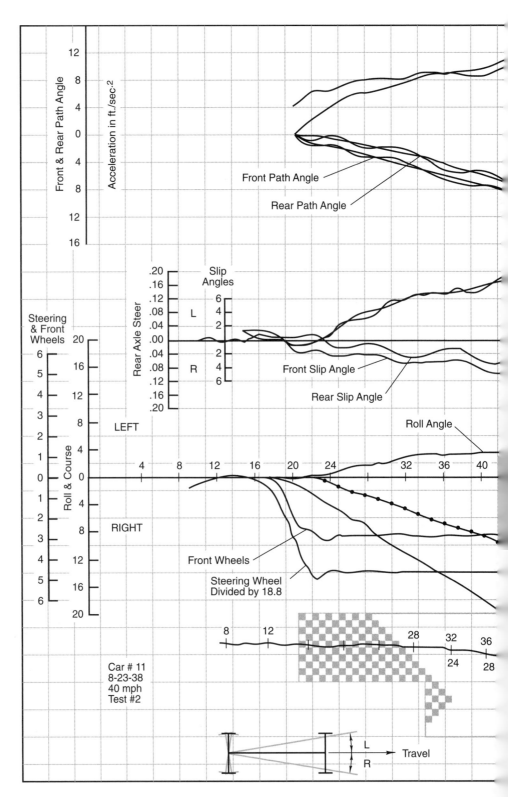

Figure 4.10 *Form in which results of checkerboard test are presented.*

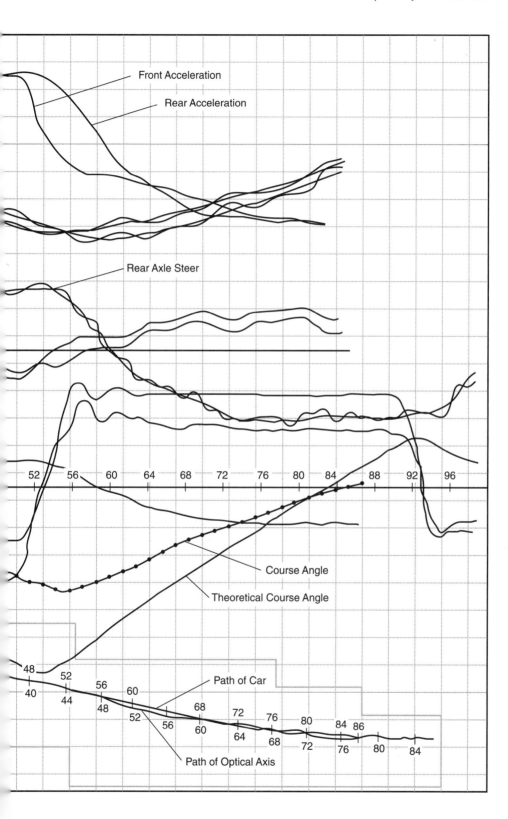

Front Acceleration

Rear Acceleration

Rear Axle Steer

52 56 60 64 68 72 76 80 84 88 92 96

Course Angle

Theoretical Course Angle

48
40 52
44 56
48 60
52 Path of Car
56 68
60 72 76
64 68 80 84 86
72 76 80
84

Path of Optical Axis

4.3 Qualitative Transient Description[29] (Schilling)

Before discussing some of the handling factors, we must try to understand just what happens to a car when we change course. We have made a theoretical study on this subject and the Proving Ground has run a number of tests on the checkerboard as reported by T. Carmichael.

From this work we have come to a pretty good understanding of what happens, but it is extremely difficult to get accurate numerical data. I shall in the following present a simplified picture of the action of a car as we have come to understand it.

We assume that at the beginning the car is moving straight ahead and that at a given moment the driver suddenly turns the steering wheel to a certain angle and holds it there. This is the simplest possible maneuver and most characteristics of the car can be demonstrated by it.

[*Yaw damping and lateral damping effects are not mentioned in these discussions but are implicitly included because steady-state is reached.*]

Robert Schilling, left, and Joseph Bidwell, right, both from GM Research. Photo Credit Cornell Aeronautical Laboratories c.1954, collection of W. F. Milliken.

---

[29] Schilling, Robert, "Handling Factors," General Motors Proving Ground report, 1938.

Turn without Roll–No Understeer or Oversteer

Start of turn [*see Figure 4.11*]—The driver has turned the front wheels by the angle δ but the car still goes straight ahead. Angle δ becomes all slip angle α_F, producing lateral force F_{YF}. This pushes the front of the car into the turn and gives it a rotary acceleration.

Transition—The front end has moved into the turn while the rear end continues straight ahead. This has given the rear end an attitude angle α_R, producing lateral force F_{YR}. This is, however, still small so that there is an excess of lateral force F_{YF} at the front. The car keeps accelerating into the turn. The radius of the curve is still very large and the centrifugal force CF is small.

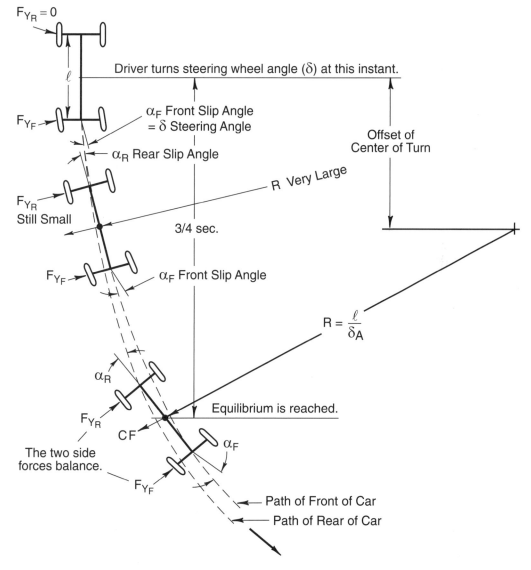

Figure 4.11 *Turn without roll—neutral steer,* δ_A = *Ackermann angle.*

Equilibrium—The attitude angle α_R has still further increased until the rear lateral force F_{YR} balances the moment of F_{YF} around the center of gravity. All forces are now in balance and the car is in equilibrium in a curve of radius R. The elapsed time is about 3/4 second. In this example the final front slip angle α_F is equal to rear slip angle α_R. The radius is ℓ/δ_A and the car neither oversteers nor understeers that radius.

If the steering angle is larger, the initial acceleration will also be larger and all forces increase proportionately. The whole process then will be run through in about the same time, though the equilibrium curve [*steady-state turn radius*] is much sharper. A change of car speed also has little effect on the time required to reach equilibrium. The distance traveled during transitions will then become longer the higher the speed.

Figure 4.12 shows the paths of three cars, all with the same total cornering stiffness front plus rear, but A is understeer, B is neutral steer, and C is oversteer.

The car B, the same as the car in Figure 4.11, neither understeers nor oversteers; the front and rear slip angles **in equilibrium** are equal [*and thus the rate of change of slip angles, in accordance with the SAE definition*]. In Figure 4.12, Car A would be the same car but with the weight shifted ahead and C with the weight shifted back. [*Provided the weight shift had no effect on cornering stiffness of the tires.*]

The effect of lowering or raising the total cornering stiffness, front plus rear, without introducing under- or oversteer is shown in Figure 4.13. If B is a car with normal inflation, E would be the same car with underinflated tires and D with overinflated tires. [*Changing inflation pressure changes cornering stiffness.*]

Of particular interest during the transition is the build-up of lateral acceleration. This is shown in Figure 4.14. At the front wheels we get a certain lateral force F_{YF}, and therefore a certain amount of lateral acceleration instantly [*ignoring tire lag*] when the steering wheel is turned. At the rear it only builds-up gradually. It may actually be negative for a very short time because k^2/ab around a vertical axis is usually smaller than unity [*where k is the radius of gyration*]. At the driver's seat it is somewhere in between, so that there should be a small instantaneous build-up, followed by a gradual increase during the transition time.

The responsiveness of a car is then characterized by two factors:

The length of the transition period
The amount of instantaneous response

This diagram of lateral acceleration at the driver's seat is repeated in Figure 4.15a, for the three cars of Figure 4.12. They all start out with the same initial response but build up at different rates. The understeering car has a low build-up and reaches equilibrium soon. The oversteering car has the largest build-up and reaches equilibrium last.

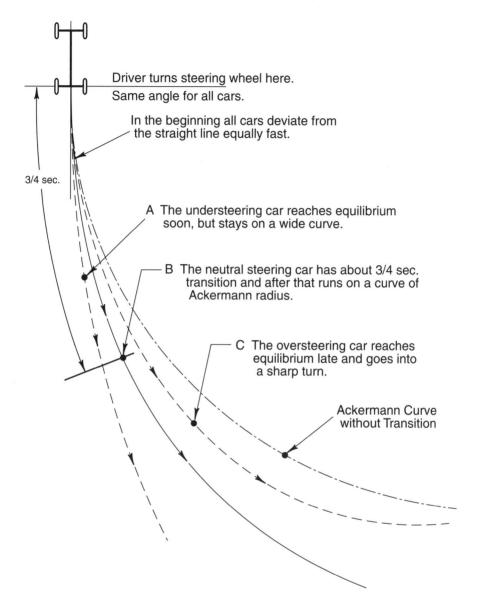

Driver turns steering wheel here.
Same angle for all cars.

In the beginning all cars deviate from
the straight line equally fast.

3/4 sec.

A The understeering car reaches equilibrium
soon, but stays on a wide curve.

B The neutral steering car has about 3/4 sec.
transition and after that runs on a curve of
Ackermann radius.

C The oversteering car reaches
equilibrium late and goes into
a sharp turn.

Ackermann Curve
without Transition

Figure 4.12 *Turn without roll—comparison of under- and oversteer.*

Figure 4.15b shows the conditions for the three cars of Figure 4.13. Here the final equilibrium acceleration is the same for all three, because they all reach a curve of the same radius. Car E with the small cornering force starts out with the smallest initial response and takes longest to reach equilibrium. Car D with the large cornering force has the largest initial response and reaches equilibrium first.

In all these cases we have assumed that the steering wheel is turned the same angle. If now we increase the steering angle of car A (Figure 4.12), and decrease the angle of car

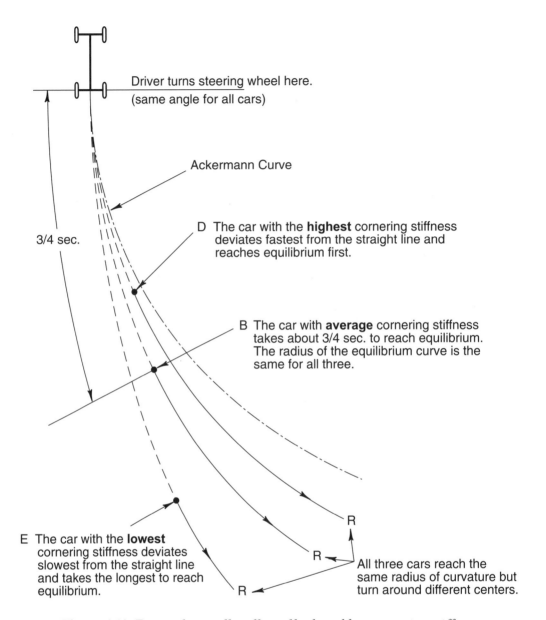

Driver turns steering wheel here.
(same angle for all cars)

Ackermann Curve

3/4 sec.

D The car with the **highest** cornering stiffness
   deviates fastest from the straight line and
   reaches equilibrium first.

B The car with **average** cornering stiffness
   takes about 3/4 sec. to reach equilibrium.
   The radius of the equilibrium curve is the
   same for all three.

E The car with the **lowest**
   cornering stiffness deviates
   slowest from the straight line
   and takes the longest to reach
   equilibrium.

R

R

R

All three cars reach the
same radius of curvature but
turn around different centers.

Figure 4.13 Turn without roll—effect of high and low cornering stiffness.

C so that they will reach an equilibrium curve of the same radius, the diagram Figure 4.15b
will become Figure 4.15c.

Here car A (understeer) shows a diagram similar to Car D (high cornering stiffness) in
Figure 4.15b, and car C (oversteer) similar to car E (low cornering stiffness) in Figure
4.15b. They are not exactly alike, and the cars will act quite differently in other respects,
but the response of high cornering stiffness and of understeer with proportionately
increased steering angles is about the same. Both show a large instantaneous response

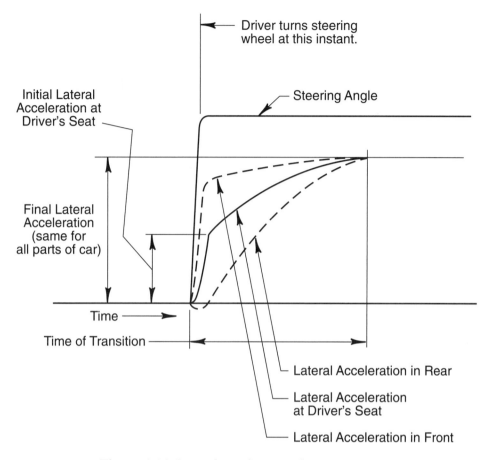

Figure 4.14 Lateral acceleration during transition.

and short transition time. Since in this case the equilibrium is never very much different from the transient condition, the driver finds it easier to "hit" a given curve with just one turn of the steering wheel and does not need to "zig-zag" the car around the turn. But this is only so if the understeer was obtained without sacrifice of total cornering stiffness. If it is produced by simply lowering the front cornering stiffness, there will be no gain in responsiveness, rather a loss.

Turn with Roll

In the cases we have considered so far, all the slip angles are produced by lateral forces and are proportional to them. That means they are proportional not only in equilibrium but during any instant during the transition and their timing is exactly the same. This is no longer true when the car rolls. Here we will find some additional slip angles or some steering angles which, even though they are roughly proportional to the lateral forces in equilibrium, have the same timing as the roll. If they are present, and they are on all cars, the transition time can never be shorter than that required to establish roll equilibrium.

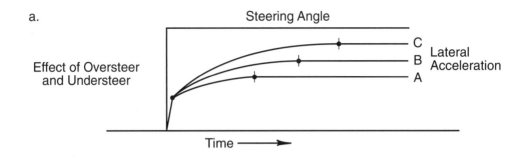

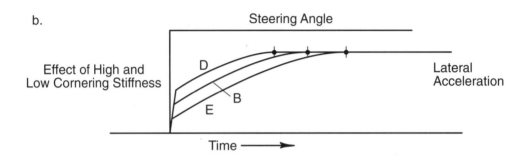

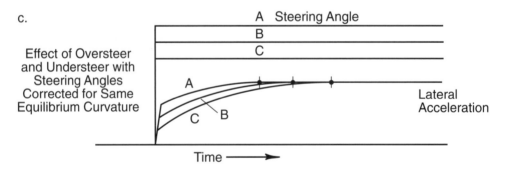

Figure 4.15 *Lateral acceleration during transition, continued.*

The roll has two effects upon car control:

> While the car is rolling, its center of gravity and the seats have a lateral velocity and lateral acceleration with respect to the wheels.

> The roll has some steering effect in adding slip angles or steering angles at the wheels [*in this section camber thrust appears to be ignored*].

The first action is explained better in Figure 4.16. This shows, at left, a car with the center of gravity 20 inches above the roll center. If a lateral force F_Y is suddenly applied at the wheels, moving them to the right, the center of gravity will tend to lag behind and the

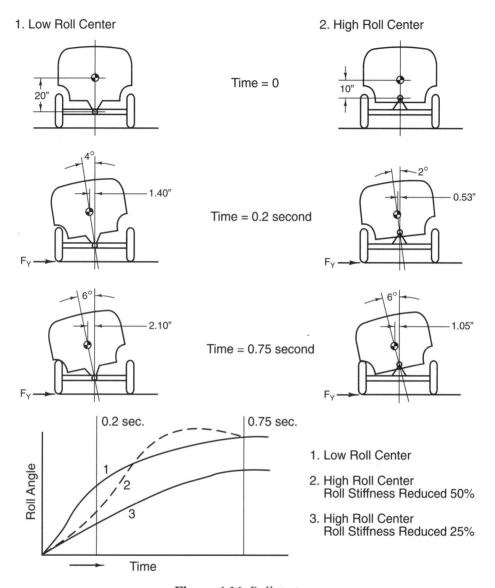

Figure 4.16 Roll timing.

car will roll more than it shifts. The roll angle during a steering maneuver as in Figure 4.11 will then build as shown for (1) at the bottom of Figure 4.16. It will increase very fast during the first 0.2 second and then more gradually until both roll and curvature are at an equilibrium.

At the right is shown the action of a car with a high roll center. The center of gravity is shown 10 inches above the roll center and the roll stiffness is assumed to be reduced in the ratio 10/20, so that the roll angle in equilibrium will be the same. Here the action of lateral force F_Y will roll the car by a smaller angle in the first 0.2 second. But since the roll stiffness is so much lower the body will tend to overshoot; we may get a roll time curve as shown for line (2) in Figure 4.16. This is, of course, very bad and we must keep the roll stiffness nearer the original value: reduce it only 25%. In that case we will get a roll time curve as line (3).

The curve of lateral acceleration as previously shown in Figure 4.14 will then appear as Figure 4.17.

Line (0) shows again the same curve as Figure 4.14 for acceleration at the driver's seat.

Line (1) corresponds to (1) on Figure 4.16 and shows the complete loss of the initial acceleration due to roll, and the delay of equilibrium.

Line (2) is car (2) in Figure 4.16. It has a better initial value due to the smaller roll, but an uneven build-up due to the over-rolling and feels like an oversteerer.

Line (3) is the combination of high roll center and medium roll stiffness (as 3 in Figure 4.16). It shows a good initial acceleration and short transition time. This is what we want to get.

The steering effects due to roll are in phase with the roll, not in phase with the lateral forces. In some cars this is quite different. But in cars that are really satisfactory the

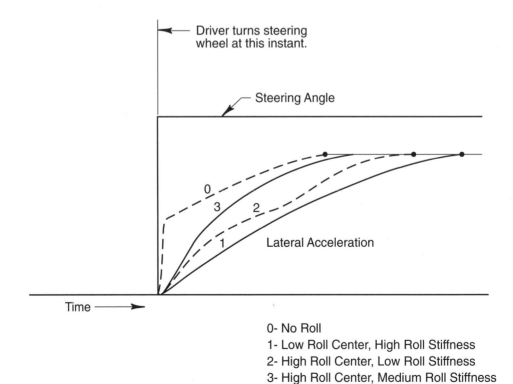

Figure 4.17 Effect of roll on lateral acceleration.

lateral acceleration and the roll angle build up at practically the same rate, as can be seen by comparing Figures 4.16 and 4.17, especially curves (3).

As a consequence the roll steering, if it is moderate, can hardly be distinguished from steering due to lateral forces during maneuvers of the kind described. It does, however, act quite differently on a road with varying camber. Here front and rear suspensions have mostly different roll angles, and are not in step with the lateral forces. The result is erratic steering unless the roll steering is kept very moderate. We have found that rear **oversteer** at four passenger load is permissible up to 5% and rear **understeer** up to 10% [*for the front-engine, rear wheel drive configuration*]. In front there should be no oversteer at all, but understeer may run as high as 25%.

4.4 Linear Analysis

In Schilling's analysis (continued from the previous section) a linear relationship between slip angle and lateral force is assumed. The variation in cornering stiffness with load is neglected in the interest of a linear analysis. Steer angles due to roll are assumed proportional to roll angle.

Based on the above assumptions, three "equilibrium" equations including the inertia force and moment are written for:

> *Lateral forces*
> *Moments about the yaw axis*
> *Moments about the roll axis*

These equations are in terms of front and rear cornering stiffness, front and rear slip angles, roll angle, roll steer ratios, inertia parameters, and roll rate/roll damping.

Based on kinematics and geometry, three additional equations are derived involving path, course, steering and slip angles, and vehicle dimensions, giving a total of six equations in terms of the following dependent variables:

> *Path angle   Lateral acceleration*
> *Yaw angle   Front slip angle*
> *Roll angle   Rear slip angle*

where V, forward speed, is constant and δ, steer angle, is the independent variable.

The characteristic equations are solved at two speeds for fixed control step input and a pulse input where the steering wheel is free after the input (free control). In all cases the fourth order equations factor into two complex roots, i.e., two modes. The first primarily involves yawing and side slipping, the second involves rolling. The calculated frequencies and dampings are given in Schilling's original chart on the following page.

Case	Condition on		First Mode		Second Mode	
	Control	Velocity ft./sec.	Frequency Hz	Specific Damping	Frequency Hz	Specific Damping
1	Fixed	60	0.72	0.69	1.07	0.38
2	Fixed	120	0.57	0.44	1.30	0.30
3	Free	60	0.73	0.34	1.33	0.30
4	Free	120	0.78	0.17	1.43	0.24

4.5 CAL Results (Segel)

The CAL research resulted in Leonard Segel's classical paper.[30] This analysis is linear based on assumptions paralleling those of Schilling's. Segel's work uses the aircraft derivative approach and a comprehensive experimental validation.

From the fourth-order characterizing equations, Segel's analysis yields two sets of conjugate complex roots which are stable (either convergent or stable oscillations). In addition, he calculates responses due to a step input of front wheel steering angle for steady-state static margins and vehicle velocities. Figures 4.18, 4.19 and 4.20 show the yawing responses for the 1953 Buick used in the experimental program.

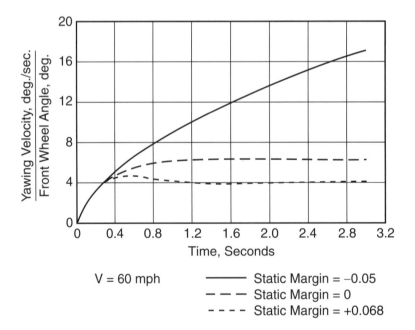

Figure 4.18 *Influence of static margin on yawing velocity response to a step input.*

---

[30] Segel, L., "Theoretical Prediction and Experimental Substantiation of the Response of the Automobile to Steering Control," The Institution of Mechanical Engineers, London, 1956.

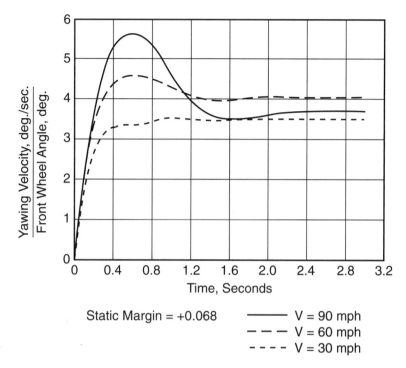

Figure 4.19 *Influence of forward velocity on yawing velocity response—understeer vehicle.*

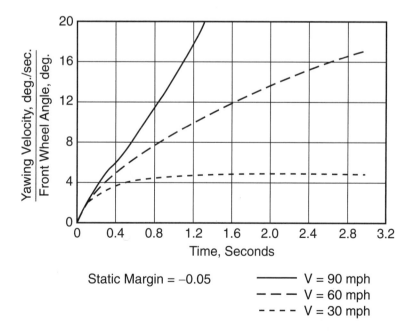

Figure 4.20 *Influence of forward velocity on the yawing velocity response—oversteer vehicle.*

The experimental validation was done on a frequency response basis. The yawing velocity and rolling velocity results are given on Figures 4.21 and 4.22, where the lines are calculated from theory and the points are recorded from experimental trials.

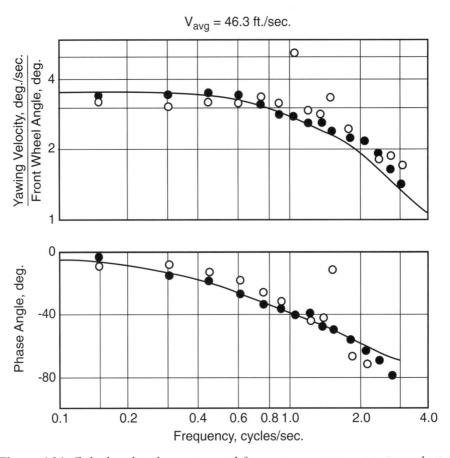

Figure 4.21 *Calculated and experimental frequency response—yawing velocity.*

4.6 Turn Entry Transient (Olley)

The Notes on Handling [*Chapter 3*] have shown that it is not enough to consider steady turns only. Geometry effects, roll steer, and lateral deflection steer, while they may not affect the steady-state slip angles, can produce drastic changes in the handling of the car.

Equally important is the fact that geometry changes can have an enormous effect on the "feel" of the car to the driver's hands on the steering wheel. And even such minor changes as a slight increase in kingpin friction may completely change the handling. One has to consider the operations of putting a car into a turn and bringing it out of the turn.

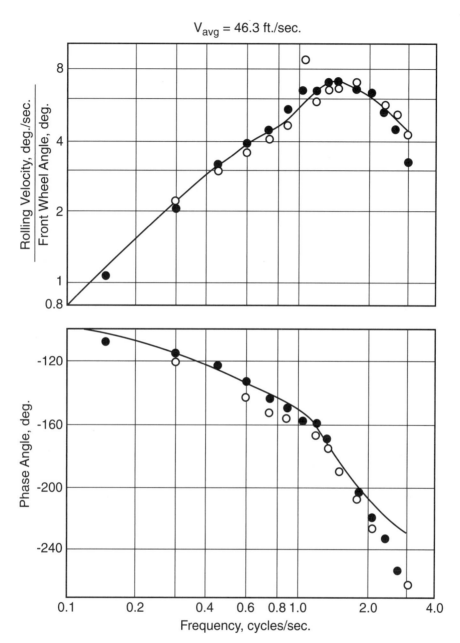

Figure 4.22 *Calculated and experimental frequency response—rolling velocity.*

The GM Proving Ground "checkerboard" tests of 1938 [*Section 4.2*] were an interesting study of a more complicated maneuver. This discussion merely concerns lane-changing at a fair road speed. But this implies negotiating an S-bend, or three separate steering operations in quick succession. The GM Pennsylvania turnpike tests of 1940 contain further studies of high speed turns, and are of particular interest in connection with S-bends.

A great deal of work has been done on a mathematical assumption of a practically instantaneous turn of the front wheels through a small angle, say, one degree. The subsequent development of front and rear slip angles is then traced. Although an instantaneous turn of the wheels, even through as little as one degree, seems improbable, because of the flexibility of the steering linkage, such an assumption seems the most reasonable approach to what actually occurs when entering or leaving a turn.

However, in connection with rapid motions of the steering wheel, it should be pointed out that the steering wheel is a double differentiating device. Assuming Ackermann steering, position of the wheel **produces** a lateral **acceleration**, which increases with the square of the road speed. So **velocity** of the steering wheel produces lateral acceleration-change, or jerk (ft./sec.^{3}).

Thus, if only for the comfort of the passengers, the steering wheel has to be held steadily or moved slowly, especially at high speeds.

In most passenger cars, unless the steering wheel is handled too fast, the actual entry of the car into a turn and the resulting roll of the car build almost simultaneously. On European cars, with low numerical steering ratios and high roll frequency, erratic handling of the steering wheel puts the passengers in considerable discomfort from spasmodic rolling of the vehicle. On American cars, with much higher steering reductions and lower roll frequency, this effect is almost entirely absent. (Consequently the less demand in America for bucket seats.)

All steering factors dependent on the roll of the car have a certain small time-lag as the roll builds after the front wheels are turned. This lag may be on the order of 0.1 sec. but depends on the mass of the vehicle, on its roll frequency, on the length of the wheelbase, on the friction or damping operating to prevent or delay the roll, etc. Suppose, for example, that a vehicle has its tire pressures adjusted for the laden and unladen conditions in such a way as to produce identical skid pad charts for the two conditions. The actual handling will still be different in the two conditions because of the lower roll frequency and reduced relative roll damping when loaded. In passenger cars, other than station wagons, the difference is small, but with high loads in trucks and light vans, it may be enough to call for completely different driving practice in the two conditions.

The connection between car roll and steering is further shown by the difficulty experienced in negotiating an S-bend at speed unless a sufficient length of straight road is provided between the two curves to permit recovery of straight road equilibrium, after the first curve and before entering the second. This is referred to particularly in the GM Proving Ground report on Pennsylvania turnpike tests.

It is also true of the simple operation of lane-changing, and is well illustrated in Figure 4.10, originally from K. A. Stonex's SAE paper of December 1940, "Car Control Factors and Their Measurement." The most difficult part of the maneuver occurs at the halfway point. Here the car has completed its right hand turn and is rolled left. The front wheels are then turned rapidly from right to left. The chart shows that during this change the left hand roll still persists while the front wheels are changing to an acceleration to the left, and the rear wheels still have an acceleration to the right. This transition interval serves to reverse the "spin" [*yaw*] of the car. And somewhat later the roll of the car is reversed, and becomes stabilized barely in time to permit the final straightening of the path at the end of the S-bend.

The whole maneuver is almost too complicated to follow, and becomes more so when one considers all the factors involved. For example, the persistency of the left hand roll, if there is roll understeer, tends to exaggerate the left hand turn after the halfway point, and thus makes the transition even more difficult.

Also, the inertia of the steering wheel enters into such a maneuver. Its effective inertia in the steering system is approximately its actual moment of inertia multiplied by the square of the steering ratio, and this may amount to more than ten times the inertia of **both** the front wheels about their kingpins. With power steering this effective inertia may be much higher, and we are all familiar with the sense of having too much flywheel effect in the steering wheel, observable in some power-steer cars. Such tests serve to illustrate the very severe practical limitations of all types of roll steer.

We can conclude that if we had sufficient wheelbase, then roll steer of any sort, except the camber steer of independent front wheels, would be a thing to avoid.

It remains to show that our wheelbases are at present "inadequate."

4.7 Moment of Inertia and Wheelbase

Introduction

In this section and the next, Olley uses the concept of "center of percussion" and its relationship to the k^2/ab ratio in yaw. By way of introduction, Dr. Hugo S. Radt wrote the following development.

Figure 4.23 shows a bicycle model at the instant of a step steer application at the front wheels, when the center of rotation can be assumed at the rear wheels.

Force equilibrium:

$$F_A - F_R = mb\dot{r} \qquad (4.1)$$

> *where br = lateral velocity at CG*
> *and $b\dot{r}$ = lateral acceleration at CG*

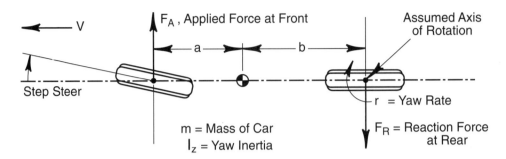

Figure 4.23 Bicycle model immediately after step steer.

Moment equilibrium:

$$aF_A - bF_R = I_z \dot{r} \qquad (4.2)$$

Eliminate F_A:
$$F_A = F_R + mb\dot{r} \qquad (4.3)$$

Then,
$$a(F_R + mb\dot{r}) - bF_R = I_z \dot{r} \qquad (4.4)$$

or,
$$(a - b)F_R = (I_z - mab)\dot{r} \qquad (4.5)$$

The reaction force
$$F_R = \left(\frac{I_z - mab}{a - b}\right)\dot{r} \qquad (4.6)$$

Or
$$F_R = \frac{(I_z/mab) - 1}{\left(\dfrac{a - b}{mab}\right)}\dot{r} \qquad (4.7)$$

$$F_R = \frac{(k^2/ab) - 1}{a - b}mab\,\dot{r} \qquad (4.8)$$

where k is the radius of gyration about a vertical axis through the center of gravity. The yaw inertia and mass are related by $I_z = mk^2$.

The center of percussion is the location of an applied force which gives no reaction force at the point of rotation. *For* $F_R = 0$, $k^2/ab = 1$ *and the center of percussion is at the front axle, Equation 4.1. In general, if*

$k^2/ab > 1$, *then* $F_R > 0$, *opposite direction to the applied force.*

$k^2/ab < 1$, *then* $F_R < 0$, *same direction as the applied force.*

Thus if $k^2/ab > 1$, the rear slip angle α_R is equivalent to the rear wheel steered to the left. If $k^2/ab < 1$, the rear slip angle α_R is equivalent to the rear wheel steered to the right.

It is also true that if the applied force occurred at the rear wheels due to a step steer (at the rear), this location would be the center of percussion if no lateral reaction force was experienced at the front wheels, i.e., $k^2/ab = 1$.

If a free body as shown in Figure 4.24 is subjected to a lateral force F along a line AA at a distance **a** from the CG, it will rotate about a point P at a distance p beyond the CG such that

$$ap = k^2 \tag{4.9}$$

where k is the radius of gyration of the body.

or $$k^2/ap = 1 \tag{4.10}$$

[The center of percussion is at AA and no lateral force is developed at P.]

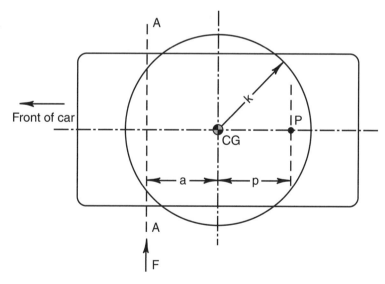

Figure 4.24 *Moment of inertia and center of percussion.*

If the line AA represents the line of the front wheels, and the force F is obtained by a steering angle, the vehicle will start to turn about P, but will be opposed by the [*force due to the*] developing slip angle at the rear tires.

It appears to be important to the handling of the car to see in which direction this slip angle develops at the rear tires, and to estimate how fast it develops. In Figure 4.25, if P

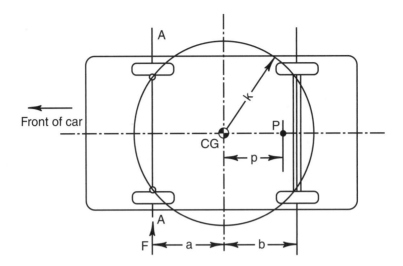

Figure 4.25 *Schematic at initial turn-in.*

is **on** the rear axle (i.e., if $k^2 = ab$) there is **no** immediate reaction at the rear tires when force F is first applied.

If P is **ahead** of the rear axle as shown (i.e., $k^2 < ab$) there is an immediate reaction from the road to the rear tires, to the **right**. In other words a small rear slip angle has appeared, creating a small **centripetal** force, which then proceeds to grow as the vehicle enters its turn.

But if P is **behind** the rear axle (i.e., $k^2 > ab$) the immediate reaction of the road on the rear tires is to the **left**, i.e., outward, and this must be reversed as the vehicle enters the turn.

One can then claim that the wheelbase is "inadequate," since at the start of a turn it is more difficult to get the car to spin [*develop yaw rate or yawing motion, not "spinning out"*] than to produce the required centripetal force at the CG. Actually the case is a little worse than this, since the car, as it starts to turn, also starts to roll.

In Figure 4.26, the lateral force from the front tires is applied at A. AB is the roll axis, and the CG has a moment arm H about the roll axis. If PP represents the center of rotation in plan, the car does not actually start to rotate about PP, but rather about an inclined axis such as DD [*due to combined rolling and yawing*]. Then the initial reaction of the road on the tires is likely to be to the left (i.e., outward) even though k^2/ab is somewhat less than 1.0.

What is clear is that, for positive [*"good" or "desirable"*] handling—without "faking" the geometry by exaggerated roll understeer at the rear tires—it is essential to have an adequate wheelbase, and that this should give a k^2/ab ratio considerably less than 1.0.

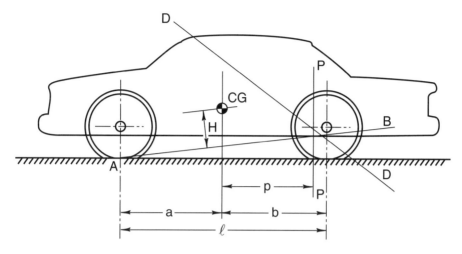

Figure 4.26 *Roll yaw motion at initial turn-in.*

It can be shown that,

$$\frac{Roll\ acceleration}{Yaw\ acceleration} = \frac{\dot{p}}{\dot{r}} = \left(\frac{H}{a}\right)\left(\frac{sprung\ mass}{total\ vehicle\ mass}\right)\left(\frac{yaw\ inertia}{roll\ inertia}\right) \qquad (4.11)$$

For a normal passenger car,

$$\frac{Roll\ acceleration}{Yaw\ acceleration} \cong \left(\frac{1}{3}\right)(1)\left(\frac{3}{1}\right) \cong 1 \qquad (4.12)$$

so Olley's 45 degree line DD in Figure 4.26 is reasonable.

The wheelbase that can be considered adequate depends on the duty demanded of the vehicle. A race car evidently requires a lower k^2/ab ratio, and must also have a lower CG and reduced roll.

Experience suggests that for stable handling of a passenger car without employing roll steer, a k^2/ab of 0.80 is about maximum. In contrast, many modern passenger cars **exceed 1.0** for this ratio. [*Olley's argument here is that, in a sudden steer maneuver, the "center of percussion" effect shouldn't create a slip angle at the rear initially opposing the development of lateral forces in the centripetal direction. A change in direction of the slip angle at the rear in the initial part of a transient is undesirable.*]

Estimating k^2/ab *in Plan View*

It is possible to form a rough estimate[31] of this ratio by regarding the vehicle as a uniform rectangular block, Figure 4.27.

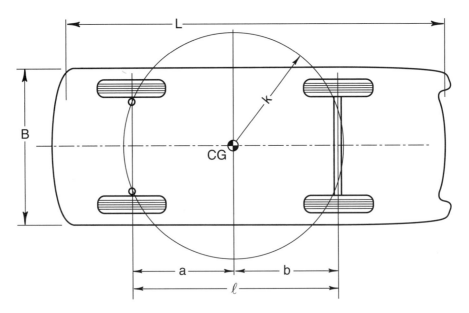

Figure 4.27 *Estimating* k^2/ab *in plan view.*

In most cases such estimates prove to be reasonably close to accurate measurements made by swinging the complete car in the horizontal plane by four cables to the wheel hubs, or other means. L is estimated effective length, generally the overall length excluding bumpers.

B, the effective width, is typically the outside width at the level of the door handles.

For a homogeneous block this would give:

$$\text{Moment of inertia about center of gravity} = m\left(\frac{L^2 + B^2}{12}\right) \tag{4.13}$$

---

[31] For estimating k^2/ab for modern cars, see:

1. Riede, P. M., R. L. Leffert, W. A. Cobb, "Typical Vehicle Parameters for Dynamic Studies Revised for the 1980's," Paper No. 840561, Society of Automotive Engineers, 1984.

2. Garrott, W. R. and M. N. Monk, "Vehicle Inertial Parameters—Measured Values and Approximations," Paper No. 881767, Society of Automotive Engineers, October 1988.

and
$$k^2 = \frac{L^2 + B^2}{12} \qquad (4.14)$$

The body consists partly of a roughly rectangular hollow shell, with more or less uniform upper and lower panels, and some smaller masses in its interior which help to reduce k^2.

There is little error in saying:

$$ab \cong \frac{\ell^2}{4} \; [\,from \; a \approx b \approx \ell/2\,] \qquad (4.15)$$

Even with an extreme weight distribution like 60/40 or 40/60, this estimate is only 4% high.

Thus if $B/L = \lambda_1$ and $\ell/L = \lambda_2$

$$\frac{k^2}{ab} \cong \frac{1 + \lambda_1^2}{3\lambda_2^2} \qquad (4.16)$$

Further than this, one can say for a passenger car, that $B/L = \lambda_1 \cong 0.375$ or $1 + \lambda_1^2 = 1.14$.

Then
$$\frac{k^2}{ab} \cong \frac{1.14}{3\lambda_2^2} = \frac{0.38}{\lambda_2^2} \qquad (4.17)$$

$\ell/L = \lambda_2$	0.5	0.6	0.616	0.70	0.80	0.872	0.90	1.0
k^2/ab	1.52	1.055	1.0	0.775	0.594	0.50	0.47	0.38

The values in the table are plotted in Figure 4.28. It is interesting that a typical "classic" car of about 1930 would have an ℓ/L ratio between 0.70 and 0.75, giving a k^2/ab ratio between 0.775 and 0.675. This would bring the center of percussion well ahead of the rear axle, and make for greater definition in handling.

4.8 Steering when Moving Forward

Time Response

If the car as sketched on Figure 4.26 is traveling at fair speed and the front wheels are turned quickly through, say, one degree, the sequence of events is somewhat as shown in Figure 4.29. (It is assumed that wheelbase ℓ is fixed, as well as the understeer characteristics.)

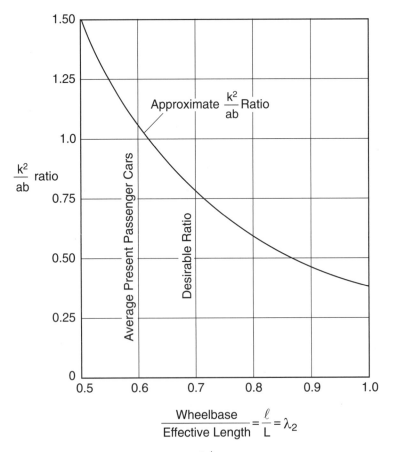

Figure 4.28 k^2/ab estimates.

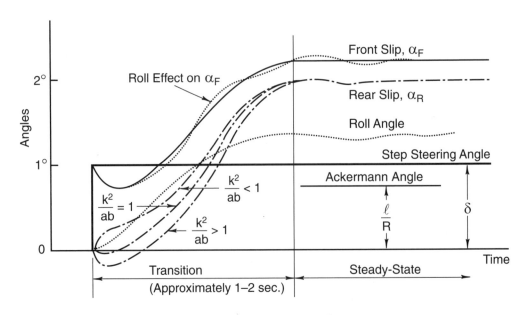

Figure 4.29 Transient time history.

During the transition period there must be an excess of lateral force from the front tires, compared with the rear, to produce the necessary yaw velocity of the vehicle around its CG. [*In the steady-state this excess is sufficient to overcome the yaw damping.*]

At the start of the turn the front slip angle α_F is identical with the steering angle δ. [*In this example, Olley uses slip and steer angles of the same sign, i.e., opposite to SAE convention.*] The rear slip angle is small, being positive when $k^2/ab < 1$, and negative when $k^2/ab > 1$. When $k^2/ab = 1$ the rear slip angle hesitates as shown above and explained earlier.

As the turn progresses α_F decreases momentarily due to the increasing yaw angle. In the case of independent front suspension (IFS) and an inclined roll axis, there is a further reason for a decrease in α_F due to the change of heading of the car from its roll angle about the inclined roll axis. [*If the roll axis is inclined at an angle θ, then there is a yaw rate component $p\sin\theta$, where $p = roll$ rate. See Chapter 3.*]

There is also a decrease in the front lateral force, though not in the slip angle α_F by reason of the roll of the car, and the consequent camber thrust on the front tires.

The momentary decrease of α_F, and of lateral force at the front, will cause a reduction of the yaw acceleration, and a consequent hesitation, which may become oscillatory as shown. And evidently this [*the hesitation*] is sensitive to the amount of roll, and the timing and damping of the roll. It is also sensitive to the lateral force required for the yaw acceleration, and hence to the k^2/ab ratio.

We have not seen any cases of an ordinary car at highway speeds (other than a car with electronic control and feedback) that oscillates as shown in Olley's Figure 4.29. If, however, there was strong roll coupling through the roll acceleration term plus roll steer and large camber change, then with low roll damping there might be some oscillation. With reasonable roll damping (30% critical) the chance of high frequency oscillation is slight.

Thus one can see further reasons for the importance of roll frequency, roll damping, and wheelbase length in handling. [*There continues to be interest in decoupling roll damping from heave, pitch and warp motions. In the coming era of active control of suspensions, damping for each mode can be set independently.*]

The greater separation between the α_F and α_R curves at the start of the turn as the k^2/ab ratio increases is simply an indication of the greater difficulty in starting the yaw rate.

Response Plots for a Modern Car

Dr. Radt, using his reasonably complete vehicle dynamics computer model, has calculated a step steer response for a modern (1990s) sporty compact car. This was done for three different values of k^2/ab: 0.8, 1.0 and 1.2. The front and rear slip angles are plotted on Figures 4.30, 4.31 and 4.32. The results generally agree with Olley's qualitative

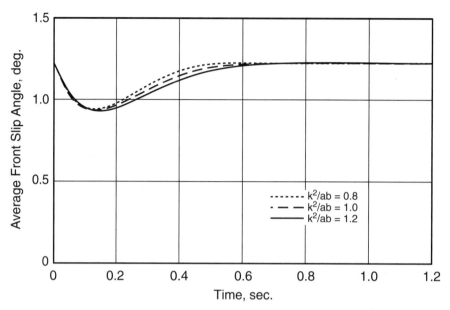

Figure 4.30 *Average front slip angles for varying* k^2/ab.

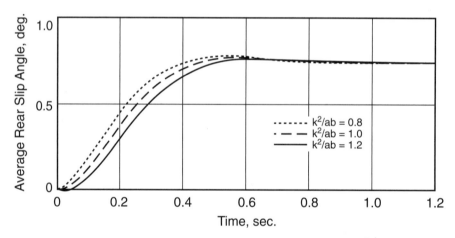

Figure 4.31 *Average rear slip angles for varying* k^2/ab.

estimates but the magnitude of the yaw inertia effect is smaller on the modern car. Radt uses Olley's sign convention for slip angle.

Steering when Moving Forward, Steady-State

The simplified bicycle model representation of a car (as in Figure 4.33) has been used in Chapter 2. First consider **forward steering**. We use the approximation that the angle subtended at the center of turn equals ℓ/R. Other variables are defined as before,

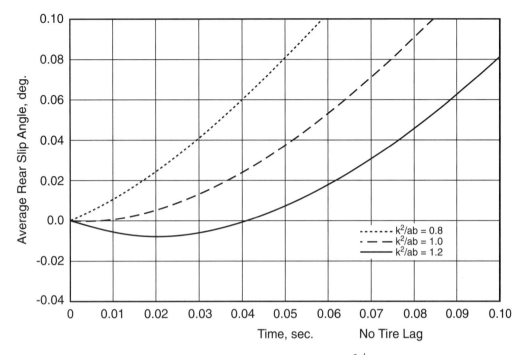

Figure 4.32 *Average rear slip angles for varying* k^2/ab, *enlarged scale.*

δ = steering angle, α_F = front slip angle, α_R = rear slip angle and β = vehicle sideslip angle at **CG**. [*Positive slip angle is defined here as yawing the wheel to the right of the local tire velocity vector, opposite to SAE sign convention.*]

Then, from the geometry:

$$\alpha_R - \frac{\ell}{R} = \alpha_F - \delta \tag{4.18}$$

or

$$\delta - \frac{\ell}{R} = \alpha_F - \alpha_R \tag{4.19}$$

$$\delta = \frac{\ell}{R} + \left(\alpha_F - \alpha_R\right) \tag{4.20}$$

and

$$\beta = \alpha_R - \frac{b}{R} \tag{4.21}$$

If $\alpha_F - \alpha_R$ is positive the car **understeers.**

Olley's above statement is not correct. *The determination of understeer or oversteer depends on the rate of change of the difference of the front and rear slip angles with lateral*

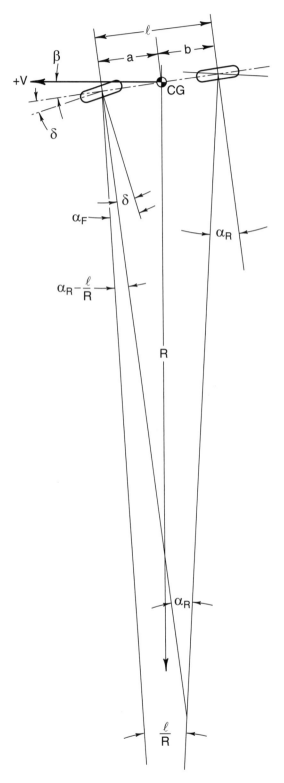

Figure 4.33 *Steering when moving forward.*

acceleration. Olley has made an oversimplification—one that continues to be a common mistake to this day. The correct approach follows:

Starting with Equation 4.20, take the derivative with respect to lateral acceleration to obtain a measure of understeer/oversteer:

$$\frac{d\delta}{dA_Y} \approx \frac{\Delta\delta}{\Delta A_Y} = \frac{\Delta(\ell/R)}{\Delta A_Y} + \frac{\Delta\alpha_F}{\Delta A_Y} - \frac{\Delta\alpha_R}{\Delta A_Y} \qquad (4.22)$$

and since the Ackermann angle is independent of lateral acceleration:

$$\frac{\Delta\delta}{\Delta A_Y} = \frac{\Delta\alpha_F}{\Delta A_Y} - \frac{\Delta\alpha_R}{\Delta A_Y} \qquad (4.23)$$

If $\dfrac{\Delta\alpha_F}{\Delta A_Y} > \dfrac{\Delta\alpha_R}{\Delta A_Y}$ *the vehicle understeers.* $\qquad (4.24)$

If $\dfrac{\Delta\alpha_F}{\Delta A_Y} < \dfrac{\Delta\alpha_R}{\Delta A_Y}$ *the vehicle oversteers.* $\qquad (4.25)$

$\Delta\alpha_F$ *tends to widen the turn and* $\Delta\alpha_R$ *tends to tighten the turn. Another perspective is given by Nordeen.*[32]

The wheelbase ℓ *is always positive. Positive radius (R) values occur when the center of curvature lies to the right of the vehicle, negative when it lies to the left. Lateral acceleration is positive to the vehicle's right and negative to the vehicle's left.*

Olley's conclusion is a simplification of Equation 4.23 based solely on the magnitudes of the slip angles. As such, Olley's conclusion breaks down for left hand turns when slip angles and lateral acceleration change sign. ***Equations 4.24 and 4.25 are the correct interpretation of understeer/oversteer*** *and have the proper units: deg./g.*

4.9 Steering when Moving in Reverse

Since Olley has just completed the steady-state for forward steering, he goes directly to the steady-state for reverse steering—then later covers the transient in reverse.

Reverse steering may be shown in the same way. See Figure 4.34.

---

[32] Nordeen, Donald L., "Vehicle Handling: Its Dependence Upon Vehicle Parameters," Paper No. S405, Society of Automotive Engineers, Detroit Section, February 3, 1964.

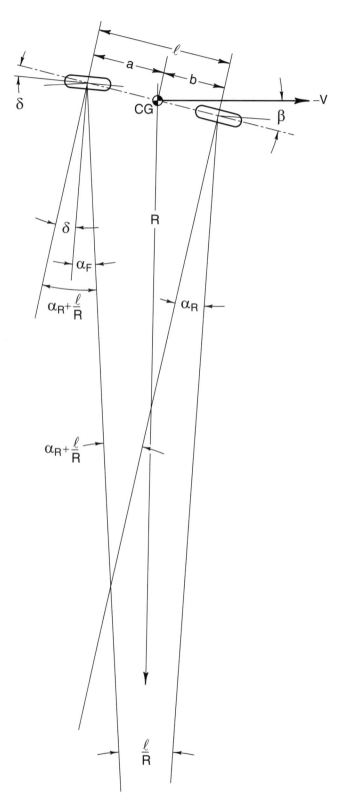

Figure 4.34 *Steering when moving in reverse.*

Geometry now gives the following relationships:

$$\alpha_R + \frac{\ell}{R} = \alpha_F + \delta \tag{4.26}$$

or
$$\delta - \frac{\ell}{R} = \alpha_R - \alpha_F \tag{4.27}$$

and
$$\beta = \alpha_R + \frac{b}{R} \tag{4.28}$$

If the car **understeers** when moving **forward** (i.e., $\alpha_F > \alpha_R$) it **oversteers** in **reverse**.

This statement is also incorrect with the same limitations as Olley's conclusion on forward steering analysis. Once again, Equation 4.23 is the valid equation, and the discussion at the end of Section 4.8 applies.

Note that switching from forward to reverse inverts the signs of the slip angles while the remainder of the terms retain their signs. **If $\Delta\delta/\Delta A_Y$ is positive when traveling forward (i.e., understeer) it is negative when traveling in reverse (i.e., oversteer).** *That is, $\Delta\alpha_F/\Delta A_Y < \Delta\alpha_R/\Delta A_Y$.*

β has changed from $\alpha_R - (b/R)$ to $\alpha_R + (b/R)$. That is, the car must be nosed-in at a much greater angle than when moving forward. [*At low speed on a fixed radius, where the slip angles are near zero, the vehicle slip angle β, in reverse, will be $+b/R$ instead of $-b/R$ (when moving forward). At other speeds there will also be a difference between the values of the slip angles when traveling forward and reverse.*]

The aligning torque due to the slip angle α_F is trying to turn the front wheels **away from center**.

When the steering angle δ is produced suddenly, or is suddenly increased in a turn, the lateral impulse at the tires is **outward** and the car rolls **inward** [*opposite the initial roll when moving forward*].

To come **out** of a turn δ is decreased, which means that the slip angle α_F is increased, and aligning torque is increased. So the steering wheel must be **forced** back to center.

Comments on Steering in Forward and Reverse

All of the above is based on Olley's slip angle convention. To put it in terms of SAE slip angle convention, change the sign of the slip angles wherever they occur. For example, Equation 4.22 becomes,

$$\frac{\Delta \delta}{\Delta A_Y} = \frac{\Delta(-\alpha_F)}{\Delta A_Y} - \frac{\Delta(-\alpha_R)}{\Delta A_Y} \qquad (4.29)$$

Equations 4.23 and 4.29 are general—valid for both left and right turns taken in either forward or reverse. See Appendix A for a detailed discussion of slip angle sign conventions. In either the Olley or SAE sign convention the vehicle is understeer if the magnitude of steer required to stay on the Ackermann path increases as the magnitude of lateral acceleration increases. The vehicle is oversteer when a reduction in steer angle is needed as lateral acceleration is increased.

There is another way to think about these steer effects, by noting that slip angles act like steer angles in that they determine the direction the tire is moving. This concept is called "slip angle steer."[33]

Consider a vehicle traveling at extremely slow speed on a constant radius path. In the limit as speed approaches zero the steer angle required to stay on this path is the Ackermann angle ℓ/R. At slow speed turning is purely geometric—no slip angles are involved. As vehicle speed increases centrifugal force develops due to the curvature of the Ackermann path. The centrifugal force is equilibrated by lateral tire forces, which implies slip angles at the tires. The front slip angle tries to lessen the path curvature, while the rear slip angle is trying to increase it. When the effect of the front is greater than that on the rear the vehicle will tend to straighten its trajectory. If the original Ackermann path (i.e., radius) is to be maintained then this tendency to "understeer" the corner needs to be overcome by additional steer angle δ as predicted by Equation 4.20. Equation 4.23 evaluates to a positive value and the vehicle is understeer.

The virtue of the "slip angle steer" concept is that one can see the several steer effects on the front and rear of the vehicle along with how the understeer or oversteer comes about. Slip angle steers can give one an indication of understeer or oversteer under conditions of lateral acceleration, but the magnitude cannot be determined without considering the rate of change of the slip angles with lateral acceleration.

Time Response in Reverse

The time diagram for a car entering a turn in **reverse** will be somewhat as shown in Figure 4.35.

---

[33] *A more complete treatment of slip angle steers is given in* Race Car Vehicle Dynamics, *pp. 168–171.*

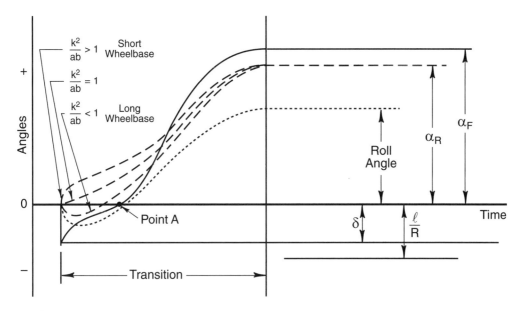

Figure 4.35 *Time history for a car that is reversing.*

The initial roll occurs in the "wrong" direction and has to reverse. The slip angle α_F also starts in the "wrong" direction, and must reverse at point A. From this point onward the aligning torque (in the absence of mechanical caster) tries to increase the steering angle and spin the steering wheel away from center.

To straighten up, the driver must forcibly return the steering angle toward zero. This **increases** lateral force on the front wheels, and therefore increases the roll angle. If these are independent front wheels the combination of increased lateral force and increased roll angle may go beyond the maximum cornering force obtainable from the tires, in which case the car will spin. Thus steering in reverse is evidently unstable except at extremely low speed.

4.10 Boat Steering and Truck in Reverse

Boat Steering

The contrasts between car steering and the steering of a ship or boat have intrigued numerous inventors, and a number of "improved" car designs have offered rear steering, one advantage of which is that such a car can enter a restricted parking space forward, instead of having to back in. Any car or truck has rear steering when running in reverse, and a variety of construction vehicles have to operate for long periods with the directing wheels at the rear. Thus the differences between the steering of ships and wheeled vehicles are of interest.

Perhaps one can caricature the case of a ship by considering only forces parallel to the centrifugal force, as in Figure 4.36.

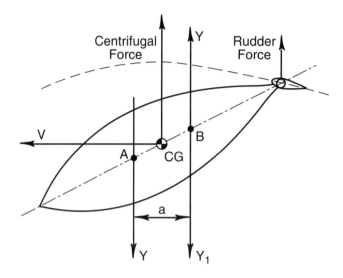

Figure 4.36 *Boat steering.*

The resistance of the water to the lateral drift of the hull may occur well forward, like Y at point A. But if $Y \times a$ represents the couple required to overcome the large yaw damping of the hull, the resultant centripetal force will be Y_1, inward at point B. Then this will be balanced by the two outward forces at the CG and at the rudder post.

Then a time diagram of the forces as the ship enters a turn would be something like Figure 4.37.

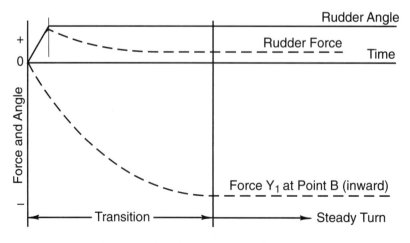

Figure 4.37 *Time response for a boat.*

If the hull is short so that the yaw damping is small the point B may not be aft of the CG. In this case, when the steady state is reached the force on the rudder post has to be inward, and the time diagram is like Figure 4.38.

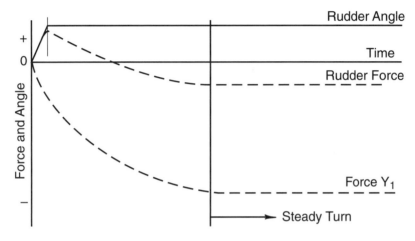

Figure 4.38 *Time response for a short hull boat.*

The torque on the rudder pivot is reversed after the start of the turn, and in the steady turn the rudder is trying to "take charge" and increase the steering angle.

Truck in Reverse

The closest thing to ship handling in a wheeled vehicle is a three-axle truck in reverse, as shown in Figure 4.39.

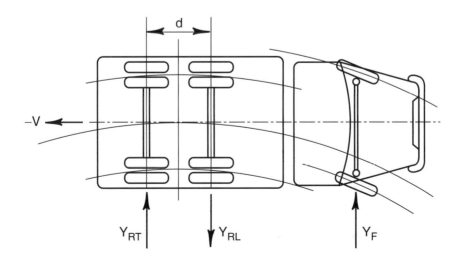

Figure 4.39 *Three-axle truck in reverse.*

Here the outward forces Y_F and Y_{RT} from the road to the front and trailing rear wheels, balance the inward force Y_{RL} on the leading rear wheels, and the couple $Y_{RT}d$ represents the yaw damping of the vehicle.

This is true only at low speed where centrifugal force is negligible. At higher speeds the two end forces decrease and Y_{RL} increases to balance the centrifugal force.

As in the case of the four-wheel trailer in Section 3.11, the yaw damping of the four rear wheels will decrease rapidly with increased speed. Above a certain speed the yaw damping becomes so small that (as in the case of the short-hulled boat) the front tires will have to provide **centripetal** force. From this speed upward the aligning torque on the front tires will reverse, and the steering wheel will try to spin toward full lock.

On any four-wheel vehicle, especially in the absence of dual rear tires or a high-friction differential, the yaw damping is so small that, at any speed above a walking pace, the forces on the front tires are inward, and the torque on the steering wheel is reversed.

On four-wheel construction vehicles, which have to do a lot of reverse running, one modification is to use a lot of "caster" on the front wheels. This is positive in forward driving and therefore negative in reverse. In reverse running the negative caster permits the vehicle to encounter a higher lateral acceleration on a turn before the steering wheel "takes charge" and tries to spin to full lock. In other words the mechanical caster tends to balance the reversed aligning torque.

4.11 Note on the Ackermann ℓ/R Approximation

Olley regularly uses ℓ/R to approximate the Ackermann steering angle, the angle required geometrically to follow a curved path of radius R, with wheelbase ℓ. In fact, this is an approximation. Dr. Radt has started from the actual (nonlinear) geometry and derived the approximate formula; see Figure 4.40.

$$h = R\cos\beta \tag{4.30}$$

$$x + a = R\sin\beta \quad \Rightarrow \quad x = R\sin\beta - a \tag{4.31}$$

$$\tan\varphi = \frac{x}{h} = \frac{R\sin\beta - a}{R\cos\beta} = \tan\beta - \frac{a}{R\cos\beta} \tag{4.32}$$

$$\tan(\varphi + \theta) = \frac{x+\ell}{h} = \frac{R\sin\beta - a + \ell}{R\cos\beta} = \tan\beta + \frac{\ell - a}{R\cos\beta} = \tan\beta + \frac{b}{R\cos\beta} \tag{4.33}$$

Hence $\quad \theta = \tan^{-1}\left[\tan\beta + \frac{b}{R\cos\beta}\right] - \tan^{-1}\left[\tan\beta - \frac{a}{R\cos\beta}\right] \tag{4.34}$

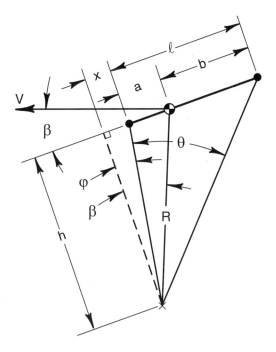

Figure 4.40 *Geometry for a low speed turn.*

But if b/R and a/R are small and β is small:

$$\theta \cong tan\,\beta + \frac{b}{R\,cos\,\beta} - tan\,\beta + \frac{a}{R\,cos\,\beta} \qquad (4.35)$$

$$\theta \cong \frac{a+b}{R\,cos\,\beta} = \frac{\ell}{R\,cos\,\beta} \cong \frac{\ell}{R} \qquad (4.36)$$

4.12 Summary

The study of transient cornering began in earnest in the 1930s and continues through this day. The earliest tests were performed with a vehicle-mounted camera and checker-board-painted pavement to record roll, pitch and yaw angles throughout the maneuver. In this chapter, Olley and his associate Schilling look at the effects of vehicle roll, tire cornering stiffness, vehicle understeer and oversteer characteristics, and radius of gyration on the quantitative response time and qualitative vehicle handling. Olley also discusses coupling of the roll and yaw motions of the vehicle, and the effect of driving in reverse instead of forward. The linear analysis performed at CAL in the 1950s still gives a very good approximation to the actual transient. More elaborate, nonlinear transient analysis is typically incorporated into elaborate computer programs and modern data acquisition can be used for correlation and validation.

CHAPTER 5

Ride

"Figuring the suspension of a car is almost entirely a matter of making useful approximations. It is not an exact science. But neither is it a blind application of rule-of-thumb principles."

**Maurice Olley, opening paragraph
from "Notes on Suspensions," 1961**

5.1 Introduction

We start logically with a simple mass on a spring, the spring being assumed to have a constant rate. If the spring has a rate K, the natural frequency of the mass, ω, is:

$$\omega = \sqrt{\frac{K}{m}} \text{ rad./sec. or } \omega = \frac{1}{2\pi}\sqrt{\frac{K}{m}} \text{ cps } [Hz] \qquad (5.1)$$

But $m = \dfrac{W}{g}$, so that

$$\omega = \frac{1}{2\pi}\sqrt{\frac{gK}{W}} = 0.159\sqrt{\frac{g}{d}} \text{ cps} \qquad (5.2)$$

where d = static deflection of spring under the weight W, Figure 5.1.

This can be expressed very simply. If **d** is in inches, **g** must also be in inches.

This chapter was reviewed by R. Thomas Bundorf, and his suggestions were incorporated.

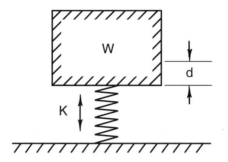

Figure 5.1 *Static deflection.*

Then: $\omega = 0.159\sqrt{\dfrac{386.4}{d}} = \dfrac{3.126}{\sqrt{d}}$ cps, or $\omega = \dfrac{188}{\sqrt{d}}$ cpm   (5.3)

This can also be written:

$$\omega = \frac{3.126}{3.16\sqrt{d/10}} \cong \sqrt{\frac{10}{d}} \text{ cps} \qquad (5.4)$$

Thus a deflection of 10 inches implies a frequency of 1 cps.

A deflection of 1 inch implies a frequency of $\sqrt{10} = 3.16$ cps or approximately 190 cpm. And a deflection of 0.1 inch implies a frequency of 10 cps = 600 cpm.

These approximations are not "accurate" but are extremely useful and are quite frequently used. For example, one can say that the unsprung weight of a passenger car front wheel is about 100 lb., and it is oscillating between a tire with a rate of about 900 lb./in. and a suspension spring of about 100 lb./in.

Consequently wheel hop frequency will be of the order of

$$\frac{188}{\sqrt{100/1000}} = \frac{188}{0.316} = 594.9 \text{ cpm} = 9.916 \text{ cps} \approx 10 \text{ cps}.$$

The "wheel rate" is the vertical rate at the wheel center due to the spring alone. (For greater accuracy we should really use the lowest point of the wheel rim rather than the wheel center. But in practice the wheel center is generally near enough.)

The "ride rate" is the **combined** rate due to the spring plus the tire.

Let K_R = ride rate
       K_W = wheel rate
       K_T = tire rate

Then since the deflections are additive [*the formula for two springs in series*]:

$$\frac{1}{K_R} = \frac{1}{K_T} + \frac{1}{K_W} \quad \text{or} \quad K_R = \frac{K_T K_W}{K_T + K_W} \tag{5.5}$$

Example—The spring gives a deflection at the wheel center of 8 inches, and the tire deflection is 1 inch. If the sprung load is 1000 lb. then

$$\text{Wheel rate,} \quad K_W = \frac{1000}{8} = 125 \text{ lb./in.}$$

$$\text{Tire rate,} \quad K_T = \frac{1000}{1} = 1000 \text{ lb./in.}$$

$$\text{Ride rate,} \quad K_R = \frac{125000}{1125} = 111 \text{ lb./in.}$$

$$\text{Effective deflection} = \frac{\text{sprung load per wheel}}{\text{ride rate at this load}} = \frac{1000}{111} = 9 \text{in.} \tag{5.6}$$

The "effective deflection" is not the actual deflection of the car spring from zero load to full load, since the spring rate is rarely constant [*due to the spring's characteristics and installation geometry*], and since the tire also deflects.

The ride rate at one end of a car may have an "effective deflection" of 9 inches [*as above*]. Then its frequency will be on the order of $188/3 = 63$ cpm.

If the effective deflection is 6 inches, the frequency is $\dfrac{188}{\sqrt{6}} = \dfrac{188}{2.45} = 77$ cpm.

Our first concern in suspension [*ride*] is with the natural resonant motions of the sprung mass of the vehicle on its springs.

By modern [*1960s*] computer methods these resonant motions can be studied much more completely than was possible a few years ago, taking full account of the actual damping characteristics of the shock absorbers, the relatively undamped tires, the "unsprung" masses (which actually ride between the spring of the tire on one side and the suspension spring on the other), the effect of flexibility in the shock absorber mounting, etc. The danger is that, with this greater facility in investigating particular cases, we may lose sight of the general principles.

5.2 Dry Friction

The figure of $188/\sqrt{d}$ for the resonant frequency is true for an undamped spring in a simple system. In such a system, without pneumatic tires, dry friction does not change the frequency, but with pneumatic tires dry friction affects the frequency very much.

In fact if one end of a car with considerable suspension friction is bounced by hand at gradually increasing amplitudes, the resonant frequency will be found to decrease considerably as the amplitude increases, Figure 5.2. While the amplitude is small, as in the range **a**, the vehicle will be bouncing on its tires only at a frequency of about 190 cpm. As the amplitude increases, assuming a total ride deflection of, say, 9 in., the frequency will gradually approach a final figure of about 63 cpm. Such suspensions are quite common. Typically they are described as riding well on rough roads, but badly on "smooth" roads [*where the car is riding primarily on the tire spring.*]

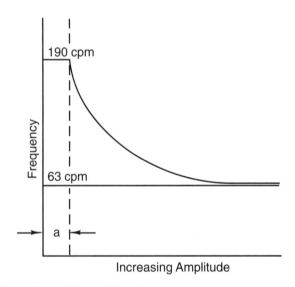

Figure 5.2 *Effect of dry friction on resonant frequency.*

Leaf springs tend, by their very nature, to have this defect, and it is only recently that interleaf liners have been produced, which permanently reduce this fault, and thus greatly increase the acceptability of the leaf spring.

It is evident in Figure 5.2 that, for a given amount of dry friction, the maximum amplitude **a**, before the friction "breaks loose" increases as the suspension is softened. **The softer the suspension the less is its tolerance for dry friction.**

In the last 30 years [*1930–1960*] on American passenger cars, the effective deflection of the car as a whole, defined as the (sprung weight)/(ride rate at CG), has approximately **doubled**, increasing from 5–6 inches to 9–12 inches. It follows that, on modern cars, dry friction has to be reduced to the utmost to give acceptable "smooth road" riding comfort.

5.3 Fluid Damping

Fluid damping has the effect of reducing the resonant frequency. But on normal car suspensions, since the damping ratio is seldom more than 25 percent of "critical," this slowing-down effect is negligible. Referring to Figure 5.3.

$$\text{Damping force} = c \times (\text{vertical velocity}) = c \frac{dz}{dt} \tag{5.7}$$

The damped frequency ω_d is related to the free frequency ω_n thus:

$$\frac{\omega_d}{\omega_n} = \sqrt{1 - \left(\frac{c}{c_c}\right)^2} \tag{5.8}$$

where c_c is the "critical" damping.[34]

Thus, for 25 percent critical damping the ratio $\omega_d/\omega_n = \sqrt{15/16} = 0.968$, a reduction in frequency of only 3.2 percent, which, in our present frequency estimates, is negligible.

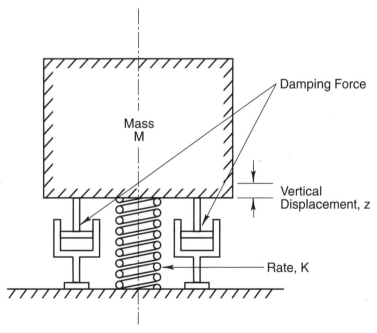

Figure 5.3 Idealized spring-mass-damper system.

[34] This relationship is derived in Rauscher, Manfred, *Introduction to Aeronautical Dynamics*, John Wiley & Sons Inc., New York, 1953, Equation 13.22e, p. 553, or Thomson, William T., *Theory of Vibration with Applications*, Prentice Hall, New Jersey, 1993, pp. 29–30. Critical damping gives no overshoot—see Figure 22.2 in *Race Car Vehicle Dynamics*, SAE R-146.

However 25 percent of critical damping represents a quite rapid damping out of any single initial disturbance. Thus the time history shown in Figure 5.4.

This fact casts considerable doubt on the usefulness of the work of Rowell and Guest, referred to later, in which the automobile is regarded as a simple mass supported on two undamped springs. However, a road surface is capable of giving repeated impulses to the wheels of a vehicle and it is under these conditions that the damping is liable to appear inadequate.

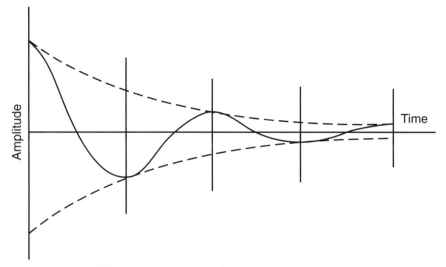

Figure 5.4 *Decay with ~25% critical damping.*

It is apparent that the work of Rowell and Guest still conveys some useful information, especially as it led to the production of the "k^2 rig" [*read "k squared rig"*], which will be referred to later.

The damping effect of conventional hydraulic shock absorbers is not by any means theoretical fluid damping in which the resistance is proportional to velocity. Yet their overall effect on the ride is quite similar to that of fluid damping. The function of the shock absorbers is to damp the ride motion of the vehicle and also the motion of the "unsprung" masses [*see also Section 6.5*].

The basic expressions are summarized as follows:

Ride rate $\Rightarrow$ *ride frequency* $\Rightarrow$ *critical ride damping (based on ride rate)*

   Ride rate, K_R *:*

$$\frac{(Tire\ rate)(wheel\ rate)}{(Tire\ rate)+(wheel\ rate)} = \frac{K_T K_W}{K_T + K_W}\ lb./in.\ or\ lb./ft. \tag{5.5}$$

Ride undamped natural frequency, ω_n :

$$\frac{1}{2\pi}\sqrt{\frac{(ride\ rate)}{(sprung\ mass)}} \quad cpm,\ cps\ or\ Hz \tag{5.1}$$

Critical ride damping:

$$2\sqrt{(sprung\ mass)(ride\ rate)}\ \ lb.\text{-}sec./ft.\ or\ lb.\text{-}sec./in. \tag{5.9}$$

Unsprung rate $\Rightarrow$ unsprung frequency $\Rightarrow$ critical unsprung damping

Unsprung rate:

$$Wheel\ rate + tire\ rate = K_W + K_T\ \ lb./in.\ or\ lb./ft. \tag{5.10}$$

Unsprung undamped natural frequency, ω_d :

$$\frac{1}{2\pi}\sqrt{\frac{(unsprung\ rate)}{(unsprung\ mass)}} \quad cpm,\ cps\ or\ Hz \tag{5.11}$$

Critical damping for unsprung:

$$2\sqrt{(unsprung\ mass)(unsprung\ rate)}\ \ lb.\text{-}sec./ft.\ or\ lb.\text{-}sec./in. \tag{5.12}$$

Consider some typical numbers as in Figure 5.5:

$$Ride\ rate = \frac{125000}{1125} = 111\ lb./in. = 1333\ lb./ft.$$

$$Sprung\ mass = \frac{1000}{32.2} = 31\ slugs$$

$$Unsprung\ mass = \frac{100}{32.2} = 3.1\ slugs$$

$$Ride\ natural\ frequency = \frac{1}{2\pi}\sqrt{\frac{1333}{31}} = 1.04\ cps = 62.4\ cpm$$

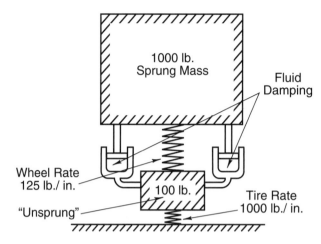

Figure 5.5 *Quarter-car ride model.*

Sprung mass critical damping based on ride rate:

$$c_c = 2\sqrt{(\text{mass}) \times (\text{rate})} = 2\sqrt{31 \times 1333} = 406 \text{ lb.-sec./ft.}$$

The unsprung mass oscillates **between** the ground and the sprung mass, i.e., against a [*combined*] spring rate of 1125 lb./in. or 13500 lb./ft. Its undamped natural frequency is therefore:

$$\text{Unsprung frequency} = \frac{1}{2\pi}\sqrt{\frac{13500}{3.1}} = 10.5 \text{ cps} = 630 \text{ cpm}$$

Critical damping for the unsprung will be $2\sqrt{3.1 \times 13500} = 410$ lb.-sec./ft.

In other words, if the shock absorbers provide 25 percent of critical damping for the ride, they will also provide approximately 25 percent for the unsprung.

It can be shown in the same way that, if the wheel rate is doubled to 250 lb./in., the ride frequency increases to 85 cpm, and critical ride damping requires 545 lb.-sec./ft. At the same time the unsprung frequency increases moderately to 665 cpm, and its critical damping would need 432 lb.-sec./ft. In other words, if 25 percent critical, or 108 lb.-sec./ft. is provided to "hold" the unsprung, it will be less than 20 percent critical for the ride. The ride will probably be underdamped.

On the other hand, if the wheel rate is halved, to 62.5 lb./in., the ride frequency decreases to 45.5 cpm, and critical ride damping requires only 296 lb.-sec./ft. Unsprung frequency is reduced to 612 cpm, and critical damping for the unsprung becomes 398 lb.-sec./ft. Or if 25 percent critical (99.5 lb.-sec./ft.) is provided for the unsprung, this becomes over 33 percent critical for the ride.

What this appears to mean is that, with a total ride deflection of about 9 inches, the amount of damping which is effective in controlling ride is about equally effective in controlling the unsprung mass.

Sample data (below) is plotted in Figure 5.6.

Given:

> *Tire rate = 1000 lb./in.*
> *Sprung mass = 31 slugs (sprung weight = 1000 lb.)*
> *Unsprung mass = 3.1 slugs (unsprung weight = 100 lb.)*

Wheel rate (lb./in.)	100	150	200	250
Ride rate (lb./ft.)	1091	1565	2000	2400
Ride frequency (cpm)	56.7	67.9	76.7	85.0
Unsprung rate (lb./ft.)	13200	13800	14400	15000
Unsprung frequency (cpm)	623	637	651	665
Damping required for critical damping of sprung mass in ride (lb.-sec./ft.)	368	441	498	545
Damping required for critical damping of unsprung mass (lb.-sec./ft.)	405	414	423	432

With a stiffer suspension, adequate damping for the unsprung tends to be inadequate for the ride. And, for an extremely soft suspension, adequate damping for the unsprung approaches more nearly to critical damping for the ride.

An extreme example is the Citroën DS19 in which the minimum damping, required to "hold" the wheels, suppresses any apparent resonant tendency in the ride of the vehicle, because of the extremely low ride rate.

Therefore, provided that other requirements such as roll and pitch stability are met there are strong arguments for soft suspensions [*in ride*].

5.4 Steel Springs: Work Storage Analysis

In this section, Olley discusses the weight of steel springs since the work (energy) storage capacity of a spring is directly related to its weight.

If one thinks of a soft suspension using normal steel springs of approximately constant rate, the weight (and cost) of spring steel soon becomes a limitation.

For instance, suppose a weight W is supported by a constant rate spring of rate K, Figure 5.7. The deflection at normal "design height" is d, and the ride clearance is z. W and z are fixed, but K and d are variable.

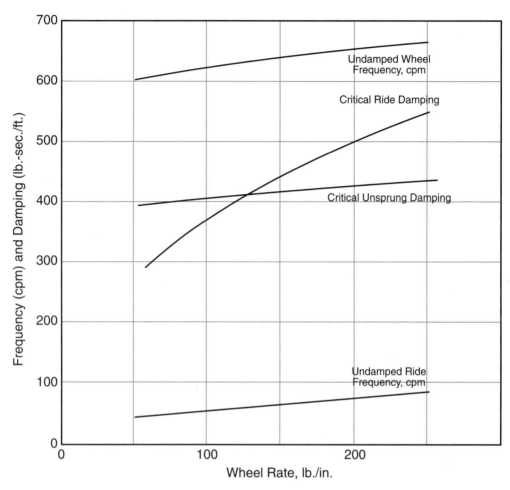

Figure 5.6 *Natural frequency and critical damping example.*

In Figure 5.8, work stored in the spring at full bump is the area under the curve

$$Work = area = \frac{1}{2}(force_{max})(d + z) \qquad (5.13)$$

but $force_{max} = rate \times (d + z)$

$$Work = \frac{1}{2}(rate \times (d + z))(d + z) \qquad (5.14)$$

$$Work = \frac{1}{2}rate(d + z)^2 \qquad (5.15)$$

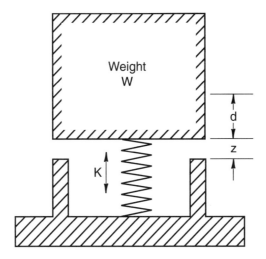

Figure 5.7 *System for spring work-storage calculation.*

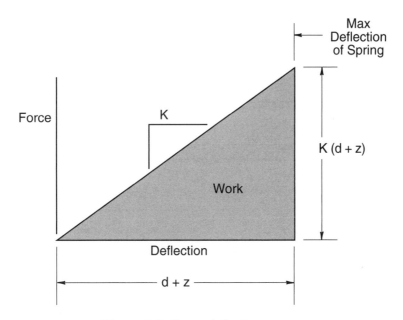

Figure 5.8 *Force-deflection curve.*

and with rate = $K = W/d$,

$$\text{Work} = \frac{W}{2d}(d+z)^2 \qquad (5.16)$$

From this it is readily shown that least work is stored, and therefore least spring steel required, when $z = d$, i.e., when deflection at normal load is equal to the ride clearance.

If we say that $d/z = n$, we find that the work stored at full bump, which determines the weight of spring steel, is:

$$\text{Work-stored} = Wz\left(\frac{n}{2} + 1 + \frac{1}{2n}\right) \tag{5.17}$$

or that

$$\frac{\text{Work-stored}}{Wz} = \left(\frac{n}{2} + 1 + \frac{1}{2n}\right) \tag{5.18}$$

Derivation of work stored at full bump:

$$\text{Work-stored} = \frac{W}{2d}(d + z)^2 = \frac{W}{2d}\left(d^2 + 2dz + z^2\right) \tag{5.19}$$

$$\text{Work-stored} = \frac{W}{2}\left(d + 2z + \frac{z^2}{d}\right) \tag{5.20}$$

$$\text{Work-stored} = \frac{Wz}{2}\left(\frac{d}{z} + 2 + \frac{z}{d}\right) \tag{5.21}$$

But $n = d/z$, *so* $\text{Work-stored} = Wz\left(\frac{n}{2} + 1 + \frac{1}{2n}\right)$ $\qquad\qquad$ *(5.22)*

which checks with Equation 5.17 stated by Olley.

Then if:

n	0.5	1	2	4	10	20
$\dfrac{\text{Work-stored}}{Wz}$	2.25	2	2.25	3.125	6.05	11.025
Increase, %	12.5	0	12.5	56.25	202.5	451.25

Hence we can say that if the ride clearance z is 3 inches, it is reasonably economical practice to provide a steel spring with a deflection at normal load of as much as 9 inches, $(d/3 = 3,\ d = 9)$.

Then $n = 3$, and percent increase is 33% [*over the optimum case of N = 1*].

Larger deflections than this demand rapidly increasing weight of spring steel.

Note—The comparison of spring weights on a basis of work stored at full bump assumes that the life of a spring depends on the **maximum** stress. This is not quite true. It also depends on the **stress range**, which becomes much less as the spring is softened. There-fore it is probable that the minimum weight (and cost) of spring steel will not actually be at the point where d = z, but will be not far from the point where d = 2z.

The statement as to the excessive weight of ultra-soft springs is still generally true, unless such softness is obtained, for a limited range, by some such "trick" device as a toggle.

See also the SAE Leaf Spring Manual on weight of active material in leaf springs.[35]

5.5 Work Stored in Springs

Work stored in a cubic inch of flat steel of rectangular section stressed in pure circular bending:

$$\frac{\sigma^2}{6E} \tag{5.23}$$

where σ is the stress in the material and E is the material's Young's modulus.

Olley gives the above formula with the requirement of **pure circular bending**. *This require-ment implies that the stress along the length of the spring is constant. This is not achieved with a single leaf spring of constant section supported at the two ends and loaded in the middle. The condition is, however, met by a "double triangular" spring in plan view with a constant thickness, t, Figure 5.9. For analysis we divide this double triangular (diamond shaped) spring into a number of strips, n, of width w and thickness t. Each strip will bend into a circle as long as all the strips are bent together (i.e., when they are stacked vertically, they give a typical leaf spring configuration).*

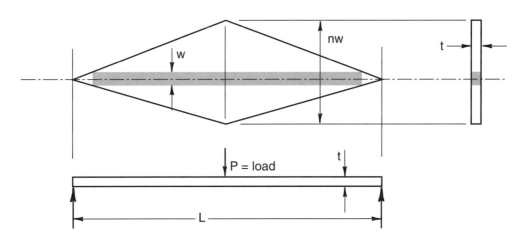

Figure 5.9 *"Triangular" leaf spring of constant thickness.*

---

[35] Design and Application of Leaf Springs, HS 788, Fourth Edition, Society of Automotive Engineers, Warrendale, Pa., 1982.

The following is a derivation[36] of the work done per unit volume.

Moment of inertia (section), $I = \dfrac{(nw)t^3}{12}$ (5.24)

Section modulus, $Z = \dfrac{(nw)t^2}{6}$ (5.25)

Bending moment on beam from concentrated load at center,

$$M = \frac{PL}{4} = Z\sigma = \frac{(nw)t^2}{6}\sigma \qquad (5.26)$$

and $P = \dfrac{2}{3}\dfrac{\sigma(nw)t^2}{L}$ (5.27)

Deflection for beam of uniform strength,

$$d = \frac{PL^3}{32EI} = \frac{PL^3}{32E\left(\dfrac{(nw)t^3}{12}\right)} = \frac{3}{8}\frac{PL^3}{E(nw)t^3} \qquad (5.28)$$

or, $P = \dfrac{8}{3}\dfrac{E(nw)t^3}{L^3}d$ (5.29)

Equating to earlier expression for load, P, gives

$$\frac{2}{3}\frac{\sigma(nw)t^2}{L} = \frac{8}{3}\frac{E(nw)t^3}{L^3}d \qquad (5.30)$$

Solve for stress, $\sigma = \dfrac{8}{2}\dfrac{Etd}{L^2} = \dfrac{4Etd}{L^2} = \dfrac{Etd}{(L/2)^2}$ (5.31)

Work done in deflecting spring (within elastic limit) is

$$W = \frac{Pd}{2} = \frac{2}{3}\frac{\sigma(nw)t^2}{L}\frac{d}{2} \qquad (5.32)$$

---

[36] Chrysler Institute notes on Suspension and Steering, C-3, 1958–60.

But from Equation 5.31,

$$d = \frac{\sigma L^2}{4Et} \qquad (5.33)$$

Thus, the work done,

$$W = \left(\frac{2}{3}\frac{\sigma(nw)t^2}{L}\right)\left(\frac{1}{2}\frac{\sigma L^2}{4Et}\right) = \frac{\sigma^2(nw)tL}{12E} \qquad (5.34)$$

Unit volume of spring is $(nw)tL/2$ *or,*

$$\frac{\textbf{Work done}}{\textbf{Unit volume}} = \frac{\sigma^2}{6E} \qquad (5.35)$$

which checks Olley (Equation 5.23).

Calling $E = 29.5 \times 10^6$ psi,

Work per cubic inch $= \dfrac{\sigma^2}{177 \times 10^6}$ \qquad or, \qquad (5.36)

Work per pound $= \dfrac{\sigma^2}{0.283\left(177 \times 10^6\right)} = \dfrac{\sigma^2}{50 \times 10^6}$ (lb.-in.)/lb. \qquad (5.37)

The total work-stored $= \dfrac{d}{2}P = \dfrac{d^2}{2}K_s$ \qquad (5.38)

[*where P is the load and K_s is the spring rate*]

Weight of working material in such a spring

$$\frac{\text{Work}}{\left(\text{Work/lb.}\right)} = \frac{d^2}{2}K_s\frac{50 \times 10^6}{\sigma^2} = \frac{25 \times 10^6}{\sigma^2}d^2K_s \qquad (5.39)$$

or \qquad Weight of working material $= \left(\dfrac{5000d}{\sigma}\right)^2 K_s$ \qquad (5.40)

Examples are given in the Leaf Spring Manual[37] showing that practical leaf springs can approach this theoretical weight within 5 or 6 percent. A rectangular section coil spring [*rectangular wire*] used in torsion [*clockspring*] has exactly the same work storage figure. The single leaf spring also has virtually the same work storage.

Round Wire Helical Spring in Compression, or Torsion Rod

Assuming that the coil spring has a reasonable "index" [*coil diameter divided by wire diameter*], and is preset so that the actual maximum stress is uniform around the wire, the work storage capacity of the coil spring and torsion rod are the same.

$$\text{Work per cubic inch} = \frac{\tau^2}{4G} \tag{5.41}$$

Again from the Chrysler Institute notes,[38] the resilience is the work stored as elastic energy. For a torsion bar or a coil spring, the work done (stored) is

$$Work\text{-}stored = \frac{\tau^2}{4G} \times \left(steel\ volume\right) \tag{5.42}$$

where τ is the shear stress and G is the shear modulus. The resilience per steel volume is derived in the Chrysler notes. Equation 5.41 (or 5.42) can be derived from Equations 21.1 and 21.9 in **Race Car Vehicle Dynamics***, p.756, noting that the work done is $WX/2 = WR\theta/2$; see Figure 21.1 for notation.*

Calling $G = 11.5 \times 10^6$ psi

$$\text{Work per cubic inch} = \frac{\tau^2}{46 \times 10^6} \text{ psi or} \tag{5.43}$$

$$\text{Work per pound} = \frac{\tau^2}{0.283\left(46 \times 10^6\right)} = \frac{\tau^2}{13 \times 10^6} \text{ (lb.-in.)/lb.} \tag{5.44}$$

$$\text{The total work stored} = \frac{\phi^2}{2} K_\phi \tag{5.45}$$

[*where K_ϕ is the torsional spring rate and ϕ is angular deflection.*]

---

[37] *SAE Spring Design Manual*, AE-11, Society of Automotive Engineers, Warrendale, Pa., 1990 [*obviously Olley was referring to an earlier version*].

[38] Chrysler Institute notes on Suspension and Steering, C-3, 1958-60.

So weight of working material in spring

$$\frac{\text{Work}}{\left(\text{Work/lb.}\right)} = \frac{\phi^2}{2}K_\phi\frac{13\times10^6}{\tau^2} = \frac{6.5\times10^6}{\tau^2}\phi^2 K_\phi \qquad (5.46)$$

or $\text{Weight of working material} = \left(\frac{2550\phi}{\tau}\right)^2 K_\phi$ (5.47)

Knowing the total deflection, the rate and the maximum stress, the design efficiency of a leaf spring or coil spring can immediately be checked by Equations 5.40 and 5.47.

Examples:

Leaf Spring	Deflection (total)	10 inches
	Rate	100 lb./in.
	Maximum stress	140000 psi

$$\text{Weight} = \left(\frac{5000\times10}{140000}\right)^2 \times 100 = 0.1275\times100 = \textbf{12.75 lb.}$$

Coil Spring	Deflection (total)	10 inches
	Rate	100 lb./in.
	Maximum stress	120000 psi

$$\text{Weight} = \left(\frac{2550\times10}{120000}\right)^2 \times 100 = 0.045\times100 = \textbf{4.5 lb.}$$

The leaf spring weighs 2.8 times as much as the coil spring. But, against this, the leaf spring, with the addition of a shackle, provides its own suspension linkage.

The numbers given in Section 5.4 on the work-stored, and therefore the spring weight versus normal deflection, apply to both types of spring. Except that as stated, the reduced stress range on the softer springs undoubtedly gives minimum weight and cost of spring steel, not when deflection equals ride clearance, but rather when deflection is at least twice the ride clearance.

5.6 Toggles and Self-Leveling

It is not practical, however, to use ultra-soft suspensions for more than an inch or so above and below design height because of the exaggerated effect of load variations, and considerations of pitch stability, etc. Therefore, such suspensions must be self-leveling, and their load deflection diagrams must have the general shape of an "S-curve."

Such a diagram is readily obtained on air suspensions, and can be obtained on a steel spring suspension by using the principle of the toggle.

Two forms of toggle are shown in Figures 5.10 and 5.11. (Also note that the **Belleville spring** is in itself a typical application of the toggle principle.)

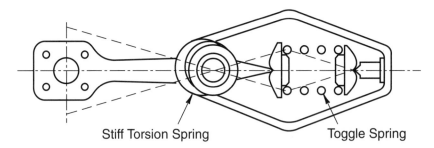

Stiff Torsion Spring   Toggle Spring

Figure 5.10 Mechanism for nonlinear springing.

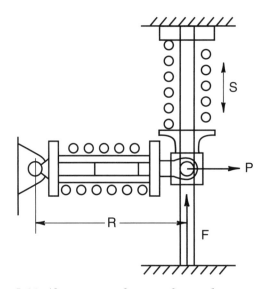

Figure 5.11 Alternate mechanism for nonlinear springing.

Typical of the toggle suspension, and of ultra-soft suspensions generally, is the load deflection diagram in Figure 5.12, giving the variation of load and rate with deflection of the spring. Between plus and minus one inch deflection the rate stays below 80 lb./in.

But this diagram does not illustrate the difficulty of providing a self-leveling device. Such a device has to adjust the wind-up of the torsion spring, as shown in the example in Figure 5.10, to balance variations in the **load**, and to keep the suspension on the "sweet spot." Figure 5.13 plots the rate against the load, and shows that, to maintain the best ride condition, any self-leveling device has to be extremely sensitive.

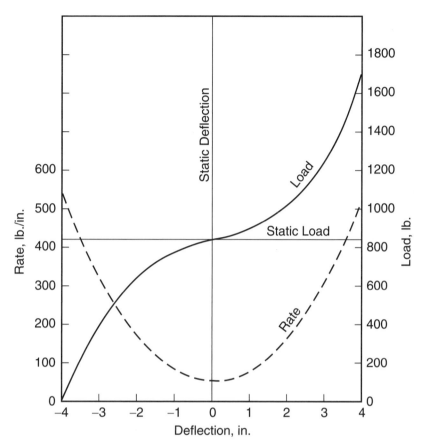

Figure 5.12 *Load deflection curve for nonlinear ride spring arrangement.*

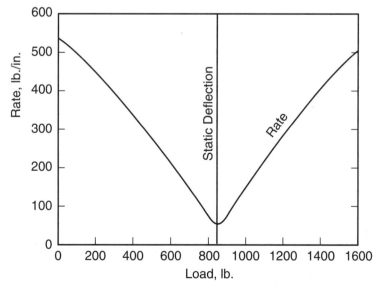

Figure 5.13 *Load against rate for nonlinear ride spring arrangement.*

Another spring arrangement for softening ride is shown in Figure 5.11. The rate at center = S − P/R. This can give any desired softness in the center position, but again, there may be difficulty in adjusting the height.

5.7 Two Degrees of Freedom

As already mentioned, the analysis of vehicle motion based on two degrees of freedom is subject to some doubt, because actual ride motions are strongly damped. The published work is that of H. S. Rowell in IAE [*Institute of Automobile Engineers*] Transactions, 1923, and James Guest in IAE Transactions of 1928.

The suggestion of these two writers that the interference of two widely dissimilar frequencies was the chief cause of discomfort in the cars of the period was amply confirmed by road tests of 1931–2 on the experimental Cadillac "k² rig," Figure 5.14. [*The pitch moment of inertia could be varied by changing weights on the front and rear of the car. The pitch and bounce centers could also be adjusted.*]

Figure 5.14 *The k² rig.*

These tests led directly to what are now regarded as fundamentals of passenger car riding comfort.

These can be briefly stated:

1. The front suspension must have a greater effective deflection than the rear. Typically front deflection should be at least 30 percent greater than rear. In other words the "spring center," at which the car, if pushed down vertically, would remain parallel with the ground, should be at least 6½ percent of the wheelbase back of the CG of the sprung mass.

2. The two frequencies of "pitch" and "bounce" should be reasonably close together within a maximum ratio of

(Pitch frequency/bounce frequency) of 1.20.

3. Ride frequencies should not be greater than 77 cpm, corresponding to an effective ride deflection in a simple system of 6 inches.

One argument for still paying attention to the work of Rowell and Guest is that it is found that the best way to develop riding comfort in a new car model is to ride it initially **without shock absorbers**, and adjust spring rates to produce the "flattest" possible ride under these conditions. Shock absorber damping is then added in small increments until adequate control is established.

This follows the general principle that the best shock control [*for ride*] is the least shock control which will do the job.

5.8 The Rowell and Guest Treatment

In Figures 5.15 and 5.16: [*Note: Figure 5.16 apears on page 299.*]

A	the front suspension (i.e., front wheel center)
B	the rear suspension (i.e., rear wheel center)
c	longitudinal distance from CG to spring center
G	CG of sprung mass m **in plane of support**
k	radius of gyration of sprung mass about the CG (ft.)
K_F	total rate of front suspension (lb./ft.)
K_R	total rate of rear suspension (lb./ft.)
O	spring center [*such that* $K_F(a+c) = K_R(b-c)$]
E	forward oscillation center [*pitch center*]
F	rearward oscillation center [*bounce center*]
z	vertical displacement at the CG
Z	vertical amplitude at the CG
θ	angular displacement about the CG

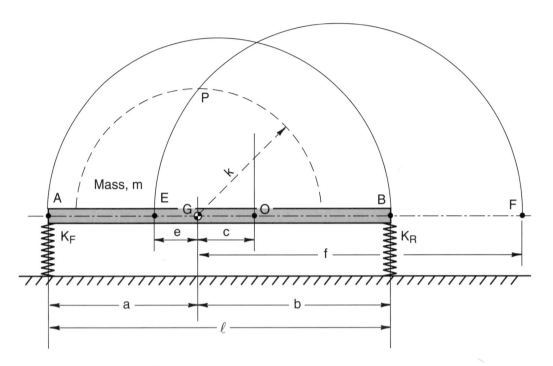

Figure 5.15 *Rowell and Guest ride diagram.*

Θ   angular amplitude about the CG
ω   any resonant frequency (rad./sec.)
ω_1 the faster of the two resonant frequencies
ω_2 the slower of the two resonant frequencies
m   sprung mass (slugs)

Spring Center O

By definition, $$K_F(a + c) = K_R(b - c) \tag{5.48}$$

Whence $$c = \frac{K_F a - K_R b}{K_F + K_R} \tag{5.49}$$

In most modern passenger cars $K_F a$ is less than $K_R b$, so the value of c is positive, i.e., back of G [*the CG of the sprung mass*].

O is the point at which the car will be pushed down parallel. [*A vertical force applied at O will compress the front and rear equally.*] It follows that a pure couple will rotate the car about O.

Vertical rate at $O = K_F + K_R$, which is a **maximum**.

Angular rate about $O = K_F(a + c)^2 + K_R(b - c)^2$ and is a **minimum**.

CG of Sprung Mass

Point G is the point at which and about which we are going to consider the car motions.

$$\text{Vertical rate at } G = \frac{1}{\dfrac{b^2}{K_F \ell^2} + \dfrac{a^2}{K_R \ell^2}} = \frac{K_F K_R \ell^2}{K_F a^2 + K_R b^2} \qquad (5.50)$$

$$\text{Angular rate about } G = K_F a^2 + K_R b^2 \qquad (5.51)$$

Pitch Stability

It has been mentioned that angular rate about O, the spring center, is a minimum. This fact becomes important in determining the pitch stability (which is very low) of "compensated" suspensions like the Packard, or small Citroën.

In the equations of motion we are concerned with three different "rates":

1. Vertical rate at $O = K_F + K_R$

2. Angular rate about $G = K_F a^2 + K_R b^2$

3. And a third rate, which is the vertical force at G per unit of rotation about G. Evidently this is $K_F a - K_R b$.

Rowell uses the symbols:

$$\alpha = \frac{K_F + K_R}{m} \qquad (5.52)$$

$$\beta = \frac{K_F a - K_R b}{m} \qquad (5.53)$$

$$\gamma = \frac{K_F a^2 + K_R b^2}{m} \qquad (5.54)$$

[*Rowell's symbols are not to be confused with the common use of these symbols: α = tire slip angle, β = vehicle sideslip angle, γ = inclination angle.*]

So that:

$$m\alpha = \text{vertical rate at the spring center, O} \tag{5.55}$$

$$m\beta = \text{vertical force per unit angle about center of gravity, G} \tag{5.56}$$

$$m\gamma = \text{angular rate about G} \tag{5.57}$$

There are two equations of motion:

$$\left.\begin{array}{l}\text{Linear:} \quad m\ddot{z} + \left(K_F + K_R\right)z + \left(K_F a - K_R b\right)\theta = 0 \\[2mm] \text{Angular:} \quad mk^2\ddot{\theta} + \left(K_F a - K_R b\right)z + \left(K_F a^2 + K_R b^2\right)\theta = 0\end{array}\right\} \tag{5.58}$$

Hence:

$$\left.\begin{array}{l}-\omega^2 mZ + \left(K_F + K_R\right)Z + \left(K_F a - K_R b\right)\Theta = 0 \\[2mm] -\omega^2 mk^2\Theta + \left(K_F a - K_R b\right)Z + \left(K_F a^2 + K_R b^2\right)\Theta = 0\end{array}\right\} \tag{5.59}$$

$$\left.\begin{array}{l}\left[\dfrac{\left(K_F + K_R\right)}{m} - \omega^2\right]Z + \dfrac{\left(K_F a - K_R b\right)}{m}\Theta = 0 \\[5mm] \dfrac{\left(K_F a - K_R b\right)}{m}Z + \left[\dfrac{\left(K_F a^2 + K_R b^2\right)}{m} - \omega^2 k^2\right]\Theta = 0\end{array}\right\} \tag{5.60}$$

From this we get:

$$\left(\omega^2 - \alpha\right)\left(\omega^2 - \frac{\gamma}{k^2}\right) = \frac{\beta^2}{k^2} \tag{5.61}$$

And hence:

$$\omega^4 - \left(\alpha + \frac{\gamma}{k^2}\right)\omega^2 + \frac{\alpha\gamma - \beta^2}{k^2} = 0 \tag{5.62}$$

This is a quadratic in ω^2. There exist two roots which can be found by the quadratic formula. The two roots are,

$$\omega_1^2 = \frac{+\left(\alpha + \dfrac{\gamma}{k^2}\right) + \sqrt{\left(\alpha + \dfrac{\gamma}{k^2}\right)^2 - 4\left(\dfrac{\alpha\gamma - \beta^2}{k^2}\right)}}{2}$$

$$\omega_2^2 = \frac{+\left(\alpha + \dfrac{\gamma}{k^2}\right) - \sqrt{\left(\alpha + \dfrac{\gamma}{k^2}\right)^2 - 4\left(\dfrac{\alpha\gamma - \beta^2}{k^2}\right)}}{2}$$

The resulting roots, ω_1 and ω_2 have the properties given by Equations 5.63 through 5.65.

$$\omega_1^2 + \omega_2^2 = \alpha + \frac{\gamma}{k^2} \tag{5.63}$$

$$\omega_1^2 \omega_2^2 = \frac{\alpha\gamma - \beta^2}{k^2} = \frac{\gamma}{k^2}\left(\alpha - \frac{\beta^2}{\gamma}\right) \tag{5.64}$$

$$\omega_1^2 - \omega_2^2 = \sqrt{\left(\alpha + \frac{\gamma}{k^2}\right)^2 - 4\frac{\alpha\gamma - \beta^2}{k^2}} = \sqrt{\left(\alpha - \frac{\gamma}{k^2}\right)^2 + 4\frac{\beta^2}{k^2}} \tag{5.65}$$

It is apparent that:

α = the square of the vertical frequency of a mass m concentrated at O. We can call this ω_o^2 [*parallel bump*].

γ/k^2 = the square of the angular frequency of the car about the center of gravity G. We can call this ω_p^2 [*pitch*].

$\alpha - \dfrac{\beta^2}{\gamma} = \dfrac{K_F + K_R}{m} - \dfrac{\left(K_F a - K_R b\right)^2}{m\left(K_F a^2 + K_R b^2\right)} = \dfrac{K_F K_R \ell^2}{m\left(K_F a^2 + K_R b^2\right)}$. This is evidently

the square of the vertical frequency of a mass concentrated at G, which we can call ω_g^2 [*bounce*].

Then one can simplify Equations 5.63 and 5.64 above to:

$$\omega_1^2 + \omega_2^2 = \omega_p^2 + \omega_o^2 \qquad (5.66)$$

$$\omega_1^2 \omega_2^2 = \omega_p^2 \omega_g^2 \qquad (5.67)$$

This is about the simplest possible statement on the two frequencies of "pitch" and "bounce" [*where ω_1 and ω_2 are frequencies about pure bounce and pitch centers for a two-degree-of-freedom system. ω_p and ω_g are pitch and bounce about axes through the center of gravity and both ω_1 and ω_2 contribute to each of them*].

There are three "special cases":

1. If $K_F a = K_R b$, i.e., spring center is at the center of gravity, G.

   Then $\qquad\qquad \beta = 0 , \; \omega_1 = \omega_p , \; \omega_2 = \omega_o = \omega_g$

   and $\qquad\qquad\qquad \dfrac{\omega_1}{\omega_2} = \sqrt{\dfrac{ab}{k^2}} \qquad\qquad (5.68)$

As Tom Bundorf points out in his review of this chapter, a further examination of the $\beta = 0$ condition is enlightening. When $\beta = 0$, as shown above, then $\omega_1 = \omega_p$, $\omega_2 = \omega_g$, and $\omega_p^2 = \gamma / k^2$ define the pitch mode about G. Also $\omega_g^2 = \alpha$, defines the parallel bump mode for mass at G.

These are seen by referring back to Equation 5.60. If Z, the vertical amplitude at G, is made zero, the second equation becomes,

$$\left[\frac{\left(K_F a^2 + K_R b^2 \right)}{m} - \omega^2 k^2 \right] \Theta = 0$$

and if Θ is not zero, then, using Equation 5.54

$$\left[\frac{\left(K_F a^2 + K_R b^2 \right)}{m} - \omega^2 k^2 \right] = \left[\gamma - \omega^2 k^2 \right] = 0$$

and $\omega^2 = \omega_p^2 = \gamma / k^2$, pitch mode.

If Θ, *the angular amplitude about G, is made zero, the first line in Equation 5.60 becomes,*

$$\left[\frac{(K_F + K_R)}{m} - \omega^2 \right] Z = 0$$

and if Z is not zero, then, using Equation 5.52,

$$\left[\frac{(K_F + K_R)}{m} - \omega^2 \right] = \left[\alpha - \omega^2 \right] = 0$$

and $\omega^2 = \omega_g^2 = \alpha$, *parallel bounce mode.*

The spring center and center of gravity coincide. The pitch center is at G and the bounce center is at ∞. *The two modes are decoupled.*

If we now look at the roots of Equation 5.62, we observe that β *occurs only in the second term under the radical. This suggests that reducing* β *to zero may have only a small effect on the two frequencies and that the frequencies obtained with* $\beta = 0$ *will be close to the actual frequencies. To check this assumption, Bundorf has prepared a spreadsheet, Table 5.1, where it will be seen that the differences are on the order of a few percent for variations in wheelbase and pitch inertias.*

2. If $k^2 = ab$ it can be shown by substitution in Equations 5.63, 5.64 and 5.65 above that:

$$\omega_1 = \sqrt{\frac{K_F}{m\,b/\ell}} \quad \text{and} \quad \omega_2 = \sqrt{\frac{K_R}{m\,a/\ell}} \tag{5.69}$$

i.e., the two ends of the car oscillate at the two frequencies of two independent simple mass-spring systems of the same ride deflections.

In the 1930s this was of academic interest, since typical k^2/ab ratios of passenger cars were then between 0.5 and 0.7. However, with increased overall length of cars, shorter wheelbases and increased overhung masses, passenger car k^2/ab ratios have generally approached or even exceeded 1.0.

Additionally Mr. Schilling has demonstrated that with the amount of damping now invariably present the actual car motion with a k^2/ab ratio of 0.8 is indistinguishable from that with $k^2/ab = 1.0$. In other words the two ends of the car now oscillate practically independently.

Table 5.1 Bundorf Spreadsheet for Case 1

Olley Natural Frequencies	Non-Equal Spring Rates					Equal Spring Rates			
						β = 0 Conditions			
	High Inertia	Low Inertia	Shorter Wheel-base	$k^2=ab$	$k^2=ab$	High Inertia	Low Inertia	$k^2=ab$	$k^2=ab$
Front spring rate, lb./in.	80	80	80	80	80	100	100	100	100
Rear spring rate, lb./in.	120	120	120	120	120	100	100	100	100
CG to front wheels, ft.	4.5	4.5	4	4.5	6	4.5	4.5	4.5	4.5
CG to rear wheels, ft.	4.5	4.5	4	4.5	4	4.5	4.5	4.5	4.5
Radius of gyration, ft.	5	4	4.5	4.501	4.900	5	4	4.501	4.501
Weight, lb.	2000	2000	2000	2000	2000	2000	2000	2000	2000
Olley term - α	38.64	38.64	38.64	38.64	38.64	38.64	38.64	38.64	38.64
Olley term - β	-34.78	-34.78	-30.91	-34.78	0.00	0.00	0.00	0.00	0.00
Olley term - γ	782.46	782.46	618.24	782.46	927.36	782.46	782.46	782.46	782.46
γ/k^2	31.30	48.90	30.53	38.62	38.62	31.30	48.90	31.30	38.62
a part of root equation	1.00	1.00	1.00	1.00	1.00	1.00	1.00	1.00	1.00
b part of root equation	-69.94	-87.54	-69.17	-77.26	-77.26	-69.94	-87.54	-69.94	-77.26
c part of root equation	1161.00	1814.06	1132.51	1432.69	1492.44	1209.37	1889.64	1209.37	1492.39
High root	42.83	53.87	42.56	46.36	38.64	38.64	48.90	38.64	38.64
Low root	27.10	33.68	26.61	30.91	38.62	31.30	38.64	31.30	38.62
Olley bump frequency squared	38.64	38.64	38.64	38.64	38.64	38.64	38.64	38.64	38.64
Olley pitch frequency squared	31.30	48.90	30.53	38.62	38.62	31.30	48.90	31.30	38.62
Olley bounce frequency squared	37.09	37.09	37.09	37.09	38.64	38.64	38.64	38.64	38.64
Olley bump frequency	6.22	6.22	6.22	6.22	6.22	6.22	6.22	6.22	6.22
Olley pitch frequency	5.59	6.99	5.53	6.21	6.21	5.59	6.99	5.59	6.21
Real high frequency, from roots	6.54	7.34	6.52	6.81	6.22	6.22	6.99	6.22	6.22
Real Low Frequency, from roots	5.21	5.80	5.16	5.56	6.21	5.59	6.22	5.59	6.21
% Difference in bump frequency	-5.0%	7.1%	-4.7%	-8.7%	0.0%	0.0%	0.0%	0.0%	0.0%
% Difference in pitch frequency	7.5%	-4.7%	7.1%	11.8%	0.0%	0.0%	0.0%	0.0%	0.0%
Bounce center using Equation 5.71*	-8.29	-2.28	-7.88	-4.51	0.00	Undefined (division by zero)			
Pitch center using Equation 5.71	3.01	7.01	2.57	4.50	0.00				
Bounce center, Eqn. 5.60, 2nd part**	-8.29	-2.28	-7.88	-4.51	0.00				
Pitch center, Eqn. 5.60, 2nd part**	3.01	7.01	2.57	4.50	0.00				

*Note: Equation does not give proper bounce center for β = 0.

**Note: Equation does not give proper pitch center for β = 0.

3. If $K_F a = K_R b$ and at the same time $k^2 = ab$, then

$$\omega_1^2 - \omega_2^2 = \frac{\ell}{mab}(K_F a - K_R b) = 0 \tag{5.70}$$

This is the sole condition for equal frequencies in pitch and bounce.

In the original discussions of 1923 and onward this condition was suggested as a possible "ideal ride." In the original "k^2 rig" it was easy to produce this condition. **And it was immediately condemned as unacceptable, since it produces a ride which has no recognizable "pattern."**

Oscillation Centers

From Equations 5.60 in the previous section on pitch stability, it is evident that

$$\frac{Z}{\Theta} = \frac{K_F a - K_R b}{m\omega^2 - (K_F + K_R)} \quad \text{or} \quad \frac{Z}{\Theta} = \frac{\beta}{\omega^2 - \alpha} \tag{5.71}$$

Since Z is the vertical amplitude and Θ is the angular amplitude at G, Z/Θ is the distance from G to each of the two centers of oscillation. These are the points E and F in Figure 5.15. The two centers correspond with the two values of ω^2 [ω_1^2 and ω_2^2].

And since, as drawn in this diagram, ω_1^2 is greater than α, ω_2^2 is less than α, and β is negative, the distance e to the **pitch center** E will be forward of the center of gravity G while the **bounce center** F will be a distance f back of G.

The product:

$$e \times f = \frac{\beta}{\omega_1^2 - \alpha} \times \frac{\beta}{\omega_2^2 - \alpha} = \frac{\beta^2}{\omega_1^2 \omega_2^2 - \left(\omega_1^2 + \omega_2^2\right)\alpha + \alpha^2}$$

$$= \frac{\beta^2}{\dfrac{\alpha\gamma - \beta^2}{k^2} - \left(\alpha^2 + \dfrac{\alpha\gamma}{k^2}\right) + \alpha^2} = \frac{\beta^2}{-\dfrac{\beta^2}{k^2}}$$

$$e \times f = -k^2 \tag{5.72}$$

It can also be shown that:

$$(e + c)(f - c) = (a + c)(b - c) \tag{5.73}$$

This completely fixes the oscillation centers so that:

1. **The product of their distances from the center of gravity G is always numerically equal to k^2.**

2. **The product of their distances from the spring center O is always numerically equal to the product of the distances of the front and rear wheels from the spring center.**

One center is always within the wheelbase, and is the "pitch center." The other, outside the wheelbase, is the "bounce center." In general the pitch motion is the faster, except in the cases where k^2 is greater than ab.

The two resonant oscillations are both angular oscillations about their respective centers. Impulses at, or near, either of the two centers will excite oscillation of the opposite type. "Pumping" near the pitch center will produce bounce, and at the bounce center will produce pitch.

On the road the two oscillations are generally occurring simultaneously, and the general motion of the car is not simple harmonic but is composed of the two frequencies. If the frequencies are very far apart, for instance, if one is twice the other, the ride motion will consist of sharp interference "kicks" and comfort is impossible.

From the rules (1) and (2) above, Professor Guest derives a simple graphical construction for fixing the oscillation centers.

This is shown in Figure 5.16.

The bar represents the sprung mass of the car.

A semicircle AHB is drawn on the wheelbase $\overline{AB}$.

Perpendiculars $\overline{GP}$ and $\overline{OH}$ are drawn from G and O to the semicircle. On $\overline{GP}$ the height $\left|\overline{GP_1}\right|$ is marked off equal to k, the radius of gyration of the sprung mass.

Then the ratio
$$\left(\left|\overline{GP_1}\right| \middle/ \left|\overline{GP}\right|\right)^2 = \frac{k^2}{ab} \tag{5.74}$$

With the center on line $\overline{AB}$, a semicircle EP$_1$HF is drawn. **Then E and F are the oscillation centers.**

This is because: $\left|\overline{EG}\right| \times \left|\overline{GF}\right| = e \times f = \left|\overline{GP_1}\right|^2 = k^2 \tag{5.75}$

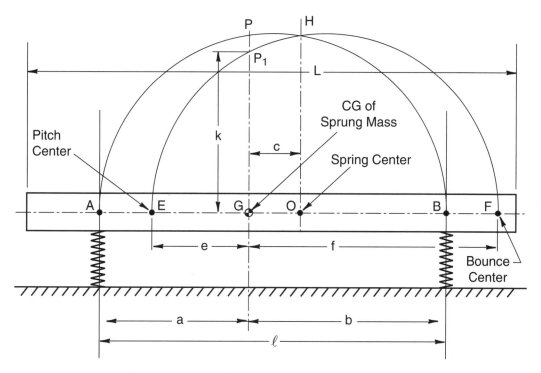

Figure 5.16 *Pitch and bounce centers, from Guest.*

and
$$\left|\overline{AO}\right| \times \left|\overline{OB}\right| = (a+c) \times (b-c) = \left|\overline{OH}\right|^2 = (e+c) \times (f-c) \qquad (5.76)$$

From this diagram one can see at once the effect of changing the position of the center of gravity G, or the spring center, or of changing the value of k^2/ab. The following observations apply to Figure 5.16:

1. In a passenger car G is not going to move much more than $\ell/10$ from the center of the wheelbase (i.e., a 60/40 distribution of the sprung weight). Thus, if we assume that $ab = \ell^2/4$ we are not likely to be more than 4 percent high. If we regard the sprung mass of the car as a uniform bar of length L, the requirement for $k^2/ab = 1.0$ is approximately that $\ell/L = 1/\sqrt{3} = 0.577$, i.e., a wheelbase equal to 0.577 of the overall length. This is exceedingly close to the proportion of wheelbase to overall length on modern [*1960s*] passenger cars, which vary between $\ell/L = 0.535$ and $\ell/L = 0.60$. This suggests a quick means of estimating the k^2/ab ratio from the dimensions of the vehicle.

2. We can change the position of O, the spring center, through a wider range. But in practice we prefer to have the spring center not more than $\ell/10$ back of the center of gravity G (a ratio of about 60/40 in the front/rear spring deflections). It can be seen that as the rear springs are stiffened or the front springs softened, the spring center O

moves back. The semicircle EP_1HF decreases in radius, and both oscillation centers move forward, F approaching the rear axle and E approaching the forward center of percussion.

3. As the k^2/ab ratio increases the two semicircles approach each other, and when $k^2/ab = 1.0$ they coincide, placing the oscillation centers at the two axles, a condition close to that of most modern passenger cars.

4. If the front and rear spring deflections are alike, i.e., spring center O coincides with G, then H coincides with P, and the semicircle EP_1HF becomes infinite [*or becomes meaningless as the bounce center moves to infinity*]. That is, the car pitches about G, and the bounce is "parallel." There is then no coupling of the pitch and bounce motions, which can each continue indefinitely (except for the damping). It was established on the k^2 rig that this was not a good condition for a "flat ride," especially at the lower speeds. Pitching can become severe at 30 mph, though the ride flattens out at high speed.

5. In some trucks, vans, truck-tractors, etc., k^2 can be substantially greater than ab. Then point P_1 moves out beyond P on the diagram, and the oscillation centers move further forward, E becoming the bounce center, outside the wheelbase, and F the pitch center. An impulse at the front then starts pitch, and at the rear, bounce. But the pitch is now slower than the bounce, so the slower motion is still started first.

6. This is the requirement for a "flat" ride, that the slower motion should be started first. The oscillation of the car produced by a single road wave is then of the form shown in Figure 5.17 and no violent pitching of the car occurs.

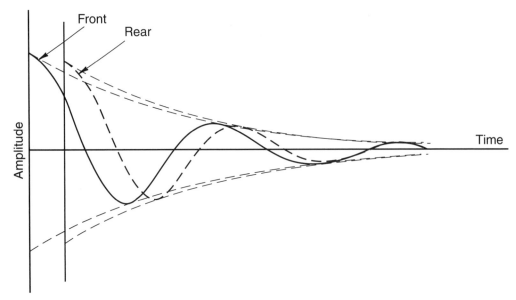

Figure 5.17 *Flat ride. See Appendices E and G for the history of this concept.*

5.9 Actual Ride Frequencies

In Section 5.1 it was mentioned that the frequency given by the simple ratio $188/\sqrt{d}$ was not "accurate."

The equations for ω_1^2 and ω_2^2 in Section 5.8 show why this is so. In general, where k^2/ab is less than 1.0, the pitch frequencies are higher and the bounce frequencies lower than indicated by $188/\sqrt{d}$.

The frequencies which do agree with $188/\sqrt{d}$ are:

1. **Equal deflections** $\left(K_F a = K_R b\right)$

    $$\text{Parallel bounce frequency} = \frac{188}{\sqrt{d}}, \text{ where d is the deflection at the CG}$$

    $$\text{Pitch frequency} = \frac{188}{\sqrt{d}} \times \sqrt{\frac{ab}{k^2}}$$

    (If $k > ab$, the pitch frequency is faster than the bounce frequency.)

2. When $k^2/ab = 1.0$ the frequencies at either end are given by $188/\sqrt{d}$.

3. In all cases the frequency ω_g in Section 5.8 is $188/\sqrt{d}$, where d is the deflection at the CG.

5.10 Height of Oscillation Centers and Sprung CG

So far the sprung mass of the car has been considered as a uniform bar. And it is remarkable that this is not too far removed from the practical case.

As stated (Section 5.8) the "wheelbase" for $k^2/ab = 1.0$, on a uniform bar, is 0.577 of the overall length of the bar. And this is extremely close to the wheelbase to overall length ratio on modern American cars [*c. 1960*], which are known to have k^2/ab ratios close to 1.0. Also, in the 1920–30 era, when effective length of sprung mass was a little longer than the wheelbase, the k^2/ab ratio of the larger closed cars was close to 0.57 to 0.62.

Actually the heights of G and the oscillation centers [*from Rowell and Guest*] are doubtful, but are generally taken as being in the plane of the wheel centers. This merely assumes that, despite the pitching or bouncing motions of the car, the wheels proceed along the road at a steady speed. It makes a small difference. For instance, suppose a complete car is swung, the height of the CG is known, and the moment of inertia about this CG is found. This is the moment of inertia of the total mass m about the total CG, which is CG_T.

The first correction is that the front and rear unsprung masses m_{uF} and m_{uR} have a CG marked CG_u, from which by straight-line relationship the sprung CG (labeled CG_s) can be drawn; see Figure 5.18.

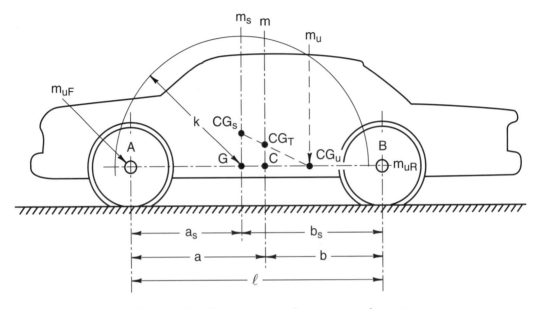

Figure 5.18 *Corrections to the moment of inertia.*

Then the moment of inertia already found must be reduced by deducting

$$m_{uF}\left(\left|\overline{AC}\right|^2 + \left|\overline{C(CG_T)}\right|^2\right) \quad \text{and} \quad m_{uR}\left(\left|\overline{BC}\right|^2 + \left|\overline{C(CG_T)}\right|^2\right).$$

This gives the moment of inertia of the **sprung mass** m_s about CG_T. From this we must deduct $m_s\left|\overline{(CG_T)(CG_s)}\right|^2$ to get the moment of inertia of the sprung mass about its own CG (point CG_s). And then, if we are to adopt the plane of the wheel centers as the reference plane, we must add $m_s\left|\overline{(CG_s)G}\right|^2$ to give the moment of inertia about G.

At the same time the **ab** quantity has also changed to $a_s \times b_s$. The total change is not great, but is worth making. For instance, a ratio of $k^2/ab = 0.622$ about CG_s may become 0.654 about G. The use of the original k^2/ab of the car as a whole, direct from the swing test, can lead to considerable errors.

And it is assumed hereafter that the oscillation centers are also in the plane of the wheel centers, i.e., in plane of $\overline{AB}$.

It may be well to repeat the statement that, although the study of two degrees of freedom has some bearing on the actual ride motions of a car or truck, it has important limitations. These are:

1. The motions are actually damped by what is usually close to 25 percent critical damping.

2. The actual ride motion is a damped motion between sprung and unsprung masses in series with a limited undamped motion between the unsprung masses and the road. Thus there are two degrees of freedom (damped) between the sprung mass and the wheels, and another two degrees of freedom (undamped) between the complete car and the road.

3. Roll of the car has been ignored, and can occur also between the rolling mass and the suspension, or between the unsprung masses and the road. **And one of the essentials of riding comfort is that the frequency of roll should be of the same order as the frequencies of pitch and bounce**.

4. IFS, if the linkage supporting the front wheels is regarded as rigid, has only one mode of wheel hop. But each front wheel has three significant rotary motions as well as wheel hop.

5. And a rear axle has six degrees of freedom: hop, lateral vibration, fore-and-aft shake, tramp, yaw, and "tilt," all of which are important, and can spoil the ride.

6. Wheel hop motions are sufficiently different in frequency from the main ride motions, so that normally the two types may be considered as "uncoupled." But there are exceptions, such as can occur in the ride of the rear end of an unladen truck, and in the "beats" in car ride occurring on severe washboard roads.

The actual ride is a much more complicated affair than can be simulated by systems of even seven or nine degrees of freedom.

5.11 Additional Material on the Two-Degree-of-Freedom Ride Model

*In Sections 5.7–5.10, Olley has summarized the published analysis by H.S. Rowell and J. Guest on the pitch and bounce motions of the **undamped** sprung mass of an automobile. Rowell's work was presented in 1923 while Guest's paper, entitled "The Main Free Vibrations of an Autocar," followed in 1928. Rowell attended Guest's presentation and actually opened the discussion that followed. Characteristic of the Institution of Automobile Engineers, the discussion was published as well as the paper. In the discussion, Rowell arrived at **Guest's conclusions** in a **more physically understandable way**.*

In the interest of completeness, Rowell's discussion is given in full below, along with some related material on ride from Olley's correspondence with Bill Milliken.

Discussion—The Main Free Vibrations of an Autocar[39]

In my [*Rowell's*] first perusal of the paper, I had some little difficulty in getting a clear physical idea of what the author [*Guest*] has called the elastically conjugate points, and therefore worked out the problem in a different way, which I think leads to interesting results.

The first part of the problem consists in finding a system of two masses m_1 and m_2, equi-momental to the sprung part of the car. The car body is shown with its equi-momental system in Figure 5.19. The center of gravity G is distant a and b from the axle positions, and the equivalent masses m_1 and m_2 are distance a' and b', from the center of gravity G. [*Note: We are using Rowell's notation in this section only—G (not CG) = center of gravity and C (not O) = spring center.*]

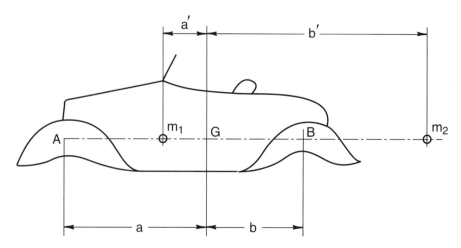

Figure 5.19 *General layout for Rowell's alternate formulation, with Rowell's notation.*

The conditions that these should be equi-momental systems are:

Equal mass or $m_1 + m_2 = m$ (1)

Common center of gravity or $m_1a' = m_2b'$ (2)

Equal moments of inertia or $m_1a'^2 + m_2b'^2 = mk^2$ (3)

where k is the radius of gyration of the car body.

---

[39] Guest, James, "The Main Free Vibrations of an Autocar," Institution of Automobile Engineers, Transactions, London, 1928. *Note: Reproduced here is Rowell's discussion of Guest's paper.*

From these three equations we can eliminate m_1, m_2 and m and so obtain the relation,

$$a'b' = k^2 \tag{4}$$

which is the condition governing the position of the equivalent masses.

The next part of the problem is to find an elastic system which is equipollent or equivalent to the springs at the axles. Suppose we have two springs of stiffnesses K_F and K_R distant a + b, the wheelbase apart, and distant p and q from the spring center C, as in Figure 5.20. The problem is to find two springs of stiffness K_1 and K_2 at distances p' and q' from C, respectively. The three conditions for equivalence of the two spring systems are as follows:

The sums of the stiffnesses must be equal,

$$K_1 + K_2 = K_F + K_R \tag{5}$$

The springs must have the same line of resultant action,

$$K_1 p' - K_2 q' = 0 = K_F p - K_R q \tag{6}$$

They must have the same angular stiffness,

$$K_1 p'^2 + K_2 q'^2 = K_F p^2 + K_R q^2 = K_2 q'(p' + q') \tag{7}$$

From (5) and (6), we have

$$(K_F + K_R)p' = K_2(p' + q') \tag{8}$$

and this combined with (7) gives

$$p'q' = \left(K_1 p'^2 + K_2 q'^2\right)/(K_F + K_R) = \left(K_F p^2 + K_R q^2\right)/(K_F + K_R) \tag{9}$$

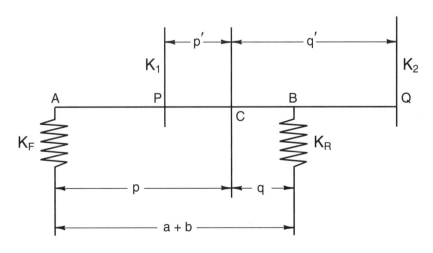

Figure 5.20 Rowell's equivalent system.

which equals h^2, say. From (5), $K_1/(K_F + K_R) + K_2/(K_F + K_R) = 1$, where $(K_F + K_R)$ is total spring stiffness. $K_1/(K_F + K_R)$ and $K_2/(K_F + K_R)$ are distributed as $q'/(p' + q')$ and $p'/(p' + q')$, respectively, thus the stiffnesses of the new springs are:

$$\left. \begin{array}{l} K_1 = (K_F + K_R)q'/(p' + q') \\ K_2 = (K_F + K_R)p'/(p' + q') \end{array} \right\} \tag{10}$$

identical in form with equations for the masses if K_1, K_2, p', q', etc. are equivalent to m_1, m_2, a', b', etc.

The next part of the problem is to place the hypothetical masses m_1 and m_2, Figure 5.19, over the fictitious springs of stiffnesses K_1 and K_2, Figure 5.20. This is simply done in Figure 5.21. Thus at the G and C, the center of gravity and the spring center, respectively, erect perpendiculars GK and CH equal [*in length*] to k and h. Bisect KH at E and draw ER at right angles to HK, cutting the car axis at R. Now with R as center, draw a semi-circle through H and K, cutting the car axis at P and Q. Then P and Q are the points of simple harmonic motion. This follows from the geometry of the circle, since:

$$\left| \overline{PC} \right| \times \left| \overline{CQ} \right| = h^2 = p'q' \quad \text{and} \quad \left| \overline{PG} \right| \times \left| \overline{GQ} \right| = k^2 = a'b'$$

Thus we have fitted two equivalent masses on to two equivalent springs. Now to invert the problem into a more practical form, and assuming the hypothesis of the author [*Guest*] that simply harmonic motion is the essence of comfort—**a hypothesis to which I** [*Rowell*] **cannot subscribe**—we require to find the spring system to give a prescribed harmonic point P.

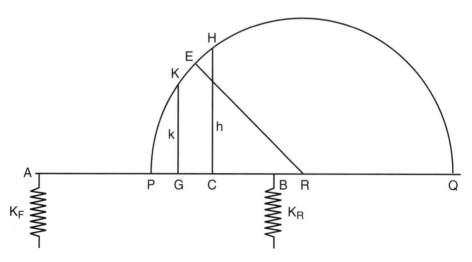

Figure 5.21 *Fitting the equivalent masses to the equivalent springs.*

Suppose in Figure 5.21 that P is decided on, and that G, the CG of the sprung mass, and GK = k (the radius of gyration) are prescribed. If a semi-circle, with center on the car axis, is drawn passing through P and K as in Figure 5.21, then from **any** point R we have the ordinate of the semi-circle CH = h, which, with one restriction, completes the solution. Thus from (6) and (9) we have:

$$K_F/K_R = q/p = \left(q^2 - h^2\right)\Big/\left(h^2 - p^2\right)$$

From (9),

$$\frac{\left(K_F p^2 + K_R q^2\right)}{\left(K_F + K_R\right)} = h^2 \tag{5.77}$$

or

$$K_F p^2 + K_R q^2 = \left(K_F + K_R\right)h^2 \tag{5.78}$$

and

$$K_R\left(q^2 - h^2\right) = K_F\left(h^2 - p^2\right) \tag{5.79}$$

Hence,

$$\frac{K_F}{K_R} = \frac{\left(q^2 - h^2\right)}{\left(h^2 - p^2\right)} \tag{5.80}$$

and from (6)

$$\frac{K_F}{K_R} = \frac{q}{p} \tag{5.81}$$

Then,

$$p\left(q^2 - h^2\right) = q\left(h^2 - p^2\right) \tag{5.82}$$

$$pq^2 - ph^2 = qh^2 - qp^2 \tag{5.83}$$

$$pq(q + p) = h^2(q + p) \tag{5.84}$$

and

$$pq = h^2 .$$

From this we proceed at once to the construction of Figure 5.22. On the wheelbase AB as diameter we draw the dotted semi-circle which intersects the semi-circle on PQ in the point H. Drop the perpendicular HC and the point C defines the spring center and the ratio of the spring stiffnesses.

I may add that the problems in practice are burdened by many complex factors, including the salesman and the customer, and they are always more difficult than the merely mathematical problems.

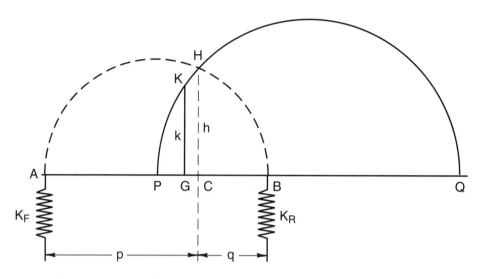

Figure 5.22 *Rowell's definition of the spring center and stiffnesses.*

By using this algebraic method we may quickly find the periods in terms which give a more realistic physical impression than Guest's equations. Clearly, the periods in terms of the new system of masses and springs are:

$$T_1 = 2\pi\sqrt{m_1/K_1} \quad \text{and} \quad T_2 = 2\pi\sqrt{m_2/K_2} \tag{11}$$

If we substitute for m_1 and m_2 in terms of m, e.g., $m_1 = mb'/(a'+b')$, and, observing that $a'+b' = p'+q'$, substituting for K_1 and K_2 the values in Equations (10), we have:

$$\left.\begin{aligned} T_1 &= 2\pi\sqrt{b'm/q'(K_F + K_R)} \\ T_2 &= 2\pi\sqrt{a'm/p'(K_F + K_R)} \end{aligned}\right\} \tag{12}$$

These equations, written in geometrical form, become:

$$\left.\begin{aligned} T_1 &= 2\pi\sqrt{m\left|\overline{GQ}\right|/\left|\overline{CQ}\right|(K_F + K_R)} \\ T_2 &= 2\pi\sqrt{m\left|\overline{PG}\right|/\left|\overline{PC}\right|(K_F + K_R)} \end{aligned}\right\} \tag{13}$$

The physical significance is very clear. The total mass is concentrated in a point at G and swinging on a weightless arm about Q or P. The resultant stiffness $K_F + K_R$ acts on the arm at C, with leverage CQ or PC according to the mode. In these equations the gravitational g is omitted, so that the masses are in slugs.

There are two other points that I should like briefly to mention. The author [*Guest*] has laid some little stress on the view that the two modes about P and Q are truly fundamental, and to that I [*Rowell*] should like to raise an objection. In the generalized coordinates of Lagrange the motions are expressed in terms of the coordinates chosen. By a transformation these coordinates can be changed so that the motions are expressed simply in harmonic motions. These are called the normal coordinates, and the author, by most ingenious processes, has given us the normal coordinates. In my work on this subject I have used various coordinates, sometimes the position of the center of gravity with rotations about that point, sometimes the spring deflections at the axles, and so on. The resultant expressions have various advantages in different applications, but the motion is always the same, and it seems to me that, while the author is obviously clear about the matter, it might mislead younger students to describe certain motions as fundamental.

The magnitude and effects of solid friction [*discussed by Guest*] are, in my opinion, very unduly minimized. During the last three or four years we [*Rowell and associates*] have done a good deal of work on spring friction [*leaf springs*], and we find that in most springs solid friction is hundreds of times greater than fluid friction. The proof of this is derived from damping curves where the crests lie with great accuracy on straight lines, as will be shown in my own paper.

[*End of Rowell comments.*]

Letter of July 16, 1959, Maurice Olley to Bill Milliken on Ride Comfort

On the subject of ride I am inconsistent in my notes, showing that I don't really understand.

I say, in one place:

> The pitch and bounce frequencies should be reasonably close together with a ratio of pitch to bounce frequency not exceeding 1.25.

But the two frequencies should not be equal. Equal frequencies can be obtained only by satisfying two requirements, k^2/ab ratio equal to unity, and equal effective deflection in front and rear suspensions. This provides theoretically only one frequency of simple harmonic motion in the vehicle. But there is no characteristic ride pattern in the vehicle and no fixed oscillation centers.

We produced this characteristic in the vehicle of 1932 known as the "k^2 rig," and dismissed it immediately as providing a **quality** of ride which was intolerably vague and "sloppy."

However, in some notes of March/57 I have a rather different idea:

> Looking once more at the use of extremely soft front springs, it will be seen that, if this front suspension has some damping so that it has little tendency to oscillate,

there will be practically only one frequency in the ride of the vehicle which will be simple harmonic motion about the forward oscillation center, which is virtually the forward center of percussion of the vehicle. Not only this, but, as the vehicle is driven forward, impulses under the front wheels will set up a slow vertical oscillation, which is immediately thereafter caught up by the faster motion of the rear suspension.

Thus no rapid pitching action or interference kicks can occur, and the vehicle is said to "ride flat."

The first statement would suggest, say, a rear [*static*] deflection of 5 inches and a front [*static*] deflection of 7.5 inches, or perhaps 6 inches rear and 8 inches front. The second would encourage, say, 6 inches rear and 11 inches or 12 inches in front, which is more like present American large cars. With air springing we can get the equivalent effective deflection of, say, 10 inches rear and 20 inches or 25 inches front.

I think the solution is that for a "flat ride" at, say, 40 mph you use a front end much softer that the rear, for a flat ride at 100 mph you use almost equal front and rear deflections.

But when you go to the limit on suspension softness in general, as for example the Citroën DS19, the usual standards of proportion between front and rear deflection no longer apply, because, with only enough damping to suppress wheel hop, you have critical damping of the ride motions, and **there are no longer any frequencies**.

As to the current objections to Rowell and Guest, that they only consider two degrees of freedom and undamped ride, it is to be stated that "ride experts" agree that the best way to work out a ride on a new model is to ride it first without shock absorbers, and develop a good action by changing spring rates, adding necessary damping only after the general ride action is satisfactory, and sparingly, since all damping harshens the ride.

As regards the modernized version of the k^2 rig, perhaps the ideal would be a vehicle with not only adjustable spring rates, but also adjustable degrees of Packard-type "compensation." What this amounts to is a means of reducing "$a \times b$" in pitch, or of greatly increasing the k^2/ab ratio, without using cast-iron bob weights as we did on the k^2 rig.

Letter of July 4, 1964, Maurice Olley to Bill Milliken on Research and Design

But I am certainly with you in the general approach, i.e., that having a general idea based on a reasonable theory, the only thing to do is to build something and see! About the only thing I ever did of any value was to build the k^2 rig on a standard 1931 Cadillac V12 7-passenger limousine. The reason for the limousine was the normally atrocious ride of the rear seat, which was behind the rear axle. The theory was that with equal spring deflection front and rear, and $k^2 = ab$, there would be only one natural ride frequency (pitch = bounce) so there would be no "beat-kick" to throw you out of the rear seat, such as always occurred when pitch frequency was 40% to 50% higher than bounce.

*Maurice Olley riding, in the 1930s. Photo credit Kettering/GMI Alumni
Foundation, Collection of Industrial History.*

We were able to show quite quickly and unquestionably that our theory was wrong. With
$k^2/ab = 1$ and equal deflections there was only one ride frequency, but at the same time
there were no definite oscillation centers. The "action" of the car on the road was unpre-
dictable. **It felt like riding a horse with no definite "gait."** So we got the idea that a
"good ride" was not the **absence** of something, such as vertical accelerations above a certain value, but was some sort of definite pattern of vertical motions, like the action of a
horse.

It was a simple step, by a certain amount of intelligent fiddling, to find the thing we should
have anticipated, that by shifting weights forward, and they making the front deflection
greater than the rear, we got a "flat" action, even with k^2/ab as low as 0.8.

If we'd had a little more knowledge and better instrumentation, we could have found out
a lot more than we did, for instance about the effects on handling of the horizontal k^2/ab
ratio. **Still we found enough to set the pattern for American passenger car suspension. IFS grew out of it as a practical way of getting a soft front suspension**.

Letter of May 15, 1957, Maurice Olley to Bill Milliken on Suspension

In this letter Olley reiterates some of the conclusions from Rowell and Guest and then goes on to discuss the possibilities of obtaining a really soft suspension by air springing. This is followed by a brief discussion of abandoning springs and controlling the load between the tires and the ground by servoed oil cylinders, predicting the control of both sprung and unsprung masses. This was eventually proven by the Lotus fully-active system using hydraulic cylinders and Moog valves, implemented in the early 1980s.

Air Springing

The other way to get a soft suspension is by air springing.

V = any volume

V_0 = atmospheric volume V_n = normal volume

p = any absolute pressure

p_0 = atmospheric pressure p_n = normalized absolute pressure

k = adiabatic index (say, 1.38)

F = load F_n = normal load

$\dot{F}$ = rate $\dot{F}_n$ = normal rate

d_n = normal effective deflection A = piston area

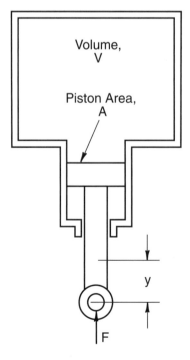

Figure 5.23 Generalized air spring.

Then
$$F = A(p - p_0) \tag{5.85}$$

$$F_n = A(p_n - p_0) \tag{5.86}$$

But $p = p_n(V_n/V)^k$ and $p_n = p_0 V_0/V_n$ (isothermal)

So,
$$F = A p_0 \left(\frac{V_0 V_n^{k-1}}{V^k} - 1 \right) \tag{5.87}$$

$$F_n = A p_0 \left(\frac{V_0}{V_n} - 1 \right) \tag{5.88}$$

$$\dot{F} = kA^2 p_0 V_0 \frac{V_n^{k-1}}{V^{k+1}} \tag{5.89}$$

$$\dot{F}_n = kA^2 p_0 \frac{V_0}{V_n^2} \tag{5.90}$$

$$d_n = \frac{V_n}{kA} \left(1 - \frac{V_n}{V_0} \right) \tag{5.91}$$

If V_n/V_0 is small, i.e., pressures are high, then d_n is approximately 7/10 of the height of a uniform column of air necessary to carry the load at the rate desired.

Now if we want to carry, say, 800 pounds with 50 inches deflection, we shall be wise first to use a 2/1 leverage and so carry a 1600 pound load at 25 inches deflection at the actual air cylinder. Suppose we use a piston of 2 in.^{2} area. Then we need 800 psi gauge pressure to carry the load.

So,
$$\frac{V_0}{V_n} = \frac{p_n}{p_0} = \frac{814.7}{14.7} = 55.5$$

$$\frac{V_n}{V_0} = 0.018$$

$$d_n = \frac{V_n}{2.76} \times 0.982 = 25 \text{ in.}$$

$$V_n = \frac{25 \times 2.76}{0.982} = \textbf{70 in.}^3$$

By simply using a reservoir of 70 in.[3] which is only say 5 in. diameter by 3-5/8 in. long, and pumping air to 800 psi, with a lever ratio of 2 to 1, we have achieved a suspension of 50 in. effective deflection, with a "spring" represented by 2.25 cubic feet of atmospheric air weighing less than 3 **ounces**.

Not only this but, despite the excessively low rate, the standing height of the vehicle can be maintained **constant**.

This looks like such an enormous advantage that the future of air springing is inevitable. This isn't the whole advantage. Notice from Equation 5.91 that if we keep V_n constant for all loads, i.e., if we pump **air**, the effective deflection d_n remains virtually constant for all loads. So the car rides practically the same at all loads.

But this may not be the ultimate in ride. Why ride on springs at all? Springs were an invention of the 17th century, which have served us well, but we may be able to do better. Instead of maintaining a constant mean lever between vehicle and ground, why not maintain a constant mean **load** between tires and ground? By modern methods of controlling the pressure in an oil cylinder, it should be possible to control both the unsprung masses and the vertical motion of the car in such a way as to virtually ignore the road surface.

What we can say is that by developing air springing we are probably approaching this condition in a logical way.

After all we mustn't forget that if a car with 6 in. bump clearance meets a 7 in. bump it must have **something** to lift it over the bump. And if it meets an upgrade is must have some thing to point it up the grade, without burying its nose on the road surface.

One thing certain. We have to start thinking about suspensions as never before.

5.12 Unsprung Weight

There is a tradition in the industry that the reduction of unsprung weight (or rather unsprung mass) improves ride. And that IFS is an example of this principle. We are told, for example, that moving brake drums inboard will improve ride by decreasing unsprung mass.

The tradition requires examination. It is evident that the so-called unsprung mass is the anvil against which the tires do their work of cushioning road bumps, so that reducing this mass allows more of the disturbance due to road roughness to pass through to the suspension.

But the "unsprung mass" is actually sprung, between the road spring above and the tire below it. So it can set up some formidable oscillations between these two springs, which have to be controlled by the shock absorbers mounted between the unsprung mass and the body. Increasing the unsprung mass demands more work from the shock absorbers, which may cause more shake of the frame and body. However, reducing the unsprung mass increases the frequency of wheel hop, and higher frequencies are more difficult to restrain by shock absorbers (because of oil foaming, elasticity of the mounts, etc.) And human tolerance of vibrations decreases rapidly as frequencies increase. All of which suggests that, although with excessive unsprung mass we should be in trouble, with too little unsprung mass we might well be in worse trouble.

Evidently, however, the usefulness of the unsprung mass as an "anvil" depends, for a given tire section, on the **absolute** mass, whereas the difficulty of controlling it depends on the **relative** values of the unsprung mass and the sprung mass above it.

For example, the large axle masses of a truck feel road irregularities less than the smaller unsprung masses of a passenger car. Yet the large unsprung masses of the truck, especially if the truck is unladen, can cause much more disturbance to the ride, and can severely damage not only the truck itself but the road surface.

This gives us an idea of the true function of unsprung mass. The mass, by making the tires work, actually improves ride, but it is important that it should not be too large in proportion to the sprung mass above it. There will be little change in ride whether the unsprung is, say, one-fifth or one-seventh of the sprung mass; but, when, as in the case of an unladen truck or a "bob-tailed" tractor, the axle mass is almost equal to the sprung mass riding on it, the problem of riding comfort is practically insoluble.

A further aspect of the problem refers to the **shape** of the unsprung mass. With any form of independent suspension the unsprung mass can be regarded as a concentrated mass. But with an axle this is not so. We are concerned with its moment of inertia in tramping motion. For example, in a truck rear axle, the great mass of the drive gears, concentrated near its center, results in **reducing** its radius of gyration. Consequently an upward impulse under one rear wheel will cause a downward impulse on the other. And this increases the tendency of the axle to tramp.

The De Dion axle, and particularly the De Dion axle with brake drums in the wheels, has a greater radius of gyration, and therefore noticeably less tendency to tramp. [*Tramp and other unsprung oscillations are discussed in Chapter 6.*]

5.13 Independent Suspension

Reduction of unsprung mass is frequently claimed as a principal advantage of independent suspension, front or rear. This is not necessarily so.

Independent suspension has two characteristics:

1. Two opposite wheels are not directly connected.
2. Each wheel travels up and down in a prescribed path.

Any rubber-tired wheel rolling over road irregularities is continually changing its rotary speed as well as developing lateral forces from slip angles and camber angles between tire and road. If two such wheels are connected by an axle, some oscillation, in the form of tramp, shimmy, wheelfight, etc. is almost bound to occur.

Independent suspension consists simply of disconnecting the wheels from each other and instead connecting each of them with the sprung mass of the car. This mass then acts as a barrier to prevent the oscillation of one wheel from affecting the other. The effectiveness of this barrier depends on the inertia of the sprung mass relative to the wheel inertia.

The front wheels, mounted on kingpins, introduce a second degree of freedom, especially because the whole steering linkage is flexible. Immediately this introduces caster wobble, which is simply a rotary oscillation of each wheel about its kingpin, as observed on all castered wheels. Caster wobble depends for its self-sustaining quality on a certain lateral flexibility or slack in the pivot mounting.

The steering linkage plays only a secondary part, as is shown by the fact that wobble occurs (at a lower frequency) even with the linkage disconnected. Since it can occur on individual wheels, IFS [*independent front suspension*] has no effect on caster wobble. In general on passenger cars the energy in caster wobble is small, and it can be damped out by a small increase in kingpin friction or by decreased caster, without loss of directional "feel."

Associated with caster wobble, but containing much greater energy, is the true **shimmy**, as seen on front axles. It is this shimmy cycle which IFS is designed to eliminate.

The shimmy cycle is associated with tramping of the two front wheels. Each wheel meets the ground toed-in. The resulting outward swerve is due to caster offset and tire aligning torque. The gyroscopic reaction from this forced swerve of both the front wheels occurs in a transverse vertical plane. And its direction is such that, if the two wheels are on either end of an axle, the lower wheel will be lifted and the upper will be slammed down on the ground. This wheel meets the ground toed-in, and the action is repeated.

The cycle is self-sustaining on a smooth, dry road, although it may have been started by a road bump. On a wet road shimmy will not occur. Also, if a steering connection to **one** front wheel is removed, shimmy will not occur.

There is the question of what constitutes independence of a pair of wheels. For example, consider the front swing axle on the Allard car. This is a true independent and, with a stiff body structure, shimmy will not occur. Because the front axle is broken and pivoted in the middle, the gyroscopic kick from one front wheel is not transmitted to the opposite wheel.

However, the forced camber change in the wheels as they move up and down makes for gyroscopic reactions liable to promote wheelfight on rough roads.

Another variation of independent suspension is the Mercedes single-joint swing axle, having the drive gear and differential mounted on the left hand swing arm. In contrast to the usual rear independent, or the De Dion axle, this independent supports the engine drive torque by unequal loading of the two rear wheels, exactly as in the case of the conventional rear axle. Also, this input torque tends to lift the rear of the car and so resists the conventional squat-back in acceleration. Yet the two rear wheels move up and down independently in prescribed paths, so the single-joint swing axle has the quality of an independent suspension.

Summarizing on independent suspension:

Reduction of unsprung mass is not a necessary feature of independent suspension, nor a necessary prescription for improved ride.

The improved ride of a De Dion axle is due, not to reduction of unsprung mass, but rather to increase in radius of gyration.

The necessary characteristics of independent suspension are:

Two opposite wheels are not directly connected.

Each wheel travels up and down in a prescribed path relative to the median plane of the car.

5.14 Multiple Suspension

Multiple spring suspension has little application to passenger cars, but more to certain military vehicles, armored cars, tanks, trucks, and certain special buses. The matter of interest is that increasing the number of pairs of supporting springs decreases the pitch stability of the vehicle.

The pitch stability is the restoring couple for a given angle of pitch. Evidently, for example, a six-spring suspension as shown in Figure 5.24 has only two-thirds the pitch stability of a four-spring suspension of the same wheelbase. Improved ride sometimes noted on such vehicles is largely due to the consequent reduction in pitch frequency.

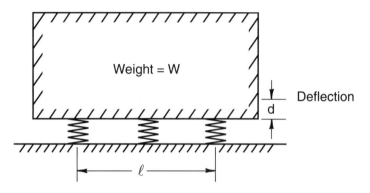

Figure 5.24 *Multiple suspension.*

The full expression for the pitch-stability of such vehicles, when springs are of equal rate and evenly spaced, is:

$$\text{Pitch stability} = \frac{W\ell^2(n+1)}{12d(n-1)} \qquad (5.92)$$

where n = number of spring pairs, d = spring deflection.

n	2	3	4	5	...	∞
Pitch stability	$\dfrac{W\ell^2}{4d}$	$\dfrac{W\ell^2}{6d}$	$\dfrac{5W\ell^2}{36d}$	$\dfrac{W\ell^2}{8d}$	...	$\dfrac{W\ell^2}{12d}$ *
Compared with four springs	1	2/3	5/9	1/2	...	1/3

*The last figure is the stability of a plank floating in water.

The ride of a "compensated" suspension, such as the Packard or 2CV Citroën, depends on the same principle of slowing down the pitch frequency by reducing the pitch stability.

5.15 Summary

Primary ride is a major component of passenger comfort. Olley begins with a thorough discussion of the quarter car (one wheel) case. He then reviews and discusses the merits (and limitations) of the simple Guest two-degree-of-freedom model.

This model yields two resonant frequencies, one which is primarily in pitch (with the oscillation center within the wheelbase) and one which is primarily in bounce (with the oscillation center outside the wheelbase). Because it is a coupled system, neither mode is pure, thus Anthony Best in his discussion of mode centers[40] characterizes the pitch mode as "bouncy pitch" and the bounce mode as "pitchy bounce." If the pitch center were at the center of gravity and the bounce center at infinity, pure pitch and pure bounce modes would result.

While we believe that Guest's mathematical development as presented by Olley is correct, we do not find it easy to get a physical understanding from it. Rowell's discussion in Section 5.11, and his summary at the end, are more satisfying in this respect. Neither Guest nor Rowell include the effects of damping.

About ten years after the Guest and Rowell work, Olley's group developed the "k^2 rig," which, for the first time, simplified subjective testing with different pitch and bounce frequencies. The k^2 rig work led to rules of thumb for designing vehicles with good primary ride characteristics, such as "flat ride." The requirement for a low natural frequency on the front of the car led to the adoption of independent front suspension at Cadillac which was widely copied. The effects of various road disturbances, speed and dampers have been studied since.[41] As speed increases, the bounce mode response increases and, as would be expected, the pitch mode response falls off.

Olley maintained an interest in ride, and in various letters he points out that coil or torsion springs are not the only way to provide a vertical spring rate—foreseeing the invention of active suspension some thirty years before its introduction.

---

[40] Milliken, W. F. and D. L. Milliken, *Race Car Vehicle Dynamics*, R-146, Society of Automotive Engineers, Warrendale, Pa., 1995, p. 795.

[41] Schilling, R. and H. Fuchs, "Modern Passenger-Car Ride Characteristics," presented at the American Society of Mechanical Engineers, New York, 1940.

CHAPTER 6

Oscillations of the Unsprung

"The trouble with these oscillations is that there are so many of them."

Maurice Olley, 1962

6.1 Introduction

As noted in the quote above, a large number of oscillation modes of axle and independent suspensions have been encountered in the history of automobile engineering. In addition to those that Olley treats in his monographs, Robert Schilling discusses some rear suspension oscillations in his "Handling Factors" report of 1938 (internal GM report). In the interest of completeness, the authors have added this material.

Olley introduces this chapter as follows:

Any axle has six degrees of freedom, namely:

Linear	Rotary
Parallel hop	Tramp
Lateral shake	Yaw
Fore and aft shake	Nod or wind-up

Some of the vibrations in these six modes can become coupled in such a way that one may feed energy into another. They can be variously excited, chiefly by the road through the tires, but also by brakes or engine torque. There is a remarkable uniformity in frequency, most of the troublesome variations occurring between 8 Hz and, say, 15 Hz.

Thus any **axle**, front or rear, opens the door to a whole family of potentially troublesome vibrations.

Independently mounted wheels have a fundamental advantage, since, in theory at least, they have only one degree of freedom and one resonant frequency. In practice they are not as good as this, since it is becoming increasingly necessary in an independent suspension to avoid a too-rigid restriction of the wheel motion to the one prescribed path. Thus further degrees of freedom are introduced, which may on occasion become troublesome.

Of the various forms of oscillation, only two are indefinitely self-sustaining on a smooth road. These are shimmy and caster wobble.

6.2 Shimmy Dynamics and Its Cures

The most dangerous form of unsprung oscillation was an old-fashioned classic "shimmy," occurring with a front axle. With the increased polar moment due to front brakes, and the use of "balloon" tires in the 1920s, shimmy became a major problem. On a smooth road, due to encountering one chance bump or pothole, or a side contact with a streetcar track, or simply due to wheel unbalance, the shimmy cycle might start without warning. This happened only at high speed, generally over 60 mph. It could shake the driver's hands off the steering wheel, or break the steering spindle or Pitman arm. It could also blow a tire, or tear a tire off its rim.

If the driver slowed down by applying brakes the immediate effect was to slow the frequency and increase the amplitude of the shimmy. The car became completely out of control. The only safe way of stopping was to use the rear brakes only [*impossible with four-wheel brakes*].

Visible black tracks were left on the road where the tread rubber had been torn off. By measuring these it was possible to figure the forces involved. For example, as shown in Figure 6.1, the vehicle was traveling 60 mph with tires rotating 620 rpm or 65 rad./sec. The tracks showed the wheel swerving outward through 10 degrees in 3 feet. The polar moment of wheel and brake drum of those days was high, approximately 2.75 slug-ft.^{2} When in the position shown in Figure 6.1 the gyroscopic torque on the front axle, trying to force the left front wheel downward would be 1830 lb.-ft. If the wheel track were 56 in., this would be equivalent to 393 lb. downward force on the left front wheel, upward on the right front wheel.

The outward swerve was evidently caused by the aligning torque at the tires, supplemented by the horizontal inertia forces at the wheel spindle due to the changes in wheel speed. Lateral oscillation of the axle and the front of the car also occurred.

As early as 1925, by work on smooth chassis rolls with shimmy excited by wheel unbalance, Rolls-Royce established the fundamental characteristics of the shimmy-cycle.

1. The energy comes from the tire contact. Wetting the rolls stopped the shimmy instantly. Lifting front of car stopped the shimmy.

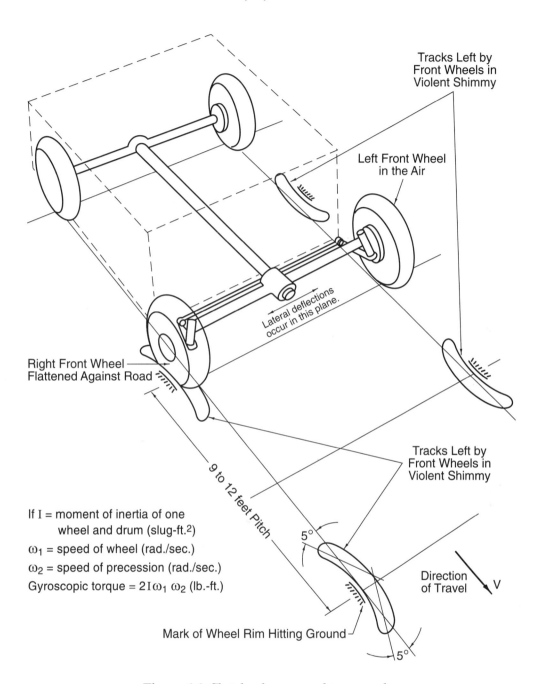

Tracks Left by
Front Wheels in
Violent Shimmy

Left Front Wheel
in the Air

Lateral deflections
occur in this plane.

Right Front Wheel
Flattened Against Road

Tracks Left by
Front Wheels in
Violent Shimmy

9 to 12 feet Pitch

If I = moment of inertia of one
wheel and drum (slug-ft.^{2})

ω_1 = speed of wheel (rad./sec.)

ω_2 = speed of precession (rad./sec.)

Gyroscopic torque = $2I\omega_1 \omega_2$ (lb.-ft.)

5°

Direction
of Travel   V

Mark of Wheel Rim Hitting Ground

5°

Figure 6.1 *Sketch of a severe shimmy cycle.*

2. One wheel alone cannot sustain shimmy. Wetting **one** drum stopped the cycle. (In this it differs completely from caster wobble.)

3. Unless the wheels turn about the kingpins together the shimmy cannot occur. Dropping [*removing*] the steering tie rod stopped the cycle. (Again this differs from caster wobble.)

4. Each wheel meets the ground toed-in, and is swerved outward by the tire contact.

5. Increasing the toe-in setting of the wheels increases shimmy excitation.

It has further been shown that increasing the aligning torque by reducing tire inflation also increases the violence of shimmy.

A real "detonation" of front wheel shimmy is seldom seen nowadays except on truck front axles. Yet, as will be shown later, the shimmy cycle is not completely cured. It still demands attention. There was often considerable doubt about what had detonated a shimmy. A driver might go for a year without a recognizable shimmy, and then have the cycle occur suddenly for no apparent cause.

Unbalance in the front wheels was only one possible cause. If both front wheels were deliberately unbalanced the shimmy tendency could be felt to increase and decrease as the two unbalances crept into opposition or back to parallel. Or one might change the relative unbalance positions by turning a street corner and find the car suddenly break into a violent shimmy. Shimmy would not occur on rough roads, but a single isolated pothole or bump in a smooth, dry road, or a glancing encounter with a raised streetcar track at considerable speed could produce a shimmy condition which only a skilled driver could handle.

An excellent way of inducing shimmy for purposes of study was on smooth chassis rolls with a considerable unbalance (say, 1/2 lb.) on each wheel rim. The relative locations of the two unbalance weights would slowly change while running, due to differences in rolling radius of the two tires. Hubcaps were removed and a white spot was placed on the end of each wheel spindle. If the room lighting were left on, the path of the spindle end was then shown as a blurred oval. At the same time, if a bright "Strobotac" light were timed somewhat **slower** than the wheel rotation speed, the white spot was seen to proceed around its oval path in the direction in which the wheel was rotating. Then what occurs is as shown in Figure 6.2 for the left front wheel.

As the unbalance weights approach 180° apart, the spindle end starts to loop (as shown in sketch A in the figure) showing the wobble "leading" the tramping motion of the axle.

The shimmy reaches a maximum vertical amplitude with a symmetrical vertical loop like Figure 6.2B, with the wobble leading the tramp by 90° of phase angle. This loop, as observed on chassis rolls, may be 3 in. high and 2 in. wide, which, at approximately 10 cycles per second, represents a considerable disturbance. It indicates a tramp of about 3 degrees, and a wobble of about 8 degrees either side of center. Observations of shimmy tracks on the road have on occasion shown greater amplitudes than this. [*Figure 6.2C shows the motion when the shimmy is dying out.*]

The question that arises is why the symmetrical motion, corresponding to **equal** toe-in and toe-out angles for the tire tracks in Figure 6.1, should represent apparently **maximum**

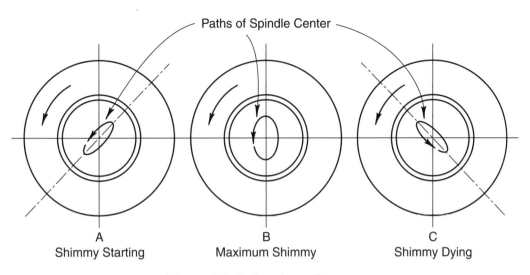

Figure 6.2 *Paths of spindle center.*

excitation of shimmy. The explanation appears to be in the "lag" in the development of full steady-state lateral force, after a slip angle occurs.

When the tire is given a small slip angle α, it has to roll approximately 2 feet before the full lateral deflection d of the tire contact patch (in Figure 6.3), corresponding to the (approximate) full steady-state lateral force, takes place. [*This distance is termed the relaxation length of the tire*]. The growth of lateral force is actually an exponential curve somewhat as sketched.

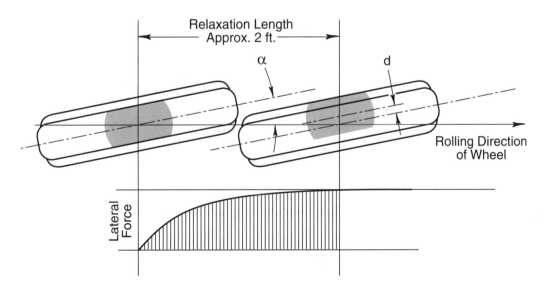

Figure 6.3 *Build-up of lateral force (relaxation length).*

The effect of this lag on a wobbling wheel in which the slip angle is changing sinusoidally is shown in Figures 6.4 and 6.5. If a wheel on a smooth chassis roll is wobbled mechanically, with means for recording lateral force and angle, the record is roughly elliptical as shown in Figure 6.4. In terms of aligning torque vs. wheel wobble, this will be like Figure 6.5, with the torque in either direction leading the angle by something more than 90°.

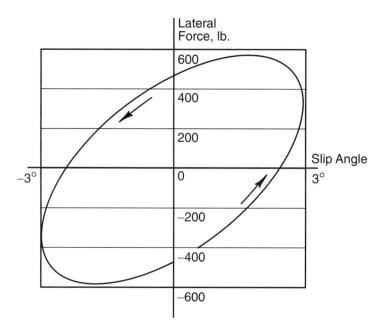

Figure 6.4 *Lateral force vs. slip angle on a wobbling wheel.*

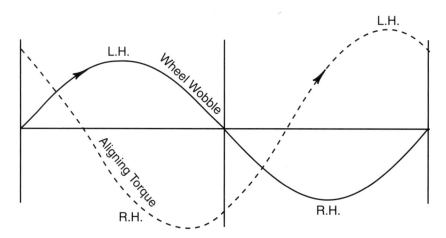

The aligning torque leads the wheel wobble by a considerable phase angle and feeds energy into the wobble motion.

Figure 6.5 *Aligning torque and wheel wobble vs. time.*

In treatments of nose-wheel "shimmy" on airplanes it is sometimes assumed that lateral slack or flexibility in the pivot mounting is necessary for the feed-in of energy. This seems an unnecessary assumption since, as shown above, the lateral flexibility of the tire casing itself will account for the wobble.

In the case of a true shimmy where the axle is tramping, and at least half of the wheel wobble is taking place out of contact with the ground, it seems clear that a symmetrical loop at the end of the wheel spindle like the middle sketch on Figure 6.2 will produce vigorous torques tending to swerve the wheels outward.

A plot of lateral force vs. slip angle on a wobbling wheel (Figure 6.4) will record an elliptical curve, due to the "lag" in the development of lateral force at any given slip angle. The aligning torque will follow the slip angle. Hence we can draw a diagram of aligning torque and wheel wobble, as Figure 6.5. [*A distance diagram is given in Figure 6.6; this is another way of looking at the same data.*]

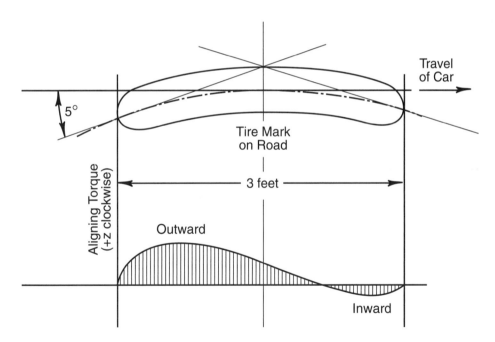

Figure 6.6 *Aligning torque plotted against distance along a tire mark on the road.*

Wheel unbalance is only one of the possible "detonators" of shimmy. A single bump or hollow in a smooth, dry road will start it, or a sudden brake application at a point where there happens to be a bump or road wave. The shimmy cycle when it builds up is the same in all cases. Many "cures" have been tried.

Center-Point Steering

This is definitely **not** a cure, since the forces delivered to the suspension mechanism by a free-running wheel are delivered, not at the ground contact A, but at the wheel center O; see Figure 6.7.

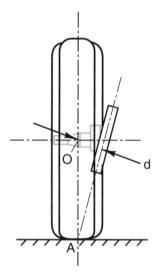

Figure 6.7 Center-point steering.

Actually, on passenger cars, a relative freedom from shimmy was frequently found when the wheel offset d was **increased**. Apparently this was due to increased damping action at the tire, due to changes in wheel speed.

Kingpin in the Wheel Plane

This has been tried frequently on passenger cars and trucks in the last 35 years [*see Figure 6.8*]. It is difficult to say whether this is a success or not. When tried 30 years ago [*c. 1930*] on passenger car front axles it was disappointing. It proved capable of breaking into a shimmy without any preliminary warning. This does not seem to be true on truck axles today, where wheel plane kingpins are found to give a marked improvement.

Parking effort is increased, since the tread rubber has to be twisted, without rolling. This construction is costly, and projecting hubcaps are liable to damage.

Drag-Link Springs

Opposed springs in the drag link (Figure 6.9) gave some relief from shimmy, which appeared to be due to slowing down the natural frequency of wheel wobble. It resulted in a great loss of definition in handling.

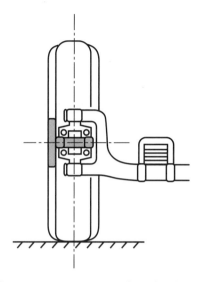

Figure 6.8 *Kingpin in the wheel plane.*

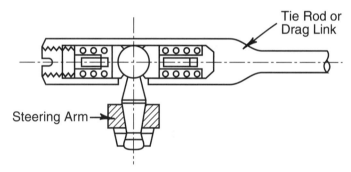

Figure 6.9 *Drag-link springs.*

Shimmy Shackle

The shimmy shackle had a similar effect to drag-link springs [*see Figure 6.10*]. Since greater masses were involved, the effective fore-and-aft flexibility could be less than in the case of the drag link. But the loss of steering definition was worse, since the whole axle could move fore and aft relative to the drag link.

Compensated Tie Rods

A suggestion made by Becker, Fromm and Maruhn[42] has been tried without success. This is shown in Figure 6.11, in one possible adaptation. This consists simply in providing two

---

[42] Becker, G., Fromm, H., and Maruhn, H., "Schwingungen in Automobillenkungen (Vibrations of the Steering Systems of Automobiles)," Krayn, Berlin, 1931.

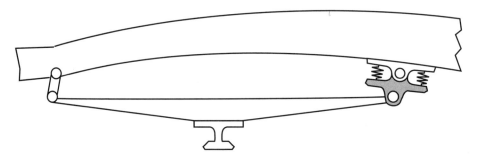

Figure 6.10 *Shimmy shackle.*

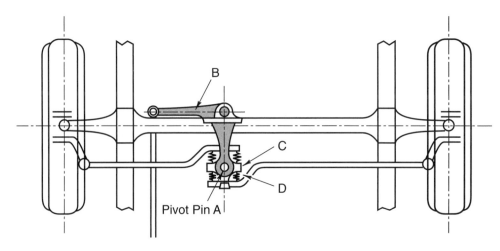

Figure 6.11 *Compensated tie rods.*

tie rods connected with a bell-crank lever **B** by means of a cross-shaped member **C**, pivoting about pin **A** on the lever. Springs **D** are inserted as shown to hold the normal toe setting. It is necessary to use wheel plane kingpins as shown, as otherwise the wheels will toe-out on the road due to their rolling resistance.

The theory is that when one wheel is forcibly swerved outward by its aligning torque, the pivot pin A will serve as a sufficiently rigid fulcrum so that the opposite wheel, instead of toeing-**in** as is usual, will also toe-out. This should make the build-up of the shimmy cycle impossible.

This has been tried, actually on a wishbone independent suspension, but not with wheel-plane kingpins. It has probably not been tried thoroughly enough to prove it out completely. Objections were that the pivot pin A proved to be far from a rigid abutment, and that shimmy, when excited by wheel imbalance, instead of being suppressed, showed some new variations. It changed from conventional shimmy to a violent wobble concentrated on one wheel, thence to the two wheels wobbling in opposite directions and so to wobble concentrated in the other wheel, and so back to the original shimmy [*a beating phenomenon with energy exchange between multiple modes*].

Practical objections are that the toe setting is very uncertain. And, on a corner, when the outer wheel feels a strong aligning torque, it tends to ease itself by increasing the slip angle of the lightly loaded inner wheel.

The "cures" for shimmy provided by devices like the shimmy shackle were all incomplete. Observation on smooth chassis rolls with wheel unbalance or on rolls with wavecams showed practically all tramping action to be accompanied by the same telltale oval loop at the end of the wheel spindle as illustrated earlier, although this was smaller and less violent than with no device. Also, peculiar "lobed" tire wear patterns showed that the shimmy cycle was still present in a reduced form.

Independent Suspension Mechanisms

The cure which can be rated as "commercially complete" is the change to independent front suspension (IFS), which suppresses shimmy by connecting the mountings of the two wheels through the entire sprung mass of the front of the car. Thus the sprung mass of the car is inserted between the two front wheel planes in such a way that the transverse gyroscopic torques of the shimmy cycle cannot produce the rapid tramp frequency of a shimmying front axle.

One can put down immediately the probable limitations on the effectiveness of independent front suspension in suppressing shimmy. For example:

1. Inertia of the sprung mass and the requirement for torsional stiffness

   The inertia of the sprung mass associated with the front wheels must be adequate to suppress shimmy. In a passenger car the only way to fulfill this requirement is to use a torsionally stiff frame-and-body assembly. Some early passenger cars with independent front suspension lacked adequate torsional stiffness. As a result these cars, although they did not break into the old fashioned shimmy, felt continually as though they were about to do so. They also wore the front tires in "lobes" just as the shimmy cycle had done.

   As a rough figure, a total torsional stiffness between the planes of the front and rear wheels of 3000 lb.-ft. per degree is found to be adequate. But, on body-frame-integral cars especially, this stiffness is often far exceeded. Eight thousand lb.-ft. per degree is not unusual and does no harm, but is an improvement as regards shake and wheelfight [*to be discussed later, Section 6.3*].

   In trucks the need for torsional stiffness is much less, apparently for two reasons. First because the moment of inertia of the cab itself is adequate to suppress shimmy, and second because the truck cab and body are separate. Relative motion between the two is not apparent to the driver.

2.   Wheel path in independent suspension

Theoretically in independent front suspension the two wheels are constrained to move up and down in planes parallel to the median plane of the car. This is so (subject to some flexibility in the wheel mounting) in such examples as the Volkswagen or the Chevrolet Dubonnet [*see Figure 3.19*]. In practically all wishbone suspensions there is some departure from parallelism. And the exact nature of this departure is of great importance to wheelfight, even though actual shimmy is avoided.

A great variety of suspension mechanisms have been used, and the fundamental differences in geometry are shown by Figures 6.12 through 6.15.

Discussion

Type 1.   **Parallel motion** (Figure 6.12) is typical of early independent front suspension designs, some of which, like the Lancia "chandelle" design, actually had the wheel support or knuckle sliding up and down on what was virtually an elongated kingpin. The Porsche design on the Volkswagen, and the Chevrolet Dubonnet designs, also have parallel motion. Most modern independent front suspension designs approach parallel motion, taking only such liberties as can be permitted without exciting wheelfight.

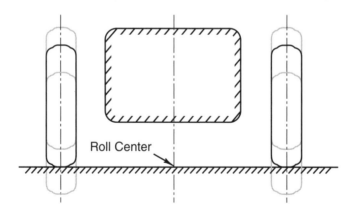

Figure 6.12 IFS with true parallel motion in ride (no track change).

Type 2.   **Parallel with track change** (Figure 6.13). This motion does not induce wheelfight. In fact the track change [*also called "tread change"*] introduces a certain amount of tire damping, effective both on ride and wheel hop [*tire damping is discussed later in this chapter*].

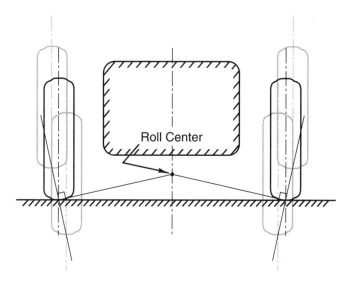

***Figure 6.13** Parallel motion with track change.*

Type 3.   **Positive swing arm** (Figure 6.14). This can be used with or without a raised roll center, since evidently the swing center O can be placed on the ground if desired. The advantage of this design is the more favorable camber position of the wheels relative to the ground on a turn. In other words the wheels do not roll quite as much as the car. On a layout the difference in camber looks small, but the handling and tire wear are extremely sensitive to such changes. The disadvantage of the design is an immediate increase in the tendency to wheelfight as the geometry is changed from parallel toward positive swing arm.

In a wishbone suspension with unequal upper and lower arms, in which consequently the effective swing arm is constantly changing, it is the effective swing arm at or near-normal design height which determines the wheelfight tendency. This tendency depends on many factors and is

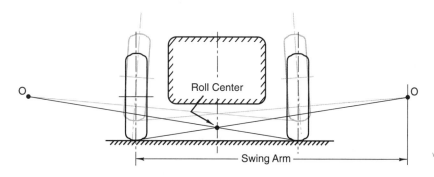

***Figure 6.14** Non-parallel motion, positive swing arm.*

extremely variable. However, if the positive swing arm at design height is much less than 100 inches wheelfight may be expected.

The extreme case of the positive swing arm is the front swing axle, as used on the Allard car. Except for a more rigid control of the up-and-down wheel motion in a fixed path, this would appear to have at least as great a tendency to wheelfight as a conventional front axle, and an equal shimmy tendency. In practice it appears to avoid actual shimmy. But it tends to lift on turns, as already noted on the rear swing axle. And this lift implies a very severe positive camber angle relative to the road on the outer tire, and hence sudden understeer and severe tire wear.

Type 4.   **Negative swing arm** (Figure 6.15) can also be arranged with various heights of swing center O, and of roll center. Or a wishbone suspension may be designed to have a negative swing arm only below design height. It is well to bear in mind that:

Negative swing arm = change toward **positive** camber as wheel rises

Positive swing arm = change toward **negative** camber as wheel rises

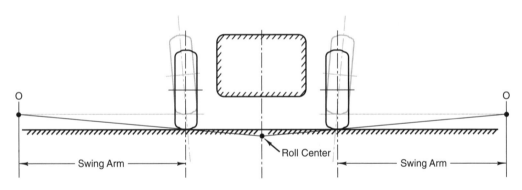

Figure 6.15 *Non-parallel motion, negative swing arm.*

The advantage of negative swing arm is a marked decrease in wheelfight. Its disadvantage is increased understeer, tire wear and tire squeal, and heavier handling.

The camber changes for various types of independent front suspensions are summarized in Figure 6.16.

3.   Steering linkage geometry in independent suspensions

Geometry of the **steering linkage** is also important in independent front suspension. Since the wheel motion is accurately controlled, the steering geometry can also be

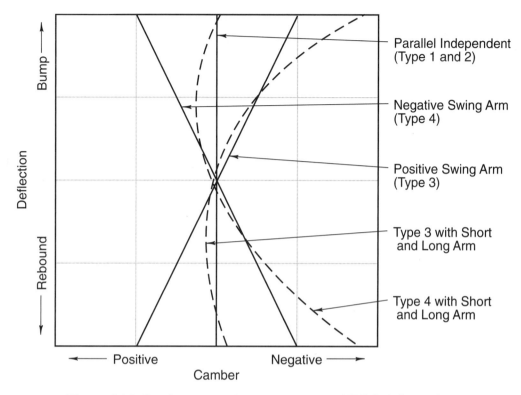

Figure 6.16 *Camber curves for various types of IFS, left front wheel.*

accurate. This is in marked contrast to conventional steering of a front axle, in which the indeterminate motion of the axle means that the steering geometry is also indeterminate.

But it was early found that theoretically "perfect" steering geometry in independent front suspension is not necessarily the best. It has been shown elsewhere that a general tendency to toe-**out** as the wheels rise may be coupled with toe-**in** above and below design height in such a way as to show advantages in wheelfight tendency and handling. [*We interpret this to mean that the first-order term is toe-out on bump, while the second-order term is toe-in on bump and toe-in on rebound.*]

6.3 Wheelfight

*In Section 6.2 Olley examined the causes and cures of shimmy, a dangerous form of unsprung oscillation and one of the **two** types which are "self-sustaining" indefinitely on a smooth road (the other is caster wobble).*

In this section, he turns to another oscillation of the unsprung called "wheelfight." Since this term is not in common use, some definitions follow:

> *In SAE Vehicle Dynamics Terminology (J670e), "Wheelfight is a rotary disturbance of the steering wheel produced by forces acting on the steerable wheels."*

> *Class notes from the Chrysler Institute of Engineering course on Suspension and Steering of 1959,[43] "A jerking oscillation of the steering wheel when driving over rough roads. It is most noticeable at 45 to 50 mph. It is usually not violent but very annoying."*

As with other motions of the unsprung mass, the definition is based on experience, not rigorous derivations. Wheelfight is not self-sustaining and requires some form of excitation at the road wheels. However, it is more than a single pulse which, according to Jim Davis at GM North American Operations, is normally referred to as "wheel kick."

As Olley and Schilling indicate, a sizable number of design and operational factors contribute to wheelfight, such as tire imbalance, gyroscopic effects from short swing arms, spindle length, steering gear resonance, wheel path on bumps, application of brakes, proximity of wheel hop frequency, etc.

Wheelfight has been largely eliminated by design in the modern passenger car, but is a regular occurrence in many race cars, as can be seen on the in-car video during races.

Introduction

When independent front suspension was first introduced in American cars in the early 1930s the victory over shimmy at first seemed far from complete. The Dubonnet "fixed kingpin" suspension, in which the kingpin rode with the sprung mass, and the suspension was inserted between the kingpin and the wheel, was completely free from the shimmy cycle, although it showed caster wobble. The freedom from shimmy was partly because of the greatly increased inertia about the kingpin.

The wishbone suspension, which was structurally better than the Dubonnet, was inferior in that it produced shakes in the car structure and in the steering wheel, which were readily seen to be suppressed remnants of the shimmy cycle. By riding ahead of an experimental car and watching its front wheels, one could see the Dubonnet front wheels running as steady discs, whereas the tires on the wishbone suspension were frequently blurred at the edges. And, when run on the chassis rolls with alternating cams to excite the wheelfight, the similarity to the shimmy cycle was unmistakable. The looping of the end of the wheel spindle was essentially the same as in shimmy.

---

[43] Chrysler Institute notes on Suspension and Steering, C-3, 1958–1960.

In independent front suspension the wheels are held upright by the car structure itself, the shaking of the car associated with wheelfight was much worse than it had been with the front axle. As already stated the first requirement on passenger cars was a torsionally stiff frame and body structure. But this alone did not cure wheelfight, although it reduced shake in the car.

Next attention was to the camber change of the wheels. It was found necessary on most cars to avoid positive swing arm effects like Type 3 in the previous section. But this varied enormously between cars. Even today some cars get away with a positive swing arm which on others is quite unacceptable.

The shimmy cycle depends on a gyroscopic couple $I\omega_1\omega_2$, where I is the rotary moment of inertia of the wheel and brake drum, ω_1 is the rotary wheel speed in rad./sec., and ω_2 is the precession velocity of the wheel about the kingpin in rad./sec. And, although the occurrence is a self-induced oscillation rather than a simple resonance, it is connected in complex ways with other resonances, for example with the frequency of wheel hop, the frequency of wheel-flap (about the kingpins), the frequency of the steering gear itself, etc.

The wheel and drum inertia I can vary considerably in passenger cars and enormously in trucks. The velocity ω_1 varies with car speed and wheel radius. The precession speed ω_2 depends on the moment of inertia about the kingpin, on flexibility in the steering linkage and in the wheel-mounting structure.

So perhaps it is not surprising that **there is no general rule for avoiding wheelfight**. On each new car model it demands a lot of "tuning" work on the road or on chassis rolls, frequently supplemented by small additions to kingpin friction, etc. An effective device is frequently to provide a fore-and-aft cushion for the lower control arm by means of a rubber-mounted strut.

Wheelfight differs from shimmy chiefly in not being self-sustaining, i.e., it requires continuous excitation by bumps or road waves. However, in some severe cases it has been found to be excited by wheel unbalance or runout, and to reach severe proportions associated with scalloped tire wear, even on smooth roads.

It can be excited on chassis rolls by almost any form of small cams mounted alternately on the two rolls. Sinusoidal cams give the most consistent excitation. And the connection with the shimmy cycle is shown by the fact that the longer the wave the greater is the excitation, since it occurs at a higher wheel speed (ω_1). Thus on 4-foot diameter rolls, two cams per roll, which will excite 10 cps (Hz) at 43 mph, will give very much stronger wheelfight excitation than four cams per roll, which excite the same frequency at only 21.5 mph.

When exciting wheelfight on chassis rolls a paint spot on the wheel spindle is used as shown in Figure 6.2. As the frequency of excitation increases, the amplitude of wheel hop increases to a maximum at resonance and then decreases almost to zero at higher speeds. If "looping" of the spindle end occurs at any frequency close to wheel hop resonance, it is seen that the steering wheel is oscillating at this frequency.

By "Strobotac" lighting it is found that the sequence of occurrences is the same as in shimmy, i.e., each wheel comes down toed-in and goes up toed-out.

The wheel which does the "fighting" is of course the steering wheel. Hence any study of wheelfight leads to an examination of the elastic resonance of the steering gear itself.

Steering Gear Resonance

If a test rig is constructed as in Figure 6.17, the steering gear will be found to have a strongly marked resonant characteristic, due to the deflections within the gear itself, the torsional flexibility of the steering wheel shaft, and the moment of inertia of the steering wheel. If a variable throw, variable speed crank is connected to the Pitman arm by a drag

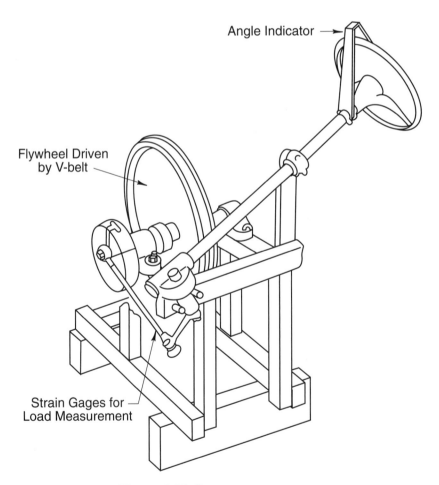

Figure 6.17 Steering gear test rig.

link as shown, it is found that, at the resonance peak, quite a short stroke (say, 3/4 inch double amplitude) is enough to produce three or four times the "correct" amplitude in the steering wheel.

If timing indicators are added, the steering wheel will be found to lag 90° behind the Pitman arm motion at resonance, and at higher frequencies the wheel motion will be almost 180° out of phase. Strain gauges on the drag link will show (Figure 6.18) the high loads falling on the gear purely due to the moment of inertia of the steering wheel.

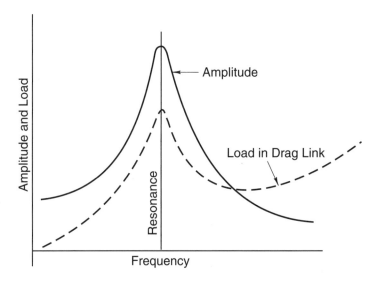

Figure 6.18 *Results of steering gear frequency sweep.*

If held at resonance for a while, breakage of the gear can result.

The thing which appears to save our steering gears from failure is that the natural frequency of the gear is commonly **below** wheel hop frequency. In one case, for example, gear resonance was found to be at 235 cpm [*or nearly 4 Hz*], while wheel hop would not normally occur below 540 cpm [*9 Hz*].

Wheelfight thus depends in part on the frequency of the steering gear being fairly close to wheel hop frequency. And it can be "tuned out" by slowing the steering gear frequency, either by increasing the moment of inertia of the steering wheel or even by reducing the diameter of the steering wheel shaft. When a wheelfight problem is cured in this way the absence of steering wheel motion is itself an indication that damaging stresses in the gear have been greatly reduced.

However, the thing to bear in mind is that the occurrence of "fight" in a steering wheel is itself a sign of potentially damaging resonance in the gear itself and, that a simple design change, which may alter the moment of inertia of a steering wheel, or possibly may stiffen a steering wheel shaft, can have the effect of introducing wheelfight, and steering breakage.

Wheelfight Cures

Wheelfight can be cured most effectively by tackling it from the other end, i.e., at the road wheel. The methods found to be most effective are:

1. Introducing some flexibility in the fore-and-aft control of the front wheels, as by rubber mounting the lower control arm.

2. Toeing the front wheels **out** as they rise. That is the conventional form of "front roll understeer."

3. Sloping the wheel arm pivots so the front wheel centers move backward as they rise.

4. Sloping the upper arm in a wishbone suspension so that immediately above design height the wheel camber is still increasing **positively**, i.e., a **negative** swing arm effect (limited by considerations of squeal and tire wear).

The feed-in of energy during wheelfight is thus similar to shimmy depending principally on tire aligning torque. As in shimmy, wetting the road or the chassis rolls will reduce or even eliminate wheelfight. Tires of different construction, giving reduced aligning torque will also give reduced wheelfight; also true with new tires before break-in.

Effect on Wheelfight (Schilling, "Handling Factors," 1938[44])

The one bad effect of swing arm action is its tendency to cause wheelfight. This has been realized earlier and is the reason why our suspensions have been built with zero camber change.

We now know four means of reducing wheelfight and have found it possible by applying these to make cars free from wheelfight, with swing arm radius as short as 100 inches.

1. Flexible steering linkage. This has been used for a number of years; it can be used only in moderation without spoiling the handling of the car.

2. Steering geometry. Oversteer error in linkage supports wheelfight and understeer error damps it. We have built as much as 10% understeer in the linkage and found quite an improvement in wheelfight without introducing any detrimental effect. Figure 6.19 shows the set-up that we use to measure the steering error and Figure 6.20 plots representative understeer and oversteer errors.

---

[44] This is an internal GM Proving Ground memo from the Milliken Research Associates files.

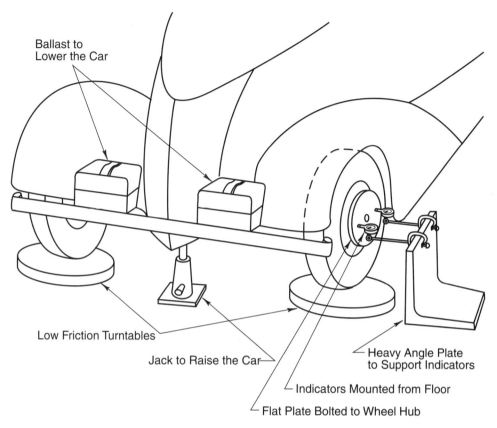

Figure 6.19 *Check of steering geometry error (bump steer measurement).*

3. High roll center causing wheel scrub is beneficial in two ways: it reduces wheel hop due to its damping effect and it produces precession torque around the kingpin opposed to wheelfight.

4. Slope of the wheel path in side view. Figure 6.21a shows what is meant. If the wheel center travels back and up as shown, its inertia force at the highest position during wheel hop (maximum compression) has an upward and also a backward component. The upward component is balanced by the reduction of pressure between tire and ground, but the backward component is not balanced by any other force. It causes a moment around the kingpin opposed to wheelfight if the slope of wheel travel is as shown. A wheel travel sloping up and forward (Figure 6.21b) will excite wheelfight.

Change of Spring Rate

Because swing arm action makes the wheel rise and drop faster than the end of the lower wishbone, it reduces the effective spring rate at the wheel. If the offset from wheel centerline to lower wishbone pin is d (Figure 6.22) the ratio of the two motions will be $(L_{fvsa} - d)/L_{fvsa}$ and the spring rate at the wheel will be reduced by $((L_{fvsa} - d)/L_{fvsa})^2$

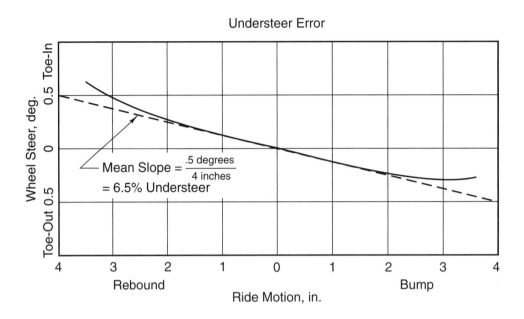

Figure 6.20 *Steering geometry error (bump steer).*

below the rate of this same suspension without swing arm action. With 100 inches swing arm and an offset as on the 1938 BOP [*Buick/Olds/Pontiac*] suspension this causes a loss of 11% in rate.

The same reduction applies to the roll rate, so that in general a heavier front stabilizer will be needed to give the same roll stiffness as on a car without swing arm action.

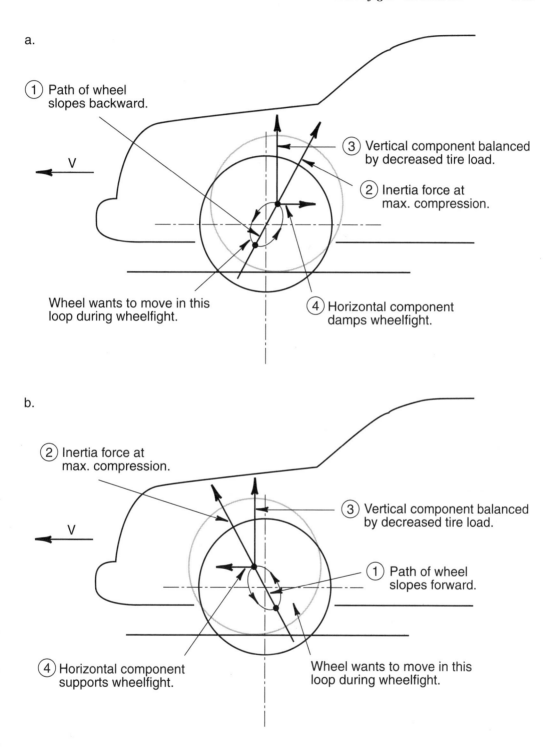

Figure 6.21 *Slope of wheel travel (side view), effect on wheelfight.*

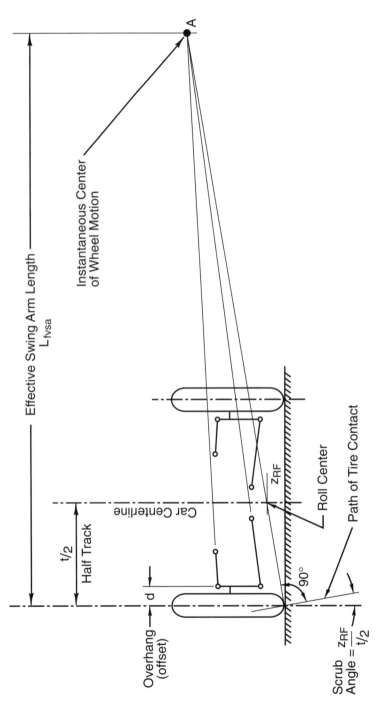

Figure 6.22 IFS front view geometry.

Reduction of Recovery Force

A good deal of the steering wheel recovery is due to the roll camber of the front wheels [*presumably from tire aligning torque due to camber*]. This is the reason why we can run our independent suspensions with zero or negative caster, while an axle car needs between two and three degrees positive caster to get the same feel—the difference is roughly equivalent to three degrees caster.

If we reduce the roll camber by 1/3 as we do with a 100 inch swing arm, we find that we have to use about 1 degree more positive caster to get the same recovery feel.

Brake Dive

1. *Geometry*

    The basic dynamics and preventive measures were described by Maurice Olley, in his report of May 25, 1937.

    There has been no attempt to introduce this factor [*anti-lift*] in rear suspensions except where it was produced incidentally on some of the new designs. We have, however, tried to build it into front suspensions of the two-ball-joint type. This attempt ran into very bad wheelfight tendencies from which we finally gained the following picture, see Figure 6.23.

    In order to get full anti-dive effect for the front suspension the point around which the wheel swings should be on the line marked "100%" [*drawn from the tire contact point to the CG*] making an angle of 22.5 degrees with the horizontal or having a slope of 0.41 [*for the example studied*]. If this point D lies below the 22.5 degree line the anti-dive effect is incomplete and proportional to the slope of a line drawn through the tire ground contact. For example—if this line has a slope of 0.26 we get: 0.26/0.41 = 64% anti-dive in front.

2. *Caster Change and Wheelfight*

    The distance from point D to the center of the wheel, L_{svsa} , we call the radius arm. This may be produced by using an actual solid radius arm or simply by the geometry of the wishbone layout. When the wheel moves up and down the kingpin centerline moves with it and swings around point D. The caster angle then changes at the rate of $1/L_{svsa}$ radian per inch or [*about*] $57/L_{svsa}$ degrees per inch.

    The load on the kingpin causes a torque around it proportional to the caster angle. If the caster angle changes during wheel hop this torque varies also and causes wheelfight. The shorter the radius L_{svsa}, the faster the variation of caster angle, and the stronger the wheelfight tendency.

    Also if point D is located at a different height than the center of the wheel, there will be a slope to the path of the center of the wheel. It has the magnitude

a.

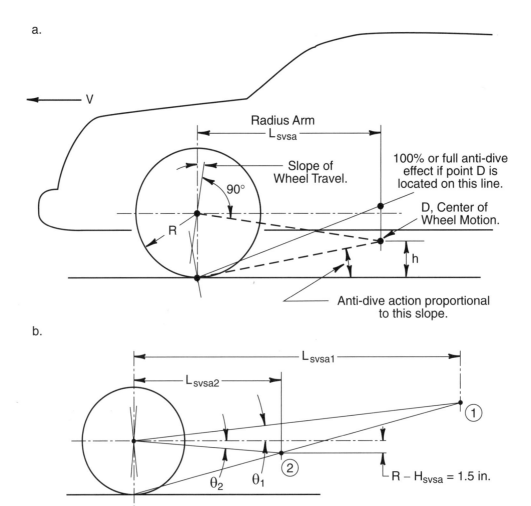

b.

Figure 6.23 Anti-dive geometry, front.

$(R - H_{svsa})/L_{svsa}$. If H_{svsa} is larger than R the slope of the wheel travel is forward, causing more wheelfight; if H_{svsa} is smaller than R the slope is backward and damps wheelfight.

By combining this with the caster change action, we can find a location giving no more wheelfight than a parallel wheel motion. For example in Figure 6.23b, point 1 gives radius arm L_{svsa1}, which is fairly large, causing small wheelfight and slope of wheel travel θ_1; this is **forward slope** and also causes wheelfight.

Point 2 is located on the same line through the tire ground contact and therefore has the same anti-dive effect. It causes radius arm L_{svsa2}, which is rather short but the slope of wheel travel θ_2 is backward. The two will cancel each other's wheelfight tendency.

Exact balance [*elimination of wheelfight for the vehicle studied*] is effected if D is about 1.5 inches below the wheel center, regardless of the amount of anti-dive effect. We built a suspension of this kind with L_{svsa} = 46 inches and $R - H_{svsa}$ = 1.5 inches and found this theory confirmed.

These dimensions give about 65% anti-dive, which is all that is needed to remove the sensation of dive completely. At the same time the caster change is only 1.5 degrees between curb weight and five-passenger load, compared to 1/2 degree on a production car. This causes no objectionable variation in steering recovery.

This ends Schilling's report.

6.4 Caster Wobble (Olley)

Caster wobble is distinguished from shimmy or wheelfight generally because it occurs with little or no tramping action, at a considerably lower frequency, and at a lower road speed. It involves less energy than shimmy, and can be eliminated by moderate increases in kingpin friction. It can occur on a single wheel. In fact "nose-wheel shimmy" on airplanes is actually an example of caster wobble. **This is the second type of wheel wobble which is indefinitely self-sustaining on a smooth road**.

Case Study–Chevrolet with Dubonnet IFS

Figure 6.24 is a drawing of the caster wobble as it was observed on a Chevrolet Dubonnet passenger car. The suspension springs played only a very small part with the car rocking about an inclined axis as shown, chiefly on the tires.

The cycle of operations was:

> Wheels
>> At A_1 the wheels have maximum left angle
>> At B_1 the wheels are straight
>> At C_1 the wheels have maximum right angle
>> At D_1 the wheels are straight.

> Car
>> At A the car is central and horizontal, turning left
>> At B the car is pointing maximum left
>> At C the car is central and horizontal, turning right
>> At D the car is pointing maximum right

The wheel wobble thus leads the displacement of the car by something less than 90° phase angle.

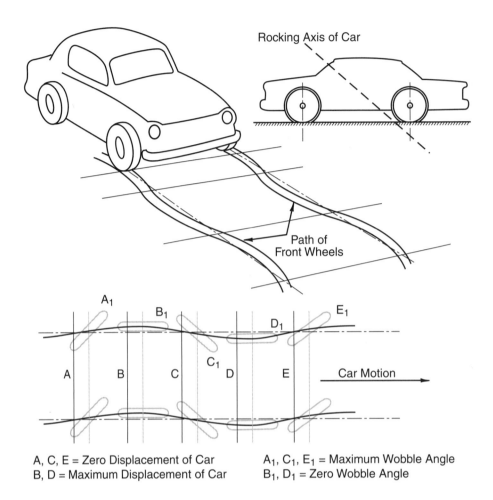

A, C, E = Zero Displacement of Car
B, D = Maximum Displacement of Car

A_1, C_1, E_1 = Maximum Wobble Angle
B_1, D_1 = Zero Wobble Angle

Figure 6.24 Caster wobble—car and wheel paths.

The maximum wheel angles occur at A_1 and C_1. Thus, during most of the passage from A to C the wheels are pointing to the left of their path of travel and are subjected to an aligning torque trying to turn them to the right. The aligning torque leads the wobble angle by something more than 90° phase angle.

The maximum lateral acceleration of the front of the car seems to occur at about A_1 or C_1, followed by maximum displacement somewhat less than 90° later.

Suitable conditions therefore exist for feeding energy both into the car motion and into the wheel wobble, provided that the wobble is first "detonated" by accidentally either deflecting the wheels or rocking the car. The source of energy is the travel of the car and the means of coupling is the aligning torque of the tires.

The controlling frequency in these tests appeared to be the rocking frequency of the car on its tires. Considerable changes could be made in the inertia about the kingpin, or in the slack or flexibility in the steering linkage, without much change in the wobble frequency. However, slack or flexibility in the linkage made the wobble more violent and increased the wheel amplitudes.

Even increased caster, though it increased the violence of wobble, did not greatly raise the frequency. Changing the tire pressure, which has an immense effect on shimmy, produced little change in caster wobble. If anything the wobble appeared worse at the **higher** pressure.

Road Speed

In this particular case road speed had a marked effect on caster wobble. It appeared worst at 20 mph, and would not occur at any speed much greater than this.

Road Surface

Wobble is self-sustaining on a smooth road or on chassis rolls. To detonate it requires an isolated bump or dip on the road, or a "flying-wedge" on the chassis rolls. Unlike shimmy, wobble can exist on one wheel only. If a car is run with no steering connection to one front wheel, this wheel will almost invariably develop caster wobble (at reduced frequency) up to a certain road speed, but will not wobble at higher speeds.

Engine Mount

The above observations apply particularly to the Chevrolet Dubonnet car, which, because of the great inertia moment about the kingpins, was especially prone to caster wobble, though completely immune from shimmy. The caster wobble occurred at an exceptionally low frequency (approximately 360 cpm [*6 Hz*]).

Perhaps because of this low frequency, the wobble was extremely sensitive to the rocking frequency of the engine on its mounts. Blocking the engine against the steering column [*with a wedge or "block"*] greatly increased the violence of the wobble. Removing the block resulted in five or six vigorous "flaps" of the engine, which stopped the caster wobble completely. The engine worked as an effective harmonic balancer.

Summary–Caster Wobble

Tentative conclusions were:

1. Caster wobble is controlled by the mixed rocking and yawing motion of the car.

2. It is self-energized, i.e., is best produced and sustained on smooth roads.

3. Is made worse by:

    Increased inertia moment about the kingpins
    A soft or slack steering linkage
    Increased caster

4. Is distinguished from shimmy by:

    Not depending on wheel tramp
    Not depending on wheel unbalance
    Not depending on gyroscopic coupling
    Occurring on a single unsteered wheel
    Being made rather worse by increased inflation
    Being affected by engine mount

5. In contrast to shimmy, the energy of any caster wobble is relatively low. It is readily damped out by friction at the kingpins, without using so much friction as to spoil the handling. Friction applied elsewhere in the steering linkage is less effective and more liable to spoil the handling.

Up to this stage we felt that we could make a very clear distinction between caster wobble and shimmy. Caster wobble occurred at a lower speed (and in fact used to be called "low speed wobble"), was of lower frequency, had little tramping action, and was easily damped out. It evidently depended partly on the inertia about the kingpin, and partly on the rocking frequency of the car. On the Chevrolet Dubonnet by greatly increasing the inertia at the kingpins and by jacking the rear wheels off the ground by a jack under the rear axle center, caster wobble could be produced as slow as 70 cpm [*1.2 Hz*].

However, since that time a lot of different varieties of caster wobble have appeared:

1. First there is the so-called nose-wheel shimmy of airplanes, which is a pure caster wobble.

2. Then some military trucks with 12 inch [*wide*] tires developed a violent wobble at about 500 cpm [*8 Hz*] and 45 mph. This had the appearance of caster wobble. There was no tramping and the vehicle was principally rocking on its tires. It proved to be easily damped out by plain thrust washers in the kingpin.

3. A third variation was the caster wobble on the light front end of the Corvair. Frequencies were actually higher than common wheel hop frequency, and were between 700 and 800 cpm. The effect on the car felt very much like a shimmy. But there was little tramping action. And this also was cured by increased friction in the lower kingpin ball.

4. On trucks, probably because of the much greater inertia of the front wheels, there appears to be generally less of a clear distinction between caster wobble and shimmy than on passenger cars. On trucks with front axles, a true shimmy can on

occasion be produced by braking on road waves. But trucks may also show caster wobble at higher frequency and higher road speed than is usual on passenger cars.

6.5 Wheel Hop

Introduction

*Classically, vehicle ride has two components or modes, i.e., **primary** ride and **secondary** ride. Primary ride, which is treated in Chapter 5, is defined by SAE J670e as "The low frequency (approximately up to 5 Hz) vibration of the sprung mass as a rigid body." Secondary ride involves unsprung mass vibrations, and is defined as "Hop— the vertical oscillatory motion of a wheel between the road surface and the sprung mass." Another definition, from the Chrysler Institute Notes, Suspension and Steering, 1959, says hop "can produce disturbing high frequency vibrations and in extreme cases contribute to loss of traction or control."*

The frequency of the hop modes is well above that of the primary mode (10 Hz and greater), so there is relatively little coupling between them. Olley discusses several types of hop, depending upon the excitation mechanism. He begins by discussing the damping of the sprung and unsprung masses.

Damping of the Sprung and Unsprung Masses

It may be useful to consider the requirements for damping the ride as compared with the damping of the unsprung mass.

Let:

M = sprung mass at one wheel (slugs)
m = unsprung mass at one wheel (slugs)
K_W = wheel rate (lb./ft.)
K_T = tire rate (lb./ft.)
ω_M = sprung mass ride frequency (rad./sec.)
ω_m = wheel hop frequency (rad./sec.)
c_{cM} = critical damping, ride (lb.-sec./ft.)
c_{cm} = critical damping, unsprung mass (lb.-sec./ft.)

Assume also: $k^2/ab = 1$

$$\text{Ride frequency} \quad \omega_M = \sqrt{\frac{K_T K_W}{M(K_T + K_W)}} \quad \text{(rad./sec.)} \tag{6.1}$$

$$\text{Unsprung frequency} \quad \omega_m = \sqrt{\frac{K_T + K_W}{m}} \quad \text{(rad./sec.)} \tag{6.2}$$

$$\text{Critical damping, ride } c_{cM} = 2\sqrt{M\frac{K_T K_W}{K_T + K_W}} \qquad (6.3)$$

$$\text{Critical damping, unsprung mass } c_{cm} = 2\sqrt{m(K_T + K_W)} \qquad (6.4)$$

If the damping, whether critical or less than critical (as for instance 25% critical), is to be equally effective in restraining the ride and the wheel hop, we have to have the condition that:

$$c_{cM} = c_{cm} \qquad (6.5)$$

or that $$M\frac{K_T K_W}{K_T + K_W} = m(K_T + K_W) \qquad (6.6)$$

or that $$\frac{m}{M} = \frac{K_T K_W}{(K_T + K_W)^2} = \frac{K_W / K_T}{(1 + K_W / K_T)^2} \qquad (6.7)$$

Thus for equally effective damping in ride and wheel hop there has to be a relationship between mass ratio and the ratio of wheel rate to tire rate. To see what this relationship is we calculate as in Table 6.1:

Table 6.1 Rate and Mass Ratios

$\dfrac{K_W}{K_T}$	m/M For Equal Damping	m/M For Half Damping on Unsprung
0.05	0.0454	0.182
0.10	0.0826	0.330
0.20	0.1389	0.556
0.30	0.1776	0.710
0.40	0.2041	0.816
0.50	0.2222	0.889
0.60	0.2342	0.937
0.70	0.2421	0.968
0.80	0.2469	0.988
1.00	0.2500	1.000

If we were content to accept half as much damping for the unsprung mass as for the ride, the m/M ratio would be increased four times.

If we assume a tire rate of 1000 lb./in., and a sprung mass of 1000 lb., Figure 6.25 shows that, with a wheel rate between 130 and 250 lb./in. and an unsprung mass between 100 and 160 lb., it is possible to arrange for damping which will be equally effective in ride and wheel hop.

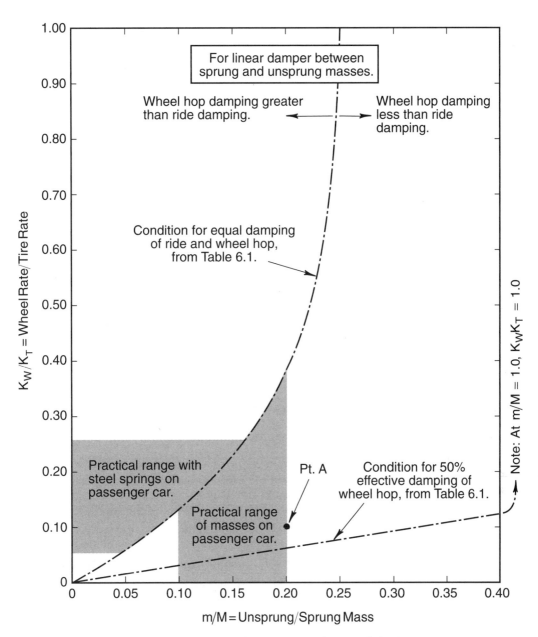

Figure 6.25 Rate and mass ratios for equal damping.

But a wheel rate of 100 lb./in. with an unsprung mass of, say, 200 lb. (point A in Figure 6.25) implies necessarily that, if the unsprung mass is to be controlled, the ride will be relatively overdamped. And a wheel rate of 50 lb./in., such as might be obtained with air-springing, almost necessarily implies that the main problem will be to control the wheel hop without noticeably overdamping the ride.

The line showing 50% effective damping of wheel hop illustrates that the ratio m/M is not very critical. In other words, departures in m/M ratio considerably to the right of the "ideal" line can be made before wheel hop becomes too much of a problem. Also, we know from experience that, in the case of a very soft suspension, the ride can be overdamped without too much discomfort, although the ride on a smooth boulevard is often disappointing due to too much damping.

We have certainly seen many more suspensions to the right or "wheel hop" side of the line than the reverse condition.

One can see from Figure 6.25 that moving left (reduction of unsprung mass) would tend to reduce wheel hop. For instance it is remarkable that an unsprung mass of a quarter of the sprung mass requires a very stiff wheel rate equal to the tire rate for theoretical equal damping of ride and wheel hop. This gives a clear explanation of the wheel hop troubles of unladen trucks.

The problem of overdamping of the ride is connected with the third form of resonance of the pneumatic-tire vehicle, because the tires have almost no damping. Thus, if the suspension springs are "stuck" by friction or too much damping, the vehicle, especially on "smooth" roads, will oscillate on its tires alone at frequencies of the order of 200 cpm [*3.3 Hz*]. These oscillations used to be much more troublesome than they are now. Reduced friction in the suspension, softer tires, and improved shock valving has reduced the occurrence of this "boulevard jerk."

Harmonic Wheel Hop Absorbers

One can see the possibilities of the harmonic wheel hop absorber illustrated in Figure 6.26. This showed considerable promise in suppressing wheel hop without transmitting any shocks to the sprung mass of the vehicle. A typical test result is shown in Figure 6.27.

The principle is fully analyzed in Den Hartog.[45] It is the same principle as the harmonic dampers used on engine crankshafts. The very small amount of damping required by the bob-weight is supplied by the air trapped in the steel shell. In practice it is found desirable to tune the absorber slightly above the wheel hop frequency, so that the greater suppression occurs at the higher frequency.

There are objections to harmonic absorbers, in that they are bulky, heavy, and quite costly. Also they ignore the fact that wheel hop is not a simple harmonic motion but an oscillation which decreases in frequency as the amplitude increases. Thus the absorber may be tuned to give desirable results on roads where the hop excitation is small, but may become ineffective on rougher road surfaces where the need for it is greater.

---

[45] Den Hartog, J. P., and Den J. Hartog (Editor), *Mechanical Vibrations*, Dover Publications, New York City, New York, April 1985. [*Obviously Olley was using an earlier edition!*]

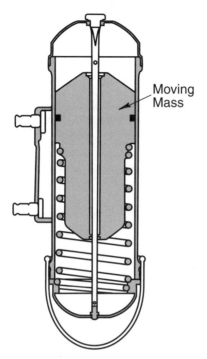

Figure 6.26 *Harmonic wheel hop absorber.*

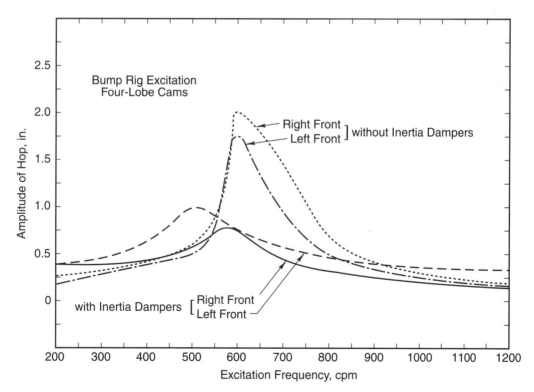

Figure 6.27 *Effect of harmonic wheel hop absorber, Citroën 2CV.*

There are other devices which appear to be equally effective. For example:

1. The provision of fore-and-aft flexibility in the wheel supports. This can have a pronounced effect on the suppression of "harshness" both on front and rear wheels (and incidentally is one of the advantages of the Hotchkiss control of rear axles).

2. Another device which is effective in suppressing shakes arising from the front wheels due to traces of the shimmy-cycle, is to design the suspension so that the wheel centers move backward, as they rise, at an angle θ of 3° to 5° from the vertical, Figure 6.28. [*This motion is termed "recession." See also Section 6.3.*]

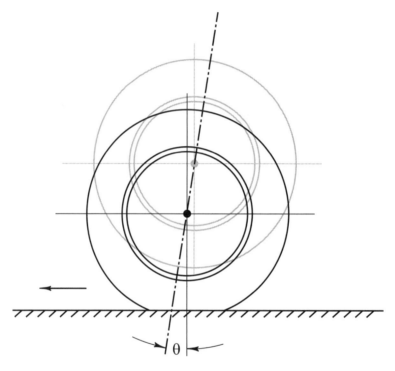

Figure 6.28 *Wheel path moving backward with ride travel.*

3. Changing the steering linkage geometry so that the wheels toe-out as they rise (roll understeer) has a similar effect.

4. Extremely effective in ride damping, and to some extent on hop damping of independent rear wheels, is the "track change" associated with swing axles. This is discussed later under damping of a swing axle [*see Section 6.12*].

Frequency of Wheel Hop

The oscillations of the unsprung mass have so far been regarded as simple harmonic, but they are not. The unsprung mass is like a bouncing rubber ball, the frequency of which decreases as the amplitude increases.

Road irregularities can throw the wheel clear of the ground, and once it is off the ground the time of its return is determined only by its upward velocity, the spring force relative to its mass, the force of gravity and the damping forces. The vertical rate of the tire has ceased to work. The resonance curve is therefore not of the common type as in Figure 6.29, left, but is as shown in Figure 6.29, right, typical of a spring having decreasing rate with increasing amplitude.

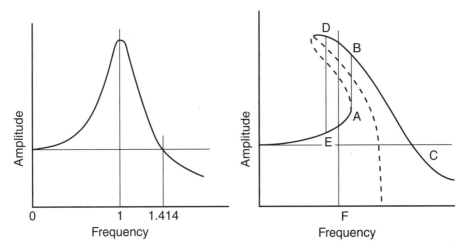

Figure 6.29 *Simplified (linear) and realistic resonance curves.*

When wheel hop is excited at increasing frequency, the amplitude will suddenly "snap" from A to B, and then decrease along the line BC. With decreasing frequency the amplitude may grow all the way to D, and then suddenly collapse to E.

This is a difficulty in bump rig testing, since with a definite exciting frequency such as F, we may obtain two entirely different amplitudes of wheel hop, depending on whether the frequency has been increased or decreased.

Shock Absorbers

For convenience of figuring it is usually assumed that the damping effect of shock absorbers is "linear," i.e., straight velocity damping. Essentially the damping force comes from forcing oil through an orifice under high pressure. If the orifice is small and short the resistance is affected very little by viscosity, but unfortunately it increases as the square of the velocity. Therefore this simple "door check" device cannot be used in a shock absorber since it would produce excessive forces at the higher amplitudes.

If the orifice is increased in area and made longer the resistance increases more nearly in direct proportion to the velocity. But the effect of viscosity changes in the oil increases, and an oil has to be found with the least possible viscosity variation with temperature.

Various types of valves (by Brouilhet, Delco-Products and others) have been devised to keep the short-orifice effect with its freedom from viscosity, and at the same time to produce a linear increase of pressure with velocity. But the variation of velocity is very great. For instance a one inch amplitude at a typical ride frequency of 1 cps [*1 Hz*] implies a maximum velocity of 0.52 ft./sec., while the same amplitude at wheel hop frequency of 10 cps gives a maximum velocity ten times as great. Thus even a straight velocity characteristic can become too great for comfort, and can overload the shock absorber and its connections. So it is necessary to insert a spring-loaded blow-off valve. The valving will therefore produce a result at the wheel somewhat as on Figure 6.30.

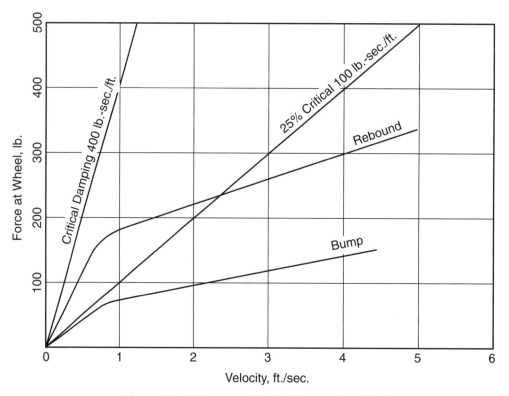

Figure 6.30 *Forces and velocities at the wheel.*

For minor ride motions, say 1 in. amplitude, or 0.52 ft./sec., the mean of the compression and rebound damping is about 40% of critical, but at 4 in. amplitude, or for a major ride disturbance, it will be only about 20% of critical.

And 1 in. amplitude of the **unsprung**, with a frequency of about 10 cps, will give a velocity of about 5.2 ft./sec. The effective damping will then be only about 12.5% of critical.

Furthermore the shock absorbers have to be more or less softly mounted to reduce shock and noise in the body. This alone involves considerable lost motion and actual time-lag in the damping of short and rapid wheel hop motions. And a further appreciable loss on such motions is caused by the actual elasticity of the oil, and by the release and re-solution of air dissolved in the oil.

All of which goes to show that in our present suspension designs, in which the shock absorber works in parallel with the suspension spring, there must be a lack of effective damping to control the more vigorous oscillations of the unsprung mass. The same statement does not apply to hydro-pneumatic suspensions like the Citroën in which the load is applied to the "spring" **through** the column of oil in the shock absorber. In this case most of the elasticity and lost motion in the damping is eliminated.

6.6 Fore and Aft Forces

When a tire on a free-rolling wheel is compressed the wheel tends to rotate faster. This occurs when the wheel encounters a road bump. The rotation must accelerate as it enters the bump, and slow down as it leaves it. This can only be done by applying forces to the wheel hub, like F_1 forward when entering and F_2 rearward when leaving the bump, Figure 6.31.

These forces may amount to several hundred pounds. As an example suppose a wheel and tire with a 12.5 in. **rolling radius** is rolling at 66 ft./sec. (45 mph). It encounters a road wave like that shown in Figure 6.31, which reduces the rolling radius momentarily by one inch. (This implies more than 1 inch compression of the tire; perhaps as much as 2 inches.)

The tire has been rotating at $(66 \times 12)/12.5 = 63.4$ rad./sec.

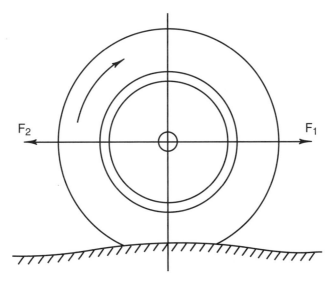

Figure 6.31 Wheel and tire rolling over a bump.

At the top of the bump it is rotating at $(66 \times 12)/11.5 = 68.9$ rad./sec.

Time interval to top of bump: $1.5/66 = 0.02275$ sec.

Average acceleration of wheel rotation: $5.5/0.02275 = 242$ rad./sec.^{2}

If the polar moment of wheel and brake drum is $1 \, \text{slug}/\text{ft.}^2$, then the accelerating torque is 242 lb.-ft, or about 240 lb. for the horizontal forces F_1 and F_2.

These are horizontal hammer-blows delivered to the wheel spindle, and balanced by horizontal forces from the road to the tire, rearward when entering and forward when leaving the bump.

Mr. Schilling points out that the rotary acceleration of a wheel in passing over a bump depends on the tire construction. For instance in a circumferentially banded tire like the Michelin X, Figure 6.32, it is probable that the bands act like a circular chain loop and maintain a uniform **linear** velocity all around the tire. In this case compressing the bottom of the tire will not change the wheel speed, since the band will bunch out ahead of and behind the contact patch and will be traveling at all points at a linear speed (relative to the wheel center) roughly equal to the speed of the car.

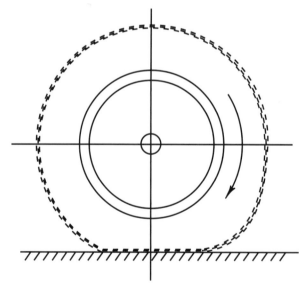

Figure 6.32 Banded (belted radial) tire, with belt modeled as a loop of chain.

Evidently we need to know more about the changes in rotation speed of tires on a wavy road surface and how these speed variations are affected by tire construction and by road surface conditions. Such speed changes appear to have a direct relation to the formation of road waves, and to wheel hop, brake hop, wheelfight, and shimmy.

6.7 Washboard Roads

With the non-simple-harmonic nature of wheel hop (Section 6.5), and its tendency to develop lower frequency with increasing amplitude, one begins to see that almost any heterogeneous road roughness of a coarse enough distribution not to be "swallowed" by the tire will excite wheel hop. And we can probably assume also, with the standard tire, that when the tire is thrown into the air the bump which has thrown it up has also spun it faster. Thus when it "lands" again it is liable to be running too fast. One begins to understand why the original roughness which had no pattern starts to develop a wave pattern in the road, Figure 6.33.

In other words, pneumatic-tired wheels tend to convert a random road roughness into a wave pattern. And this action is cumulative, since the increasing wave pattern increases wheel hop, which accelerates the formation of waves. The changes in wheel speed which occur with changes in wheel radius perhaps account for the general form of washboard ripples on gravel roads, which consist of relatively narrow ridges on a generally flat surface. (But it is difficult to account for the remarkable uniformity of the 30 in. pitch on gravel roads all over the world.) [*The authors have been unable to find any experimental data proving or disproving Olley's thoughts on the formation of washboard roads.*]

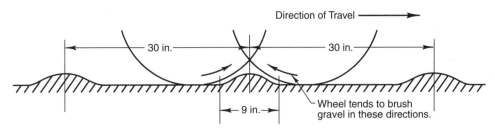

Figure 6.33 Idealized washboard formation on gravel road.

When four cams of roughly the washboard shape are placed on 4 foot diameter chassis rolls, the linear pitch is approximately 38 in., which is close enough to gravel washboard to form a useful test, Figure 6.34.

It is observed that the resulting wheel and car motions depend on the amount of shock absorber action. If the wheel hop frequency is 9 cps for a fairly vigorous hop, the maximum excitation will occur at about $9 \times 3.14 = 28.3$ ft./sec. or 19.3 mph.

When there is little shock absorber action and when the exciting frequency is slightly different from the natural frequency, the end of the car on the rolls tends to "beat," the wheels sometimes hitting the cams and at other times hitting between the cams. And when the beat frequency reaches the ride frequency of the car, which may be approximately 1 cps [*1 Hz*] (for 9 in. effective deflection), the plunging of the car on the rolls may become unmanageable. This particular beating effect in the ride has been a major cause of complaint from parts of the world (such as Africa and the Middle East) where gravel roads are habitually unscraped, and develop really violent washboard surfaces.

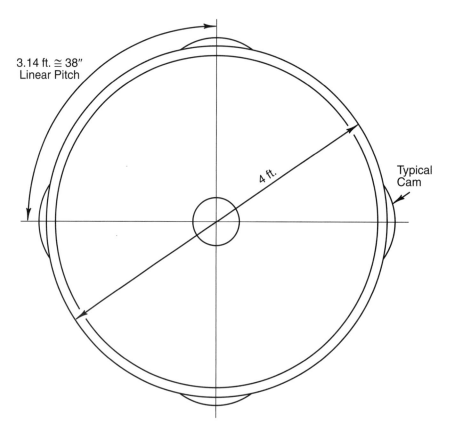

3.14 ft. ≅ 38″
Linear Pitch

4 ft.

Typical
Cam

Figure 6.34 Cams added to chassis roll to simulate washboard.

If we can rush through this beating condition on the rolls, and double the speed to about 39 mph it is sometimes possible to produce a condition where each wheel is virtually "skipping" one cam, and producing a 9 cps wheel hop from a nominal 18 cps excitation. And in this case the right hand wheel is quite likely to pick up its excitation alternately to the left hand wheel, so that we have tramping action excited by parallel cams.

Another very common occurrence in rig testing on rear axles is that, if the cams on the two rolls are not exactly parallel, the cams that hit the tires an inch or so "later" will produce violent wheel hop while the other side will ride practically with no hop at all. Thus the right hand wheel may hop with the rolls running in one direction, and the left hand wheel when rotation is reversed.

So we begin to get an explanation of why washboard roads, when well developed, frequently show two superposed wave systems: one transverse representing parallel hop, and the other diagonal representing tramp. (See Figure 6.35 based on a main highway in South Africa about ten years ago [*c. 1950*], a typical example of a crossed washboard pattern.)

With adequate damping of the unsprung masses, however, we do not find the wheel hop occurring at half the frequency of the excitation, but rather find the wheels hopping at the

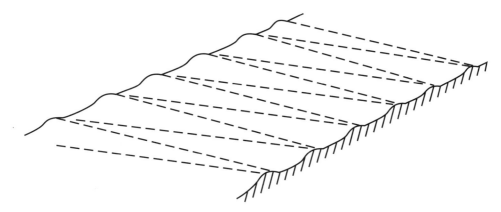

Figure 6.35 *Mixed parallel and diagonal wave pattern in washboard road.*

forced frequency imposed by the cams on the chassis rolls or by the wave spacing on the road. Mr. Schilling points out that at this high frequency of forced oscillation the wheel hop will be almost 180° out of phase with its excitation, so that the wheels will be "down" as they pass over the bumps, thus compressing the gravel in the ridges. But apparently the scrubbing action as sketched on Figure 6.33 still exists, since it is quite clear from observation that the ridges continually grow. Evidently, closer studies of the motions of tires on wavy road surfaces of all sorts are needed in order to **see** the hopping and rotary scrubbing motions of the tire on the road. Thus we might find whether in fact "banded" tires do not tend to produce washboard roads and do resist wheelfight.

It appears possible that the initial formation of a corrugated road surface is not connected with wheel hop but is inherent in the intermittent nature of the motion of the tread rubber through the contact area. In Figure 6.36 the rolling radius is about 3/8 in. greater than the standing height. It follows that, from A to B and again from C to D, the tread rubber is sliding backward on the road, whereas from B to C it is sliding forward. However, by analyzing scratch patterns from rolling tires it is seen that this relative sliding is not uniform. At one point the sliding will be all backward, and a few inches farther along nearly all the sliding will be forward. This is considered to be the cause of "scalloped" wear of any tires which are not being used for traction.

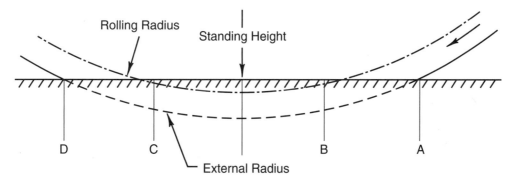

Figure 6.36 *Analysis of tread motion in the tire print.*

It appears that the same cause might lead to a relatively fine-pitched initial corrugation in the road. Then the fact that the wheel hop oscillation is nonlinear means that wheel hop can be excited by a multiple of its natural frequency, so that the initial finer corrugation may be built up into the 30 in. pitch washboard by reason of the wheel hop frequency.

Gravel roads are becoming uncommon in this country, and unscraped gravel is quite rare. But this is not so in much of the export territory.

In "cohesive" rather than "granular" road surfaces (in asphalt, for example) wave formation also occurs, but is quite different from gravel washboard. In general it appears to be more nearly sinusoidal in form, and it is much longer in pitch, typically from 5 to 9 feet. One of its major causes is certainly brake hop, as shown by its rapid growth at the approaches to traffic lights. However, waves are formed even in concrete expressways far away from stoplights and can be clearly traced to oscillations of the unsprung masses in commercial vehicles.

6.8 Brake Hop

In Section 9.11, Sudden Brake Application, the high torques which might be applied to the wheels for short time intervals are discussed. It is pointed out that in brake hop we are vitally interested in the rotation of the brake backing plates which occurs in brake dive, or in other words in the **length of torque arm**.

Type 1: Consider a simple case of a "pusher type" Dubonnet front suspension as shown in Figure 6.37.

The brake backing plate is bolted to the arm, and the anti-dive angle θ_F is such that, in forward braking, dive is over-corrected and the front of the car **lifts** slightly, the car as a whole stopping level. This is true in steady braking. But in sudden brake application quite different things happen.

When a sudden torque T_F is applied to the two front wheels the upward force on the front of the car is:

$$\frac{T_F}{L_{svsa}} - \frac{A_X W h}{\ell} \tag{6.8}$$

where T_F = torque applied to both front wheels, lb.-in.
L_{svsa} = length of the torque arm, in.
A_X = deceleration in g-units (before wheels stop turning)
W = vehicle weight, lb.
h = static height of CG, in.
ℓ = wheelbase, in.

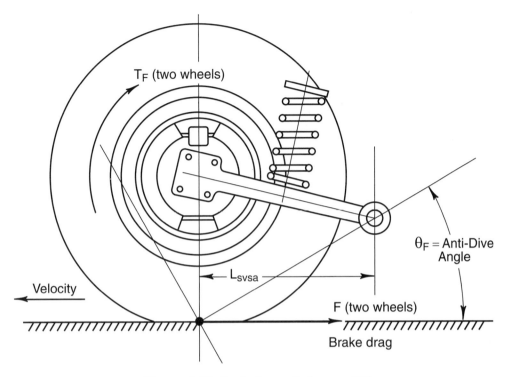

Figure 6.37 *Brake hop—Dubonnet IFS.*

And if the sprung mass of the front of the car is W_F/g and t is the duration of the high torque before the wheels stop,

Vertical velocity of front of car:

$$V = \frac{\left(\dfrac{T_F}{L_{svsa}} - \dfrac{A_X W h}{\ell}\right) tg}{W_F}$$ (6.9)

For example, we might assume:

$W_F = 1800$ lb.
$L_{svsa} = 1$ ft.
$T_F = 4200$ lb.-ft.
$W = 4000$ lb.
$h/\ell = 0.20$
$t = 0.1105$ sec.
$A_X = 0.96g$

Then $V = (3432 \times 0.1105)/56 = 6.77$ ft./sec.

The lift of the front end in this short time interval:

Lift $= Vt/2 = 0.374$ ft. $= 4.5$ in.

Actually the rebound stops would have picked the wheels off the road before this full lift occurred. And the flattening of the tire would have reduced the initial acceleration. But even if the vertical velocity when the rebound stops engage is only 3 ft./sec., the front of the car will sail through the air for about 0.18 sec, which at 45 mph is a [*longitudinal*] leap of 12 feet! This can occur with this type of short pusher-arm suspension, and can be stopped only by putting a restriction valve in the hydraulic lines to the front brakes. It is probably the most severe example of brake hop, though perhaps it might be better called "brake jump."

In the case of the Porsche, or the Chevrolet Dubonnet suspension (see Figure 3.19 and Chapter 9, Anti-Dive Geometry), although the arms are short and there is some anti-dive effect, no rotation of the backing plate with brake dive occurs, and there is therefore no vertical impact between the wheels and the ground when brakes are suddenly applied.

With an effective arm length L_{svsa} of 3.5 ft., such as may occur in an anti-dive layout on a wishbone suspension, the vertical acceleration of the front end due to panic braking will be negligible, and this form of brake hop does not exist.

This same sort of brake hop can and does occur in reverse on a rear axle when sudden braking is used with a short torque arm. In this case there is frequently no definite rebound stop, and therefore there is danger of damaging the rear shock absorbers.

Type 2: The more usual type of brake hop is the reverse of the above and occurs at the rear wheels of cars with short torque arms, on sudden brake application, Figure 6.38.

When a sudden brake torque is applied to the rear wheels the lifting force at the rear tires is $T_R/L_{svsa} - W_R$.

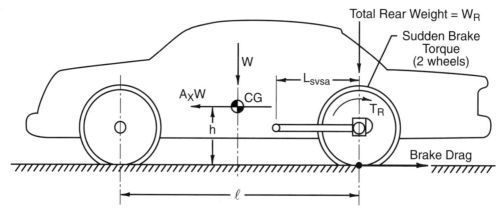

Figure 6.38 Brake hop—axle rear suspension with short torque arms.

When $L_{svsa} < T_R/W_R$ the rear wheels can theoretically lift right off the road. This can occur only momentarily, as the rear wheels stop almost instantly and torque T_R disappears. However, if we take the theoretical case and consider $T_R = 3300$ lb.-ft. and $W_R = 2000$ lb. the limiting length for the torque arm $L_{svsa} = 1.65$ ft. or 20 in.

It is a coincidence that this is just about the length of the short torque tubes recently introduced on some small German cars. Referring to Chapter 9, Anti-Dive Geometry, it is stated that the assumption of instantaneous application of braking is not realistic and that, in a conventional passenger car, the elasticity of the drive train was such that the rear wheels stopped first, while stalling of the engine occurred some appreciable time later.

The violent oscillations which are set up both in the brake lines and in the suspension and driveline by a panic brake stop are undoubtedly only an extreme form of those which occur on any sudden brake application. Wheels which take 1/10 second to stop in sudden braking seem well adapted to set up brake hop oscillations at 10 cps. Thus it is perhaps not surprising that it is found possible to use short torque tubes as above without brake hop, **by using exceptionally soft drive springs in the clutch driven disc** [*manual transmission only*].

The oscillatory nature of sudden brake application undoubtedly encourages brake hop. Probably the driveline flexibility in the conventional car is an essential factor also. Packaged powerplants, as in rear engine or front drive cars, will have different brake hop characteristics, which may be better or worse depending on internal "tuning" variations.

The only general statements on forward [*car moving forward*] brake hop in rear wheels appear to be:

- It is not directly connected with anti-dive angle θ_R.
- It is directly connected with the length of the effective torque arm, L_{svsa}.
- It is greatly affected by torsional oscillations in the driveline, and in fluid drive or in cases of extremely flexible drivelines can be virtually nonexistent.

Forward brake hop of the type under discussion is a **rough road** phenomenon. In contrast the "brake jump" discussed before [*following Equation 6.9*] occurred principally on smooth, hard roads. There is an interesting similarity between forward brake hop and reverse power hop.

6.9 Reverse Power Hop

If the drive gears are carried in the axle, and the axle is controlled by torque arms as shown in Figure 6.38, the same types of torque reaction which produce forward brake hop can also produce power hop in reverse. The torque reaction on the axle casing and torque arms is trying to lift the rear wheels, and particularly the left rear wheel, off the ground, as shown in Figure 6.39.

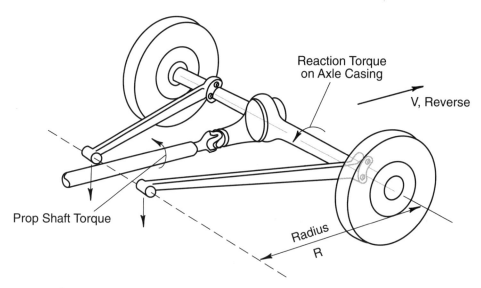

Figure 6.39 Power hop in reverse—axle controlled by torque arms.

In the case of power hop, soft clutch drive springs, such as helped forward brake hop problems, can do no good, since the engine torque will have closed them solid. But torsional frequencies in the driveline prove to be just as important in power hop as in brake hop. And in particular the rocking frequency of the engine on its mounts is of first importance. If this happens to be close to the wheel hop frequency, and if the torque arm radius R is less than about 45 in., then reverse power hop is difficult to avoid.

When reverse power hop builds up really seriously, as when attempting to climb a gravel hill in reverse, hopping of the left rear wheel, rocking of the powerplant, and torque surges in the driveline can become enough to cause serious damage particularly to the reverse pinion in the transmission.

Besides the radius R of the torque arm and the rocking frequency of the powerplant, power hop is obviously concerned with the rear wheel track, with the effective width of the rear spring base, with the rear axle reduction ratio, and with the rear shock absorbers. It is also dependent on the type of transmission, fluid drive being much less liable to power hop than synchromesh. Besides the damping action provided by shock absorbers, the small but "punctual" damping provided by dry friction as in leaf springs, has a noticeable effect in discouraging power hop.

A torque arm, offset to the right of center, is designed to equalize the vertical load on the two rear tires whether driving forward or in reverse. It is therefore probably effective in reducing reverse power hop. Thus we might list:

Factors affecting reverse power hop

Torque arm radius
Powerplant mount—frequency of driveline

Transmission type
Rear wheel track
Rear spring base (and roll rate)
Reduction ratio
Shock absorber position and setting
Suspension friction
Offset torque arm

Finally we have to admit that the conventional rear axle is liable to power hop, and that possibly the only complete escape is either a De Dion axle or independent rear wheels in which the drive gears are mounted on the sprung mass of the vehicle.

Forward power hop is rarely troublesome in passenger cars, but frequently encountered in trucks, where it is associated with beaming vibrations of the frame, and with "cab-nod," etc.

Note on Reverse Power Hop (Offset Torque Arm)

This note originally appeared at the end of Olley's monograph. We have moved it forward so that it follows the original section on reverse power hop, above.

It has been pointed out that the notes above on reverse power hop are not satisfactory. A test has just been made with an offset torque arm arranged as in Figure 6.40.

The arrangement is similar to that in Figure 6.39 except that the left hand torque arm is changed to a simple radius rod, being **pivoted** to the axle as shown. This leaves the right hand torque arm to take all the torque reaction. The front end of this arm is attached to the

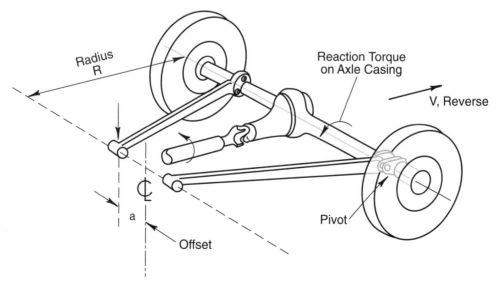

Figure 6.40 *Reverse power hop—offset torque arm.*

chassis 14 in. to the right of centerline [*distance a*], and the projected length R of the radius arm is 52 in. The ratio R/a is 3.7, which happens to be the same as the axle ratio.

The result is that in reverse power hop, instead of the left rear wheel doing most of the hopping, both rear wheels hop equally. But the hop still occurs.

The true description of reverse power hop is probably that, as the torque on the rear wheels builds up, the torque reaction on the axle casing pulls the rear of the vehicle down, compressing the rear springs. This does not change the vertical load on the rear tires (in the above case, with the offset torque arm). But when the torque on the rear tires reaches their traction limit the tires slip, and the torque momentarily disappears, releasing the rear springs, and allowing the rear of the vehicle to spring back up, beyond "design height." Bouncing of the rear of the vehicle and severe torque surges in the driveline occur, with periodic changes in rear wheel torque and in the load on the rear tires. This can continue indefinitely at a frequency intermediate between wheel hop frequency and the bounce frequency at the rear of the vehicle.

The effect on gravel roads is severe because of the sudden disintegration of the road surface at the traction limit. And the effect with a fluid drive is less severe because of fluid damping in the driveline. The effect of engine mount tuning is explained by the fact that an engine rocking frequency drastically lower than the power hop frequency will tend to avoid torque surges in the driveline.

6.10 Axle Tramp

Reference has been made to the fact that a conventional rear axle, when exercised on a bump rig, shows a clear tendency to tramp rather than to bounce parallel. A very clear example of this is seen on the bump rig when cams on the two rolls are not quite parallel. In the condition shown in Figure 6.41, an upward acceleration of the left rear wheel will tend to move the axle about the opposite center of percussion. Because of the considerable mass concentrated at A, the center of percussion will be at some point like B, well within the wheel track. Consequently the right rear wheel will be forced downward at the time that its cam, which is slightly delayed, hits it. Thus the "later" cam will deliver a much harder blow.

The result will be that, in the case shown, the right rear wheel will do nearly all the hopping when the wheels are driven forward as shown. When the rotation is reversed hopping will concentrate in the left rear wheel.

There have been many cases where even truly parallel cams will not sustain parallel wheel hop, the motion still tending to concentrate in one wheel. In such cases the hopping motion can be forced from one side to the other by bearing down heavily on the side which is hopping.

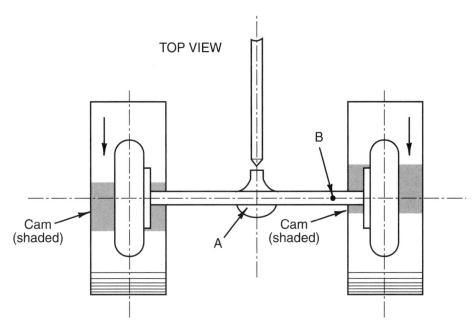

Figure 6.41 *Axle tramp on bump rig with offset cams (chassis rolls with cleats).*

On a De Dion axle with no concentrated mass at its center this reluctance to hop parallel is not seen, and the same tendency is seen on the road, with an almost complete absence of cross-shake.

Independent rear suspension (of all types) is equally free from a tramping tendency.

"Sculling Action"

When a rear axle is excited on the bump rig by alternate cams, tramping action occurs through the whole scale of frequency, Figure 6.42. But the nature of the tramping

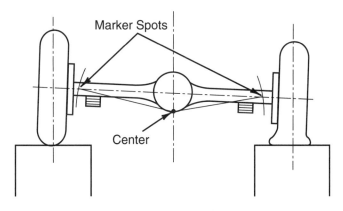

Figure 6.42 *Bump rig with alternate cams, low frequency. Rear view of Figure 6.41.*

changes with the frequency. Marker spots are placed at the ends of the axle as shown. At low frequencies the oscillation is seen to occur about a low center as shown. As the frequency increases the center of the tramp oscillation rises.

At high frequency, well above tramp resonance the oscillation center will have moved upward as shown in Figure 6.43. Neither of these extreme conditions will produce any considerable cross-shake in the car.

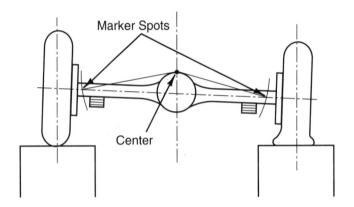

Figure 6.43 *Bump rig with alternate cams, high frequency.*

But at an intermediate frequency, generally rather close to tramp resonance, each of the marker spots may be seen to move in a vertical elliptical loop, as shown in Figure 6.44.

The tire treads move in inclined elliptical loops as shown, each tire moving outward in its lowest position. Thus the whole axle tramps with a "sculling" action.

The tire on the downward wheel is seen to be pulled outward thus (Figure 6.45), and it is evident that **camber thrust** contributes something to the feeding of energy into the tramp, and to the violence of the cross-shake induced by the sculling action.

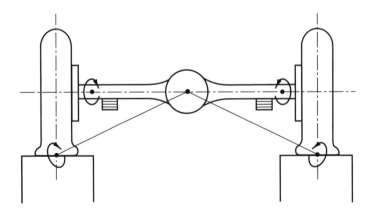

Figure 6.44 *Bump rig with alternate cams, intermediate frequency.*

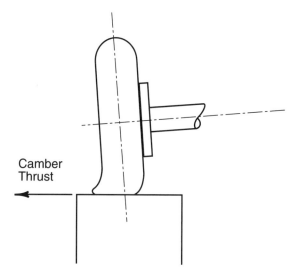

Figure 6.45 *"Sculling action" due to camber thrust, on a rolling road.*

But, if the roll axis of the **axle** is inclined for **roll understeer** [*see Figure 3.5*] the descending wheel is toed-out, as shown in Figure 6.46, when it meets the chassis roll. In case of, say, 2 in. of tramp at the wheels and a 10% roll understeer this toe-out angle may be 0.2 degree, which with the wheel flattened down on the chassis roll, could make the outward force F_Y as much as 40 or 50 lb.

This must be the explanation that roll understeer is found to be an important factor in increasing sculling action of the axle and consequent cross-shake of the car. And finally yaw of the axle in this same toe-out direction can come from the force F_X needed to speed up the downward wheel due to its decreasing rolling radius. If there is flexibility

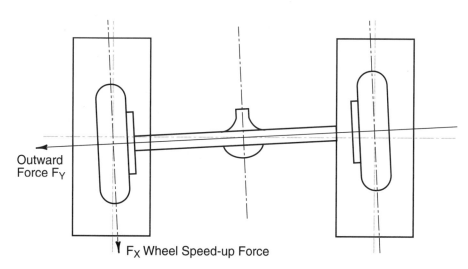

Figure 6.46 *"Sculling" action on the chassis rolls, top view.*

in the axle mounting, permitting such yawing motion, the outward force F_Y from slip angle thrust can be greatly increased.

I have never seen this sculling tendency strong enough to sustain an axle tramp of this nature on a smooth road. But it can greatly exaggerate axle tramp on road waves or washboard, or axle tramp induced by wheel unbalance or runout.

6.11 Crane-Simplex Linkage

Probably the best way to conduct road tests on an experimental car of any new type, in order to determine the most desirable roll steer condition for the rear axle, is by an experimental installation of the link control shown in Figure 6.47. The rear springs are shown shackled at both ends. Thus braking and driving **torques** are carried by the springs. But braking and driving **thrusts** and the "steering geometry" of the rear axle are entirely controlled by the two radius rods.

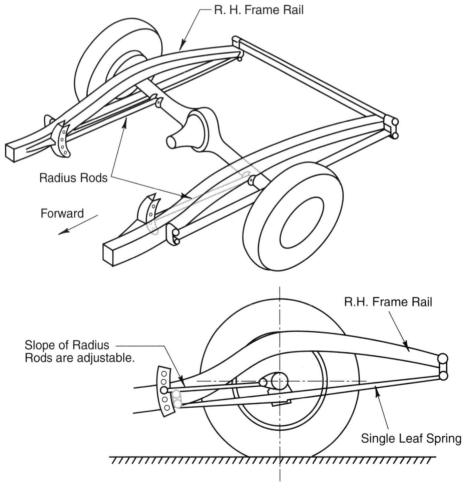

Figure 6.47 *Crane-Simplex linkage.*

By providing means such as the channel sectors shown for changing the slope of these rods at design height, rapid changes may be made in the rear roll steer. It might be desirable, for instance, to have provision for changing from 10% oversteer to 15% understeer. The percent roll steer is identical to the slope of the rods from horizontal at design height. Motion of the front shackle is actually so small that a plain spring end with a sliding pad or cam face is just as good.

The purpose of this test on any new experimental model is first of all to discover how much rear understeer is required for adequate handling stability. While the increase of rear understeer always produces an amazing improvement in the "feel" of directional stability, no more understeer than absolutely needed should be used (with the conventional axle) and this same test will show why this is so.

Increasing roll understeer:

- Increases road shock and "harshness"
- Increases lift of the rear end in brake-dive, and squat in acceleration
- Greatly increases axle tramp, and consequent cross-shake of the rear end on rough roads

The increased axle tramp is not merely a matter of cross-shake and discomfort in the rear seat. Far more serious is the effect on handling. When the rear wheels tramp it is seen that the tires leave the road. Bearing in mind that a tire must roll two feet or more in contact with the road before delivering the full lateral force for a given slip angle, it is easy to see that tires which will not stay on the ground represent a great loss in cornering capability. Consequently it can be stated that the greatest fault in a rear axle with excessive roll understeer is its tendency to go into a sudden **oversteer** on a rippled road turn. (But the above remarks apply to conventional rear axles. They do not apply to De Dion axles or independents. The heavier the mass of the differential at its center, the worse is the tramping tendency of the conventional axle.)

6.12 Damping of a Swing Axle

In sharp contrast to the conventional axle with its tramping tendency, one of the best features of the swing axle is the fact that lateral motion of the tire treads on the road caused by the ride motions provides considerable damping action on the ride, and may possibly provide some damping on the wheel hop. In any case, since the swing axle is an independent with only one degree of freedom, wheel hop tendency is much less than with an axle.

Ride damping with a swing axle depends on the cornering stiffness of the tire, i.e., on the lateral stiffness of the tire casing. It is appreciable even at touring speeds, though it varies inversely with car speed. When the vehicle bounces on the road the tire treads move in sinusoidal paths as in Figure 6.48. Suppose the amplitude of car bounce is Z, such that at any instant the vertical displacement is:

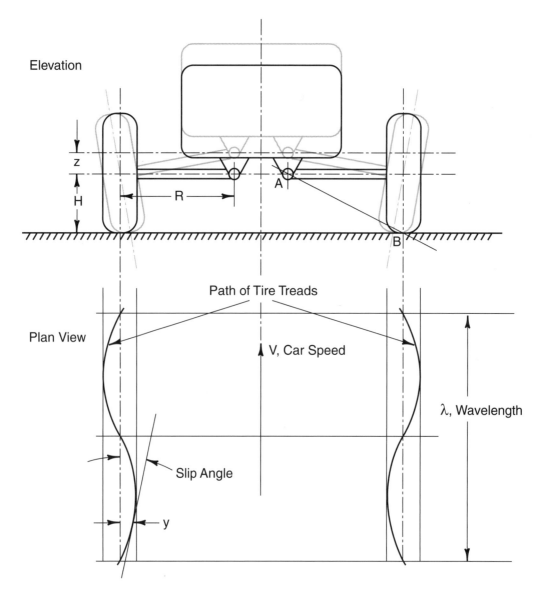

Figure 6.48 *Swing axle in ride, large track changes.*

$$z = Z\sin \omega t \qquad (6.10)$$

where t is time, and ω is the bounce frequency in radians per second.

Then vertical velocity $\quad \dot{z} = \dfrac{dz}{dt} = Z\omega\cos \omega t \qquad (6.11)$

Lateral displacement $\quad y \cong \dfrac{H}{R}z = \dfrac{H}{R}Z\sin \omega t \qquad (6.12)$

and lateral velocity

$$\dot{y} = \frac{H}{R}Z\omega\cos\omega t = \frac{H}{R}\dot{z} \qquad (6.13)$$

The slip angle in radians:

$$\alpha = \frac{\dot{y}}{V} = \frac{H}{R}\frac{\dot{z}}{V} \qquad (6.14)$$

If C is the cornering stiffness of the tire in lb./rad., the lateral force at the tire tread at any instant

$$F_y = C\alpha = C\frac{H}{R}\frac{\dot{z}}{V} \qquad (6.15)$$

And the resultant **vertical** force on the car body:

$$F = \frac{H}{R}F_y = \frac{CH^2}{VR^2}Z\omega\cos\omega t \qquad (6.16)$$

This force varies sinusoidally and is (on these assumptions) 180 degrees out of phase with the vertical velocity. When the body is at its maximum velocity downward the lift from the tire cornering force is at a maximum upward. Therefore this is **equivalent to a fluid damping of the riding motion**.

It is useful to estimate the value of this damping force.

The damping coefficient is evidently $\dfrac{CH^2}{VR^2}$

If   M = sprung mass on one wheel (slugs)
     m = unsprung mass on one wheel (slugs)
     K_W = wheel rate (lb./ft.)
     K_T = tire rate (lb./ft.)

And if the k^2/ab ratio for the sprung mass $\cong 1$, then

Bounce frequency

$$\omega = \sqrt{\frac{K_T K_W}{K_T + K_W}\frac{1}{M}} \qquad (6.17)$$

Critical damping coefficient

$$c_{cM} = 2\sqrt{\frac{K_T K_W}{K_T + K_W}M} = 2M\omega \qquad (6.18)$$

Wavelength $$\lambda = \frac{2\pi V}{\omega}$$ (6.19)

Example

Let $\left.\begin{array}{l} H = 12.5 \text{ in.} \\ R = 25 \text{ in.} \end{array}\right\} \Rightarrow \frac{H}{R} = 0.50$

$W = 900 \text{ lb.} \Rightarrow M = W/g = 900/32.2 = 27.95 \text{ slugs}$

$K_W = 140 \text{ lb./in.} = 1680 \text{ lb./ft.}$

$K_T = 1000 \text{ lb./in.} = 12000 \text{ lb./ft.}$

Then   Ride rate $= \dfrac{K_T K_W}{K_T + K_W} = 1474 \text{ lb./ft.}$

Ride frequency $= \omega = \sqrt{\dfrac{1474}{27.95}} = 7.26 \text{ rad./sec.} = 69.5 \text{ cpm}$

If cornering coefficient $C' = 0.167 = \dfrac{C}{W}$

then $C = C'W = 0.167 \times 900 = 150 \text{ lb./deg.} = 8600 \text{ lb./rad.}$

and $\dfrac{CH^2}{R^2} = 2150 \text{ lb./rad.}$

Critical damping coefficient, $c_{cM} = 2M\omega = 2 \times 27.95 \times 7.26 = 406 \text{ lb.-sec./ft.}$

Wavelength, $\lambda = \dfrac{2\pi}{\omega} V = 0.865V$ (ft.)

Velocity (mph)	10	20	30	40	50	60
Velocity (ft./sec.)	14.7	29.3	44	58.7	73.3	88
Damping coefficient (lb.-sec./ft.)	146	73.3	49	36.6	29.3	24.5
% Critical damping	36	18	12	9	7.2	6
Wavelength λ (ft.)	12.7	25.3	38	50.7	63.3	76

Compared with the 25% critical damping required for normal ride control, the damping figures quoted above are quite significant, even up to 60 mph. They are plotted in Figure 6.49 and account for the fact that (on dry roads at least) not much shock absorber action is required or is even admissible in a swing axle.

Figure 6.49, however, shows the damping running up toward infinity at low speeds and we know this is not true. When the vehicle is standing, the change in wheel track as it bounces acts primarily to stiffen the suspension because of the lateral elasticity of the tire casing. And it is logical to suppose that at low road speeds, well below 10 mph, this stiffening effect predominates.

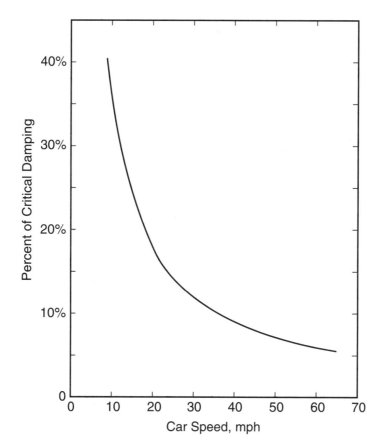

Figure 6.49 *Swing axle tire damping.*

We can probably compare the wavelength λ with the distance lag [*relaxation length*] of the tire, which we might assume to be 2 feet. Then, below a wavelength of, say, 8 feet the stiffening effect rather than the damping effect would predominate. This agrees in a general way with actual experience on swing axles in which at extreme low speeds the ride is usually rather stiff-legged, while the high speed ride is exceptionally well damped.

It may be well to take a look at the damping of the unsprung mass. If Z is the vertical amplitude of wheel hop, vertical force on wheel due to tire slip angle (assuming constant cornering stiffness):

$$F = \frac{CH^2}{VR^2} Z\omega \cos \omega t \tag{6.20}$$

where ω = wheel hop frequency in rad./sec.:

$$\omega = \sqrt{\frac{K_T + K_W}{m}} \tag{6.21}$$

Critical damping coefficient

$$c_{cm} = 2\sqrt{m(K_T + K_W)} = 2m\omega \tag{6.22}$$

Let unsprung weight equal 100 lb. (that is, $m = 100/32.2 = 3.10$ slugs)

Then, $K_T + K_W = 13680$ lb./ft.

Wheel hop frequency, $\omega = \sqrt{\dfrac{13680}{3.10}} = 66.3$ rad./sec. $= 635$ cpm

Critical damping coefficient, $c_{cm} = 2 \times 3.10 \times 66.3 = 412$ lb.-sec./ft.

The critical damping coefficient for the unsprung mass is virtually the same as for the ride. Thus theoretically the damping of the unsprung mass is equally effective. But, when we look at the value of λ, the wavelength, this looks very doubtful.

Velocity (mph)	10	20	30	40	50	60
Velocity (ft./sec.)	14.7	29.3	44	58.7	73.3	88
Wavelength in wheel hop (ft.)	1.39	2.78	4.17	5.57	6.95	8.33

At the high speed of 60 mph, it seems probable that appreciable wheel hop damping may occur. But it seems clear that at lower speeds up to 30 mph, the effect of the changing wheel track is principally to increase the ride rate. (Observation on the bump rig does not entirely agree. There appears to be more damping of wheel hop than above estimates would suggest. Evidently more experimental work on the development of lateral forces in tires under oscillating changes of slip angle is required. Also it seems probable that these tire characteristics vary enormously both with changes in tire construction and with changes in tire characteristics caused by mileage.)

6.13 Note on Raised Roll Center without Swing Axle

It should be noted that the ratio H/R for the swing axle indicates the slope of the line AB in Figure 6.48 and is a measure of rate of change of the wheel track. Just as in the case of brake "anti-dive" angles, there is no necessary connection with the actual construction details of the swing axle. Thus a parallel independent of "**Type 2**" (Section 6.2, Figure 6.13, "Parallel with Track Change") with a raised roll center has the same ride damping, for a given rate of track change, as a swing axle. However, as the damping coefficient depends on $(H/R)^2$, the damping effect is very small for small lifts of the roll center. The damping effect probably begins to be appreciable for inclinations of the line AB of about 15°, corresponding to a lift of about 8 in. of the roll center with a 60 in. wheel track.

6.14 Handling Factors (Report by Robert Schilling, GMPG, 1938[46])

In this report, Schilling considers some oscillation modes of the unsprung that Olley does not cover; also he amplifies some of Olley's coverage. At the risk of some redundancy, it has seemed best to present the Schilling material exactly as it appears in his report.

Waddle and Side Chuck

These actions have been previously described by Maurice Olley. I repeat here his illustration Figure 6.50. Figure 6.51a shows the desirable combination in more detail. In Figure 6.51b the axle is shown in tramped position due to a changed road camber.

If the change from (a) to (b) in Figure 6.51 is fast enough, the mass of the body will remain almost stationary since it is about five times as large as that of the axle. That means the axle has to swing around the roll center. It develops an inertia force F_I at the axle center and two side slip forces F_Y at the tires. These are transmitted to the body at the roll center and tend to rock it counterclockwise around the center of gravity. The spring deflections produce vertical forces F which tend to cause clockwise rocking. At the correct roll center height the two moments balance and the body does not roll at all.

This action will take place if the axle is made to tramp at frequencies from 400 to 700 cycles per minute—wheel hop frequency or slightly slower. All larger axle motions are of this frequency.

From our experience during the last year [*1937–38*] we have drawn the following conclusions:

Rear   The highest roll center location tried so far—about 16 in.—proved the best and must be just about correct because on the road the feeling of waddle has com-

---

[46] This is an internal GM Proving Ground memo from the Milliken Research Associates files.

a. Parallel independent.

b. Axle with high
   roll center.

c. Axle with correct
   roll center height.

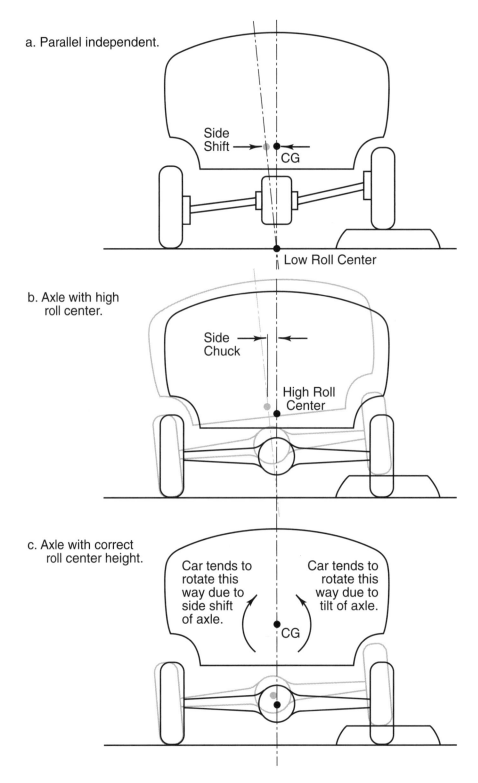

Figure 6.50 *Olley on waddle.*

a.

b.

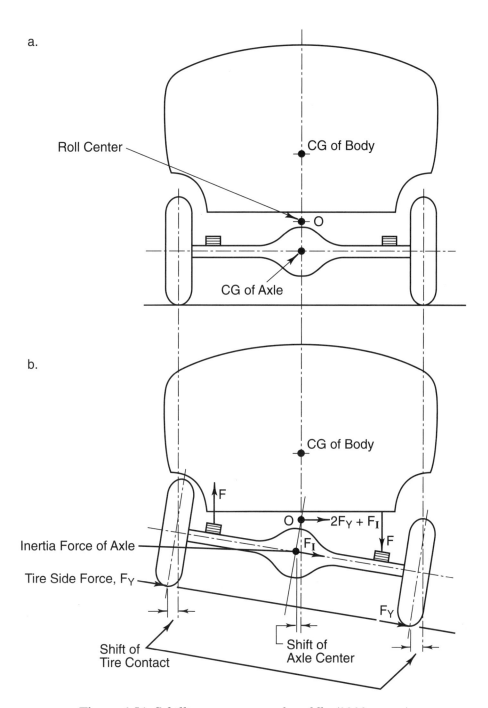

Figure 6.51 *Schilling on tramp and waddle (1938 report).*

pletely disappeared. The car can be driven over the worst potholes with the rear seat evidently moving ahead in a straight line.

This is confirmed by observation on the bump rig. If the axle here is made to tramp by running on alternate cams, the wheel hop resonance does not produce any appreciable side motion of the body. When running up and down the speed range, this resonance is hardly noticeable in the rear seat.

Front   The roll center height of 10 inches that we tried proved far too high. There was a very marked side chuck. The driver and front seat passenger could feel and see it on a road with variable camber. The worst of it was that it kept changing the direction of the car and therefore gave the impression of interfering with the steering.

This action lowers the **desirable** front roll center to somewhere under 5 inches. The high limit seems to vary for different cars and we don't seem to know yet what determines it.

Wheelhouse Clearance

If the rear roll axis is lifted from 10 to 16 inches the lateral motion of the tires toward the wheel housing due to a 6 degree roll will be reduced by 1/2 inch. That means that it is permissible to reduce the wheel housing clearance and widen the seat by one inch.

Tire Scrub

We said already that a high roll center is impossible without "scrub" (on the drawing layout). Figure 6.51b shows that this scrub actually occurs on the road. This has not shown any bad effect on tire wear for rear roll centers up to 16 inches. But we have noticed cupping on front tires with very short mileage when using 10 inches front roll center height. This effect has disappeared at 6 inches front roll center.

Scrub Damping

Figure 6.51b also shows that the scrub forces F_Y produce a moment around the roll center opposed to the tramp motion of the axle. This provides very efficient tramp damping. On the bump rig we have observed that axles with high roll center have much less tramp amplitude than those with low roll center. If the lateral velocity of the axle is v and the car speed is V the angle of the tire path with respect to the car centerline is v/V. The lateral force F_Y is proportional to this slip angle and therefore also proportional to lateral velocity and inverse to car speed. The tramp damping due to scrub becomes less at high speed.

On the front wheels these forces also enter into the wheelfight cycle, since they produce precession [*or aligning*] torques around the kingpins. Their timing is opposed to the wheelfight motion caused by other factors, so that they tend to stop it. At low speed they are much larger than others and are liable to cause a particular type of wheelkick of their own. However, this does not appear for less than 6 inches front roll center height.

Rear Axle Side Shake

One very important effect of a high roll center on a rear axle is the suppression of axle side shake. How this cycle looks on a car with roll center below the axle center is again shown in Figure 6.52. From an observation of the bump rig we plot Figure 6.53. This shows on top the usual wheel hop curve, as measured at the wheel center, and at bottom the side shake amplitude at the center of the axle. We see that at low speed [*or low frequency*] the side shake is an almost fixed percentage of the hop as it must be with the oscillation center observed, but instead of decreasing in proportion to the hop, it builds up to its own resonance and drops only after that.

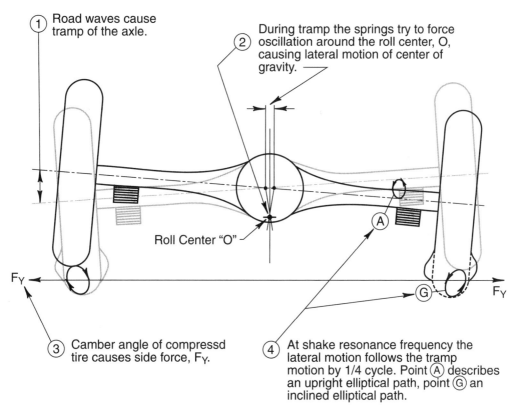

① Road waves cause tramp of the axle.

② During tramp the springs try to force oscillation around the roll center, O, causing lateral motion of center of gravity.

Roll Center "O"

F_Y

③ Camber angle of compressd tire causes side force, F_Y.

④ At shake resonance frequency the lateral motion follows the tramp motion by 1/4 cycle. Point Ⓐ describes an upright elliptical path, point Ⓖ an inclined elliptical path.

⑤ Point Ⓖ travels outward when the side force, F_Y, is directed outward. The cycle receives energy from the road.

A   G F_Y

Figure 6.52 Rear axle side shake, low roll center.

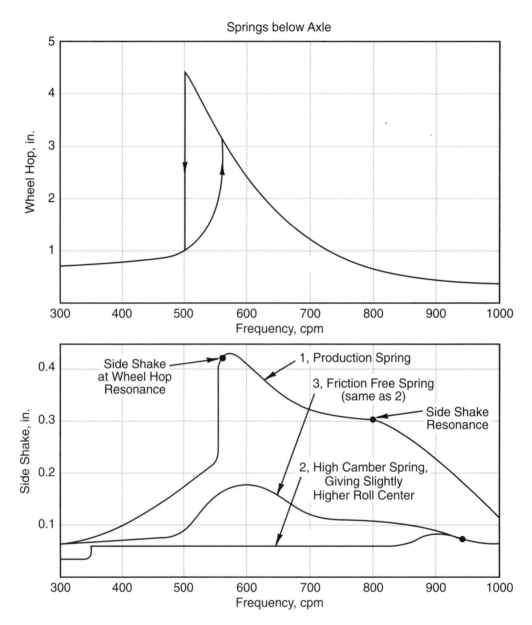

Figure 6.53 *Rear axle side shake vs. excitation frequency.*

We found the following means effective to control side shake:

- Friction in the springs. This is very effective but will spoil the ride and handling if applied in sufficient amount. It also is not reliable since it usually changes during the life of the spring.

- Higher lateral stiffness, to move the resonance farther away from the wheel hop resonance. This must be done in any case, the resonance should be at least 900 cpm. But since it is not easy to increase the stiffness very much with a conventional Hotchkiss design, it is usually impossible to stop side shake by this means alone.

- Higher roll center, to reduce the excitation of wheel hop.

A slight raising of the roll center by using higher camber springs combined with a tension shackle, which increased the lateral stiffness, has given us side shake curves like those shown in Figure 6.53(2). This, however, still relied somewhat on the friction in the springs. The same geometry with an almost friction free spring is also shown as curve (3).

The most reliable results have always been obtained with a roll center above the axle center. The cycle then appears as shown in Figure 6.54 and gives curves like those shown in Figure 6.55.

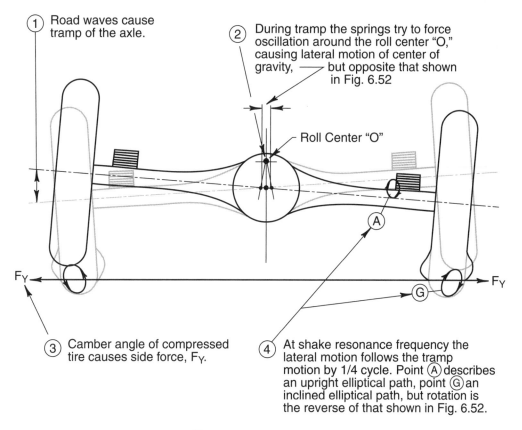

Figure 6.54 Rear axle side shake, high roll center.

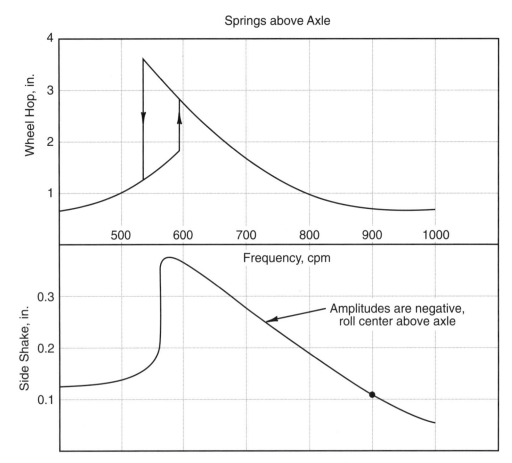

Figure 6.55 *Rear axle side shake vs. excitation frequency, high roll center.*

This set-up on the bump rig shows considerable side motion of the axle but no resonant condition. The difference from Figure 6.52 is mainly due to the fact that here during resonance the camber forces of the tire are opposed to the lateral motion and are therefore damping forces. With a low roll center they were in the same direction as the motion and therefore increasing it.

With high roll center it is not necessary to rely on spring friction anymore to keep the axle under control, but it is still very desirable to keep the shake resonance far above wheel hop resonance. The reason is as follows:

In the case of low roll center, where the side shake partially energizes itself from the road, we get a picture that looks about like Figure 6.56a. A single bump will start the side shake and it will then tend to increase due to the self-energization along limit lines (1). The damping forces tend to decrease it along lines (2). The result will be a slow decrease along lines (3), so that we get some four or five shakes from every single road bump.

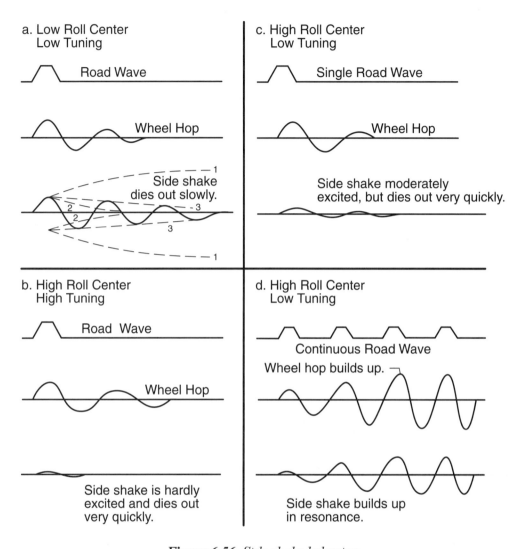

Figure 6.56 Side shake behavior.

With the high roll center and high tuning [*a high natural frequency in side shake*] we get a picture like Figure 6.56b. Here the difference in tuning plus the strong inherent damping keep the first amplitude very small. After the bump is passed there is no energization and the motion is stopped very quickly. The same is still true if the tuning is low, say, about the same as wheel hop, only the side shake will pick up a little more from the hop due to the closer tuning, Figure 6.56c.

Side shake gets very serious, however, if a series of waves are encountered that are just about spaced right for wheel hop, Figure 6.56d. Here the wheel hop will build up and from it in turn the side shake will build up to quite large amplitudes. This can only be avoided by tuning the side shake considerably higher, so that even if there is wheel hop, the side shake will remain small.

Camber Change or Swing Arm Action

This action can only be controlled when an independent suspension is used and therefore at present interests us only for our front suspensions. The instantaneous center of motion of a wheel is the intersection of the two wishbone centerlines in front view. If the distance from this point to the wheel is L the camber will change at the rate of 1/L radian or 57/L degrees per inch of wheel travel.

In a plot of camber angles against standing height—see Figure 6.57—the tangent at normal standing height must have the same slope, 57/L. Due to the uneven length of the wishbones, the length L will vary with the standing height as the slope of the curve varies.

Roll Cambering

On our present production cars [*1938*] the camber change is practically zero, the swing arm infinite at normal standing height. This means that when the car rolls the wheels roll with it and the average change of camber left and right is equal to the roll angle of the car. It has been pointed out repeatedly that this is a cause of loss of cornering capability and of tire squeal, although the understeer that results improves the handling.

Figure 6.58a shows the camber angles between tires and road for the 1938 BOP [*Buick/Olds/Pontiac*] suspension and Figure 6.58b for a swing arm of 100 inches. With the known tire characteristics we can compute the steering effect due to this cambering action.

The computed values are also shown in Figures 6.58a and 6.58b. They amount to 19% understeer at 5 degrees roll angle in the first case and 13% in the second case. This is a very material change and must be balanced by some other factor in order to maintain the handling of the car.

The beneficial effects of reduced wheel camber are:

- Less tire wear and squeal because the tires are not "rolled under" so much and because the slip angles are smaller. Figure 6.59 shows the speeds of incipient squeal as measured on the skid pad for a car with infinite swing arm and one with 100 inch swing arm.

- The cornering stiffness of the tire is not reduced so much by camber. The steering reaction at low lateral acceleration is quicker, and the car has a generally better response. Even at very high lateral accelerations it is still possible to steer the car quickly and easily.

6.15 Summary

With highly compliant suspensions in use today (2000), oscillations of the unsprung masses may be even more troublesome than they were in Olley's day. These oscillations

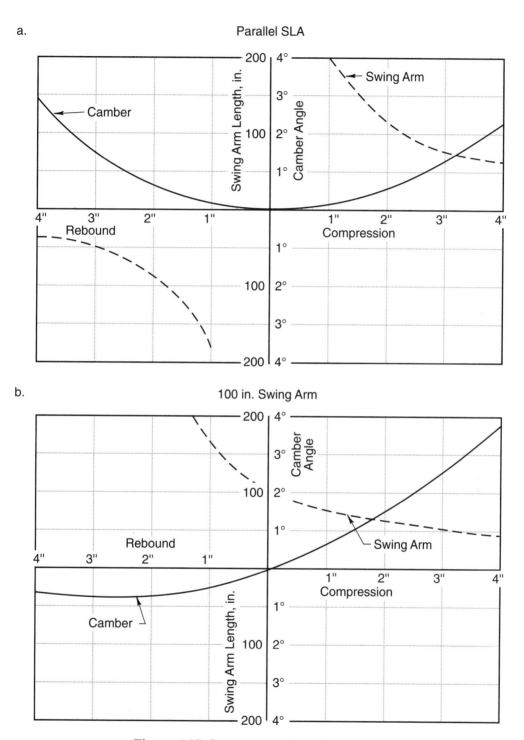

Figure 6.57 *Swing arm and camber change.*

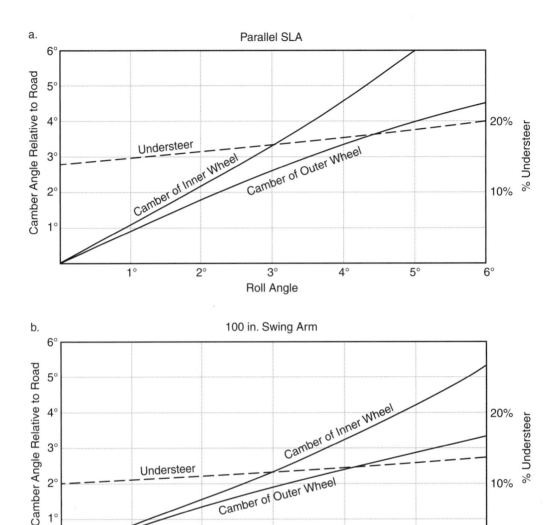

Figure 6.58 *Roll cambering of front wheels.*

can be violent and may damage the structure of the vehicle. Less severe cases may still contribute to structural fatigue, and may also degrade the ride (i.e., shake) and handling (i.e., steering wheel "wheelfight"), or make unacceptable noises. Numerous forms of oscillation have been categorized and at least two of these, shimmy and caster wobble, are self-sustaining—even on smooth roads. Oscillations of the unsprung masses take a toll on roadways as well as vehicles, evidenced by "washboard" dirt/gravel roads and waves in asphalt, often seen in the braking zone before an intersection. Solutions to control these oscillations are often complex—chassis stiffness, suspension geometry, steering geometry, drivetrain characteristics, tire characteristics, mass ratios (sprung to unsprung), damping, friction and compliances are all possible contributors.

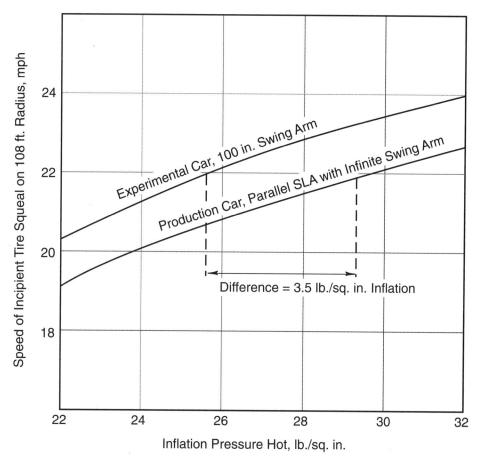

Figure 6.59 *Reduction of tire squeal due to swing arm action.*

Hopefully, unsprung mass oscillations are found in lab tests or in vehicle development, before a new design is committed to production. One major advance since Olley wrote these notes has been the introduction of new vibration (and acoustic) test equipment to supplement or replace "bumpy" chassis rolls. Various types of shaker and bump rigs now exist which can provide a wide range of simulated road inputs to a test vehicle. Modal analysis, a relatively new measurement and analysis technique, has supplanted the single channel capability of the Strobotac. Multi-channel modal testing typically uses accelerometers to measure the motion of a structure and allows detailed visualization of vibrational modes and frequencies.

Springfield, Mass., April 1922, with Springfield-built 40/50 hp Rolls-Royce ("Silver Ghost" type). Believed to be near Olley's home. Left to right: Olley's sister Florence, unknown, Mrs. Norma Marie Olley, Maurice Olley. Photo Credit Rolls-Royce Heritage Trust.

CHAPTER 7

Suspension Linkages

"And although I have called my linkage solutions 'approximate' the results obtained are frequently much more accurate than the drawing layouts and serve to correct errors in the layouts."

Maurice Olley
Letter to Bill Milliken, 1958

7.1 Introduction

In this chapter, Olley is tackling a subject of great interest to him—suspension linkage analysis. He frequently refers to it in his correspondence, noting that he had returned to the subject on several occasions to improve and expand his treatment. Traditionally, the kinematics of suspensions and steering systems were designed on the drafting board but Olley recognized that an analytical approach, however approximate, offered a basic level of understanding worth going after.

Olley demonstrates his facility in engineering mathematics—not then common in design circles. He makes useful simplifying assumptions and proceeds to develop solutions which give reliable results in the normal range of suspension and steering system movements. We found this chapter to be an education in how suspensions really work and an example of why Olley was such a great engineer. His approach is a balanced one of intuition, physical insight, and applied mathematics. A student would do well to absorb this chapter before relying on modern suspension computer programs for design studies.

Olley starts by outlining his basic assumptions. In Section 7.2 he applies them to a simplified double A-frame front suspension without offsets, i.e., the suspension links extend to the wheel center plane. He calculates roll center height, camber change and lateral scrub.

This chapter was reviewed by R. Thomas Bundorf, and his suggestions were incorporated.

In the next section, 7.3, he develops the correct slope of the steering tie rod for minimizing bump steer. Sections 7.4 and 7.5 extend this steering analysis to include anti-dive and swept A-frames (rotational axis non-parallel to vehicle centerline). Section 7.6 repeats the analysis with offset A-frames and 7.7 gives a numerical example showing that including the offsets in the analysis is desirable.

Section 7.8 changes from front suspension to a link rear axle, comparing the front view analysis of double A-frames to the side view of a link rear axle suspension. The controlling parameters are similar and a numerical example is included. The analysis is extended to include offsets in Section 7.9, with a comparison between a numerical example and a drawing layout. The remaining sections analyze ride and wheel rates, effects of camber and the use of torsion springs.

In short, this chapter describes a reasonably comprehensive treatment of suspension and steering kinematics.

Approximate solution of linkage problems is useful in connection with all types of front and rear suspensions containing radius arms, including wheel and steering geometry, wheel rates, etc.

The solutions all depend on approximations to the circular arc, Figure 7.1b, and chiefly on the simplest approximation, namely:

$$y \cong \frac{z^2}{2R} \tag{7.1}$$

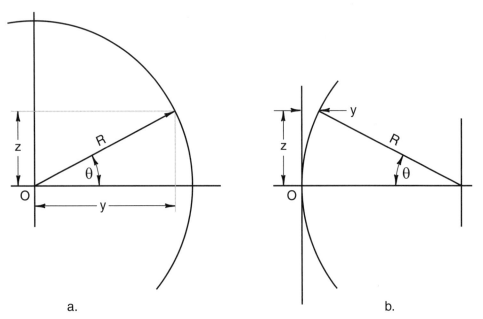

a.   b.

Figure 7.1 Circular arc.

This is actually a parabolic arc, and is inaccurate to the extent that if $\theta = 30°$, so that $z = R/2$, this will give $y = 0.125R$ instead of the correct figure of **$y = 0.134R$**.

To derive the approximation consider the following: The equation for a circle with origin at the center, using Figure 7.1a is:

$$y^2 + z^2 = R^2 \tag{7.2}$$

Note we use y and z to place the linkage analysis in the SAE coordinate system, where x is the longitudinal axis of the vehicle.

If the origin is moved to the circle's circumference (Figure 7.1b), y^2 is replaced by $(y - R)^2$, and the equation becomes,

$$(y - R)^2 + z^2 = R^2 \tag{7.3}$$

or
$$y^2 - 2yR + R^2 + z^2 = R^2 \tag{7.4}$$

and
$$z^2 = 2Ry - y^2 \tag{7.5}$$

Olley assumes y^2 is small and can be neglected compared to 2Ry, then,

$$z^2 \cong 2Ry \quad \text{and} \quad y \cong \frac{z^2}{2R} \tag{7.6}$$

*This is the equation for a parabola, i.e., it is in the form $y = z^2/2p$, where p is the distance between the directrix and the focus. Note that the **true** value of y is given by,*

$$y = R - R\cos\theta \tag{7.7}$$

and for $\theta = 30°$, $y = R(1 - 0.866) = 0.134R$

The statement $y = z^2/2R$ is really the first step in a series:

$$y = \frac{z^2}{2R}\left(1 + \frac{z^2}{4R^2} + \frac{z^4}{8R^4} + \cdots\right) \tag{7.8}$$

and even the second step $y = \dfrac{z^2}{2R}\left(1 + \dfrac{z^2}{4R^2}\right)$ would give great increase in accuracy.

The series relationship is developed as follows:

Start with the Equation 7.5 for a circle with origin of the axis system on the circumference, i.e.,

$$y^2 - 2yR + z^2 = 0 \tag{7.9}$$

This is a quadratic equation of the form, $ay^2 + by + c = 0$, whose solution is,

$$y = \frac{-b \pm \sqrt{b^2 - 4ac}}{2a} \tag{7.10}$$

In terms of Equation 7.9, the solution is (choose the minus sign solution):

$$y = \frac{2R - \sqrt{4R^2 - 4z^2}}{2} \tag{7.11}$$

$$y = R - \sqrt{R^2 - z^2} \tag{7.12}$$

$$\frac{y}{R} = 1 - \sqrt{1 - \frac{z^2}{R^2}} \tag{7.13}$$

The last term (square root) can be expressed as a series using the binomial expansion which in general form is,

$$(a \pm b)^n = a^n \pm \frac{n}{1}a^{n-1}b \pm \frac{n(n-1)}{2!}a^{n-2}b^2 \pm \frac{n(n-1)(n-2)}{3!}a^{n-3}b^3 \pm \cdots \tag{7.14}$$

In our case, $a = 1$, $b = -z^2/R^2$, and $n = 0.5$

  1st term is: 1

  2nd term is: $\left(\frac{0.5}{1}\right)(1)^{-0.5}\left(-\frac{z^2}{R^2}\right) = +\frac{z^2}{2R^2}$

  3rd term is: $\left(\frac{0.5}{1}\right)\left(\frac{-0.5}{2}\right)(1)^{-1.5}\left(-\frac{z^2}{R^2}\right)^2 = +\frac{z^4}{8R^4}$

4th term is: $\left(\dfrac{0.5}{1}\right)\left(\dfrac{-0.5}{2}\right)\left(\dfrac{-1.5}{3}\right)(1)^{-2.5}\left(-\dfrac{z^2}{R^2}\right)^3 = +\dfrac{z^6}{16R^6}$

Hence,

$$\sqrt{1 - \frac{z^2}{R^2}} = 1 + \frac{z^2}{2R^2} + \frac{z^4}{8R^4} + \frac{z^6}{16R^6} + \cdots \tag{7.15}$$

and

$$\frac{y}{R} = 1 - 1 + \frac{z^2}{2R^2} + \frac{z^4}{8R^4} + \frac{z^6}{16R^6} + \cdots \tag{7.16}$$

$$y = \frac{z^2}{2R} + \frac{z^4}{8R^3} + \frac{z^6}{16R^5} + \cdots \tag{7.17}$$

$$y = \frac{z^2}{2R}\left(1 + \frac{z^2}{4R^2} + \frac{z^4}{8R^3} + \cdots\right) \tag{7.18}$$

For example with $\theta = 30°$ [*using the first two terms of this series*], this will give:

$$y = 0.125R\left(1 + \frac{1}{16}\right) = 0.1328R \tag{7.19}$$

It would be desirable to include this second term, but the results become too complicated for use except in special cases.

It is well to bear in mind that, if R is 10 inches, the error in taking $y = z^2/2R$ is 0.090 inch, when $\theta = 30°$, but is only 0.006 inch when $\theta = 15°$. The approximation will give realistic results at or near the design position of a suspension, but is not generally accurate near bump and rebound positions. However, the results are useful, as will be seen in Figure 7.2.

When the arm is not initially horizontal but has an initial "lift" a, the expression for y becomes:

$$y \cong \frac{(z + a)^2 - a^2}{2R} = \frac{z^2}{2R} + \frac{za}{R} \tag{7.20}$$

(This is subject to the same error when angle θ becomes large.)

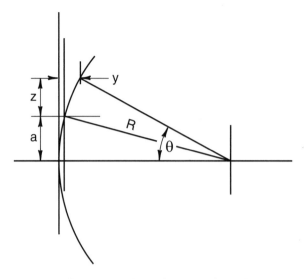

Figure 7.2 *Arm shown with "lift."*

7.2 Front Suspension with No Offsets (First Approximation)

Referring to Figure 7.3:

$$y_1 \cong \frac{z^2}{2R_1} + \frac{za}{R_1} \tag{7.21}$$

$$y_2 \cong \frac{z^2}{2R_2} + \frac{zb}{R_2} \tag{7.22}$$

Assume for the moment that the contact point of the tire, P, moves vertically, i.e., that $R_3 = \infty$ and $y_3 = 0$. There is no lateral motion or scrub of the tire in this case. For small motions, triangles PHy_1 and $P(H - h)y_2$ can be assumed to be similar and the lateral motions y_1 and y_2 are proportional to their height above the ground point P, which acts as a pin joint. By manipulation, this assumption yields Equations 7.23 through 7.26.

$$\frac{y_2}{H - h} = \frac{y_1}{H} \quad or \quad \frac{y_2}{H - h} - \frac{y_1}{H} = 0 \tag{7.23}$$

and

$$\frac{Hy_2}{H - h} - y_1 = 0 \tag{7.24}$$

$$Hy_2 - (H - h)y_1 = 0 \tag{7.25}$$

or

$$\frac{H}{h}y_2 - \frac{(H - h)}{h}y_1 = 0 \tag{7.26}$$

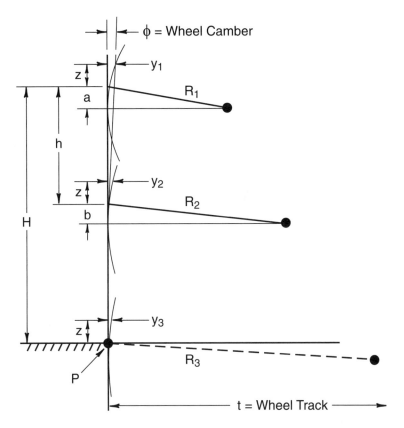

Figure 7.3 *Left front suspension, viewed from behind.*

If $R_3 \neq \infty$, as in Figure 7.3, then y_3 exists and $y_3 = \dfrac{H}{h} y_2 - \dfrac{(H-h)}{h} y_1$.

This can also be seen by superposition. First assume y_2 is zero. The wheel link then pivots about the end of link R_2 to produce an outward scrub at P equal to $(H-h) y_1/h$. Then assume y_1 is zero. The wheel link then pivots about the end of link R_1 to produce an inward scrub at P equal to Hy_2/h. The resulting scrub is given by Olley's Equation 7.27.

$$y_3 = \frac{H}{h} y_2 - \frac{H-h}{h} y_1 \qquad (7.27)$$

Inserting the solutions for y_1 and y_2 from Equations 7.21 and 7.22 gives Olley's next equations:

$$y_3 = \frac{H}{h}\left(\frac{z^2}{2R_2} + \frac{zb}{R_2}\right) - \frac{H-h}{h}\left(\frac{z^2}{2R_1} + \frac{za}{R_1}\right) \qquad (7.28)$$

$$y_3 = \frac{z^2}{2h}\left(\frac{H}{R_2} - \frac{H-h}{R_1}\right) + \frac{z}{h}\left(\frac{Hb}{R_2} - \frac{(H-h)a}{R_1}\right) \tag{7.29}$$

Hence:
$$\frac{dy_3}{dz} = \frac{z}{h}\left(\frac{H}{R_2} - \frac{H-h}{R_1}\right) + \frac{1}{h}\left(\frac{Hb}{R_2} - \frac{(H-h)a}{R_1}\right) \tag{7.30}$$

This is the "rate of tread [*track*] change" and can be used to indicate the **height of the roll axis.** *In Figure 7.4, a line at 90° to the slope dy_3/dz points to the linkage instant center, which then allows the roll center height to be calculated.*

Thus, when $z = 0$,
$$\frac{dy_3}{dz} = \frac{1}{h}\left(\frac{Hb}{R_2} - \frac{(H-h)a}{R_1}\right) \tag{7.31}$$

Then the height of roll center above the ground is:

$$z_R = \frac{t}{2}\frac{1}{h}\left(\frac{Hb}{R_2} - \frac{(H-h)a}{R_1}\right) \tag{7.32}$$

Due to Olley's sign convention, this gives a negative sign to a roll center that is above ground. Equation 7.32 and Figure 7.4 assume that the roll center is in the center of the car—left-right symmetry—and $z_R/(t/2) = dy_3/dz$.

The consistency of handling may be affected if the roll center moves as the car moves up and down on bumps, as z changes. Since the roll center height is linearly related to dy_3/dz then $d(dy_3/dz)/dz = d^2 y_3/dz^2$ is a measure of its movement. This is found by differentiating Equation 7.30.

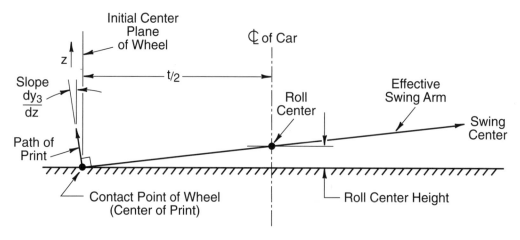

Figure 7.4 *Roll center construction, left front suspension.*

From dy_3/dz we get:

$$\frac{d^2y_3}{dz^2} = \text{curvature} \cong \frac{1}{R_3} = \frac{1}{h}\left(\frac{H}{R_2} - \frac{H-h}{R_1}\right) \tag{7.33}$$

This is zero when $H/(H-h) = R_2/R_1$, i.e., **when the lengths of the arms vary inversely as the heights of their outer ends from the ground, the tire contacts move in a straight line, i.e., the height of the roll axis remains fixed as the car moves up and down**. If also a = b, **there is no tread change**. The roll axis is on the ground, and the tire contacts move vertically.

R_3 is the effective radius of tire contact point motion. It is not the linkage instant center radius which is derived in Equation 7.39. This illustrates that the motion of points on a mass controlled by a four-bar linkage is not strictly defined by the instant center. The path of any mass point moves normal to the instant center, and the rotation of the mass is inversely proportional to the distance to the instant center, but the point may have a path radius that is much shorter, due to the continuing change of the instant center as the links are reoriented with wheel motion.

Camber Change

To avoid a confusing number of minus signs in the figuring, we have to call camber angle, ϕ, **positive** as drawn on Figure 7.3, even though we refer to this generally as **negative camber**.

Instead of Olley's inversion of the sign of camber angle, we've chosen to use wheel inclination angle, γ. For a left front wheel, negative camber angle is equal to positive inclination angle and Olley's derivation is correct. On the right hand wheels, negative camber is equal to negative inclination angle. A more complete explanation is given in Race Car Vehicle Dynamics, *Section 2.8 "SAE Tire Axis System."*

Then, camber [*inclination*] angle, γ (in radians): [*from 7.21 and 7.22*]

$$\gamma = \frac{y_1 - y_2}{h} = \frac{z^2}{2h}\left(\frac{1}{R_1} - \frac{1}{R_2}\right) + \frac{z}{h}\left(\frac{a}{R_1} - \frac{b}{R_2}\right) \tag{7.34}$$

Whence

$$\frac{d\gamma}{dz} = \frac{z}{h}\left(\frac{1}{R_1} - \frac{1}{R_2}\right) + \frac{1}{h}\left(\frac{a}{R_1} - \frac{b}{R_2}\right) \tag{7.35}$$

When z = 0,

$$\frac{d\gamma}{dz} = \frac{1}{h}\left(\frac{a}{R_1} - \frac{b}{R_2}\right) \tag{7.36}$$

The "camber [*inclination*] change radius" at design height is thus:

$$\gamma \cong \frac{d\gamma}{dz} z = \frac{z}{h}\left(\frac{a}{R_1} - \frac{b}{R_2}\right) \qquad (7.37)$$

But $\gamma \cong z/R$, *where R is the "inclination change radius"*

or
$$R = \frac{z}{\dfrac{z}{h}\left(\dfrac{a}{R_1} - \dfrac{b}{R_2}\right)} = \frac{h}{\left(\dfrac{a}{R_1} - \dfrac{b}{R_2}\right)} \qquad (7.38)$$

The camber [*inclination*] change radius

$$R = \frac{h}{(\text{slope upper arm}) - (\text{slope lower arm})} \qquad (7.39)$$

R is the distance to the linkage instant center. The height of the linkage instant center above ground is $H - R(a/R_1)$. *The angle of the line from tire contact patch to the linkage instant center is,*

$$\frac{H - R(a/R_1)}{R} = \frac{H}{R} - \frac{a}{R_1}$$

Substituting for R:

$$\frac{H}{h}\left[\frac{a}{R_1} - \frac{b}{R_2}\right] - \frac{a}{R_1} = -\frac{1}{h}\left[\frac{Hb}{R_2} - \frac{(H-h)a}{R_1}\right]$$

which is the negative of Equation 7.31, therefore Olley's "rate of tread [track] *change" does define the slope of a line to the linkage instant center.*

If $a/R_1 > b/R_2$ the camber [*inclination*] change radius is positive, meaning that the center of swing is **inside** the wheel, as in Figure 7.5.

A less usual arrangement is $a/R_1 < b/R_2$, which puts the center of swing outside the wheels, and thus gives an "inverted" swing axle effect.

When $a/R_1 = b/R_2$, i.e., **upper and lower arms are parallel, camber change radius is infinite. There is no camber change at this point**.

Certain constants are involved. These are:

$$\frac{1}{R_1} - \frac{1}{R_2} \text{ which can be called } P_1$$

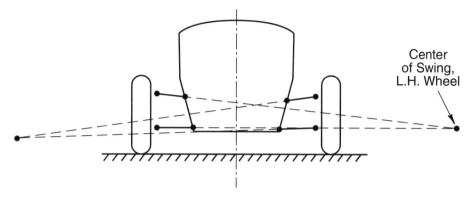

Figure 7.5 *Positive swing arm location.*

$\dfrac{a}{R_1} - \dfrac{b}{R_2}$ which can be called Q_1

$\dfrac{H}{R_2} - \dfrac{H-h}{R_1}$ which can be called P_2

$\dfrac{Hb}{R_2} - \dfrac{(H-h)a}{R_1}$ which can be called Q_2

Then:

Camber [*inclination*] angle: $\gamma = \dfrac{1}{h}\left(\dfrac{P_1 z^2}{2} + Q_1 z\right)$ (7.40)

Ride camber [*inclination*]: $\dfrac{d\gamma}{dz} = \dfrac{1}{h}\left(P_1 z + Q_1\right)$ (7.41)

[*Ride*] Camber change radius [*at design height*] $= \dfrac{h}{Q_1}$ (7.42)

Tread [*track*] change: $y_3 = \dfrac{1}{h}\left(\dfrac{P_2 z^2}{2} + Q_2 z\right)$ (7.43)

Ride scrub: $\dfrac{dy_3}{dz} = \dfrac{1}{h}\left(P_2 z + Q_2\right)$ (7.44)

[*Ride*] Scrub radius [*at design height*] $= \dfrac{h}{P_2}$ (7.45)

Roll center height [*at design height*]: $z_R = \dfrac{t}{2h}Q_2$ (7.46)

7.3 Steering Linkage (without Anti-Dive)

The way in which the steering tie rod is attached to the system affects steering introduced by ride and roll motion. The following analysis assesses the effect of the location, length and angle of the steering tie rod.

In Figure 7.6, B is the outer steering ball and A_1 is the inner ball in the theoretically perfect position.

Symbols y_1, y_2 and z are as in Section 7.2. [*Equations 7.21 and 7.22*]

The following ratios can be written,

$$\frac{y_1}{H} = \frac{y_2}{H-h} = \frac{y_4}{H-h+h-c} = \frac{y_4}{H-c}$$ (7.47)

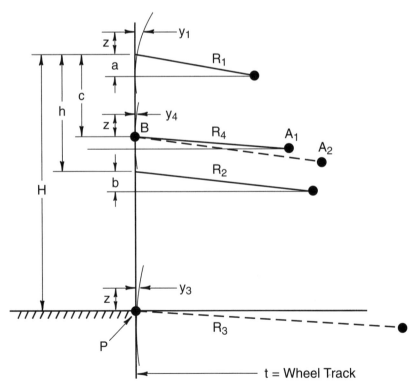

Figure 7.6 *Left front wheel viewed from behind, including steering linkage.*

Since $y_1 = \gamma H$ *or* $H = y_1/\gamma$,

$$\frac{y_4}{\dfrac{y_1}{\gamma} - c} = \frac{y_2}{\dfrac{y_1}{\gamma} - h} \quad\Rightarrow\quad \frac{y_4}{y_1 - c\gamma} = \frac{y_2}{y_1 - h\gamma} \tag{7.48}$$

$$y_4(y_1 - h\gamma) = y_2(y_1 - c\gamma) \tag{7.49}$$

$$y_4 y_1 - y_2 y_1 = y_4 h\gamma - y_2 c\gamma = \gamma(y_4 h - y_2 c) \tag{7.50}$$

But $\gamma = (y_1 - y_2)/h$, $\quad y_4 y_1 - y_2 y_1 = \dfrac{y_1 - y_2}{h}(y_4 h - y_2 c) \tag{7.51}$

$$(y_4 - y_2)y_1 = (y_1 - y_2)\left(y_4 - y_2\frac{c}{h}\right) \tag{7.52}$$

$$y_4 - y_2 = \left(1 - \frac{y_2}{y_1}\right)\left(y_4 - y_2\frac{c}{h}\right) \tag{7.53}$$

Solve for y_4: $\qquad\qquad y_4 = y_1 - \dfrac{c}{h}y_1 + \dfrac{c}{h}y_2 \tag{7.54}$

Then $\qquad\qquad\qquad y_4 = \dfrac{c}{h}y_2 + \left(1 - \dfrac{c}{h}\right)y_1 \tag{7.55}$

or $\qquad y_4 = \dfrac{z^2}{2h}\left(\dfrac{c}{R_2} + \dfrac{h-c}{R_1}\right) + \dfrac{z}{h}\left(\dfrac{cb}{R_2} + \dfrac{(h-c)a}{R_1}\right) \tag{7.56}$

This defines the motion of the outer steering tie rod ball.

$$\frac{dy_4}{dz} = \frac{z}{h}\left(\frac{c}{R_2} + \frac{h-c}{R_1}\right) + \frac{1}{h}\left(\frac{cb}{R_2} + \frac{(h-c)a}{R_1}\right) \tag{7.57}$$

When $z = 0$, $\qquad \dfrac{dy_4}{dz} = \dfrac{1}{h}\left(\dfrac{cb}{R_2} + \dfrac{(h-c)a}{R_1}\right) \tag{7.58}$

This is the correct slope of the steering tie rod at design height for "perfect" [*non-interfering*] **steering geometry.**

The curvature,
$$\frac{d^2y_4}{dz^2} = \frac{1}{h}\left(\frac{c}{R_2} + \frac{(h-c)}{R_1}\right) = \frac{1}{R_4} \qquad (7.59)$$

So the correct length of tie rod is:

$$R_4 = h\bigg/\left(\frac{c}{R_2} + \frac{(h-c)}{R_1}\right) \qquad (7.60)$$

Supposing that the steering linkage is to the **rear** of the kingpin, and that the slope of the tie rod is increased, like [*the dashed line in Figure 7.6*] $\overline{BA_2}$, then the wheels will **toe-out** as they rise. This is "roll understeer," and is useful for handling stability and for reducing wheelfight. Also, if the tie rod is longer than the correct length [*extend solid line past point A_1*], the wheels **toe-in** above and below center. The combined effect [*like $\overline{BA_2}$*], as illustrated by the path of the end of the wheel spindle, S, on the left front wheel, is as shown in Figure 7.7.

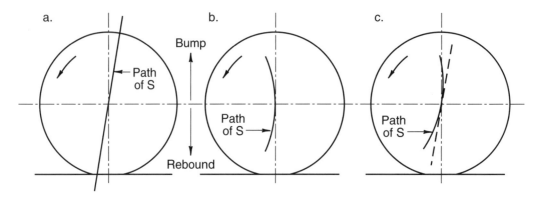

Figure 7.7 *Tie rod effect on path of the wheel spindle, left front wheel.*

In Figure 7.7, part "a." shows an understeer slope due to slope of the tie rod; "b." shows toe-in above and below center due to length of tie rod; "c." shows effect of slope and length combined. On a corner there is little change in angle on the outer, heavily loaded wheel [*bump*] while the slip angle on the inner, lightly loaded wheel [*rebound*] is **reduced**. This is beneficial to handling and tire wear.

To get comparable results with steering linkage **ahead** of the kingpin, the tie rods $\overline{BA_2}$ must be **shorter** than the theoretical length, and the inner ball A_2 has to be set **above** the theoretical height A_1.

7.4 Effect of Anti-Dive on Steering Linkage Layout

When anti-dive geometry is arranged as shown in Figure 7.8, there is an important effect on steering linkage layout.

The length of the equivalent radius arm:

$$L = \frac{h}{\tan \alpha} \qquad (7.61)$$

For perfect steering the lateral shifts (the **y's** of Figures 7.1, 7.2, 7.3 and 7.6) remain unchanged, whereas the vertical displacements (z in the earlier sketches) are reduced in the ratio $(L-d)/L$. Thus for rearward steering linkage, the correct **length** of tie rod is **reduced** in the ratio $((L-d)/L)^2$, and the correct **slope** of tie rod is **increased** in the ratio $L/(L-d)$.

It was not apparent to the authors how Olley arrived at the length and slope of the steering tie rod (for "perfect" steering) for the anti-dive case. The following derivation, which confirms Olley's results, was performed by MRA Associate, Edward Kasprzak.

The side view (Figure 7.8) gives the relationship $L = h/\tan \alpha$.

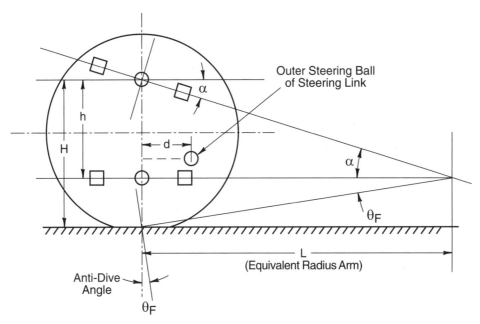

Figure 7.8 *Anti-dive layout, looking at left front wheel.*

With anti-dive, $\alpha \neq 0$, and L has a finite value (unlike the earlier case with no anti-dive, where $\alpha = 0$ and $L \to \infty$). Olley assumes that the lateral shifts of the A-arms and the outer steering ball joint remain unchanged, but the presence of anti-dive requires recalculation of the vertical shift. By similar triangles, Figure 7.9, it is seen that the vertical shift at the outer steering ball, z', can be calculated from the vertical shift at the wheel center, z, by:

$$z' = \frac{L-d}{L} z \qquad (7.62)$$

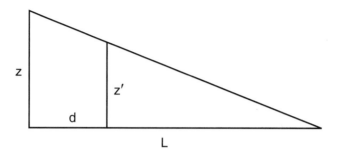

Figure 7.9 *Similar triangles used for tie rod location calculation.*

where d is the distance of the outer steering ball aft of the wheel center.

This change in vertical shift (with no change in lateral shift) requires the inner steering ball location be recalculated to maintain "perfect steering." From Olley's earlier derivation (Equation 7.56):

$$y_4 = \frac{z^2}{2h}\left(\frac{c}{R_2} + \frac{h-c}{R_1}\right) + \frac{z}{h}\left(\frac{cb}{R_2} + \frac{(h-c)a}{R_1}\right)$$ (7.63)

We are interested in the vertical motion at the outer steering ball, which is z', not z. Noting that $z = \left(L/(L-d)\right)z'$, and substituting into Equation 7.63:

$$y_4 = \left(\frac{L}{L-d}\right)^2 \frac{z'^2}{2h}\left(\frac{c}{R_2} + \frac{h-c}{R_1}\right) + \left(\frac{L}{L-d}\right)\frac{z'}{h}\left(\frac{cb}{R_2} + \frac{(h-c)a}{R_1}\right)$$ (7.64)

Taking the first derivative:

$$\frac{dy_4}{dz'} = \left(\frac{L}{L-d}\right)^2 \frac{z'}{h}\left(\frac{c}{R_2} + \frac{h-c}{R_1}\right) + \left(\frac{L}{L-d}\right)\frac{1}{h}\left(\frac{cb}{R_2} + \frac{(h-c)a}{R_1}\right)$$ (7.65)

The new slope at design height ($z' = 0$) is:

$$\frac{dy_4}{dz'} = \left(\frac{L}{L-d}\right)\frac{1}{h}\left(\frac{cb}{R_2} + \frac{(h-c)a}{R_1}\right)$$ (7.66)

*In comparison with the previous (no anti-dive) **slope** (from Equation 7.58):*

$$\frac{New}{Old} = \frac{\dfrac{dy_4}{dz'}}{\dfrac{dy_4}{dz}} = \frac{\left(\dfrac{L}{L-d}\right)\dfrac{1}{h}\left(\dfrac{cb}{R_2} + \dfrac{(h-c)a}{R_1}\right)}{\dfrac{1}{h}\left(\dfrac{cb}{R_2} + \dfrac{(h-c)a}{R_1}\right)} = \frac{L}{L-d}$$ (7.67)

*Therefore, the **slope increases**.*

Taking the second derivative:

$$\frac{d^2 y_4}{dz'^2} = \left(\frac{L}{L-d}\right)^2 \frac{1}{h}\left(\frac{c}{R_2} + \frac{h-c}{R_1}\right) = \frac{1}{R_4'} \qquad (7.68)$$

gives the new tie rod length as:

$$R_4' = \left(\frac{L-d}{L}\right)^2 h \bigg/ \left(\frac{c}{R_2} + \frac{(h-c)}{R_1}\right) \qquad (7.69)$$

*In comparison with the previous (no anti-dive) **length** (from Equation 7.60):*

$$\frac{New}{Old} = \frac{R_4'}{R_4} = \frac{\left(\dfrac{L-d}{L}\right)^2 h \bigg/ \left(\dfrac{c}{R_2} + \dfrac{(h-c)}{R_1}\right)}{h \bigg/ \left(\dfrac{c}{R_2} + \dfrac{(h-c)}{R_1}\right)} = \left(\frac{L-d}{L}\right)^2 \qquad (7.70)$$

*Therefore, the **length decreases**.*

There is another potential source of error when using anti-dive with a rear steering linkage; see Figure 7.10. As the equivalent radius L is decreased by increased anti-dive, the path of the outer steering ball becomes increasingly U-shaped, departing more and more from a circular arc. [*This may be easier to see with a diagram like Figure 17.21.*[47]]

When **forward** steering linkage is used with anti-dive, the correct **length** of tie rod **increases** in the ratio $((L+d)/L)^2$, and its **slope decreases** in the ratio $L/(L+d)$. Also, its path becomes closer to a true circular arc. With anti-dive geometry there are thus some significant advantages in **forward** steering linkage.

7.5 Wheel Motions with Arm-Planes at an Angle to the Transverse Plane

From R.B. Burton's "Coil Spring Wishbone Suspension"[48] notes of March 1949 (Report 132-83) one is inclined to think that these cases may be solved by projecting arm lengths and all motions in the transverse plane (see pages 34 and 110 in Burton's report).

---

[47] Milliken, W. F. and D. L. Milliken, *Race Car Vehicle Dynamics*, R-146, Society of Automotive Engineers, Warrendale, Pa., 1995, p. 632.

[48] The authors do not have a copy of this internal GM report.

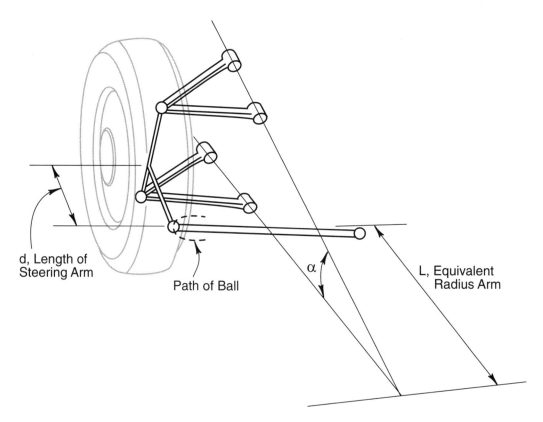

d, Length of Steering Arm

Path of Ball

α

L, Equivalent Radius Arm

Figure 7.10 Effect of side view swing arm length on path of outer steering ball.

Thus if α in Figure 7.11 is the angle in plan view the arm lengths would become $R_1/\cos\alpha$ and $R_2/\cos\alpha$ [*where R_1 and R_2 are lengths in the transverse plane (upper view in figure)*]. This may have been acceptable in suspensions of 1948/9. But with today's more complex geometry [*c. 1960*], **it is quite important to project the motions in the plane of swing**, as shown in Figure 7.11.

Lateral movement y in the plane of swing can then be projected as $y\cos\alpha$, in the transverse plane. It is particularly necessary to project **all steering geometry points** in the plane of swing, with due allowance for anti-dive, etc. [*Thus with arm planes at an angle, the skew projected view (Figure 7.11, lower panel) gives the correct length and angles for calculation of ride steer.*]

7.6 Greater Accuracy (Allowance for Offsets)

So far the linkage has been dealt with as though the outer ends of the upper and lower arms were in the plane of the wheel. This has had some advantages in showing general principles, but particularly in connection with link controlled **rear axles**, it has proved necessary to allow for the offsets. This is also necessary when calculating wheel rates in wishbone front suspension.

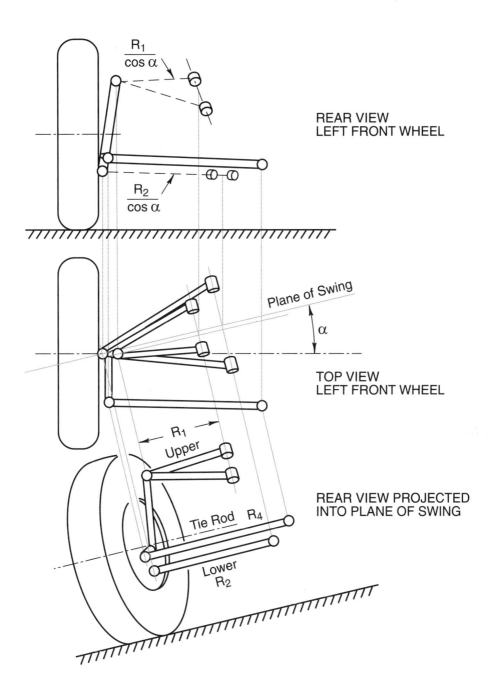

$\dfrac{R_1}{\cos \alpha}$

REAR VIEW
LEFT FRONT WHEEL

$\dfrac{R_2}{\cos \alpha}$

Plane of Swing

α

TOP VIEW
LEFT FRONT WHEEL

R_1

Upper

REAR VIEW PROJECTED
INTO PLANE OF SWING

Tie Rod R_4

Lower
R_2

Figure 7.11 *Projecting motion into the plane of swing.*

In Figure 7.12,

    d = offset upper arm
    e = offset lower arm
    z = lift of wheel center
    z_1 = lift of upper arm ball
    z_2 = lift of lower arm ball
    y_1 = lateral displacement, upper ball [*see Figure 7.3*]
    y_2 = lateral displacement, lower ball
    y_3 = lateral displacement at tire contact (P)

$$y_1 \cong \frac{z_1^2}{2R_1} + \frac{z_1 a}{R_1} \tag{7.71}$$

$$y_2 \cong \frac{z_2^2}{2R_2} + \frac{z_2 b}{R_2} \tag{7.72}$$

The equations above follow directly from Section 7.1 (Equation 7.20), where it was shown that for a single arm, the lateral deflection for a lift "a" is approximately,

$$y \cong \frac{z^2}{2R} + \frac{za}{R} \tag{7.73}$$

Camber (Inclination) Change (γ)

γ, as drawn in Figure 7.12 is considered positive [*wheel leans inward as it rises*].

$$z_1 = z - d\gamma \quad \text{or} \quad z_1^2 = z^2 - 2dz\gamma + (d\gamma)^2 \tag{7.74}$$

$$z_2 = z - e\gamma \quad \text{or} \quad z_2^2 = z^2 - 2ez\gamma + (e\gamma)^2 \tag{7.75}$$

*Where d is **not** the derivative operator and the second-order term will be omitted.*

Whence,
$$y_1 - y_2 \cong \frac{z_1^2}{2R_1} + \frac{z_1 a}{R_1} - \frac{z_2^2}{2R_2} - \frac{z_2 b}{R_2} \tag{7.76}$$

$$y_1 - y_2 \cong \frac{z^2 - 2dz\gamma}{2R_1} + \frac{az - ad\gamma}{R_1} - \frac{z^2 - 2ez\gamma}{2R_2} - \frac{bz - be\gamma}{R_2} \tag{7.77}$$

$$y_1 - y_2 \cong \frac{z^2}{2}\left(\frac{1}{R_1} - \frac{1}{R_2}\right) + z\left(\frac{a}{R_1} - \frac{b}{R_2}\right) - \gamma\left(\frac{ad}{R_1} - \frac{be}{R_2}\right) - z\gamma\left(\frac{d}{R_1} - \frac{e}{R_2}\right) \tag{7.78}$$

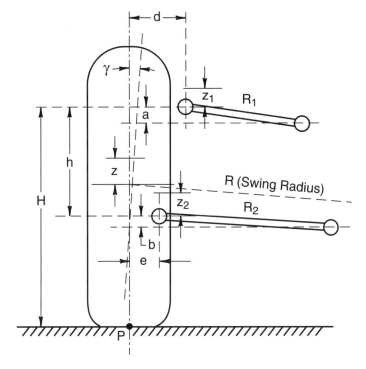

Figure 7.12 *Layout of independent suspension with lateral offsets.*

To simplify, let:

$$\frac{1}{R_1} - \frac{1}{R_2} = P_1 \qquad \frac{a}{R_1} - \frac{b}{R_2} = Q_1$$

$$\frac{d}{R_1} - \frac{e}{R_2} = U_1 \qquad \frac{ad}{R_1} - \frac{be}{R_2} = V_1$$

Then:

$$y_1 - y_2 = \frac{P_1 z^2}{2} + Q_1 z - V_1 \gamma - U_1 z \gamma \qquad (7.79)$$

$$\gamma = \frac{y_1 - y_2}{h} = \frac{1}{h}\left(\frac{P_1 z^2}{2} + Q_1 z - V_1 \gamma - U_1 z \gamma\right) \qquad (7.80)$$

or

$$\gamma = \frac{0.5 P_1 z^2 + Q_1 z}{h + V_1 + U_1 z} \qquad (7.81)$$

Olley now differentiates this expression. The normal form for differentiating the division of two variables, u and v, is given by the "Quotient Rule" as:

$$\frac{d}{dx}\left(\frac{u}{v}\right) = \frac{vu' - uv'}{v^2} = \frac{v\dfrac{du}{dx} - u\dfrac{dv}{dx}}{v^2} = \frac{\dfrac{du}{dx} - \dfrac{u}{v}\dfrac{dv}{dx}}{v} \tag{7.82}$$

In Olley's Equation 7.81,

$$u = 0.5P_1z^2 + Q_1z \quad \text{and} \quad \frac{du}{dz} = P_1z + Q_1$$

$$v = h + V_1 + U_1z \quad \text{and} \quad \frac{dv}{dz} = U_1$$

Also, note that $\gamma = u/v$

Whence
$$\frac{d\gamma}{dz} = \frac{P_1z + Q_1 - U_1\gamma}{h + V_1 + U_1z} \tag{7.83}$$

Equation 7.83 represents the rate of camber change with ride travel. An example quantifying the influence on steering arm lateral offsets for Equations 7.81, 7.83 and the following equations relating to tread change is presented in Section 7.7 (Table 7.1).

Tread Change (One Wheel)

From geometrical proportioning,

$$y_3 = \frac{H}{h}y_2 - \frac{H-h}{h}y_1 \tag{7.84}$$

Olley now references Equations 7.71 & 7.72, and 7.74 & 7.75, substituting into the above expression for y_1 and y_2 in terms of z. After expanding and collecting terms, the following expression results:

$$\begin{aligned}
y_3 = {} & \frac{z^2}{2h}\left(\frac{H}{R_2} - \frac{H-h}{R_1}\right) + \frac{z}{h}\left(\frac{Hb}{R_2} - \frac{(H-h)a}{R_1}\right) \\
& - \frac{z\gamma}{h}\left(\frac{He}{R_2} - \frac{(H-h)d}{R_1}\right) - \frac{\gamma}{h}\left(\frac{Hbe}{R_2} - \frac{(H-h)ad}{R_1}\right)
\end{aligned} \tag{7.85}$$

Let:
$$\frac{H}{R_2} - \frac{H-h}{R_1} = P_2 \qquad \frac{Hb}{R_2} - \frac{(H-h)a}{R_1} = Q_2$$

$$\frac{He}{R_2} - \frac{(H-h)d}{R_1} = U_2 \qquad \frac{Hbe}{R_2} - \frac{(H-h)ad}{R_1} = V_2$$

Then
$$y_3 = \frac{1}{h}\left(\frac{1}{2}P_2 z^2 + Q_2 z - \gamma\left(U_2 z + V_2\right)\right) \tag{7.86}$$

and
$$\frac{dy_3}{dz} = \frac{1}{h}\left(P_2 z + Q_2 - U_2 \gamma - \frac{d\gamma}{dz}\left(U_2 z + V_2\right)\right) \tag{7.87}$$

When $z = 0$, since $\gamma = 0$ as well,

$$\frac{dy_3}{dz} = \frac{1}{h}\left(Q_2 - \frac{d\gamma}{dz}V_2\right) \tag{7.88}$$

Note: Compare Equations 7.81, 7.83 and 7.87 with 7.40, 7.41 and 7.44 to see the additional factors introduced as correction for offsets.

7.7 Comparison Example–Front Suspension without and with Offsets

As a numerical example of such corrected figuring on a front suspension, consider Figure 7.13 and Table 7.1.

$R_1 = 10$ in.	$R_2 = 16$ in.
$a = 1$ in.	$b = 0.5$ in.
$d = 6$ in.	$e = 3$ in.
$H = 20$ in.	$h = 10$ in.

Then:

$P_1 = +0.0375$	$P_2 = +0.250$
$Q_1 = +0.06875$	$Q_2 = -0.375$
$U_1 = +0.4125$	$U_2 = -2.25$
$V_1 = +0.50625$	$V_2 = -4.125$

The plot in Figure 7.14 shows that, although on the rebound side the differences are negligible, on the bump side the corrections are well worth making. This type of correction is quite necessary in figuring link-controlled rear axles, and is essential when figuring wheel rates.

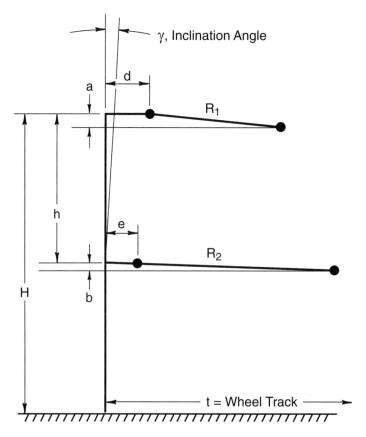

Figure 7.13 *Layout showing offsets.*

Table 7.1 Data from Rough and Corrected Methods

Wheel travel, z (in.)	−3.0	−2.0	−1.0	0.0	1.0	2.0	3.0
Inclination γ (deg.)							
Rough method	−0.215	−0.358	−0.286	0.0	0.501	1.215	2.15
Corrected method	−0.232	−0.370	−0.283	0.0	0.460	1.073	1.83
Inclination change radius $1/(d\gamma/dz)$ (in.)							
Rough method	−228.5	−1600	+320	+145	+97	+73.5	+55.2
Corrected method	−220	−2700	+303	+153	+106	+83.3	+70
Tread change, one wheel (in.)							
Rough method	0.225	0.125	0.050	0.0	−0.025	−0.025	0.0
Corrected method	0.226	0.1253	0.049	0.0	−0.020	−0.009	+0.035
Roll center height (in.)							
Rough method	—	—	—	1.09	—	—	—
Corrected method	—	—	—	1.01	—	—	—

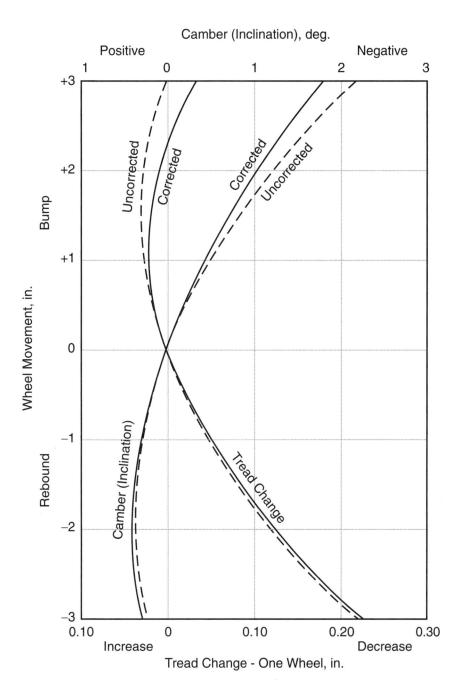

Figure 7.14 *Results—uncorrected, and corrected for offsets.*

7.8 Link Suspension Rear Axle

Consider first an arrangement as in Figure 7.15 with no offsets of the pivot points on the axle.

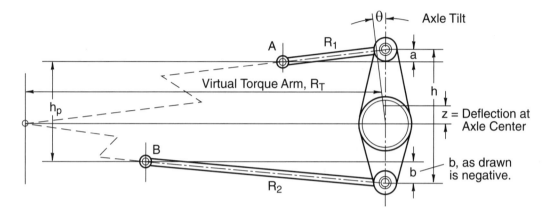

Figure 7.15 *Rear axle, left side view.*

If we define two quantities:

(a) Difference of inverse of upper and lower radii

$$\frac{1}{R_1} - \frac{1}{R_2} = P$$

(b) Difference of slopes of upper and lower arms at design height

$$\frac{a}{R_1} - \frac{b}{R_2} = Q$$

We then have:

$$\theta \cong \frac{1}{h}\left(\frac{1}{2}Pz^2 + Qz\right) \tag{7.89}$$

[*This is comparable to camber for an independent suspension; see Equation 7.40 at the end of Section 7.2.*]

$$\frac{1}{R_T} = \frac{d\theta}{dz} \cong \frac{1}{h}(Pz + Q) \quad \text{or} \quad R_T = \frac{h}{Pz + Q} \tag{7.90}$$

[*This is comparable to ride camber for an independent suspension; see Equation 7.41 at the end of Section 7.2.*]

If R_{T_0} = torque arm length at design height, then evidently:

$$R_{T_0} = \frac{h}{Q} = \frac{\text{height between pins}}{\text{difference of arm slopes}} \qquad (7.91)$$

Having accepted a figure for h, and for R_{T_0}, the desired torque arm at design height, the difference of slope of the two radius arms is fixed, regardless of their length.

We can rewrite Equation 7.89 as:

$$\theta \cong \left(\frac{Pz^2}{2h} + \frac{z}{R_{T_0}} \right) \qquad (7.92)$$

This shows that, for equal bump and rebound strokes,

Bump:
$$\theta_{(+z)} \cong \left(\frac{Pz^2}{2h} + \frac{|z|}{R_{T_0}} \right) \qquad (7.93)$$

Rebound:
$$\theta_{(-z)} \cong \left(\frac{Pz^2}{2h} - \frac{|z|}{R_{T_0}} \right) \qquad (7.94)$$

Total tilt of axle:
$$\theta_{(+z)} - \theta_{(-z)} = \frac{2|z|}{R_{T_0}} \qquad (7.95)$$

In other words, the total change of axle tilt (or pinion nose angle) is the same as if we had used a solid torque arm or torque tube of length R_{T_0}. And, within the limits of the approximation, this is true whatever the lengths of the radius arms. But **with the linkage we can do what is impossible with a solid torque arm**. We can distribute the change in axle tilt between the bump and rebound strokes in any proportion we like. This is done by manipulating the value of P, i.e., the relationship of the upper and lower arm lengths.

Evidently, from Equations 7.93 and 7.94,

$$\theta_{(+z)} + \theta_{(-z)} = \frac{Pz^2}{h} \quad \text{or} \quad P = \frac{h}{z^2}\left(\theta_{(+z)} + \theta_{(-z)} \right) \qquad (7.96)$$

Example

Suppose h = 8.5 in. and desired torque arm R_{T_0} = 50 in.

Then from Equation 7.91

$$Q = \frac{h}{R_{T_0}} = \frac{8.5}{50} = 0.170$$

i.e., upper and lower arms at design must include an angle of

$$(0.170 \text{ rad.}) \times (57.3 \text{ deg./rad.}) = 9.75 \text{ deg.}$$

If we are concerned with bump and rebound strokes of ±3.75 in., then from Equation 7.95, the total tilt change, bump to rebound:

$$\theta_{(+z)} - \theta_{(-z)} = \frac{7.5}{50} = 0.150 \text{ rad.} = 8.6 \text{ deg.}$$

To clear the pinion nose from the floor in bump position, it may be desired to take 7° of tilt in the 3.75 in. bump stroke, leaving −1.6° for the rebound. Then,

$$\theta_{(+z)} + \theta_{(-z)} = 5.4 \text{ deg.} = 0.0943 \text{ rad.}$$

and from Equation 7.96,

$$P = \frac{8.5 \times 0.0943}{14.06} = 0.057$$

A convenient length for R_2 may be, say, 25 in. Then,

$$P = \frac{1}{R_1} - \frac{1}{R_2} \quad \text{or} \quad R_1 = \frac{1}{P + (1/R_2)}$$

$$R_1 = \frac{1}{0.057 + 0.040} = 10.3 \text{ in.}$$

It is desirable to look for the change in the virtual torque arm in the extreme bump and rebound positions.

From Equation 7.90, $$R_T = \frac{h}{Pz + Q}$$

At 3.75 in. bump, $$R_T = \frac{8.5}{(0.057 \times 3.75) + 0.170} = 22.1 \text{ in.}$$

At 3.75 in. rebound, $R_T = \dfrac{8.5}{0.170 - 0.214} = -193$ in.

R_T becomes infinite, i.e., **rate** of tilt becomes zero, when (from Equation 7.90)

$$z = -\frac{Q}{P} = -\frac{0.170}{0.057} \text{ , i.e., at 3 in. rebound}$$

On bump, at 3.75 inches, $\theta = 7$ degrees and R_T is positive at 22.1 inches. At neutral position, $\theta = 0$ degrees and $R_T = 50$ inches, as designed. At –3 inches rebound, $\theta = -1.7$ degrees, its maximum negative angle, and begins to return to positive; $R_T = \infty$ and begins to become negative. For example, at –3.75 inches rebound, the axle tilt is –1.6 degrees and R_T is negative at –193 inches.

The whole layout is extremely favorable to good behavior in traction and braking. The only difficulty is that the vertical distance h_p between the forward pivots A and B, is necessarily small, so that the fore-and-aft loads on these pivots, particularly in forward traction, are high.

If the upper and lower pivots on the axle are reasonably close to the vertical plane through the axle center, the above approximations apply with fair accuracy. But when the upper and lower pins are offset considerably, these approximations are not adequate to give either θ, the tilt angle, or R_T, the torque arm radius. It is necessary to apply the corrections for offset already worked out for IFS. These give excellent results on link controlled axles, as shown in the next section.

7.9 Rear Axle Linkage with Offsets

In Figure 7.16:

    z = travel of axle
    z_1 = travel of upper pivot z_2 = travel of lower pivot
    d = upper offset   e = lower offset
    a = lift of upper arm   b = lift of lower arm (shown as negative in figure)
    θ = tilt angle

Horizontal travels, x_1 and x_2, as before. [*x_1 and x_2 are longitudinal displacements and are analogous to the lateral displacements y_1 and y_2 used earlier in this chapter.*]

$$z_1 \cong z + d\theta \tag{7.97}$$

[*$d\theta$ is not a derivative*]

$$z_2 \cong z + e\theta \tag{7.98}$$

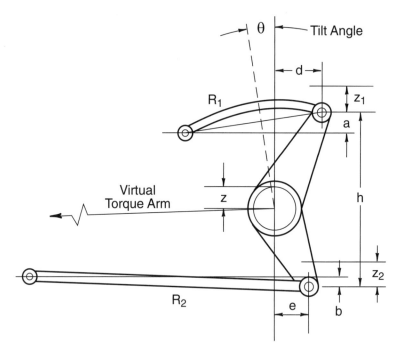

Figure 7.16 Rear axle with offset link mounting.

$$z_1^2 \cong (z + d\theta)^2 \cong z^2 + 2dz\theta \tag{7.99}$$

$$z_2^2 \cong (z + e\theta)^2 \cong z^2 + 2ez\theta \tag{7.100}$$

$$x_1 = \frac{z_1^2}{2R_1} + \frac{az_1}{R_1} = \frac{z^2}{2R_1} + \frac{az}{R_1} + \frac{d\theta}{R_1}(z + a) \tag{7.101}$$

$$x_2 = \frac{z_2^2}{2R_2} + \frac{bz_2}{R_2} = \frac{z^2}{2R_2} + \frac{bz}{R_2} + \frac{e\theta}{R_2}(z + b) \tag{7.102}$$

$$\theta = \frac{x_1 - x_2}{h} = \frac{z^2}{2h}\left(\frac{1}{R_1} - \frac{1}{R_2}\right) + \frac{z}{h}\left(\frac{a}{R_1} - \frac{b}{R_2}\right)$$

$$+ \frac{\theta}{h}\left[z\left(\frac{d}{R_1} - \frac{e}{R_2}\right) + \left(\frac{ad}{R_1} - \frac{be}{R_2}\right)\right] \tag{7.103}$$

Let:

$$\frac{1}{R_1} - \frac{1}{R_2} = P_1 \qquad \frac{a}{R_1} - \frac{b}{R_2} = Q_1$$

$$\frac{d}{R_1} - \frac{e}{R_2} = U_1 \qquad \frac{ad}{R_1} - \frac{be}{R_2} = V_1$$

Then:

$$\theta = \frac{1}{h}\left(\frac{1}{2}P_1z^2 + Q_1z + V_1\theta + U_1z\theta\right) \qquad (7.104)$$

or,

$$\theta = \frac{0.5P_1z^2 + Q_1z}{h - V_1 - U_1z} \qquad (7.105)$$

Applying these corrections to the virtual torque arm radius:

$$\frac{d\theta}{dz} = \frac{1}{R_T} = U_1\frac{0.5P_1z^2 + Q_1z}{\left(h - V_1 - U_1z\right)^2} + \frac{P_1z + Q_1}{h - V_1 - U_1z} = \frac{P_1z + Q_1 + U_1\theta}{h - V_1 - U_1z} \qquad (7.106)$$

$$R_T = \frac{h - V_1 - U_1z}{P_1z + Q_1 + U_1\theta} \qquad (7.107)$$

Note the correction for offsets:

For tilt angle θ: Subtract $V_1 + U_1z$ from the denominator.

For tilt change rate $1/R_T$: Add $U_1\theta$ to the numerator and subtract $V_1 + U_1z$ from the denominator.

The equations for rear axle with offsets are analogous to the equations for independent suspension with offsets.

Example

Consider an actual layout, Figure 7.17.

$R_1 = 14.8$ in. $\qquad\qquad R_2 = 25.5$ in.
$a = 1.0$ in. $\qquad\qquad b = -2.3$ in.
$d = 5.10$ in. $\qquad\qquad e = 2.05$ in.
$h = 9.15$ in.

$$P_1 = \frac{1}{R_1} - \frac{1}{R_2} = 0.0283$$

$$Q_1 = \frac{a}{R_1} - \frac{b}{R_2} = 0.0675 + 0.0902 = 0.1577$$

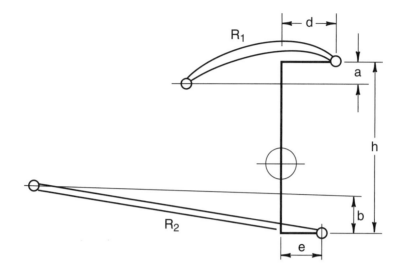

Figure 7.17 Rear axle layout for the example.

$$U_1 = \frac{d}{R_1} - \frac{e}{R_2} = 0.344 - 0.0805 = 0.2635$$

$$V_1 = \frac{ad}{R_1} - \frac{be}{R_2} = 0.344 + 0.185 = 0.529$$

Figure 7.18, which plots pinion angle from the drawing layout, and from the calculated values [*in Table 7.2*] corrected for offset, shows the almost complete agreement up to ±4 inches deflection. The change in torque arm radius is also shown. For preliminary figuring the first "rough" method is recommended, after which the corrections for offset are easily applied, as in the above example.

7.10 Ride Rates and Wheel Rates

In the SAE Handbook[49] under Ride and Vibration Terminology:

Wheel rate is defined as the change of wheel load at the center of tire contact per unit vertical displacement of the sprung mass **relative to the wheel**, at a specified load [*also called wheel center rate*]. And it is also stated that, if the wheel camber varies, the displacement should be measured relative to the **lowest point on the rim centerline**.

Ride rate (containing both wheel and tire deflection) concerns the change of wheel load per unit displacement of the sprung mass **relative to the ground.**

---

[49] These definitions can now be found in Vehicle Dynamics Terminology, SAE J670e.

Table 7.2 Axle Calculations without and with Offsets

First method					
z (in.)	−4	−2	0	2	4
$0.5P_1z^2$	0.2264	0.0566	0	0.0566	0.2264
Q_1z	−0.6308	−0.3154	0	0.3154	0.6308
$0.5P_1z^2 + Q_1z$	−0.4044	−0.2588	0	0.3720	0.8572
θ (rad.)	−0.0442	−0.0283	0	0.0407	0.0937
θ (deg.)	−2.53	−1.62	0	2.335	5.37
P_1z	−0.1132	−0.0566	0	0.0566	0.1132
$P_1z + Q_1$	0.0445	0.1011	0.1577	0.2143	0.2709
$d\theta/dz$	0.00486	0.01105	0.01722	0.02345	0.0296
Torque arm R_T (in.)	206	90.5	58	42.6	33.8

Correction for offset					
$h - V_1 - U_1z$	9.158	8.8845	8.621	8.3575	8.084
θ (rad.)	−0.0441	−0.0293	0	0.0445	0.1060
θ (deg.)	−2.52	−1.68	0	2.55	6.075
$P_1z + Q_1 + U_1\theta$	0.0335	0.0934	0.1577	0.2260	0.2988
$d\theta/dz$	0.00346	0.0105	0.0183	0.0270	0.0370
Torque arm R_T (in.)	289.0	95.2	54.7	37	27
Corrected pinion angle (deg.)*	0.98	1.82	3.5	6.05	9.575

*Actual pinion angle at design is 3.5°.

The selection of the "rim point" as above is based on the discussion in R.B. Burton's report of 1949 on the Coil Spring Wishbone Suspension (GM Product Study 2, No. 132-83). In this report (p. 71) tests are quoted tending to show that, in a wheel which changes camber, the effective point of load application is at or near the intersection of the lowest part of the tire-seat with the center plane of the wheel [*see Figure 2.19*].

This simply says that, when a wheel takes a camber angle, like γ, Figure 7.19, the load application point moves sideways from A to B. This is evidently a convention which will give approximately correct results when figuring ride rates on such things as swing axles. But it will not do to accept the same convention when considering cornering conditions with lateral forces at the tires, as Figure 7.20.

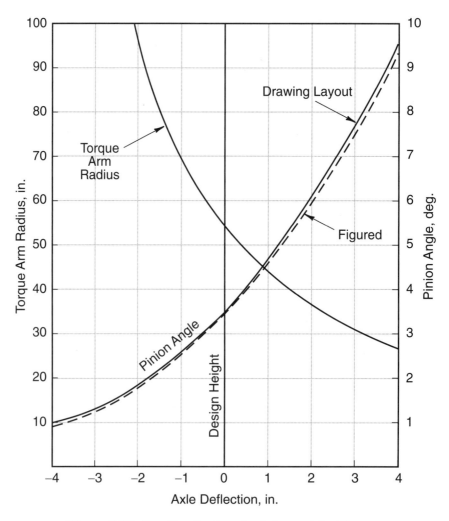

Figure 7.18 *Results of axle calculations with offsets.*

Since the bottom of the tire in Figure 7.20 is displaced laterally by the lateral force, the resultant must go through Point C. The forces are shown.

In this case the resultant force must be applied at a point somewhere **below** the road surface.

In the case of an axle where the wheels stay vertical, Figure 7.21, there is no problem. [*The modern way to account for lateral tire deflection is with tire overturning moment, M_X, per SAE Tire Axis System, J670e[49].*]

The **wheel rate** at the rim point P, is the spring rate K_S. If K_T is the tire rate, the ride rate, K_R, is:

$$K_R = \frac{K_T K_S}{K_T + K_S} \tag{7.108}$$

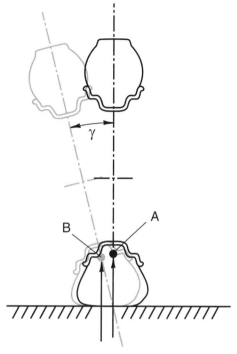

Figure 7.19 *Rim point with cambered wheel (narrow bias ply tire).*

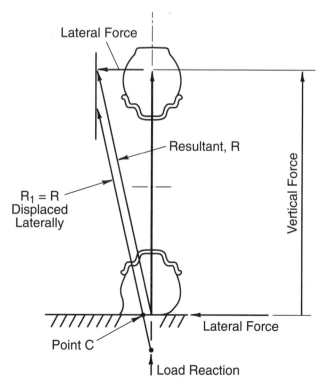

Figure 7.20 *Rim point with applied lateral force.*

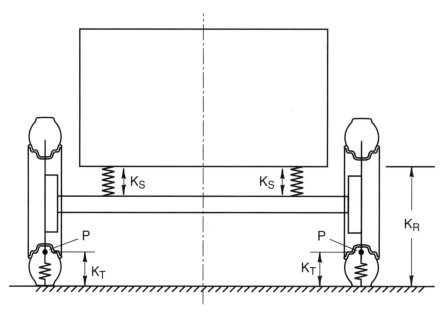

Figure 7.21 *Rim point for axle suspension (no camber).*

For a parallel independent the same is true. But on a swing axle or any independent where wheel camber changes, there is room for considerable doubt.

Consider first a swing axle, Figure 7.22.

Definition of symbols:

O = suspension pivot on chassis
T = spring torque about O
T_O = angular spring rate about O
$R = W$ = wheel load (neglect unsprung mass)
z = height of bump travel
P = initial rim point
P_1 = rim point after bump travel
r = distance from the rim point to O along the wheel plane
r_1 = vertical distance from the rim point to O
L = side view swing arm length at design height
L_1 = side view swing arm length after bump travel
θ = swing arm angle after bump travel (zero at design height)

The spring produces an angular rate:

$$T_O \equiv \frac{dT}{d\theta} \tag{7.109}$$

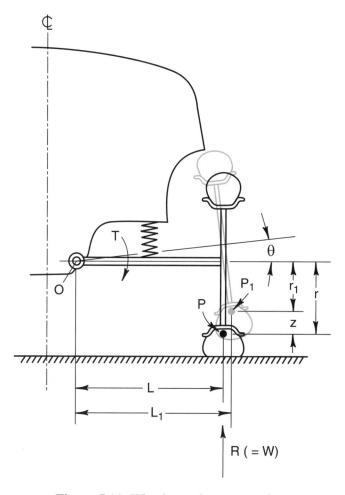

Figure 7.22 *Wheel rate for swing axle.*

about the center pivot O. Neglect the unsprung weight and assume that road reaction R = W, the load per wheel. Then at any angle θ,

$$T = W(L\cos\theta + r\sin\theta) \qquad (7.110)$$

or

$$W = \frac{T}{L\cos\theta + r\sin\theta} \qquad (7.111)$$

Hence by differentiation [*Edward Kasprzak filled in the steps that Olley "leaves out"*],

Olley wants to find dW/dz, the vertical rate of the suspension. By the "Chain Rule" we know:

$$\frac{dW}{dz} = \frac{dW}{d\theta}\frac{d\theta}{dz} \qquad (7.112)$$

First the $dW/d\theta$ term:

The "Quotient Rule" (Equation 7.82) says:

$$\frac{d}{dx}\left(\frac{u}{v}\right) = \frac{\dfrac{du}{dx} - \dfrac{u}{v}\dfrac{dv}{dx}}{v} \tag{7.113}$$

Here, $\quad u = T$
$\qquad du/d\theta = T_O$
$\qquad v = L\cos\theta + r\sin\theta$
$\qquad dv/d\theta = r\cos\theta - L\sin\theta$
$\qquad u/v = W$

So $\qquad\qquad \dfrac{dW}{d\theta} = \dfrac{T_O - W(r\cos\theta - L\sin\theta)}{L\cos\theta + r\sin\theta} \tag{7.114}$

Now, the $d\theta/dz$ term:

Start with $z = r - r_1 = r + (L\sin\theta - r\cos\theta)$ and differentiate both sides with respect to z:

$$\frac{d}{dz}(z) = \frac{d}{dz}(r) + \frac{d}{dz}(L\sin\theta - r\cos\theta) \tag{7.115}$$

$$1 = 0 + \frac{d}{d\theta}(L\sin\theta - r\cos\theta)\frac{d\theta}{dz} \tag{7.116}$$

$$1 = (L\cos\theta + r\sin\theta)\frac{d\theta}{dz} \tag{7.117}$$

So $\qquad\qquad \dfrac{d\theta}{dz} = \dfrac{1}{(L\cos\theta + r\sin\theta)} \tag{7.118}$

Combining terms: $\qquad \dfrac{dW}{dz} = \dfrac{dW}{d\theta}\dfrac{d\theta}{dz}$

$$\frac{dW}{dz} = \left(\frac{T_O - W(r\cos\theta - L\sin\theta)}{L\cos\theta + r\sin\theta}\right)\left(\frac{1}{(L\cos\theta + r\sin\theta)}\right) \tag{7.119}$$

Wheel rate: $\qquad \dfrac{dW}{dz} = \left(\dfrac{T_O - W(r\cos\theta - L\sin\theta)}{(L\cos\theta + r\sin\theta)^2}\right) \tag{7.120}$

But $r\cos\theta - L\sin\theta = r_1$, and $L\cos\theta + r\sin\theta = L_1$ (see Figure 7.22)

So [*without camber thrust*], Wheel rate $= \dfrac{dW}{dz} = \dfrac{T_O - Wr_1}{L_1^2}$ (7.121)

If we wanted to read the wheel rate directly, we should need to set the rim points P on knife edges resting on platform scales, which must roll freely sideways to give correct results, Figure 7.23. We probably should not do this, but should get the **ride rates**, with tires, in this way, and then figure the wheel rates on the principle that:

$$\text{Wheel rate} = \frac{(\text{tire rate}) \times (\text{ride rate})}{(\text{tire rate}) - (\text{ride rate})}$$ (7.122)

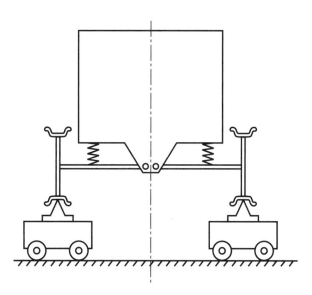

Figure 7.23 *Conceptual method for direct reading of wheel rate on swing axle.*

As an example, suppose that:

Normal load, $W_0 = 900$ lb.
L = 24 in.
r = 7 in.
$T_O =$ constant $= 75420$ lb.-in./rad.

Figure 7.24 shows the load and wheel rate figures which would be obtained by testing on knife edges as above.

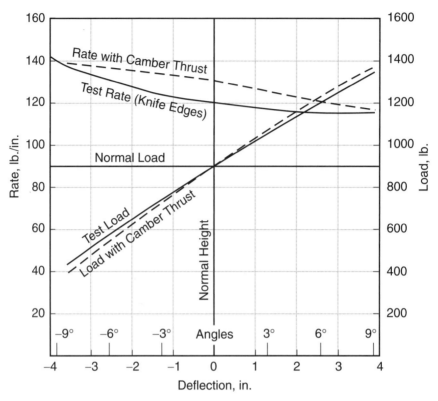

Figure 7.24 *Swing axle wheel rate.*

7.11 Camber Thrust

Section 7.10 represents about the best we can do in the way of wheel rate testing on a swing axle in the laboratory. But it seems highly improbable that this represents the rate of the suspension when running on the road.

The camber thrust on a running wheel is nearly proportional to the load on the wheel (at moderate loads) and to the tangent of the camber angle γ; see Figure 7.25. The resultant of W vertical and W tan γ horizontal is a force $W/\cos\gamma$, in the plane of the wheel. (It is this which allows bicycles to steer almost entirely by camber thrust, while remaining stable on corners.) If this is assumed, then the actual **wheel rate** on the road can be derived as follows:

Olley's goal is the wheel rate, dW/dz, which is equal to $\dfrac{dW}{d\gamma}\dfrac{d\gamma}{dz}$.

He assumes that for a cambered wheel the resultant force (vertical and horizontal at the bottom of the tire) is in the plane of the wheel. This is an assumption based on some early tire tests of narrow tires. It appeared to be valid for camber change less than, say, 10°. If this is true, then $WL/\cos\gamma = T$, or $W = T\cos\gamma/L$, where W is the vertical force on the tire at the road surface.

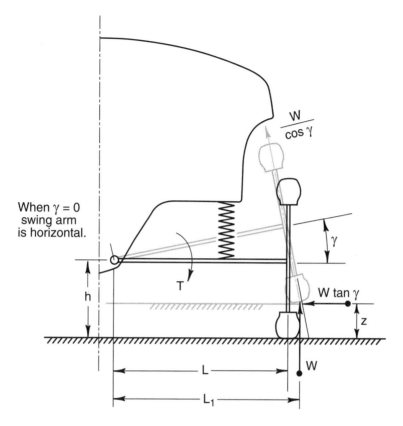

Figure 7.25 *Wheel rate including estimated effects of camber thrust.*

Differentiating this gives $dW/d\gamma = (\cos\gamma/L)(dTd\gamma) - T\sin\gamma/L$, *which simplifies to:*

$$dW/d\gamma = T_O\cos\gamma/L - T\sin\gamma/L$$

where the first term is due to the assumption that the resultant force is in the wheel plane, i.e., W varies directly as $\cos\gamma$. The second term is a correction term.

From Figure 7.25 it can be shown that $z = h(1 - \cos\gamma) + L\sin\gamma$. Hence, $dz/d\gamma = L\cos\gamma + h\sin\gamma = L_1$, the horizontal distance from the swing arm pivot to the bottom of the displaced tire. (L_1 will be greater than L.)

Finally,
$$\frac{dW}{dz} = \frac{dW/d\gamma}{dz/d\gamma} = \frac{T_O\cos\gamma/L - T\sin\gamma/L}{L\cos\gamma + h\sin\gamma} \tag{7.123}$$

$$\frac{dW}{dz} = \frac{1}{L}\frac{T_O\cos\gamma - T\sin\gamma}{L\cos\gamma + h\sin\gamma} \tag{7.124}$$

And [*with $L_1 = L\cos\gamma + h\sin\gamma$*],

$$\frac{dW}{dz} = \frac{T_O\cos\gamma - T\sin\gamma}{L_1 L} \tag{7.125}$$

At design height, when $z = 0$, and $\gamma = 0$,

$$\frac{dW}{dz} = \frac{T_O}{L^2} \tag{7.126}$$

i.e., the effect of the height h above the road in reducing the wheel rate disappears. [*This is different than when camber thrust is neglected. Both relationships are plotted on Figure 7.24.*]

If we assume, as before,

> Normal load, $W_0 = 900$ lb.
> L = 24 in.
> r = 7 in.
> T_O = constant = 75420 lb.-in./rad.

and say that h = 12 in., the figured load and rate are as indicated in Figure 7.24. The rate at design height is increased about 11 lb./in over the "test rate."

7.12 Toe-In–Swing Axle with Diagonal Pivot

If the axle has a diagonal pivot, Figure 7.26, the wheels toe-in as they rise and fall. Although the effect of this at and near the design position is negligible, this must serve to stiffen the suspension appreciably in the bump position.

It appears, therefore, that the true vertical wheel or ride rate of a swing axle can be obtained only when the wheel is rolling on a flat surface.

7.13 Wheel Rates–Wishbone Suspension

The spring rate, measured at the wheel center, can be determined in several ways. Olley's computational method is presented below, but, in the 1960s the solution time (using a slide rule) was long, and this method was not popular. Instead, the standard way to calculate wheel rates used the graphical method—and this was so well established that Olley only mentions it in passing at the end of his original write-up. We present an additional example of the graphical method at the end of this section, taken from another source.

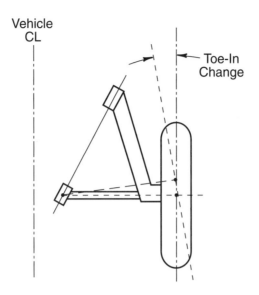

Figure 7.26 *Swing axle with diagonal pivot.*

There are various ways of working out the wheel rates on a wishbone suspension. Assume that the load is applied through the lower arm at the outer pivot B, see Figure 7.27. Then it is possible to figure or to test the vertical rate at B.

But this is not the wheel rate because the vertical deflection z is not generally equal to z_2 at B.

Because of the relatively small change of camber it makes no great difference whether we measure the wheel rate at the rim point P, at the wheel center O, or at B′, which is the projection of point B on the wheel disc. So we'll take point B′, which is most convenient.

And we can also assume that height h, which is $\overline{A'B'}$ on the wheel disc, is constant. It is not necessary to assume that $dT/d\theta$, or T_O, the angular rate of the lower arm, is constant. The camber changes are not so great that one need worry about the effect of camber thrust on the ride rate, as one did in the case of the swing axle.

Then we can apply the **corrected** figures for camber change, as obtained in Section 7.6, to getting the wheel rate at B′ [*with offsets*].

It was there found that if:

$$\frac{1}{R_1} - \frac{1}{R_2} = P_1 \qquad \frac{a}{R_1} - \frac{b}{R_2} = Q_1$$

$$\frac{d}{R_1} - \frac{e}{R_2} = U_1 \qquad \frac{ad}{R_1} - \frac{be}{R_2} = V_1$$

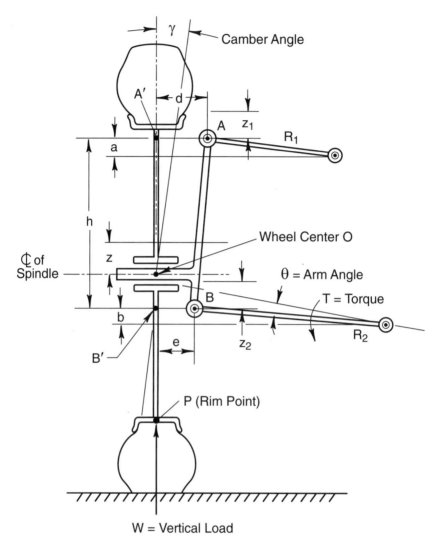

Figure 7.27 *Wheel rate nomenclature including tire.*

Then:

[*Equation 7.80*] $\gamma = \dfrac{y_1 - y_2}{h} = \dfrac{1}{h}\left(\dfrac{1}{2}P_1 z^2 + Q_1 z - V_1 \gamma - U_1 z \gamma\right)$ (7.127)

Whence

[*Equation 7.83*] $\dfrac{d\gamma}{dz} = \dfrac{P_1 z + Q_1 - U_1 \gamma}{h + V_1 + U_1 z}$ (7.128)

Let $S = h + V_1 + U_1z$. Then,

$$\frac{d}{dz}\left(\frac{d\gamma}{dz}\right) = \frac{d^2\gamma}{dz^2} = \frac{d}{dz}\left(\frac{P_1z + Q_1 - U_1\gamma}{S}\right) \qquad (7.129)$$

$$\frac{d^2\gamma}{dz^2} = \frac{S\left(P_1 - U_1(d\gamma/dz)\right) - \left(P_1z + Q_1 - U_1\gamma\right)U_1}{S^2} \qquad (7.130)$$

$$\frac{d^2\gamma}{dz^2} = \frac{SP_1 - SU_1(d\gamma/dz) - \left(P_1z + Q_1 - U_1\gamma\right)U_1}{S^2} \qquad (7.131)$$

But from Equation 7.128,

$$\left(h + V_1 + U_1z\right)\frac{d\gamma}{dz} = P_1z + Q_1 - U_1\gamma = S\frac{d\gamma}{dz} \qquad (7.132)$$

So, $$\frac{d^2\gamma}{dz^2} = \frac{SP_1 - SU_1(d\gamma/dz) - SU_1(d\gamma/dz)}{S^2} \qquad (7.133)$$

$$\frac{d^2\gamma}{dz^2} = \frac{P_1 - 2U_1(d\gamma/dz)}{S} \qquad (7.134)$$

and $$\frac{d^2\gamma}{dz^2} = \frac{P_1 - 2U_1(d\gamma/dz)}{h + V_1 + U_1z} \qquad (7.135)$$

By the principle of equal work at the arm or at the wheel:

$$Wdz = Td\theta \qquad (7.136)$$

[*dz and dθ **are** derivatives*]

or $$W = T\frac{d\theta}{dz} \qquad (7.137)$$

But $\theta = \dfrac{z - e\gamma}{R_2}$, so $$\frac{d\theta}{dz} = \frac{1}{R_2}\left(1 - e\frac{d\gamma}{dz}\right) \qquad (7.138)$$

and $$W = \frac{T}{R_2}\left(1 - e\frac{d\gamma}{dz}\right) \qquad (7.139)$$

Also, since $W = T\dfrac{d\theta}{dz}$, the wheel rate:

$$\frac{dW}{dz} = \left(\frac{d\theta}{dz}\right)\left(\frac{dT}{dz}\right) + T\frac{d^2\theta}{dz^2} \tag{7.140}$$

$$\frac{dW}{dz} = \left(\frac{d\theta}{dz}\right)\left(\frac{dT}{dz}\right)\left(\frac{d\theta}{d\theta}\right) + T\frac{d^2\theta}{dz^2} \tag{7.141}$$

$$\frac{dW}{dz} = \left(\frac{dT}{d\theta}\right)\left(\frac{d\theta}{dz}\right)^2 + T\frac{d^2\theta}{dz^2} \tag{7.142}$$

with $T_O = dT/d\theta$
$$\frac{dW}{dz} = T_O\left(\frac{d\theta}{dz}\right)^2 + T\frac{d^2\theta}{dz^2} \tag{7.143}$$

$$\frac{dW}{dz} = \frac{T_O}{R_2^2}\left(1 - e\frac{d\gamma}{dz}\right)^2 - \frac{Te}{R_2}\frac{d^2\gamma}{dz^2} \tag{7.144}$$

*Note: The **first** term is the static term (linear) which holds at trim. The **second** term (nonlinear) corrects for departure from trim. In the example of Section 7.7 the first term is much larger.*

We can apply this to the example of Section 7.7, with the additional information:

Normal load $= W_0 = 700$ lb.
Angular rate $= T_O = 22520$ lb.-in./rad. (constant)

Then we get the results in Table 7.3, plotted in Figure 7.28.

The load deflection diagram can also be obtained from force diagrams on a layout, Figure 7.29, if we can estimate the vertical loads at the outer joint of the lower arm at various deflections.

For instance in the force diagram, if AB represents the vertical load in one position, BC is the tension in the lower arm, and AC is the force along diagonal DA. Then, if DE $=$ AC, EF is the compression in the upper arm, and DF is the vertical force at the rim point P; and similarly at other positions.

Reasonably accurate predictions of wheel rate have been made in this way.

Table 7.3 Wishbone Suspension Wheel Rate

Ride position z (in.)	−3	−2	−1	0	1	2	3
Camber γ (deg.)	−0.232	−0.370	−0.284	0	0.460	1.073	1.83
θ (deg.)	−10.7	−7.13	−3.53	0	3.5	6.96	10.4
$d\theta/dz$ (rad./in.)	0.0633	0.0626	0.0619	0.0613	0.0607	0.06025	0.0598
T (lb.-in.)	7200	8600	10013	11400	12773	14135	15485
W (lb.)	456	539	620	700	775	852	926
Rate dW/dz By intervals (lb./in.)	83	81	80	75	77	74	—
Rate dW/dz (lb./in.) Equation 7.144	84	81.9	79.7	78.1	76.4	74.6	74.25

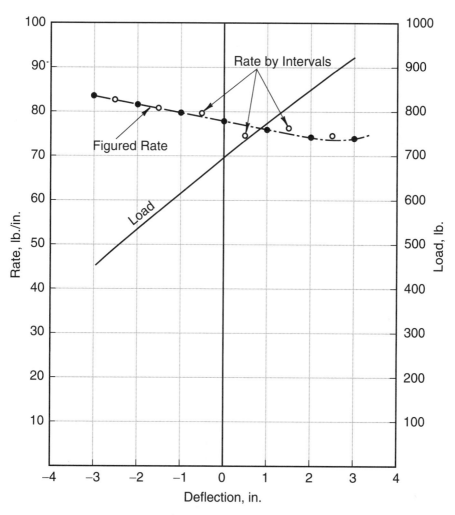

Figure 7.28 Wishbone suspension wheel rate.

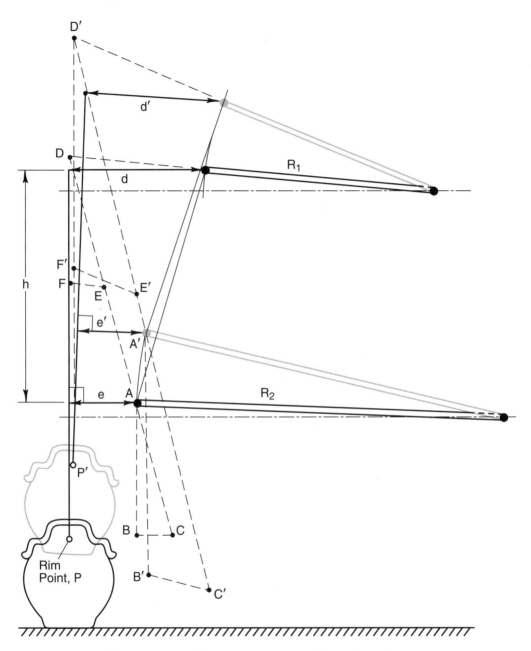

Figure 7.29 *Wishbone suspension—Olley's force diagram.*

At the time that Olley was writing his notes, a graphical method using force vectors drawn to an arbitrary scale was commonly used when figuring wheel rates. This procedure is based on the simple rule that if three forces are present on a mass in equilibrium, the vector sum of any two must be equal to the third; further, that they must intersect, else there would be an unbalanced couple (moment). The material below, including Figure 7.30 is taken from the General Motors Institute class notes.

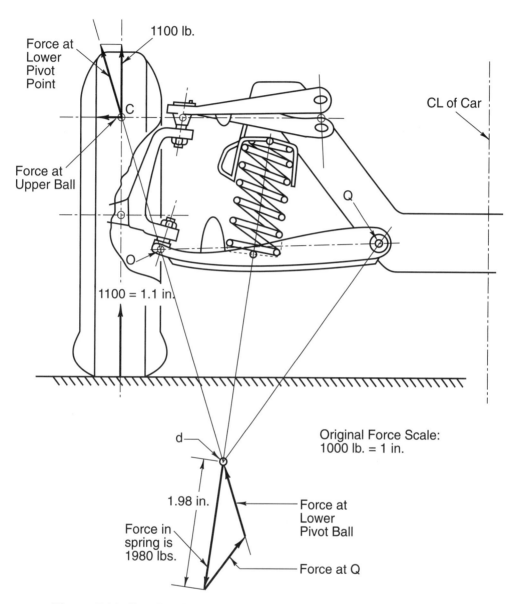

Figure 7.30 *Graphical method for determining wheel rate (from Mola).*

Graphical Procedure [Mola[50]]

The forces in the spring at various positions of the wheel center can be found by a graphical method. This procedure is simple, quick and it is a good check to the analytical approach used previously [*similar to Olley's procedure*]. Figure 7.30 shows the suspension at design load and the necessary steps employed to obtain graphically the force in the spring.

---

[50] Mola, Simone, "Fundamentals of Vehicle Dynamics," Product Engineering Department, General Motors Institute, 1967.

1. Establish a force scale, for example, 1000 lbs. = 1 in. Draw the force acting at the wheel centerline; 1100 lbs. = 1.1 in.

2. For equilibrium the lines of action of the forces at the upper and lower ball joints and at the wheel center line must all cross at point C. This is equivalent to the analytical condition:

$$\Sigma M_O = 0$$

As shown, the forces in the upper and lower arm can be scaled from the drawing.

3. Again, equilibrium of the lower control arm requires that the forces acting upon it must cross point d. The spring force scaled from the drawing (1980 lbs.) agrees quite well with the one obtained [*in Mola*] from the analytical solution.

7.14 Tread [*Track*] Change Radius

Some attention is necessary to the tread change radius.

For instance at one time a "fixed kingpin" wishbone suspension was designed, roughly as shown in Figure 7.31.

The tread change radius R_3 was then short, like the suspension arms. Lateral forces like F on corners then have the effect of a toggle, and greatly reduce the wheel rate on the outside wheel, causing a loss of roll-stability.

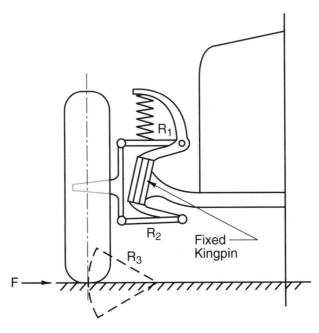

Figure 7.31 Wishbone suspension with fixed kingpin.

7.15 Effect of Camber Change on Wheel Rate

In Section 7.13, the wheel rate dW/dz has been given in Equation 7.144, to bring out the importance of $d\gamma/dz$ which is the inverse of the camber change radius, in its effect on the wheel rate. This is a matter frequently ignored in the development of a wishbone suspension. **Any change in the slope of the upper or lower arm in the design position, or any change in the offset, e, changes the wheel rate.**

When, for instance, the slope of an upper arm at design is changed, certain changes in ride or handling characteristics are noted, which are often ascribed to changes in wheel camber, or height of roll center. Actually they may be due largely to change of ride or roll rates, due to an increase or decrease of $d\gamma/dz$.

An increased divergence of the arms will **increase** $d\gamma/dz$, i.e., **shorten** the camber change radius, and **decrease** the ride and roll rates, and vice versa.

7.16 Vertical Rate of Arm and Torsion Spring

This is discussed in SAE Torsion Spring Manual,[51] and useful charts are included to show the changes in load, rate and effective deflection which occur.

Yet, even in patent specifications, it is often erroneously stated that the lowest rate occurs when the arm is horizontal. Probably the simplest way of looking at it is that, **relative to angle θ**, the rate of increase of the vertical distance AB is the horizontal distance BC, and the rate of "increase" of BC is **minus** AB.

Assume θ is a small angle, although Olley draws it as a large angle in Figure 7.32. Olley says, "**relative to angle θ**, the rate of increase of the vertical distance AB is the horizontal distance BC." *This follows from,*

$$\theta \cong \frac{AB}{BC} \tag{7.145}$$

Then,
$$\frac{\Delta AB}{\Delta\theta} = \frac{dAB}{d\theta} = BC \tag{7.146}$$

Now by observation, the rate of increase of BC with θ = −AB, i.e., BC will increase as AB is shortened (everything is linear so far).

Hence, since
$$T = P \times \left|\overline{BC}\right| \tag{7.147}$$

---

[51] SAE Spring Design Manual, AE-11, Chapter 2, Section 4, Society of Automotive Engineers, Warrendale, Pa., 1990.

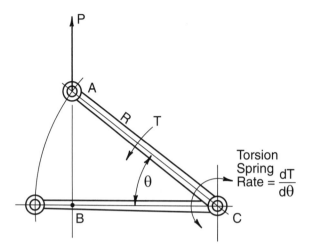

Figure 7.32 *Arm attached to torsion spring.*

$$\frac{dT}{d\theta} = \frac{dP}{d\theta} \times |\overline{BC}| + P \times \frac{d|\overline{BC}|}{d\theta} \qquad (7.148)$$

$$\frac{dT}{d\theta} = \frac{dP}{d\theta}|\overline{BC}| - P|\overline{AB}| \qquad (7.149)$$

or

$$\frac{dP}{d\theta} = \frac{\dfrac{dT}{d\theta} + P|\overline{AB}|}{|\overline{BC}|} \qquad (7.150)$$

Then

$$\frac{dP}{d\overline{AB}} = \frac{dP}{d\theta}\frac{d\theta}{d\overline{AB}} \qquad (7.151)$$

$$\frac{dP}{d\,\overline{AB}} = \frac{(dT/d\theta) + P\overline{AB}}{\overline{BC}} \times \frac{d\theta}{d\,\overline{AB}} \qquad (7.152)$$

But

$$\frac{1}{\dfrac{d\,\overline{AB}}{d\theta}} = \frac{1}{\overline{BC}} \qquad (7.153)$$

and

$$\frac{dP}{d\overline{AB}} = \frac{(dT/d\theta) + P\overline{AB}}{\overline{BC}^2} \qquad (7.154)$$

In the Spring Manual,[52] *the position of lowest rate occurs for negative θ's. The manual has design plots for all combinations of design variables.*

7.17 Position of Springs

A fallacy, also seen in patent specifications, is that the spring **position** in an independent suspension, has an effect on roll stability. For example, on the Scarab rear engine car the rear springs on the swing axle are raised with the idea of increasing roll stability (as shown in Figure 7.33).

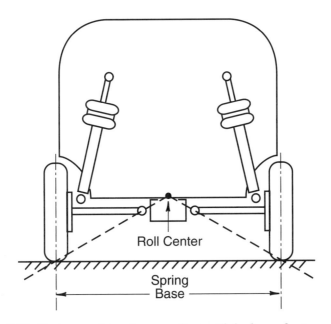

Figure 7.33 *Spring position has no effect with **independent** suspension.*

The spring position has no effect whatever on any form of independent suspension, since the height of the roll center is determined entirely by the geometry of the wheel motion. Also, the spring base on any independent suspension is always equal to the wheel track.

An axle is entirely different; see Figure 7.34. Here, for instance, changing from springs below axle to springs above axle can raise the roll center and have a marked effect on roll stability. And the roll stability also depends on the **square** of the spring base, so that spring separation is extremely important.

---

[52] SAE Spring Design Manual, AE-11, Society of Automotive Engineers, Warrendale, Pa., 1990.

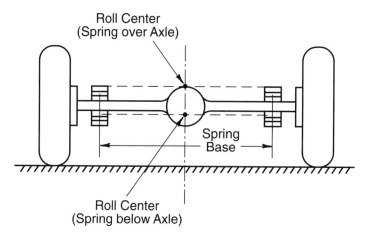

Figure 7.34 *Spring position may have large effects with **axle** suspension.*

7.18 Summary

Suspension linkage problems are now routinely solved with the use of computers, running either CAD software or specialized linkage analysis programs. Computer methods are typically more accurate than Olley's methods or the graphical methods that came before. However, these programs are complex and usually compiled—the internal workings are not accessible to the user—requiring the user to place a certain amount of trust in the program author(s). In conversations with students (typically Formula SAE race car designers), it has become obvious to us that the use of canned software has not improved the general understanding of linkage problems, and in fact the opposite has occurred. "Blind trust" in the computer has led to some amusing (and time consuming) design flaws at the student level. We are also aware of similar problems at the corporate level, where mistakes are much more expensive.

Using Olley's simplified methods, hand calculations to check the automated methods can be easily made. A simplified analysis is usually a good way to get a feel for the basic trends in any complex and/or nonlinear problem. Note that we are not advocating a return to manual calculation of suspension linkages, we are simply suggesting that some combination of drawing layouts, graphical (force vector) methods, and manual calculations may aid the understanding of these complex problems. While Olley only discusses a few suspension types, his methods can be extended to other types with a little imagination. In particular, the parabolic approximation to the circular arc of a simple link simplifies the calculations significantly.

In Wales, c. 1924–5. Left to right: Maurice Olley, Olley's stepmother, Norma Marie Olley, Olley's brother Arthur. Photo credit Rolls-Royce Heritage Trust.

CHAPTER 8

Roll, Roll Moments and Skew Rates

"Surely there is nothing very marvelous in a machine weighing a couple of tons, which, even when built so low—as the CG within two feet of the ground—still loses 50% of its potential cornering ability by lateral weight transfer?"

Maurice Olley

8.1 Introduction

In this chapter Olley fills in some details on roll rates that were assumed in earlier chapters. There is an interesting discussion of skew rates, now called warp rates. He also discusses compensated (longitudinally interconnected) suspensions.

The study of static roll rates and roll moments can become fairly complicated. And there is considerable difference between roll caused by an applied moment and roll caused by lateral force applied at the CG which is the usual condition encountered on the road.

8.2 The Roll Axis

The roll axis is discussed in Section 2.5 but we still lack a definition of it. The best definition seems to be that the roll axis defines, in the median plane of the car, a transverse plane in which horizontal lateral forces applied to the rolling mass of the car will move the car sideways **without** causing it to roll; see Figure 8.1 for the basic geometry.

It follows that forces applied above the roll axis (as at the CG) will cause roll. Also that forces, if any, applied below the roll axis will cause "banking" (like a bicycle).

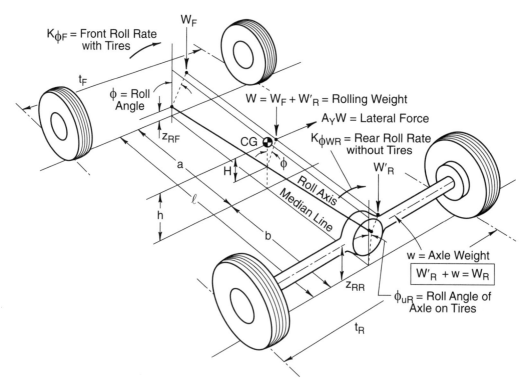

Figure 8.1 *Basic geometry of the roll axis model, including roll of the rear axle on the tires.*

In considering suspension at either end of the car we shall also be discussing "roll centers." These are obviously the points where the roll axis intersects the transverse planes of the front or rear wheel pairs.

There are three main types of suspension to consider:

1. The axle.
2. Independent suspension without tread [*track*] change.
3. Independent suspension with tread change.

Axle

The axle holds the wheels upright because it is a rigid member from wheel to wheel and this forms a traveling "trestle" on which the sprung mass is supported. When the sprung mass is subjected to a roll moment it rotates through an angle about a center in the median plane, the height of which is determined by the suspension mechanism.

In a Hotchkiss rear axle the roll center is normally close to the plane containing the front and rear spring eyes. On other suspensions the roll center height is determined by some form of centering mechanism such as a Panhard rod, or other linkage. (See Section 3.3.)

The conditions governing the distribution of the roll moments to the front and rear tires are rather fully discussed in the following pages. No simple statement confined to one end of the car can fully cover the subject. The point to note here is that in general on an axle with leaf springs, the height of the roll center z_{RR} is controlled by the height of the spring eyes, and that $K_{\phi WR}$ (the rear roll rate without tires) is $\lambda(1/2)K_R t_S^2$ lb.-in./rad. (see Figure 8.2). The constant, λ, which may be 1.30 or so, is due to the fact that the leaf spring rate is raised by the twisting and side bending of the springs in roll.

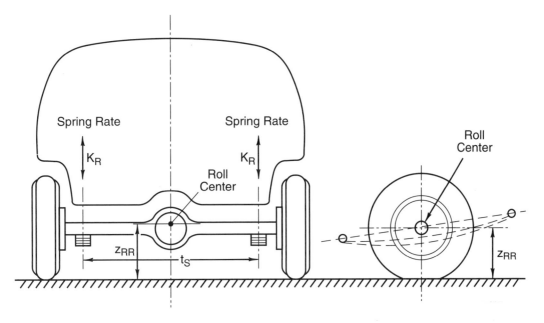

Figure 8.2 *Roll center location, axle with leaf springs.*

The stability in roll of such a suspension is thus dependent on t_S^2, and on the height of the roll center, which in turn depends on the placing of the rear springs.

In a truck rear axle the springs are frequently deep in section and placed **above** the axle, thus raising the roll center and increasing stability. But dual rear wheels may make the spring separation only **half** of the mean wheel track, in which case the rear roll rate is relatively very low.

In other types of suspensions the **height** of the rear springs does not affect the roll axis. In independents this height depends only on the rate of tread-change. And on coil spring rear axles the roll center height is controlled by some form of linkage.

The full treatment for distribution of roll moments, etc., is given below, referring to Figure 8.1.

A_Y = lateral acceleration (in g-units)
$K_{\phi F}$ = front roll rate **with** tires (lb.-ft./rad.)
$K_{\phi WR}$ = rear roll rate **without** tires (lb.-ft./rad.)
$K_{\phi TR}$ = axle roll rate on its tires (lb.-ft./rad.)
ϕ = roll angle of vehicle relative to ground (rad.)
ϕ_{uR} = roll angle of axle relative to ground (rad.)
h = total height of CG of rolling mass above ground (ft.)
H = height of the CG above the roll axis (ft.)
z_{RF} = height of front roll axis (ft.)
z_{RR} = height of CG of axle (assumed same as height of rear roll center) (ft.)
t_F = front wheel track (ft.)
t_R = rear wheel track (ft.)
W_F = front rolling weight (lb.)
W_R' = rear rolling weight (lb.)
w = rear unsprung weight (lb.)
W_R = total rear weight: $W_R = W_R' + w$ (lb.)
ΔW_F = front weight transfer (lb.)
ΔW_R = rear weight transfer (lb.)

Equilibrium of rolling mass:

$$K_{\phi F}\phi + K_{\phi WR}\left(\phi - \phi_{uR}\right) = \left(A_Y + \phi\right)\left[W_F\left(h - z_{RF}\right) + W_R'\left(h - z_{RR}\right)\right] \qquad (8.1)$$

The term $W_F\left(h - z_{RF}\right) + W_R'\left(h - z_{RR}\right)$ is a constant. Call it M_c, the rolling moment constant.

Then $\qquad K_{\phi F}\phi + K_{\phi WR}\left(\phi - \phi_{uR}\right) = M_c\left(A_Y + \phi\right) \qquad (8.2)$

From which $\qquad \phi = \dfrac{A_Y M_c + K_{\phi WR}\phi_{uR}}{K_{\phi F} + K_{\phi WR} - M_c} \qquad (8.3)$

Equilibrium of axle:

$$K_{\phi TR}\phi_{uR} = K_{\phi WR}\left(\phi - \phi_{uR}\right) + W_R z_{RR}\left(A_Y + \phi_{uR}\right) \qquad (8.4)$$

From which $\qquad \phi_{uR} = \dfrac{M_c\left(A_Y + \phi\right) + W_R z_{RR} A_Y - K_{\phi F}\phi}{K_{\phi TR} - W_R z_{RR}} \qquad (8.5)$

Then,

Front weight transfer $\qquad \Delta W_F = \dfrac{K_{\phi F}\phi + A_Y W_F z_{RF}}{t_F} \qquad (8.6)$

Rear weight transfer $\qquad \Delta W_R = \dfrac{K_{\phi TR}\phi_{uR}}{t_R}$ $\qquad\qquad$ (8.7)

The roll moment distribution and its effect upon steering are fully discussed in Chapter 2, Equations 2.40 to 2.49.

The above treatment and Figure 8.1 applies particularly to IFS with a rear axle. It is shown in Chapter 2 that it can also be applied to IFS with a swing axle. The modifications necessary for a vehicle with front and rear axle suspensions will be obvious. The following are some descriptions of [*other*] suspension types.

Independent without Tread [Track] Change

This applies not only to true parallel action independents, Figure 8.3a, but to any independent, such as Figure 8.3b, with its roll center on the ground. K is now the vertical rate of spring plus tire [*overall ride rate per wheel*], and the roll rate $K_{\phi F}$ will include the tire.

In the absence of a roll stabilizer [*anti-roll bar*]:

$$K_{\phi F} = \left(1/2\right) K t_F^2 \text{ lb.-in./radian (if lengths are in inches).} \qquad (8.8)$$

The rolling mass in case (a) is the sprung plus unsprung. In case (b) the two wheels usually do not roll quite as far as the sprung mass. But the difference is generally small, and the unsprung is usually added as part of the rolling mass. [*Terry Satchell points out that this is worth accounting for as a function of camber gain, when the unsprung is heavy.*]

The rolling moment at the front end is then $W_F h \left(A_Y + \phi\right)$.

It is a mistake to say that this is necessarily resisted by the roll moment $K_{\phi F}\phi$, since the total roll moment is resisted front and rear in proportion to the front and rear roll rates. **What can be said is that in any form of independent, with or without tread change, unless it is fitted with a "stabilizer" or a "de-stabilizer," the roll rate is always** $K_{\phi F} = \left(1/2\right) K t_F^2$ **(lb.-in./rad.).**

or $\qquad\qquad K_{\phi F} \text{ (lb.-ft./deg.)} = \dfrac{\left(1/2\right) K t_F^2}{12 \times 57.3} = \dfrac{K t_F^2}{1375} \qquad\qquad$ (8.9)

$$\text{Roll rate} = \dfrac{\left(\text{ride rate, one wheel}\right) \times \left(\text{wheel track}\right)^2}{1375} \qquad (8.10)$$

The importance of this is that ride rate and roll rate figures are frequently quoted from tests, which do not satisfy these conditions. In such cases it can be confidently stated that errors have been made in one or both of the readings.

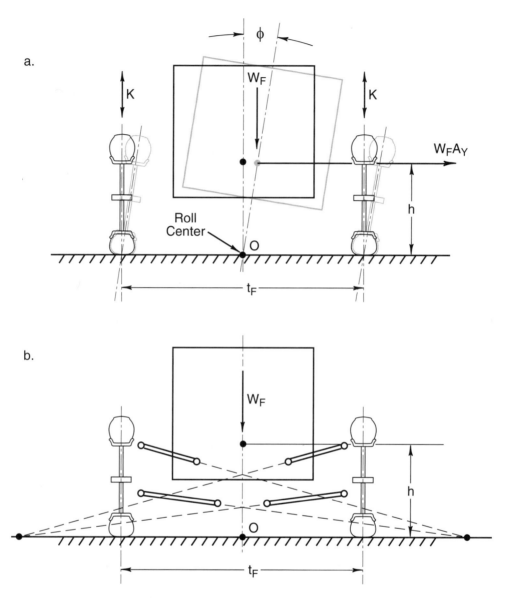

Figure 8.3 *Independent suspensions without tread (track) change.*

The stabilizer [*also called "anti-roll bar"*], principally used in front, adds to the roll rate without increasing the ride rate, Figure 8.4.

The de-stabilizer [*also called "camber compensator"*], principally used on rear swing axles, adds to the ride rate without increasing the roll rate, see Figure 8.5. [*Another common mechanical arrangement is the "Z-bar," which looks like an anti-roll bar but with the lever arms pointing in opposite directions. It also carries load and increases the ride rate, but does not increase the roll rate.*]

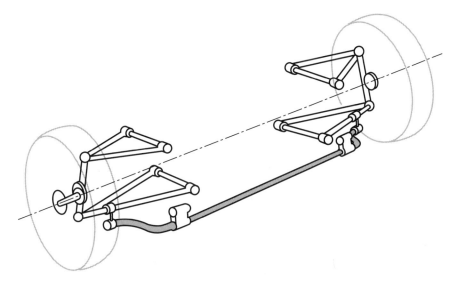

Figure 8.4 *Stabilizer or anti-roll bar.*

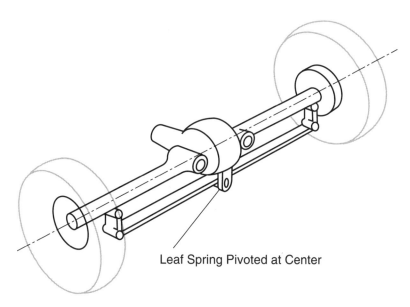

Leaf Spring Pivoted at Center

Figure 8.5 *De-stabilizer—pivoted transverse leaf spring (or camber compensator).*

Independent with Tread Change

A variation in the wishbone suspension which is becoming popular [*c. 1960*] is shown in Figure 8.6. In this case, there is tread change as shown by the raised roll center z_{RF}. If $R_1 H = R_2 (H - h)$, the rate of tread change is constant, i.e., the "scrub line" AB is a straight line, and z_{RF} is constant.

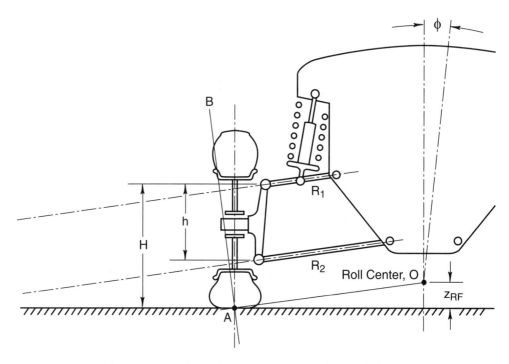

Figure 8.6 *Independent suspension with tread change.*

On a turn, the outer wheel rolls through about the same angle as the car, but the inner wheel rolls **more** (which is undesirable for tire wear and squeal). The difference between the inner and outer wheel is not significant as regards roll moment distribution, and it is usual simply to add the unsprung to the spring for the total rolling mass. When figuring the distribution of roll moments it is [*also*] usual to ignore the slight side shift of the roll center O which occurs when the car rolls. In other words the treatment is like that based on Figure 8.1. [*Depending on the choice of suspension type and actual geometry, the side shift in the roll center with roll may be large and it may make sense to use a more sophisticated type of analysis that includes the full kinematics.*]

Swing Axle

In Chapter 2, the swing axle was dealt with as a simple independent with a raised roll center. That is, the unsprung weight was ignored and the tire deflection was simply added to the spring deflection. This was a reasonable approximation for its purpose. But for a more accurate study it would be better to consider the swing axle as shown in Figure 8.7, in which case it closely resembles a conventional axle, except for the high roll rate due to the wide spring base and the high roll center.

Roll rate **without** tires: $K_{\phi WR} = (1/2)\, K t^2$ (8.11)

Roll rate of unsprung on tires: $K_{\phi TR} = (1/2)\, K_T t^2$ (8.12)

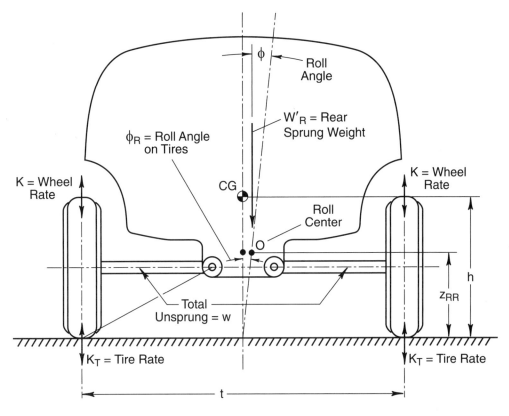

Figure 8.7 *Swing axle (rear view).*

The solution for roll moment distribution is then exactly the same as for the rear axle (earlier in this section). However, this does not intend to say that the swing axle handles or rides exactly like a rigid axle with high roll rate and high roll center.

Attention is directed to Section 7.11 in which it is pointed out that we have no means of testing the actual ride or roll rates on a swing axle, including the effect of camber thrust. Also, the notes on swing axle steering (Section 2.9) are not complete, since they do not cover the important condition of a swing axle running in a lightly loaded position with positive camber on the wheels. This positive camber position of the swing axle, and the resulting oversteer, is probably the greatest fault of the swing axle. However, a compensating advantage is the damping effect of the changing wheel track. (See Section 6.12.)

8.3 Intermediate Designs of Independent Suspension

Between the parallel independent with its roll center on the ground and the swing axle, with its high roll center, there are any number of intermediate designs, of "semi-swing" independents in which the center of swing of each wheel may be at or beyond the center of the opposite wheel, giving a roll center such as O (Figure 8.8) which may be only 6 inches or so above the ground. In calculating roll moment distribution on this type of

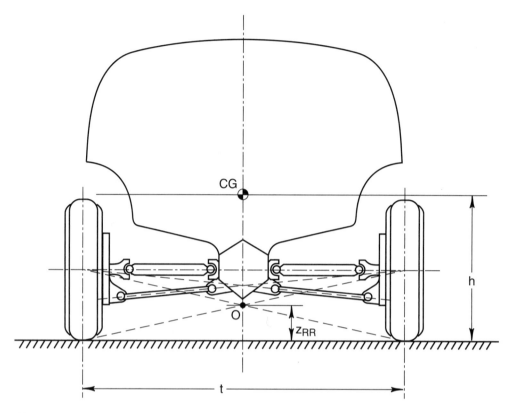

Figure 8.8 Intermediate design of independent suspension (late Corvair type shown).

suspension it is probably satisfactory to include 50 percent of the unsprung weight as rolling weight [*sprung weight*], and the other 50 percent as rolling only on the tires. Since these suspensions are independents, it follows that the spring base in roll is equal to the wheel track.

Generally speaking such compromise designs as these have proven extremely successful in rear suspensions with respect to ride, handling, tire life, lack of wheel hop, etc.

8.4 De Dion Axles

In most cases (Figure 8.9) De Dion axles are mounted similarly to conventional Hotchkiss axles and require no special consideration. Advantages over conventional axles are:

- Elimination of the mass of the drive gears and casing at the axle center. This greatly reduces the tendency of the axle to tramp, and the consequent side shake of the car.
- Rear wheels can be toed-in or given negative camber for improved cornering.

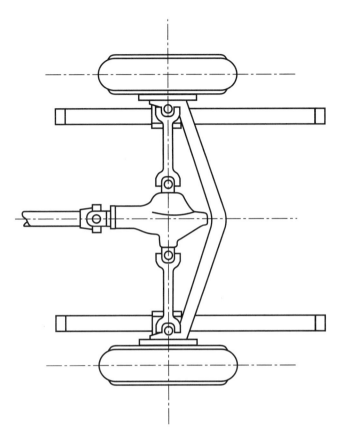

Figure 8.9 *Typical De Dion axle on leaf springs.*

- Unsprung weight is reduced.
- Interference with the rear floor can be reduced.

A particular variation of the De Dion axle used on Mercedes race cars prior to World War II is worthy of note; see Figure 8.10.

The axle is stiff in bending, but made in two halves connected by a rotary sleeve joint. If the car rolls through an angle ϕ, the wheels tilt in the opposite direction through an angle γ, such that $\gamma = -\dfrac{r}{R}\phi$. [*If the vertical distance moved by the torque arm at the wheel end is x, then* $\phi = \dfrac{x}{t/2}$, *and the wheel camber change is* $-\dfrac{r}{R}\dfrac{x}{t/2} = -\dfrac{r}{R}\phi.$]

This undoubtedly gives an appreciable advantage in rear roll-steer. [*Olley may have meant "an appreciable advantage in rear roll **camber**," which is in the understeer direction with this design.*] (However, Mercedes race cars now [*1950s*] employ a form of low-center swing axle.)

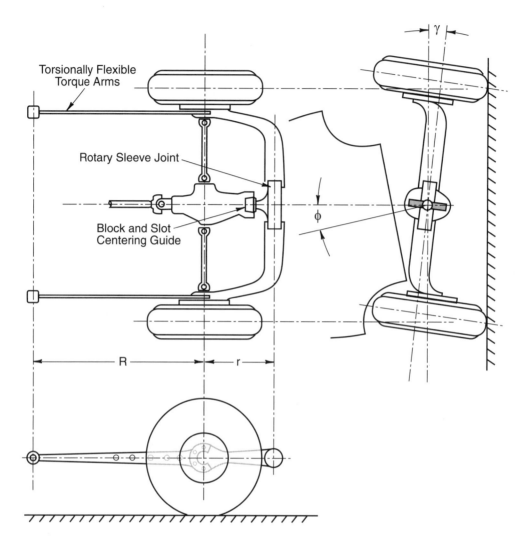

Figure 8.10 *Mercedes De Dion axle.*

8.5 Skew Rates [*Warp*]

Perhaps skew rates have not previously received enough attention. Under static conditions, or when moving at moderate speed over a warped road surface, the **skew stiffness of a car's suspension controls the torsional distortion forces which fall on the frame and body**.

Imagine the car with its front and rear wheel pairs standing on two seesaws as shown in Figure 8.11, the front plank being pivoted near ground level, while the rear is pivoted somewhere near the rear axle roll center. Then if the two planks are tilted in opposite directions in such a way that the tilting moments on the two planks are equal and opposite, the car will remain upright, and the tilting moment at **either** end divided by the **sum** of the tilt angles of the two planks is the measure of the skew rate of the suspension.

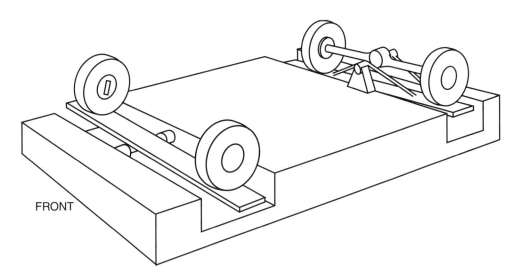

Figure 8.11 *Test rig for determining skew rates.*

For example the roll rate at the front of a conventional passenger car may be 350 lb.-ft./degree, and at the rear 240 lb.-ft./deg. Then the skew rate will be the combination of the two or

$$\frac{350 \times 240}{350 + 240} = 142 \text{ lb.-ft./deg.} \tag{8.13}$$

8.6 Longitudinal Interconnection–Compensated Suspension

A completely different condition exists in a compensated suspension such as the Packard torsion-rod suspension (Figure 8.12) in which, while the total roll rate of the vehicle remains perfectly normal, the skew rate may be exceedingly small. [*Other examples of this are the longitudinal coil springs in the French Citroën 2CV and the Moulton Hydrolastic and Hydragas fluid interconnected suspensions used on English cars from the BMC1100/MG Sedan to the MGF.[53] The Lotus Active Suspension[54] was programmed "modally" and the skew or warp rate could be set to any desired value over a wide range.*]

The principal feature of this type of suspension is a great reduction in pitch **stability**, and hence a reduction in pitch **frequency**. But the low skew rate is an important incidental advantage.

---

[53] Moulton, Dr. A. E. "Moulton Suspension, Past and Future," Sir Henry Royce Memorial Foundation Lecture, IMechE, London, June 2000.

[54] Williams, D. A. and P. G. Wright, US Patent 4,625,993, 1986.

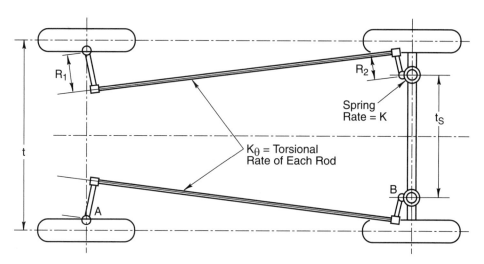

Figure 8.12 *Packard torsion-rod suspension.*

Total Roll Rate for Compensated Suspension

Suppose the car is rolled left so motion up at A (assumed parallel independent) is z inches.

$$\text{Motion up at B} = z \times \frac{t_S}{t} \text{ inch.} \tag{8.14}$$

$$\text{Torsion in rod} = z\,K_\theta\left(\frac{1}{R_1} + \frac{t_S}{tR_2}\right) \tag{8.15}$$

$$\text{Compression in rear spring} = \frac{t_S}{t}Kz \tag{8.16}$$

$$\text{Moment on front end} = z\frac{K_\theta}{R_1}\left(\frac{1}{R_1} + \frac{t_S}{tR_2}\right)t \tag{8.17}$$

$$\text{Moment on rear end} = z\frac{K_\theta}{R_2}\left(\frac{1}{R_1} + \frac{t_S}{tR_2}\right)t_S + \frac{zKt_S^2}{t} \tag{8.18}$$

$$\text{Total moment (front and rear)} = zK_\theta\left(\frac{t}{R_1} + \frac{t_S}{R_2}\right)\left(\frac{1}{R_1} + \frac{t_S}{tR_2}\right) + \frac{zKt_S^2}{t} \tag{8.19}$$

$$\text{Angle of roll} = \frac{2z}{t} \tag{8.20}$$

Therefore,   Total Roll Rate $= \dfrac{K_\theta}{2}\left(\dfrac{t}{R_1}+\dfrac{t_S}{R_2}\right)^2+\dfrac{Kt_S^2}{2}$ (8.21)

If $K_\theta = 9820$ lb.-in./rad.
          $t = 60$ in.
          $t_S = 44$ in.
          $R_1 = 14$ in.
          $R_2 = 12$ in.
          $K = 100$ lb./in.

$$\text{Total roll rate } = \frac{9820}{2}\left(\frac{60}{14}+\frac{44}{12}\right)^2+\frac{100}{2}(44)^2$$

$$= 311000 + 96800 = 407800 \text{ lb.-in./rad.} \qquad (8.22)$$

$$= 593 \text{ lb.-ft./deg.}$$

Skew Rate

Suppose,   Motion up at A $= x$ (8.23)

                Motion down at B $= y$ (8.24)

Then,   Torsion in rod $= K_\theta\left(\dfrac{x}{R_1}-\dfrac{y}{R_2}\right)$ (8.25)

                Compression of rear springs $= \pm Ky$ (8.26)

        Roll moment on front end $= \dfrac{K_\theta t}{R_1}\left(\dfrac{x}{R_1}-\dfrac{y}{R_2}\right)$ (8.27)

Opposing moment on rear end $= t_S\left[Ky-\dfrac{K_\theta}{R_2}\left(\dfrac{x}{R_1}-\dfrac{y}{R_2}\right)\right]$ (8.28)

These must be equal or:

$$\frac{K_\theta t}{R_1}\left(\frac{x}{R_1}-\frac{y}{R_2}\right)=t_S\left[Ky-\frac{K_\theta}{R_2}\left(\frac{x}{R_1}-\frac{y}{R_2}\right)\right] \qquad (8.29)$$

$$K_\theta\left(\frac{t}{R_1}+\frac{t_S}{R_2}\right)\left(\frac{x}{R_1}-\frac{y}{R_2}\right)=Kt_S y \qquad (8.30)$$

Or

$$y = x \frac{\dfrac{K_\theta}{R_1}\left(\dfrac{t}{R_1} + \dfrac{t_S}{R_2}\right)}{Kt_S + \dfrac{K_\theta}{R_2}\left(\dfrac{t}{R_1} + \dfrac{t_S}{R_2}\right)} \tag{8.31}$$

$$\text{Total angle} = \frac{2x}{t} + \frac{2y}{t_S} \tag{8.32}$$

$$\text{Skew rate} = \frac{\text{moment at either end}}{\text{total angle}} = \frac{\dfrac{K_\theta}{R_1}\left(\dfrac{x}{R_1} - \dfrac{y}{R_2}\right)t}{\dfrac{2x}{t} + \dfrac{2y}{t_S}} \tag{8.33}$$

Example:

Let $\qquad K_\theta = 9820$ lb.-in./rad., and other quantities as above.

Then

$$y = \frac{702 \times 7.952}{4400 + (818 \times 7.952)}x = 0.511x \tag{8.34}$$

$$\text{Skew rate} = \frac{9820 \times 60}{14 \times 2}\left(\frac{\dfrac{1}{14} - \dfrac{0.511}{12}}{\dfrac{2}{60} + \dfrac{2(0.511)}{44}}\right) \tag{8.35}$$

$$\text{Skew rate} = 10731 \text{ lb.-in./rad.} = 15.6 \text{ lb.-ft./deg.}$$

which compares with 142 lb.-ft./deg. for a normal car.

The skew rate is therefore only about 15.6/593 or about 2.5% of the total roll rate, as compared with 142/593 or 24% of the total roll rate on a standard car. (Note: The compensated suspension is, however, figured without a front stabilizer, which would affect the skew rate considerably.)

8.7 Roll Stability

The roll of a car on a turn depends on the roll rates at the two ends and the height of the CG of the rolling mass above the roll axis.

If a car has independent suspension without tread change at both ends (as on some European cars) the roll axis is on the ground. The entire mass of the car, sprung plus unsprung, rolls on a turn. And the moment arm of the CG above the roll axis is the height of the CG from the ground, which may be two feet or more.

Rolling moments are therefore high, and, if the spring "deflections" are to be high enough for comfort, some supplementary springs operating only in roll have to be provided for adequate roll stability. (In contrast one might consider the Corvair in which the moment arm of the CG around the roll axis is only about 11 inches.)

From time to time, car designs are produced in which the roll axis is raised until the CG of the rolling mass is actually **below** the roll axis. Roll **rates** then become unnecessary and in their absence the car will "bank" on corners like a bicycle. The belief has been that such a vehicle will ride and handle in every way like a bicycle. But this is a mistake, since the bicycle is an entirely different case from the four-wheeled vehicle. It actually steers by banking and lacks entirely the lateral oscillations of the four-wheeled vehicle. [*Bicycles/motorcycles have their own types of dynamic problems.*]

This whole question of roll axis height is best discussed in Schilling's "Handling Factors" of September 23, 1938, quoted at length in Chapter 6 in the discussion of waddle and side chuck.

There is thus some optimum height of roll axis. But it is not possible to select an arbitrary "best height." The situation is continually changing as car suspensions are softened and as dry-friction is reduced. Much of the "waddle" of cars with a low roll axis in the past (for example the original SLA cars of 1932–33) was partially due to suspension **friction**. And some European front drive cars with roll axis on the ground show little tendency to waddle. On the contrary it is cars with a high roll axis which tend to show lateral jerk, and lateral control linkage, such as Panhard rods, have to be softened to overcome it.

Scale Effects

The same scale effects mentioned in Section 9.4 as applying to pitch stability of a vehicle also apply to its stability in roll. That is, if a small car is built to three-fourths of the scale of a large car it will have to have only about nine-sixteenths of the spring deflection to be equally stable in roll. Its frequency in roll will be about 33 percent higher. The only escape from this is to build the small car exceedingly low.

Roll Stabilizer

With normal disposition of masses in a passenger car, and in the absence of a roll stabilizer, the roll frequency tends to be appreciably lower than the frequencies in pitch and bounce. For best riding comfort it is desirable to keep all three frequencies fairly close together. Therefore a roll stabilizer can be used which can contribute as much as 25 percent to the overall roll stiffness of the vehicle without interfering seriously with the riding comfort. This stabilizer can take the form shown in Figure 8.13.

If L = total length of the torsion rod and I = its polar moment, the torsional stiffness of the rod, K_θ, is:

$$K_\theta = \frac{T}{\theta} = \frac{GI}{L} \text{ lb.-in./rad.} \tag{8.36}$$

G = *shear modulus. For a round bar,* $I = \pi d^4/32$.

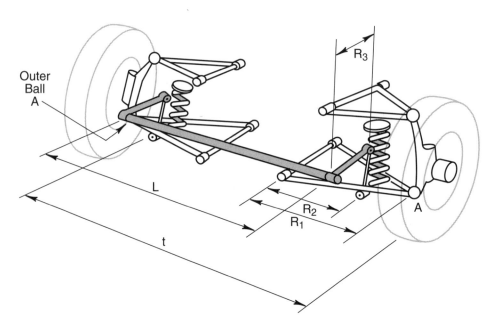

Figure 8.13 *Roll stabilizer (anti-roll bar).*

In roll only half the rod length operates for each wheel. Therefore linear rate at either of the outer wishbone balls (point A) is:

$$K_A = \frac{2K_\theta}{R_3^2} \times \frac{R_2^2}{R_1^2} \text{ lb./in.} \tag{8.37}$$

Then the added roll rate: $K_{\phi\text{aux.}} = \dfrac{4K_\theta R_2^2 \left(\dfrac{t}{2}\right)^2}{R_1^2 R_3^2}$ lb.-in./rad. (8.38)

$$K_{\phi aux.} = \frac{K_{\theta}R_2^2 t^2}{688 R_1^2 R_3^2} \quad \text{lb.-ft./deg.} \tag{8.39}$$

In practice, because of tire deflection, bending of the R_3 arm, and deflection of the rubber joints, the actual added roll rate may not be much more than half the theoretical.

Also, because of the rubber connections, the roll stabilizer adds appreciably to the ride rate. In testing ride and roll rates without stabilizer, it is therefore necessary to disconnect **both ends** of the stabilizer.

With the stabilizer bar, the two wheel ride rate is unaffected except for wind-up of any rubber bushings. However, the one wheel bump rate is increased and this rate depends on both ride springs and the stabilizer bar rate.

8.8 Roll Axis Measurement

Some confusion frequently arises with regard to the roll axis. For example, observations by eye or camera under a car while traveling on the road will not show the sprung mass of the car rotating about the roll axis. However, it can be demonstrated experimentally; see Figure 8.14.

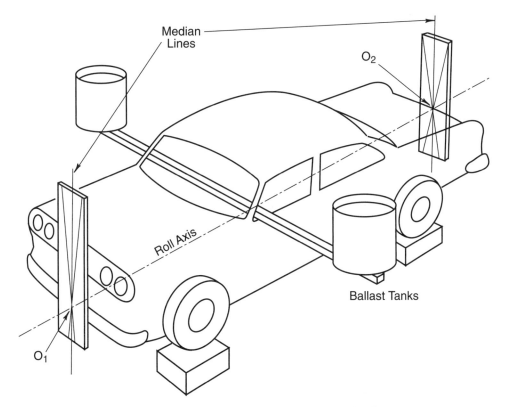

Figure 8.14 *Experimental determination of roll axis.*

The car is made to roll statically by applying a roll moment by such means as water ballast tanks as shown, or by shifting ballast bags on a cross beam. [*Since Olley wrote this, a number of kinematic and compliance test machines have been developed and are used around the world, for making this and other types of measurement.*]

Tires are overinflated, or knife edges on the wheel rims may be used [*or measurements may be made at the wheel centers with the chassis clamped to a rigid table*]. In the case of an independent suspension with tread change, the wheel supports must move freely sideways.

Suitable sighting boards inscribed with vertical median lines are attached at each end of the vehicle and adjusted to bring median lines vertical. When the vehicle is rolled statically by shifting ballast, the points O_1 and O_2 are found by using two transits, or by multiple camera exposures. The line joining these two points is the roll axis. [*Note that with many types of suspension, the roll axis is not in a fixed location; it changes with ride and roll position. Other methods of analysis may be used to account for this, but the roll axis concept remains useful for visualization.*]

8.9 Summary

As noted above, the roll axis in essence is a linear concept. It follows from design layouts and simple axle suspensions and continues to be used. It gives a good feel for the workings of the suspension, and simple vehicle dynamics analysis using a roll center at each end of a vehicle will often give results that are reasonably accurate. Unfortunately, in many cases the roll center moves with ride and roll travel of the suspension, especially with independent suspensions. This then leads to involved geometric methods for tracking the movement of the roll center, which removes much of the attraction of this method.

In more recent analyses an alternate formulation has been used, which consists in treating the force balance on each wheel independently. This has been called by several different names including lateral-force-anti[55] (the change in normal force as a result of a lateral force) and with this alternative formulation no fixed roll center is assumed. At any given ride position, an independent suspension moves about some instant axis, which appears in front (or rear) view as an instant center. If a line is drawn from the tire con-

[55] McHenry, Raymond E., "Research in Automobile Dynamics—A Computer Simulation of General Three-Dimensional Motions," Paper No. 710361, Society of Automotive Engineers, Warrendale, Pa., June 1971.

[56] Milliken, W. F. and D. L. Milliken, *Race Car Vehicle Dynamics*, R-146, Society of Automotive Engineers, Warrendale, Pa., 1995.

tact to this point, a virtual swing arm is constructed and the inclination of this arm determines the coupling between the lateral and vertical forces for that ride position. Figures 17.6 and 17.21 in Race Car Vehicle Dynamics[56] *show the instant axis concept.*

The material in this chapter is presented in the original order that it appears in Olley's notes. It seemed better to keep the notes on skew rates and compensated suspension (interconnection) with the discussion of the roll axis and the de-stabilizer (camber compensator) than to move these to another part of the book.

Onboard the S.S. Berengaria, 1936. Left to right: Olley's daughter Diane, Olley's wife Norma Marie Olley, Maurice Olley. Photo credit Rolls-Royce Heritage Trust.

CHAPTER 9

Fore and Aft Forces

"My present belief is that the ordinary passenger car, say, five years hence, will be front drive with IFS, perhaps with a rear axle or with parallel type IRS. It is the safest handling vehicle for an unskilled driver, under all road conditions."

Maurice Olley, 1953

9.1 Introduction

This chapter covers a number of topics, all related to longitudinal acceleration. Olley presents calculations to approximate the maximum traction available before wheel spin, discusses brake distribution and then devotes considerable effort to the effects of anti-dive and anti-squat. The chapter ends with a discussion of sudden brake application and the ramifications of this violent event.

9.2 Maximum Traction

In this section, Olley first calculates the load changes due to acceleration (for a solid axle) and then calculates the longitudinal force available for acceleration.

Traction forces, F_{XLR} and F_{XRR}, are applied at **each** rear wheel; see Figure 9.1. Wind resistance force is ignored. So is the small rolling resistance at the two front wheels. Thus the total tractive force F_X at the rear tires is employed in accelerating the vehicle.

Let: W = total weight of vehicle, lb.
W_F = vertical load, front tires, lb.
W_R = vertical load, rear tires, lb.
t_R = rear wheel track, in.
G = axle ratio
R = wheel radius, in.

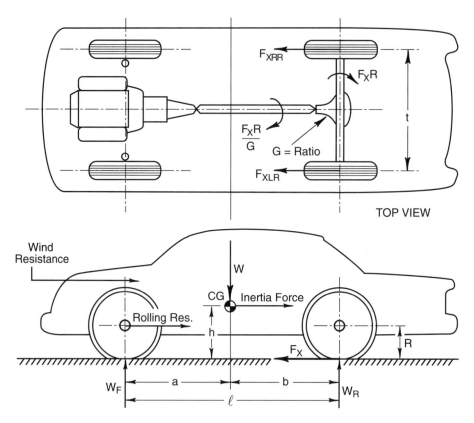

Figure 9.1 *Layout for engine torque reaction and maximum traction.*

A_X = longitudinal acceleration, g
μ = traction coefficient
$K_{\phi T}$ = total roll rate, lb.-ft./deg.
$K_{\phi F}$ = front roll rate, lb.-ft./deg.
$K_{\phi R}$ = rear roll rate, lb.-ft./deg.

Then
$$W_R = W\frac{a}{\ell} + F_X\frac{h}{\ell} \qquad (9.1)$$

But $F_X = WA_X$ (this neglects the rotational acceleration of the wheels). Therefore,

$$W_R = W\left(\frac{a}{\ell} + A_X\frac{h}{\ell}\right) \qquad (9.2)$$

Torque of powerplant, (engine) × (transmission ratio):

$$T_D = F_X R / G \qquad (9.3)$$

If we assume body-frame to be torsionally stiff, T_D is distributed:

Torque on front wheels
$$\frac{K_{\phi F}}{K_{\phi T}}T_D = \frac{K_{\phi F}}{K_{\phi T}}\frac{F_X R}{G} \tag{9.4}$$

Torque on rear wheels
$$\frac{K_{\phi R}}{K_{\phi T}}T_D = \frac{K_{\phi R}}{K_{\phi T}}\frac{F_X R}{G} \tag{9.5}$$

So total drive torque falling on rear axle is

$$\left(1 - \frac{K_{\phi R}}{K_{\phi T}}\right)\frac{F_X R}{G} = -\frac{K_{\phi F}}{K_{\phi T}}\frac{F_X R}{G} \tag{9.6}$$

[*Change in*] vertical load on left rear wheel due to drive torque [*assuming a counterclockwise driveshaft rotation*]:

$$\Delta W_{LR} = +\frac{K_{\phi F}}{K_{\phi T}}\frac{F_X R}{G}\frac{1}{t_R} \tag{9.7}$$

[*Change in*] vertical load on right rear wheel due to drive torque:

$$\Delta W_{RR} = -\frac{K_{\phi F}}{K_{\phi T}}\frac{F_X R}{G}\frac{1}{t_R} \tag{9.8}$$

Total load on left rear wheel:

$$W_{LR} = \frac{W}{2}\left(\frac{a}{\ell} + A_X\frac{h}{\ell}\right) + \left(\frac{WA_X}{2}\frac{K_{\phi F}R}{K_{\phi T}G(t_R/2)}\right) \tag{9.9}$$

$$W_{LR} = \frac{W}{2}\left[\frac{a}{\ell} + A_X\left(\frac{h}{\ell} + \frac{K_{\phi F}R}{K_{\phi T}G(t_R/2)}\right)\right] \tag{9.10}$$

Total load on right rear wheel:

$$W_{RR} = \frac{W}{2}\left[\frac{a}{\ell} + A_X\left(\frac{h}{\ell} - \frac{K_{\phi F}R}{K_{\phi T}G(t_R/2)}\right)\right] \tag{9.11}$$

With a **standard free differential** [*open differential*] the maximum acceleration, $A_{X\,max}$, is limited by the adhesion of the right rear wheel.

To fill in some steps left out of the original:

$$F_{Xmax} = \mu W \left(\frac{a}{\ell} + A_{Xmax} \left(\frac{h}{\ell} - \frac{K_{\phi F} R}{K_{\phi T} G(t_R/2)} \right) \right) \tag{9.12}$$

But, $\qquad A_{Xmax} = \dfrac{F_{Xmax}}{W} = \mu \left(\dfrac{a}{\ell} + A_{Xmax} \left(\dfrac{h}{\ell} - \dfrac{K_{\phi F} R}{K_{\phi T} G(t_R/2)} \right) \right)$ $\qquad$ (9.13)

and, $\qquad W \times A_{Xmax} = \mu W \left(\dfrac{a}{\ell} + A_{Xmax} \left(\dfrac{h}{\ell} - \dfrac{K_{\phi F} R}{K_{\phi T} G(t_R/2)} \right) \right)$ $\qquad$ (9.14)

or $\qquad\qquad A_{Xmax} = \dfrac{\mu \dfrac{a}{\ell}}{1 - \mu \left(\dfrac{h}{\ell} - \dfrac{K_{\phi F} R}{K_{\phi T} G(t_R/2)} \right)}$ $\qquad$ (9.15)

With a **locked differential**, the maximum tractive force available from the left rear:

$$F_{XLR\,max} = \mu \frac{W}{2} \left(\frac{a}{\ell} + A_{Xmax} \left(\frac{h}{\ell} + \frac{K_{\phi F} R}{K_{\phi T} G(t_R/2)} \right) \right) \tag{9.16}$$

Maximum tractive force available from the right rear:

$$F_{XRR\,max} = \mu \frac{W}{2} \left(\frac{a}{\ell} + A_{Xmax} \left(\frac{h}{\ell} - \frac{K_{\phi F} R}{K_{\phi T} G(t_R/2)} \right) \right) \tag{9.17}$$

Total tractive force: $\qquad W \times A_{Xmax} = \mu W \left(\dfrac{a}{\ell} + A_{Xmax} \dfrac{h}{\ell} \right)$ $\qquad$ (9.18)

or $\qquad\qquad A_{Xmax} = \dfrac{\mu \dfrac{a}{\ell}}{\left(1 - \mu \dfrac{h}{\ell} \right)}$ $\qquad$ (9.19)

Consider some values. Let:

$W = 4000$ lb.
$a/\ell = 0.50$
$h/\ell = 0.20$
$K_{\phi F}/K_{\phi T} = 2/3$ (typical value with front stabilizer [*anti-roll bar*])
$$\frac{R}{(t_R/2)} = \frac{12.5}{30} = 0.417$$
$G = 3$

Then
$$\frac{K_{\phi F} R}{K_{\phi T} G(t_R/2)} = \frac{2 \times 0.417}{9} = 0.0925 \qquad (9.20)$$

Load on left rear wheel:

$$W_{LR} = \frac{W}{2}\left(\frac{a}{\ell} + A_X\left(\frac{h}{\ell} + \frac{K_{\phi F} R}{K_{\phi T} G(t_R/2)}\right)\right) = 2000(0.5 + 0.2925 A_X) \qquad (9.21)$$

Load on right rear wheel:

$$W_{RR} = \frac{W}{2}\left(\frac{a}{\ell} + A_X\left(\frac{h}{\ell} - \frac{K_{\phi F} R}{K_{\phi T} G(t_R/2)}\right)\right) = 2000(0.5 + 0.1075 A_X) \qquad (9.22)$$

If we take $\mu = 1.0$ (a dry road), then:

With free differential,

$$A_{Xmax} = \frac{\mu \dfrac{a}{\ell}}{1 - \mu\left(\dfrac{h}{\ell} - \dfrac{K_{\phi F} R}{K_{\phi T} G(t_R/2)}\right)} = \frac{0.5\mu}{1 - 0.1075\mu} = \mathbf{0.56g} \qquad (9.23)$$

Maximum tractive force on each wheel:

$$F_{XLR} = F_{XRR} = 0.56 \times 2000 = 1120 \text{ lb.}$$
$$\text{Total: } F_X = 2240 \text{ lb.}$$

With a locked differential,

$$A_{Xmax} = \frac{\mu \frac{a}{\ell}}{\left(1 - \mu \frac{h}{\ell}\right)} = \frac{0.5}{1 - 0.2} = \mathbf{0.625g} \tag{9.24}$$

Tractive force:

Left rear wheel: $F_{XLR} = 2000\left(0.5 + \left(0.625 \times 0.2925\right)\right) = 1366$ lb.
Right rear wheel: $F_{XRR} = 2000\left(0.5 + \left(0.625 \times 0.1075\right)\right) = 1134$ lb.
Total $= 2500$ lb.

1. Note that a car, resembling a standard car in general specifications, has lost approximately 10% in maximum acceleration due to the lifting effect on the right rear wheel, with a free differential. With a locked differential this loss is restored.

    It is also restored by:

    *   Any suspension with the drive gears fixed to the sprung mass, i.e.,
        De Dion axle
        Independent rear suspension
        Conventional swing axle

    *   Or by the use of an offset torque arm, as covered in Section 3.3.

2. Note also that the single joint swing axle (as on Mercedes cars) does **not** have equal vertical loads on the two rear wheels, but carries the drive shaft torque by unequal loading of the two rear wheels, just like a conventional rear axle. (See Figure 9.13 below.)

3. Note also that the loss in maximum acceleration is reduced by,
    *   Smaller wheels or wider track, i.e., reducing $R/(t_R/2)$
    *   Greater reduction in axle gears, i.e., increasing G
    *   Reducing front stabilizer, i.e., reducing $K_{\phi F}/K_{\phi T}$
    *   Increasing height of CG or reducing wheelbase, i.e., increasing h/ℓ
    *   Increasing weight on rear wheels, i.e., increasing a/ℓ

    However we are really interested, not so much in A_{Xmax} as in A_{Xmax}/μ. This is the ratio:

$$\frac{A_{Xmax}}{\mu} = \frac{\text{maximum acceleration}}{\text{maximum acceleration with four wheel drive}} \tag{9.25}$$

For an axle with free differential (or a single-joint swing axle),

$$\frac{A_{X\,max}}{\mu} = \frac{a/\ell}{1 - \mu\left(\dfrac{h}{\ell} - \dfrac{K_{\phi F}R}{K_{\phi T}G(t_R/2)}\right)} \tag{9.26}$$

For a locked differential, an axle with offset torque arm or a "sprung differential,"

$$\frac{A_{X\,max}}{\mu} = \frac{a/\ell}{1 - \mu\dfrac{h}{\ell}} \tag{9.27}$$

Front Drive

The front drive passenger car will in general have a sprung differential, rather than a truck-type driving axle. So the limitation of $A_{X\,max}$ due to lifting one wheel will not exist.

Then, evidently,
$$\frac{A_{X\,max}}{\mu} = \frac{b/\ell}{1 + \mu\dfrac{h}{\ell}} \tag{9.28}$$

[*This was checked by taking moments about the rear tire contact patch.*]

Figure 9.2 shows the comparison of front drive with sprung differential, and rear axle with free differential. The verticals show $A_{X\,max}/\mu$ which is also **maximum tractive effort vs. tractive effort with four wheel drive** expressed as percentage of four wheel drive.

These quantities are plotted against percent of load on front wheels. The practical range is between a 40/60 weight distribution (typical rear engine) and a 60/40 distribution (typical front drive).

The total probable range of h/ℓ for a passenger car is between 0.175 and 0.225, as shown in Figure 9.2. The probable range of friction coefficient is between 1.0 for dry, smooth concrete, and 0.30 for wet blacktop.

At 50/50 weight distribution on dry concrete the front drive is at a disadvantage, having a maximum traction only 0.417 of four wheel drive, as compared with 0.56 for the rear axle, with free differential.

On the wet road, however, this disadvantage is much less, 0.475 for the front drive, and 0.515 for the rear axle.

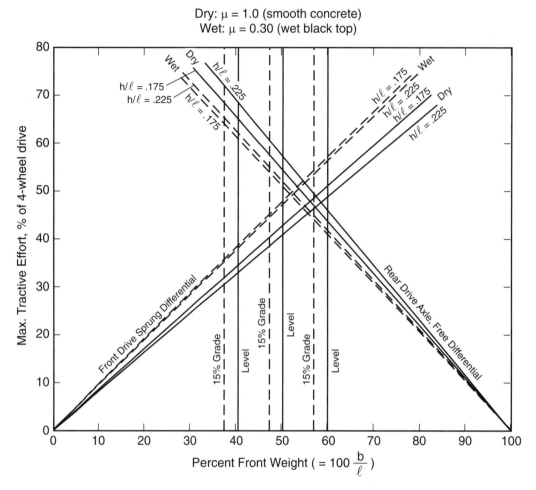

Figure 9.2 *Comparison of maximum tractive effort vs. weight distribution.*

At a 60/40 weight distribution, which is probable on a front drive, the front drive car has 50% of four wheel traction on the dry road, and almost 57% on wet road. In this latter case it has an important advantage over the rear axle with 50/50 weight distribution. [*Note: These numbers depend on* h/ℓ.]

Grades

The effect of grades is shown most simply by shifting the weight distribution points to the left. Thus, on a 15% grade, the 40/60 weight distribution becomes approximately 37/63, and the 60/40 becomes 57/43. This is shown by the broken lines in Figure 9.2. The grade is an advantage to the rear drive and a disadvantage to the front drive car.

9.3 Brake Distribution

The distribution of braking between front and rear wheels is a compromise between the requirements of high and low traction coefficients, i.e., between traction coefficients of dry and wet roads.

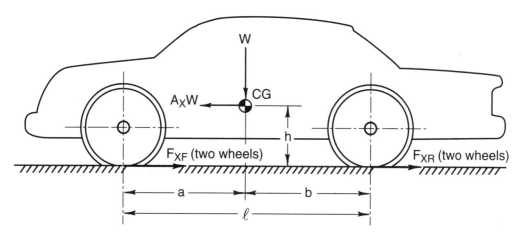

Figure 9.3 *Brake distribution for maximum braking.*

During forward braking:

Weight on front wheels:
$$W_F = W\left(\frac{b}{\ell} + A_X\frac{h}{\ell}\right) \tag{9.29}$$

Weight on rear wheels:
$$W_R = W\left(\frac{a}{\ell} - A_X\frac{h}{\ell}\right) \tag{9.30}$$

If μ = traction coefficient, then

Braking capacity, front wheels: $\mu W\left(\dfrac{b}{\ell} + A_X\dfrac{h}{\ell}\right)$ $\qquad(9.31)$

Braking capacity, rear wheels: $\mu W\left(\dfrac{a}{\ell} - A_X\dfrac{h}{\ell}\right)$ $\qquad(9.32)$

Total brake force: $\qquad\qquad\qquad F_{XF} + F_{XR}$ $\qquad(9.33)$

These need to be multiplied by tire loaded radius to arrive at brake torque.

When $F_{XF} = \mu W\left(\dfrac{b}{\ell} + A_X\dfrac{h}{\ell}\right)$ the front wheels lock.

When $F_{XR} = \mu W \left(\dfrac{a}{\ell} - A_X \dfrac{h}{\ell} \right)$ the rear wheels lock.

But if λ is the proportion of front wheel braking and $1 - \lambda$ is the proportion of rear wheel braking, then

$$F_{XF} = \lambda A_X W \quad \text{and} \quad F_{XR} = (1 - \lambda) A_X W \tag{9.34}$$

So, front wheels lock when $\qquad A_X = \dfrac{\mu \dfrac{b}{\ell}}{\lambda - \mu \dfrac{h}{\ell}}$ $\qquad$ (9.35)

or rear wheels lock when $\qquad A_X = \dfrac{\mu \dfrac{a}{\ell}}{(1 - \lambda) + \mu \dfrac{h}{\ell}}$ $\qquad$ (9.36)

Example 1:

Let: $\quad a/\ell = b/\ell = 0.50$
$\quad\quad\;\; h/\ell = 0.20$
$\quad\quad\;\; \lambda = 0.60$ and $1 - \lambda = 0.40$

Then front wheels lock when $\quad A_X = \dfrac{0.5\mu}{0.6 - 0.2\mu}$ $\qquad$ (9.37)

And rear wheels lock when $\qquad A_X = \dfrac{0.5\mu}{0.4 - 0.2\mu}$ $\qquad$ (9.38)

Dry road:
$\quad \mu = 1.0$
$\quad$ Fronts lock when $A_X = 0.5/0.4 = \mathbf{1.25}$
$\quad\quad$ (This is above traction coefficient, i.e., front wheels will not lock.)
$\quad$ Rears lock when $A_X = 0.5/0.6 = \mathbf{0.833}$

Wet road:
$\quad \mu = 0.30$
$\quad$ Fronts lock when $A_X = 0.15/0.54 = \mathbf{0.278}$
$\quad$ Rears lock when $A_X = 0.15/0.46 = \mathbf{0.326}$
$\quad\quad$ (This is above traction coefficient, i.e., rear wheels will not lock.)

Example 2:

[*Same as Example 1, but with*]: $\lambda = 0.55$ and $1 - \lambda = 0.45$

Then front wheels lock when $A_X = \dfrac{0.5\mu}{0.55 - 0.2\mu}$ (9.39)

And rear wheels lock when $A_X = \dfrac{0.5\mu}{0.45 - 0.2\mu}$ (9.40)

Dry road:
> $\mu = 1.0$
> Fronts lock when $A_X = 0.5/0.35 = \mathbf{1.43}$ (no lock)
> Rears lock when $A_X = 0.5/0.65 = \mathbf{0.77}$

Wet road:
> $\mu = 0.30$
> Fronts lock when $A_X = 0.15/0.49 = \mathbf{0.306}$ (no lock)
> Rears lock when $A_X = 0.15/0.51 = \mathbf{0.294}$

This is more clearly seen by a braking diagram, Figure 9.4.

On a dry road, with 60/40 brake distribution, the rear brake force meets the brake capacity line at point A, where $A_X = 0.833$. From then on the rear wheels are locked, but extra deceleration can be obtained from the front brakes, as shown by line BC.

With 55/45 brake distribution the rear wheels lock sooner, at point D, representing $A_X = 0.77$. Extra deceleration is obtained from the front brakes along line EC.

The argument for the 55/45 distribution is shown in the wet road portion of the diagram. On the wet road, with 60/40 distribution, the front wheels will lock first, at point F, representing $A_X = 0.278$.

With a 55/45 distribution, the rear wheels will still lock first, at point G, representing $A_X = 0.294$.

Probably there are some reasons for keeping the 55/45 distribution, even though it sacrifices some stopping power on dry roads. However, point G shows that on wet roads there is only a negligible margin against locking all wheels.

With improvements in highway surfaces and tire treads, there is an increasing tendency to adopt brake distributions, such as 60/40, which are more favorable to dry roads.

Although an instructive way of plotting brake performance, Olley's Figure 9.4 is based on certain assumptions. In the first place, it assumes a constant friction coefficient for a given tire/road combination and omits tire load sensitivity and tire temperature effects. The brake capability is linear with wheel loads and hence longitudinal deceleration A_X. In practice, brake distribution is often based on hydraulic line pressure and the geometry

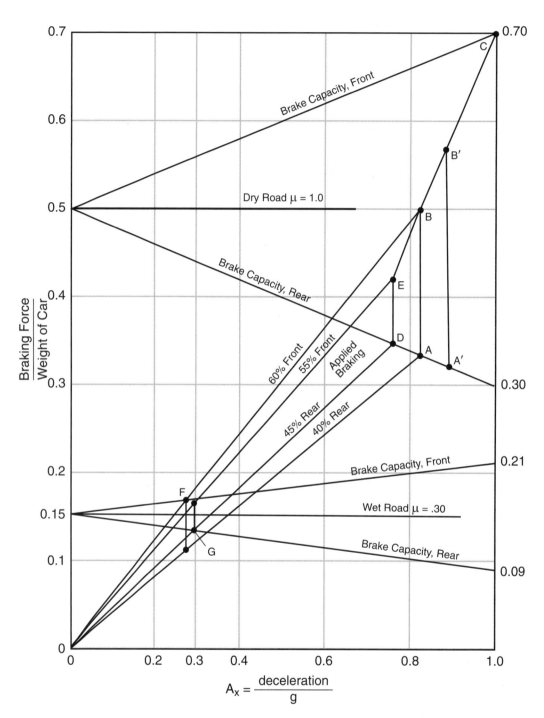

Figure 9.4 Braking diagram.

of the actuating mechanism, but Olley defines brake distribution in terms of the relative front and rear braking forces.

To construct the diagram he first calculates the front and rear "brake capacities", which depend on the vehicle CG location (horizontal and vertical), i.e., $a/\ell, b/\ell, h/\ell$, W and μ as a function of A_X. The slope of these lines (upper portion of the diagram) can be modified by changing these parameters to give higher and lower values for the front and rear brake capacities at $A_X = 1.0$, but the sum of these capacities must equal the assumed friction coefficient.

*He now assumes some distribution of the front and rear braking forces, for example 60% front, 40% rear (these lines start at the origin). For example, if at $A_X = 0.3$ the braking forces of the front (~0.12) and rear (~0.18) are added, they sum to 0.3 on the vertical scale. In the example (dry road) the 40% rear distribution line intersects the rear brake capacity and the rear wheels are locked up at Point A. At the **same** A_X (horizontal scale) the front brakes are at point B. The front brakes are operating far below their capacity and as they are applied harder, B moves up BC and a line connecting A and B moves to the right (for example A'B'). Thus the brake distribution continues to move further to the front as B progresses toward C.*

In summary, the Olley braking diagram applies to a specific situation for a given μ and vehicle CG location, and for brake forces proportional to load.

9.4 Brake Dive

To simplify the figuring, without serious error, it seems best to ignore the small weight transfer of the unsprung masses and consider the elements in Figure 9.5 as representing **sprung mass only**.

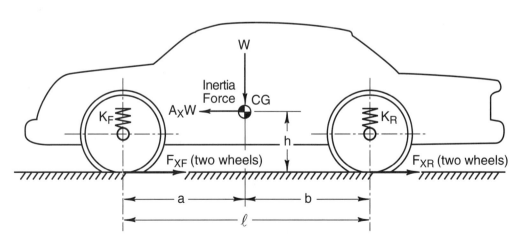

Figure 9.5 *Definitions for brake dive analysis.*

Probably a more serious omission is that the effective mass of the car is increased by the rotary inertia of the four wheels and the flywheel, etc., and when we say that $F_{XF} + F_{XR} = A_X W$ we ignore this.

Let K_F = front spring rate (two wheels)
        K_R = rear spring rate (two wheels)
        A_X = deceleration (g)

The couple causing brake dive is $A_X W h$ and the resulting downward force on front springs and lifting force on rear springs is $A_X W h / \ell$. Then, if the front and rear suspensions are "neutral," i.e., nothing is done geometrically to resist brake dive:

Front end will drop $\dfrac{A_X W h}{K_F \ell}$

Rear end will lift $\dfrac{A_X W h}{K_R \ell}$

The angle of brake dive (in radians) is then $\dfrac{A_X W h}{\ell^2}\left(\dfrac{1}{K_F} + \dfrac{1}{K_R} \right)$

Or, if d_F is the front static deflection at normal load and d_R is the rear static deflection at normal load, we can say that:

$$\frac{W}{K_F} = \frac{\ell}{b} d_F \ \text{ and } \ \frac{W}{K_R} = \frac{\ell}{a} d_R$$

Therefore, the angle of brake dive is $\dfrac{A_X h}{\ell}\left(\dfrac{d_F}{b} + \dfrac{d_R}{a} \right)$

Note that the "static deflections" enter into the equation as dimensions of the car. Therefore, if the car is scaled down, to obtain equal dive angles its spring deflections must be scaled down in the same ratio. Thus the smaller car must be relatively stiffer sprung and must have higher ride frequencies.

The opinion that a heavy car rides better than a light one is not justified. But it is true that a **large** car can ride better than a small one with equal stability in pitch and roll.

Actually the case of the smaller car is much worse than is shown by straight scale effects, because of the need to contain the same size of human beings. This means that, on the smaller car, without drastic redesigning, the height h of the CG cannot be reduced appreciably.

Consider then that the wheelbase ℓ and its parts **a** and **b**, are reduced to 3/4 of their original dimensions, while **h** remains unchanged. Then, for the same angle of brake dive, the deflections d_F and d_R, must be only nine-sixteenths of the original, or, if for the larger car they were, say, 9 in., they can be little more than 5 in. for the smaller car.

The angle through which the car with neutral suspension squats back in acceleration is also given by:

$$\frac{A_X h}{\ell}\left(\frac{d_F}{b} + \frac{d_R}{a}\right) \tag{9.41}$$

but the lower value of A_X due to driving only one pair of wheels, determines that the squat in acceleration is less than the brake dive angle.

Braking Example

Let $W = 4000$ lb.
        $h = 24$ in.
        $\ell = 120$ in.
        $A_X = 1.0g$
        $K_F = 225$ lb./in.
        $K_R = 275$ lb./in.

Then vertical forces on either end: $\dfrac{A_X W h}{\ell} = 800$ lb.

In braking, drop in front is: $\dfrac{A_X W h}{K_F \ell} = 3.56$ in.

Lift in rear is: $\dfrac{A_X W h}{K_R \ell} = 2.91$ in.

Brake dive angle is: $\dfrac{6.47}{120} \times 57.3 = 3.10°$

This of course is a steady-state figure. It will be exceeded, if the suspension stops will allow, on sudden brake applications.

9.5 Anti-Dive Geometry

No changes in configuration within the car, except a reduction in h/ℓ, can change the actual weight transfer $A_X W h/\ell$ on front and rear **tires**. But the dive angle, and the weight transfer on the front and rear **springs**, can be reduced or can even be reversed by arranging the wheel supporting mechanism to have the effect of a radius arm (Figure 9.6).

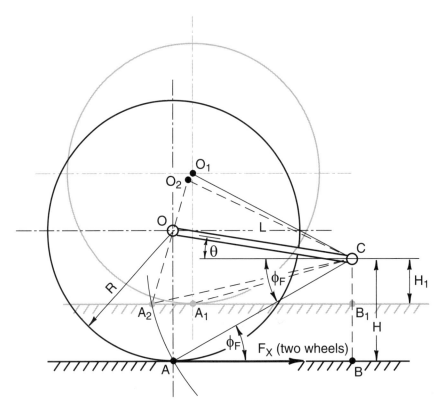

Figure 9.6 *Anti-dive geometry, front wheels.*

Suppose, for example, that a front wheel of radius R is supported by a single radius arm OC, of length L which is pivoted at C, and bolted to the brake backing plate at O. The arm makes an angle θ with the horizontal, bringing the pivot C to a height H from the ground.

When the brakes are applied, the braking force F_{XF} causes a turning moment $F_{XF}H$ around pivot C and increases the vertical load between tires and ground at point A by $(F_{XF}H)/L\cos\theta$.

Evidently, if $F_{XF}\tan\phi_F$ is equal to the weight transfer due to braking, the height of the suspension at this end of the car will not change (in steady-state braking). If the height of the pivot C changes from H to H_1, the wheel center O moves to O_1 and the ground contact A moves to A_1. Then ϕ_F has been reduced from BAC to B_1A_1C, and the anti-dive effect has been reduced.

We can write,
$$\tan\phi_F = \frac{H}{L\cos\theta}$$
(9.42)

From which,
$$\cos\theta = \frac{H}{L\tan\phi_F}$$
(9.43)

Also, $$sin\,\theta = (R - H)/L \qquad (9.44)$$

Then, $$tan\,\theta = \frac{sin\,\theta}{cos\,\theta} = \frac{(R-H)/L}{H/(L\,tan\,\phi_F)} \qquad (9.45)$$

$$tan\,\theta = (R-H)\,tan\,\phi_F/H \qquad (9.46)$$

and, at any height, $$tan\,\phi_F = H\,tan\,\theta/(R-H) \qquad (9.47)$$

Usually this is not the most convenient way to look at the anti-dive effect.

When the height H has been reduced to H_1, the tire will have been compressed, and center O will not have moved quite as far as O_1. So it is not too far wrong if we assume that the original triangle AOC has swung up to the position A_2O_2C, and that the new angle ϕ_F is B_1A_2C.

Then we can say that the curve AA_2, representing the path of the original contact point, determines the change in ϕ_F, and so determines the anti-dive effect at various standing heights.

As an example, consider the Porsche front suspension consisting of two equal short radius arms which are initially horizontal, Figure 9.7. There is no anti-dive angle at normal standing height. But, as the car dives, a position A_1 is soon reached at which the weight transfer is balanced and no further dive takes place. (And this occurs without

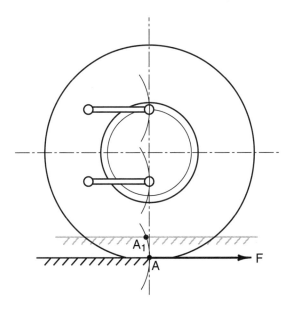

Figure 9.7 Porsche-type IFS (c. 1960).

change of caster angle or rotation of the brake backing plate. The same was true of the Chevrolet Dubonnet suspension.)

Or suppose a wishbone suspension with both arms tilted forward at an angle ϕ to the horizontal, Figure 9.8. Then a braking force F_{XF} produces a vertical component $F_{XF} \tan \phi$, although there is no rotation of the brake backing plate, no change of caster and no radius arm.

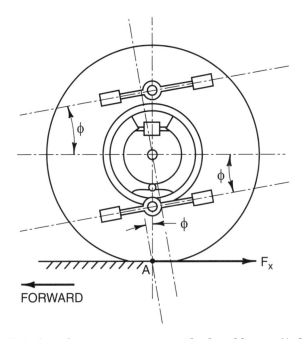

Figure 9.8 *Anti-dive geometry using tilted wishbones (A-frames).*

Now we can consider the conditions to prevent brake dive for the complete car, see Figure 9.9. The total braking force is F_X. It is divided, in the design of the car, λF_X in front and $(1 - \lambda) F_X$ at the rear.

Then if a horizontal line $B_F B_R$ through the CG is divided at point C in the proportion

$$\frac{B_F C}{B_R C} = \frac{\lambda}{1 - \lambda} \tag{9.48}$$

the lines $A_F C$ and $A_R C$, making angles ϕ_F and ϕ_R with the horizontal, define the path angles of the contact points (at right angles to $A_F C$ and $A_R C$) required to resist brake dive completely.

For
$$\tan \phi_F = \frac{h}{\lambda \ell} \quad \text{and} \quad \tan \phi_R = \frac{h}{(1 - \lambda) \ell} \tag{9.49}$$

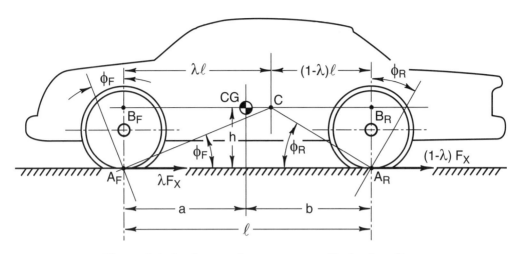

Figure 9.9 *Brake anti-dive geometry, all wheels rolling.*

Thus $\qquad \lambda F_X \tan \phi_F = \dfrac{F_X h}{\ell}$ and also $(1-\lambda)F_X \tan \phi_R = \dfrac{F_X h}{\ell}$ $\qquad$ (9.50)

The above relationship for 100% anti-dive on the front (with outboard brakes) can be derived from a consideration of the forces and moments involved. Refer to Figure 9.9.

First we should note that load changes at the front (and rear) wheels due to a horizontal inertia force at the CG will be the same (in steady-state) whether the vehicle has anti-dive geometry or not. However, the body attitude can be controlled by the designer. The front brake force, λF_X, produces a moment $\lambda F_X h$ about point C. If this moment is divided by the distance $B_F C$ a vertical force is produced at point A_F. This force is directed downward and is generated by the suspension swing arm, i.e., it is a kinematic effect of the suspension. It is assumed to act on the hub carrier (knuckle) in parallel with the suspension spring. It tends to move the wheel down relative to the car body and lengthen the spring.

At the CG there is a reversed effective inertia force equal to F_X (the total braking force). Taking moments about A_R (the rear tire ground contact point) gives:

$$F_X h = F_V \ell \qquad (9.51)$$

*where F_V is the vertical force at the front track. It acts on the hub carrier in parallel with the spring and **tends** to shorten the spring. In the case of 100% anti-dive the two forces noted above are equal and the spring length remains constant—there is no pitch of the body and no movement of the unsprung.*

Equating the two forces, from the linkage and from the body inertia gives:

$$\frac{F_X h}{\ell} = \frac{\lambda F_X h}{B_F C} \qquad (9.52)$$

But h = SVSA (side view swing arm) height
    $B_F C$ = SVSA length

So that $$\frac{F_X h}{\ell} = \lambda F_X \frac{(SVSA\ height)}{(SVSA\ length)} = \lambda F_X \tan \phi_F \qquad (9.53)$$

where ϕ_F is the slope of the swing arm.

Note that SVSA length is the projected length of any physical suspension linkage with instant center (IC) on the line defined by ϕ_F.

Equations 9.49 and 9.50 are true only up to the point where the wheels slide. When this occurs the proportion of braking, front and rear, is no longer determined by the design, but by the load distribution.

Figure 9.10 illustrates the condition above the point of wheel slip [*slide*]. If μ is the coefficient of tire traction, the inertia force at the CG is μW. [*We now know that tire friction, μ, is generally a function of load, i.e., tire load sensitivity. The following derivation would be improved if different values for μ were used for front and rear tires which operate at different loads*].

If $$F_{XF} \tan \phi_F = \frac{\mu W h}{\ell} \quad \text{and} \quad F_{XR} \tan \phi_R = \frac{\mu W h}{\ell} \qquad (9.54)$$

there will be complete anti-dive [*with all four wheels locked*].

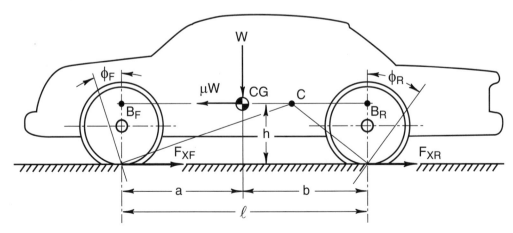

Figure 9.10 *Brake dive geometry, all wheels locked (or slipping).*

But

$$F_{XF} = \mu\left(\frac{Wb}{\ell} + \frac{\mu Wh}{\ell}\right) = \frac{\mu W}{\ell}(b + \mu h) \tag{9.55}$$

and

$$F_{XR} = \frac{\mu W}{\ell}(a - \mu h) \tag{9.56}$$

So, for complete anti-dive with all wheels slipping [*skidding*],

$$(b + \mu h)\tan\phi_F = h \quad \text{or} \quad \tan\phi_F = \frac{h}{b + \mu h} \tag{9.57}$$

and

$$(a - \mu h)\tan\phi_R = h \quad \text{or} \quad \tan\phi_R = \frac{h}{a - \mu h} \tag{9.58}$$

Hence in Figure 9.10, if $B_FC = b + \mu h$ and $B_RC = a - \mu h$, this represents the condition of zero brake dive. (Note that the desirable angles ϕ_F and ϕ_R now vary with the coefficient of tire traction. As μ decreases, ϕ_F increases and ϕ_R decreases.)

Example

Let $a = b$
  $h/\ell = 0.225$ (for the sprung mass)
  $\lambda = 0.6$ and $(1 - \lambda) = 0.4$ (below the point of wheel skid)

Then if $\tan\phi_F = \dfrac{h}{0.6\ell} = 0.375$, front end will not drop

and if $\tan\phi_R = \dfrac{h}{0.4\ell} = 0.562$, rear end will not lift.

Hence $\phi_F = 20.5°$ and $\phi_R = 29.5°$.

This is the condition below the point of wheel skid.

But, above the point of wheel skid [*Note that Olley now uses $h/\ell = 0.2$ instead of 0.225.*]:

If $\mu = 1.0$ (dry road)

$$\frac{b + \mu h}{a - \mu h} = \frac{b + \mu(h/\ell)\ell}{a - \mu(h/\ell)\ell} = \frac{0.5\ell + 0.2\ell}{0.5\ell - 0.2\ell} = \frac{0.7\ell}{0.3\ell}$$

$$\tan\phi_F = \frac{h}{0.7\ell} = 0.321 \quad \text{and} \quad \phi_F \approx 18°$$

$$\tan \phi_R = \frac{h}{0.3\ell} = 0.750 \text{ and } \phi_R \approx 37°$$

If $\mu = 0.30$ (wet road)

$$\frac{b + \mu h}{a - \mu h} = \frac{b + \mu(h/\ell)\ell}{a - \mu(h/\ell)\ell} = \frac{0.5\ell + 0.06\ell}{0.5\ell - 0.06\ell} = \frac{0.56\ell}{0.44\ell}$$

$$\tan \phi_F = \frac{h}{0.56\ell} = 0.400 \text{ and } \phi_F \approx 22°$$

$$\tan \phi_R = \frac{h}{0.44\ell} = 0.510 \text{ and } \phi_R \approx 27°$$

In hard braking on a dry road, we need $\phi_F = 18°$ and $\phi_R = 37°$, and we have $\phi_F = 20.5°$ and $\phi_R = 29.5°$. So ϕ_F is too big, and ϕ_R is too small. Consequently both ends will lift slightly. With all wheels skidding on a wet road there would be little change in the posture of the car. However in actual practice a complete cancellation of brake dive is seldom attempted. It is more usual to make ϕ_F about 10°, while ϕ_R may be anything from 0° to 25°.

There are several objections to complete anti-dive. For example:

1. A car which stops absolutely flat gives a severe shock to the passengers on severe brake application. A reasonable amount of dive serves as a "cushion."

2. In most front suspension designs the anti-dive geometry entails considerable change in caster angle. The caster angle increases as the wheel rises, implying more caster when heavily loaded, which makes for heavy steering.

3. There is increased difficulty in getting an accurate steering geometry. See Sections 7.3 and 7.4.

4. Excessive angles, ϕ_R, at the rear involve considerable variation in the rotation speed as the wheels move up and down on a broken road surface, and these may cause severe rattling in the drive gears and transmission. With fluid transmission some increase in ϕ_R angles seems permissible.

5. Also, forward brake hop and reverse power hop are likely to occur at the rear end. [*See Section 6.8 onward.*]

9.6 Power Squat

It is clear that when the rear wheels are driven and the car accelerates (or even if it is just using the rear traction to climb a hill, or to overcome air resistance) the car tends to lift up in front, and "squat" at the rear.

Nothing in the way of suspension geometry can be done to reduce the front end lift (since there are no horizontal [*tire*] forces there) but a lot of things can be done at the rear to prevent the squat. Unlike complete cancellation of brake dive, the squatting of the rear end is often **overcorrected** without difficulty.

Since the total traction force $F_{XR} \approx A_X W$ and weight transfer to the rear is $A_X W h / \ell$, if $\tan \phi_{R'} = h/\ell$ the rear squat is cancelled entirely.

And since h/ℓ is about 0.225, the angle $\phi_{R'}$ required is about 12.5°.

Or, with a 12.5 in. wheel radius, a horizontal torque arm at the axle center 55.5 in. long (12.5/0.225) will prevent rear squat [*i.e., 12.5/55.5 = 0.225 for* h/ℓ].

On the other hand if the torque arm is still shorter, as shown in Figure 9.11, so that line AC passes through the CG, then the total lifting force of the traction $F_{XR} \tan \phi_R$ is applied at the CG and the car will lift at either end [*i.e., both ends*] through a distance inversely proportional to the spring rates, and will remain almost horizontal in acceleration.

$$F_{XR}h = moment\ about\ CG \qquad (9.59)$$

This moment divided by b gives downforce at rear tire patch.

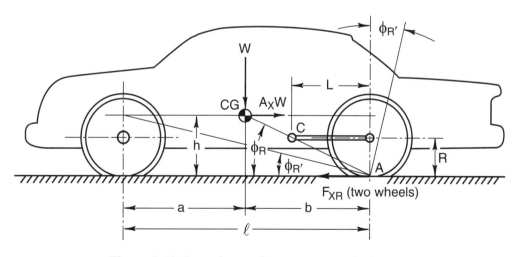

Figure 9.11 *Basic layout for anti-squat calculations.*

But,
$$F_{XR}h/b = F_{XR}\frac{(SVSA\ height)}{(SVSA\ length)} = F_{XR}\tan\phi_R \qquad (9.60)$$

*For the sum of the vertical forces to equal zero, there is a **lift** at the CG equal to $F_{XR}h/b$ in the **up** direction.*

Evidently, if the CG is central, this calls for a torque arm only about 28 in. long. A few years ago such a short radius of axle motion would have been considered unacceptable, for reasons already stated. However, with fluid drives, softer tires, lighter axles and better roads, there are signs that an effective torque arm shorter than 55 in., and frequently less than 30 in. is now tolerable for ordinary road use.

But it should be kept in mind that a radius arm such as AC is not essential to the elimination either of brake dive or traction squat. It is the path of the contact point which matters. Thus it is the path of the contact point with the brakes locked in the case of brake dive, and with the drive gears locked in the case of power squat. [*This path is at right angles to the effective swing arm AC.*]

For example, suppose the car sketched in Figure 9.9 to have IFS and a De Dion axle, and that both ends are fitted with "inboard" brakes in which the backing plates [*chassis reaction points*] are attached to the sprung mass. Then, when the brakes or drive gears are locked, the ground contact points A_F and A_R follow the motion of the **wheel centers** and since these will move more or less vertically, there is no appreciable anti-dive or anti-squat effect.

On a conventional axle both the brake shoes and the drive gears are carried on the axle. So the path of the rear ground contact A_R is the same in both braking and driving.

A particular note is required on rear axles controlled by short and long arm linkages as illustrated in Section 7.8. It was there pointed out that the effective torque arm on such linkages varied throughout the stroke, being quite short at the bump position and becoming very long or even "negative" at rebound.

The scale layout in Figure 9.12 shows that the path of the contact point is close to a straight line. Thus the steady-state brake dive correction is practically constant throughout the ride range. But it will be shown later in Section 9.11 that, in sudden or "panic" braking, it is the effective torque arm radius and not the path of the contact point which controls brake hop. Thus the long torque arm radius at rebound accounts largely for the freedom from brake hop on this type of suspension.

9.7 Mercedes Single-Joint Swing Arm

It has already been pointed out that this design [*shown in Figure 9.13*] produces the same difference in vertical load on the right and left tires as does a conventional axle. But in

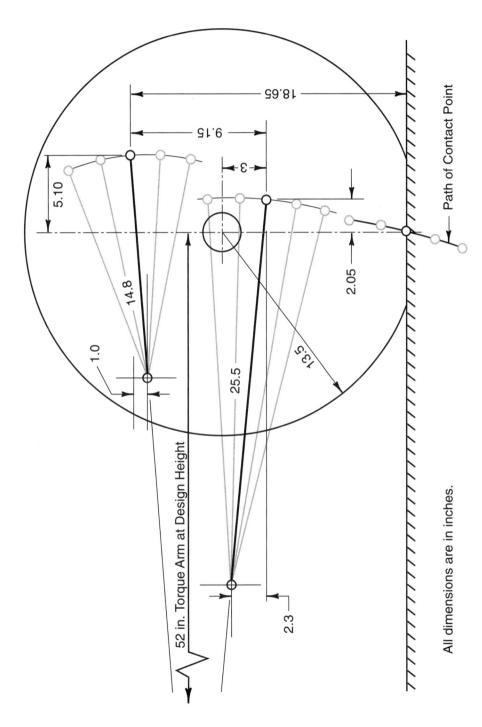

Figure 9.12 Rear link suspension, path of contact point.

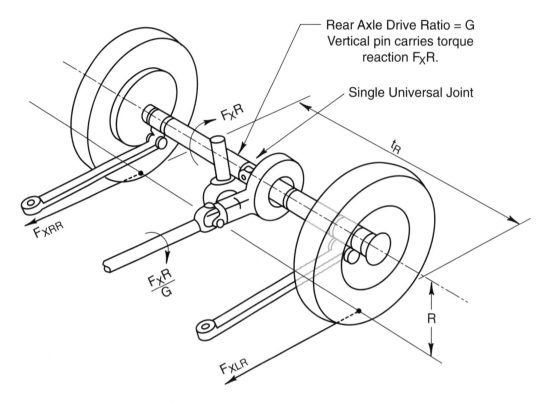

Figure 9.13 *Mercedes single-joint swing axle.*

the process it develops a vertical lift, $F_X R / G(t_R/2)$, on the centerline of the car, tending to resist power squat. This opposes the weight transfer $F_X h/\ell$. The net transfer of load to the rear **springs** is then,

$$F_X\left(\frac{h}{\ell} - \frac{R}{G(t_R/2)}\right) \tag{9.61}$$

So that if
$$\frac{h}{\ell} = \frac{R}{G(t_R/2)} \tag{9.62}$$

there will be no drop of the rear end in acceleration. If we say that $h/\ell = 0.225$ and $R/(t_R/2) = 0.417$, this gives $G = 0.417/0.225 = 1.85$. Or, with an axle ratio of say 3.7 the "squat" at the rear would be 50% corrected.

The lift actually entails rotation of the rear wheels and angular motion of the ground contact point like $\phi_{R'}$ on Figure 9.11. Thus, when the left rear wheel lifts a distance z with the drive shaft held, both rear wheels rotate forward through an angle $z/(Gt_R/2)$, or $\tan\phi_R = R/(Gt_R/2)$.

Taking $R/(t_R/2) = 0.417$ and $G = 3.7$, this will give $\phi_R = 6.5°$, which corresponds to about 50% correction of squat.

An interesting feature is that, when the left rear wheel hops on a rough road, it does change the drive shaft speed, but when the right rear wheel hops it does not. This suggests a difference in action of the two wheels in forward braking. Since the brake torque is carried by the vertical pin, allowing no rotation of the axle in the fore and aft plane, there is no resistance to brake dive.[57]

9.8 Vehicles with Axles Controlled by Leaf Springs

This section is followed directly by extra material that Olley put at the end of one of the monographs, which corrects and expands on portions of this section.

Vehicles with axles controlled by leaf springs present some special problems in connection with brake dive and power squat [*see also Chapter 10*]. We shall need to look back a few years.

Consider the typical "classic" car of Figure 9.14, with horizontal symmetrical leaf springs front and rear. It is like the car shown in Figure 9.3, i.e., there are no anti-dive or anti-squat effects. The height of the center of the main [*spring*] plate from the ground is H_F in front, and H_R at the rear. And we'll assume "berlin" (centered) eyes.

Then the braking torque on the front springs is $F_{XF}H_F$. And, if it is a Hotchkiss rear axle, the torque on the rear springs is $F_{XR}H_R$.

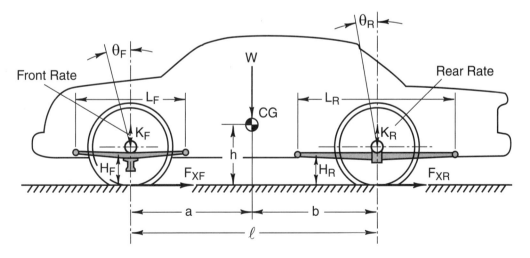

Figure 9.14 *"Classic" suspension—axles on leaf springs front and rear.*

---

[57] A summary of the anti-dive, anti-squat relationships for calculating the percentages is given in Milliken, W. F. and D. L. Milliken, *Race Car Vehicle Dynamics*, R-146, Society of Automotive Engineers, Warrendale, Pa., 1995, pp. 617–620.

Since the springs are symmetrical, the wind-up stiffness of the springs is $K_F L_F^2/4$ in front, and $K_R L_R^2/4$ at the rear. (These are in lb.-in. per radian.)

Thus the wind-up angle in front: $\theta_F = \dfrac{4 F_{XF} H_F}{K_F L_F^2}$ (9.63)

And at the rear: $\theta_R = \dfrac{4 F_{XR} H_R}{K_R L_R^2}$ (9.64)

Suppose that:
$\quad$ $F_{XF}/F_{XR} = 1.5$ (braking divided 60/40)
$\quad$ $L_F = 40$ in.
$\quad$ $L_R = 56.5$ in.
$\quad$ $H_F = H_R$

Then,

$$\frac{\theta_F}{\theta_R} = 3 \frac{K_R}{K_F} \qquad (9.65)$$

If
$$\frac{\theta_F}{\theta_R} = 1, \; K_F = 3 K_R$$

Or, in other words, to make the front and rear wind-up angles equal, **the front springs must be three times as stiff as the rear**. This was about the proportion of spring rates actually used on these cars, and which made a "flat ride" impossible.

Actually torque arms or torque tubes were frequently used, which prevented wind-up of the rear springs. But usually nothing was done to prevent wind-up of the front springs.

As an example if:
$\quad$ $F_{XF} = 1000$ lb.
$\quad$ $H_F = 11$ in.
$\quad$ $K_F = 300$ lb./in.

The front wind-up angle:

$$\theta_F = \frac{44000}{300 \times 1600} \times 57.3 = 5.25°$$

Thus negative caster on brake application was almost inevitable.

But, not content with this, frames were shortened by making the front springs unsymmetrical with the shorter end **in front; see Figure 9.15**.

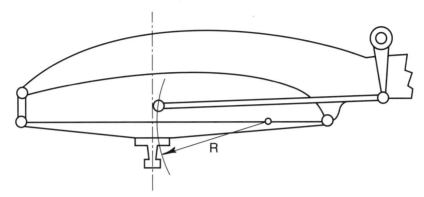

Figure 9.15 *Unsymmetrical front spring, shorter end in front.*

This was one of the first appearances of unsymmetrical leaf springs. It was frequently argued that it was necessary to have the longer spring "half" at the rear to improve the steering geometry. This is a fallacy, as the radius of action R of the spring always shortens as the spring is made unsymmetrical in **either direction**.

It is necessary to distinguish between unsymmetrical springs and "biased" springs, Figure 9.16.

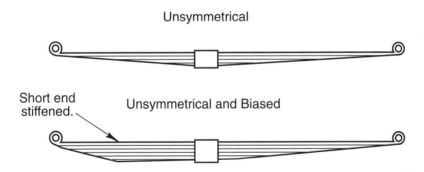

Figure 9.16 *Unsymmetrical vs. unsymmetrical and biased leaf spring construction.*

The unsymmetrical spring can still be designed to bend in circular arcs and to store as much work per pound of metal as a symmetrical spring. The biased spring is artificially stiffened at one end to resist brake dive or power squat, and sacrifices something in the efficient use of spring steel.

Using the symbols of Figure 9.17, if a = b = L/2 (for a symmetrical spring),

$$R = \frac{3a^3}{3a^2 + a^2} = \frac{3a^3}{4a^2} = 0.75a \qquad (9.66)$$

which is a relationship given in the Spring Manual.[58] *This says that for a **cantilever** spring the center of the eye moves in a path with a radius of 0.75L, where L is the length of the main leaf. This assumes the spring bends in a circular arc shape with leaves of constant cross section properly stepped for uniform strength. For a completely **symmetrical** spring the R is given in terms of L, the overall spring length, hence R/L = 0.75/2 = 0.375.*

The radius of action R of an unsymmetrical spring, Figure 9.17, of which end B is fixed, is given by:

$$R = \frac{3a^2b}{3a^2 + b^2}$$
(9.67)

Or if $a = \tau L$ and $b = (1 - \tau)L$:

$$\frac{R}{L} = \frac{3\tau^2(1 - \tau)}{3\tau^2 + (1 - \tau)^2}$$
(9.68)

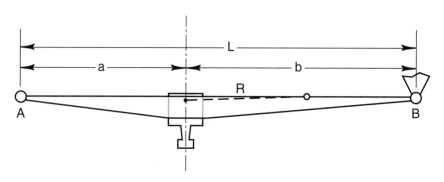

Figure 9.17 *Layout of unsymmetrical leaf spring.*

This is plotted in Figure 9.18 and it is noted that, whichever end of the spring is shortened, the radius of action is decreased below the optimum value, for a symmetrical spring of R/L = 0.375. Actually, a figure for R/L of 0.350 is not far off for all practical **unbiased** springs.

The next important feature of unsymmetrical springs is that, for a given vertical rate, they **decrease** in wind-up stiffness as they are made more unsymmetrical.

---

[58] SAE Spring Design Manual, AE-11, Society of Automotive Engineers, Warrendale, Pa., 1990.

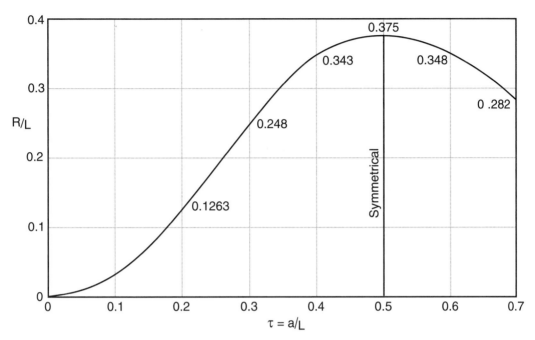

Figure 9.18 *Radius of action of an unsymmetrical leaf spring with the **rear** eye (pivot) fixed to the sprung mass.*

Wind-Up of Unsymmetrical Spring

In Figure 9.19:

> Wind-up torque = T
> Angle of wind-up = θ

1. For all springs. whether biased or not:

$$z_1 = \frac{T}{LK_1} \quad \text{and} \quad z_2 = -\frac{T}{LK_2} \tag{9.69}$$

Wind-up angle: $\qquad \theta = \dfrac{z_1 - z_2}{L} = \dfrac{T}{L^2}\left(\dfrac{1}{K_1} + \dfrac{1}{K_2}\right)$ $\qquad$ (9.70)

Wind-up stiffness: $\qquad \dfrac{T}{\theta} = \dfrac{L^2}{(1/K_1) + (1/K_2)}$ $\qquad$ (9.71)

Under torque, the deflection at the axle [*due to this torque*]:

$$z = \frac{1}{L}(bz_1 + az_2) = \frac{T}{L^2}\left(\frac{b}{K_1} - \frac{a}{K_2}\right) \tag{9.72}$$

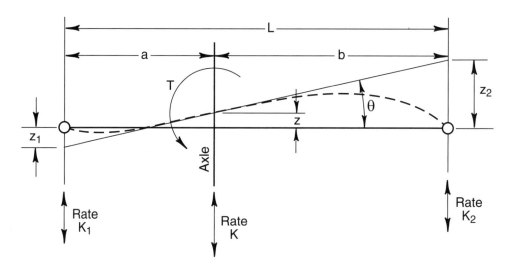

Figure 9.19 Wind-up of unsymmetrical spring.

Under vertical load, W, at the axle:

$$z_1 = \frac{Wb}{LK_1} \quad \text{and} \quad z_2 = \frac{Wa}{LK_2} \tag{9.73}$$

and

$$z = \frac{1}{L}(bz_1 + az_2) = \frac{W}{L^2}\left(\frac{b^2}{K_1} + \frac{a^2}{K_2}\right) \tag{9.74}$$

So

$$\frac{z}{W} = \frac{1}{K} = \frac{1}{L^2}\left(\frac{b^2}{K_1} + \frac{a^2}{K_2}\right) = \frac{K_1 a^2 + K_2 b^2}{K_1 K_2 L^2} \tag{9.75}$$

2. For unbiased springs only

Let ΣI = sum of moment of inertia of the plate sections.

Then

$$\frac{1}{K_1} = \frac{a^3}{2E\,\Sigma I} \quad \text{and} \quad \frac{1}{K_2} = \frac{b^3}{2E\,\Sigma I} \tag{9.76}$$

So

$$\frac{1}{K} = \frac{1}{2EL^2\,\Sigma I}\left(a^3 b^2 + a^2 b^3\right) = \frac{a^2 b^2}{2EL\,\Sigma I} \tag{9.77}$$

Or

$$2E\,\Sigma I = \frac{Ka^2 b^2}{L} \tag{9.78}$$

The origin of the above expressions, with 2EΣI in the denominator, is clarified as follows: As shown in Chapter 10, where leaf springs are treated as a "form of link motion," the deflection at the end of a single leaf is,

$$z = \frac{WL^3}{EI} \qquad (9.79)$$

where   *W = the load at end of single leaf*
   L = the effective link length
   E = Young's Modulus
   I = moment of inertia of the section

When this formula is applied to a multi-leaf spring, Olley develops a multiplying factor based on a series representation of the number of spring leaves. He shows that a large number of leaves are required to "approach the flexibility of a theoretical spring with **circular bending,** *" a requirement of the link representation of a leaf spring. For an infinite number of leaves, this factor is 1/2 and*

$$\frac{z}{W} = \frac{L^3}{2EI} \qquad (9.80)$$

Thus, since W/z = K ,
$$\frac{1}{K} = \frac{L^3}{2EI} \qquad (9.81)$$

Equation 9.81 is the basis for Equation 9.76, from which Equation 9.78 is derived using the relationship for springs in parallel.

Under torque, **lift of axle**:

$$z = \frac{T}{L^2}\left(\frac{b}{K_1} - \frac{a}{K_2}\right) = \frac{T}{2EL^2\Sigma I}\left(a^3 b - ab^3\right) \qquad (9.82)$$

or
$$z = \frac{T}{LK}\left(\frac{a}{b} - \frac{b}{a}\right) = \frac{T}{K}\left(\frac{a-b}{ab}\right) \qquad (9.83)$$

Note that $ab/(b-a)$ is the equivalent torque arm, R, so that under torque,

$$z = \frac{-T}{K \times (\text{torque arm})} = \frac{-T}{KR} \qquad (9.84)$$

Wind-up angle [*under torque*]:

$$\theta = \frac{T}{L^2}\left(\frac{1}{K_1} + \frac{1}{K_2}\right) = \frac{T}{2EL^2 \Sigma I}\left(a^3 + b^3\right) \tag{9.85}$$

or $\quad \theta = \frac{T}{LKa^2b^2}\left(a^3 + b^3\right) = \frac{T}{LK}\left(\frac{L^3 - 3abL}{a^2b^2}\right) = \frac{T}{K}\left(\frac{L^2 - 3ab}{a^2b^2}\right) \tag{9.86}$

The wind-up stiffness,

$$\frac{T}{\theta} = \frac{Ka^2b^2}{L^2 - 3ab} = \frac{Kab}{\left(L^2/ab\right) - 3} \tag{9.87}$$

If $a = \tau L$, $b = (1 - \tau)L$:

$$\frac{T}{\theta} = K\frac{\tau(1 - \tau)L^2}{\left(1/\tau(1 - \tau)\right) - 3} \tag{9.88}$$

And since wind-up stiffness of a symmetrical spring is $KL^2/4$, the relative wind-up stiffness of an unsymmetrical spring:

$$\frac{T/\theta}{KL^2/4} = \frac{4\tau(1 - \tau)}{\left(1/\tau(1 - \tau)\right) - 3} \tag{9.89}$$

Wind-up stiffness as a function of asymmetry, τ, is given in the table below and is plotted on Figure 9.20.

τ	0.30	0.333	0.35	0.40	0.45	0.50
$\dfrac{T/\theta}{KL^2/4}$	0.447	0.592	0.655	0.823	0.943	1.0

Note on Wind-Up Stiffness of Leaf Springs

It has been found that Section 9.8 on wind-up stiffness does not completely cover the situation. As a matter of fact there are two significant wind-up stiffnesses of an unsymmetrical leaf spring, one in which the axle is free to move up and down relative to the car, and the other in which it is not. These might be called "free" and "fixed" wind-up stiffness. All slow movements, as in acceleration or braking, occur with the axle free, but rapid vibrations of the axle such as occur due to torque reaction of a four-cylinder engine, leave the standing height of the car virtually undisturbed, and are therefore classed as fixed-axle oscillations.

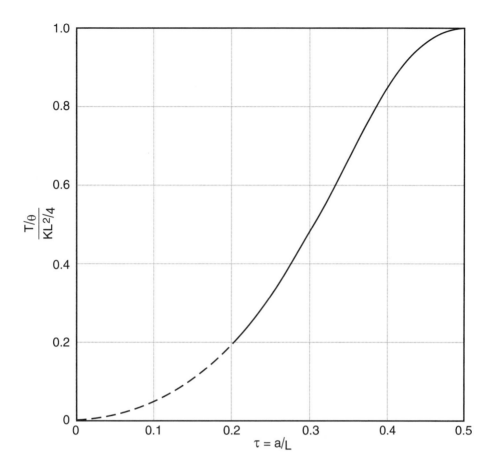

Figure 9.20 *Wind-up stiffness comparison—unsymmetrical spring vs. symmetrical spring.*

Increasing the eccentricity of a leaf spring rapidly reduces its "free" wind-up stiffness, but has much less effect on the "fixed" stiffness.

It has been shown earlier in Section 9.8 that the free wind-up stiffness of an unsymmetrical (but "unbiased") spring [*see Figure 9.16*] is given by:

$$\frac{T}{\theta} = \frac{Kab}{\left(L^2/ab\right) - 3}$$

(9.90)

where:

        T = wind-up torque
        θ = wind-up angle
        K = spring rate at axle
        L = spring length
        a = distance from axle to front of spring
        b = distance from axle to rear of spring

or, if: $a = \tau L$ and $b = (1 - \tau)L$

$$\frac{T}{\theta} = KL^2 \frac{\tau(1 - \tau)}{(1/\tau(1 - \tau)) - 3} \qquad (9.91)$$

The "fixed" wind-up stiffness (see Figure 9.19) is evidently:

$$\frac{T}{\theta} = K_1 a^2 + K_2 b^2 \qquad (9.92)$$

where K_1 and K_2 are the spring rates of the front and rear ends. And if the spring is unbiased, $K_1/K_2 = b^3/a^3$, or

$$K_1 = K\frac{b^2}{aL} \quad \text{and} \quad K_2 = K\frac{a^2}{bL} \qquad (9.93)$$

Thus fixed $$\frac{T}{\theta} = \frac{K}{L}\left(ab^2 + a^2b\right) = Kab = KL^2\tau(1 - \tau) \qquad (9.94)$$

Then, comparing the wind-up rates with that of a symmetrical spring, we have:

$$\frac{\text{Free rate}}{\text{Symmetrical}} = \frac{4\tau(1 - \tau)}{(1/\tau(1 - \tau)) - 3} \quad [\textit{axle free to move relative to car}] \qquad (9.95)$$

$$\frac{\text{Fixed rate}}{\text{Symmetrical}} = 4\tau(1 - \tau) \quad [\textit{axle fixed relative to car}] \qquad (9.96)$$

τ	0.2	0.3	0.333	0.35	0.40	0.45	0.50
$\dfrac{\text{Free rate}}{\text{Symmetrical}}$	0.197	0.477	0.593	0.65	0.822	0.943	1.00
$\dfrac{\text{Fixed rate}}{\text{Symmetrical}}$	0.64	0.84	0.889	0.91	0.96	0.98	1.00

Hence we can redraw Figure 9.20 as Figure 9.21.

Figures 9.20 and 9.21 show the loss in wind-up stiffness through making the spring unsymmetrical. A spring with a 40/60 division has lost 18% in wind-up stiffness. And a 1 to 2 division [*33/67*] loses over 40%.

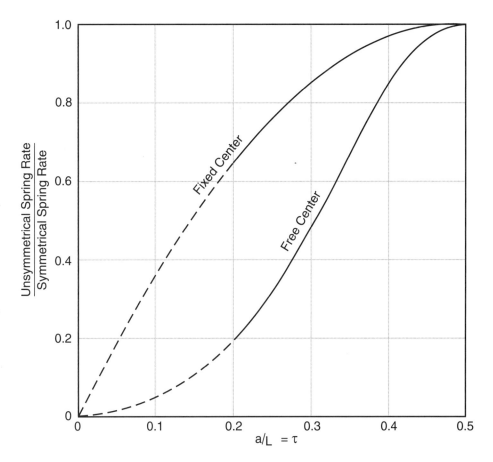

***Figure 9.21** Wind-up stiffness comparison—unsymmetrical spring vs. symmetrical spring—recalculated.*

The important things in the above notes are:

- Unsymmetrical springs have **less** wind-up stiffness for a given ride rate.
- The action radius of unsymmetrical springs is somewhat shorter than three-eighths of spring length.
- The lift or drop of the spring center under wind-up torque is given by

$$\frac{\text{Applied torque}}{(\text{Spring rate}) \times (\text{Effective torque arm})} \tag{9.97}$$

(For the case of "biased" springs, see Section 10.9.)

This, however, is not the whole tale. Whenever a wind-up torque occurs it is also associated with a weight transfer, and this also tends to tilt an unsymmetrical spring. So the actual spring wind-up is a combination of the two effects. In the case of the old unequally divided front springs the two wind-up effects were added. In the case of modern unsymmetrical rear springs the lifting effect of the short front half of the spring both reduces power squat and reduces wind-up.

Examples show this:

1. Old front spring in braking, Figure 9.22

$$\text{Weight transfer} = \left(F_{XF} + F_{XR}\right)\frac{h}{\ell} \tag{9.98}$$

Front spring deflection due to transfer:

$$d_F = \left(F_{XF} + F_{XR}\right)\frac{h}{K_F\ell} \tag{9.99}$$

Tilt of spring due to transfer:

$$\theta_F = \frac{d_F}{R} = \left(F_{XF} + F_{XR}\right)\frac{h}{K_F\ell R} \tag{9.100}$$

Tilt due to torque: $\quad \theta_F = \dfrac{T}{K_F} \times \dfrac{\left(L^2/ab\right) - 3}{ab} = \dfrac{F_{XF}H_F}{K_Fab}\left(\dfrac{L^2}{ab} - 3\right)$ (9.101)

Drop due to torque: $\quad\quad\quad\quad d_F = \dfrac{F_{XF}H_F}{K_FR}$ (9.102)

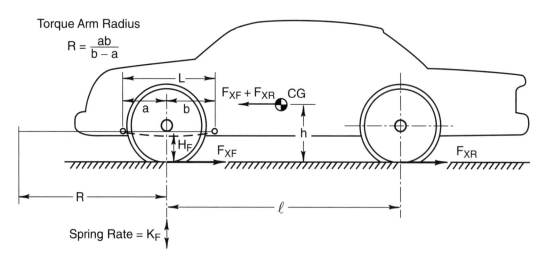

Figure 9.22 Unsymmetrical front leaf spring in braking.

Total wind-up angle: $\theta_F = \dfrac{1}{K_F}\left(\dfrac{(F_{XF}+F_{XR})h}{\ell R} + \dfrac{F_{XF}H_F}{ab}\left(\dfrac{L^2}{ab} - 3 \right) \right)$ (9.103)

Total drop: $d_F = \dfrac{1}{K_F}\left((F_{XF}+F_{XR})\dfrac{h}{\ell} + \dfrac{F_{XF}H_F}{R} \right)$ (9.104)

Let K_F = 300 lb./in.
       F_{XF} = 1000 lb.
       F_{XR} = 667 lb.
       L = 40 in.
       a = 16 in.
       b = 24 in.
       H_F = 11 in.
       h/ℓ = 0.225 for sprung mass

Then $R = \dfrac{16 \times 24}{8} = 48$ in.

Note: $R = ab/(b-a)$, the equivalent torque arm radius. R is defined earlier, Equation 9.84.

Total wind-up angle (degrees):

$$\theta_F = \frac{57.3}{300}\left(\frac{1667 \times 0.225}{48} + \frac{11000}{384}\left(\frac{1600}{384} - 3 \right) \right)$$ (9.105)

$$\theta_F = \underset{(\text{from transfer})}{1.49°} + \underset{(\text{from torque})}{6.36°} = 7.85°$$ (9.106)

Total drop:

$$d_F = \frac{1}{300}\left((1667 \times 0.225) + \frac{11000}{48} \right)$$ (9.107)

$$d_F = \underset{(\text{from transfer})}{1.25 \text{ in.}} + \underset{(\text{from torque})}{0.765 \text{ in.}} = 2.015 \text{ in.}$$ (9.108)

(This does not consider the tilt of the car due to the drop, since we are only concerned with the one end.)

Of the drop of the front end only 1.25 in. is due to the transfer. But this is increased 60% by the wind-up of the unsymmetrical spring. Of the wind-up, 81% comes from the torque and 19% from the transfer.

With a wind-up of nearly 8 degrees (steady-state) it is easy to see why we were in trouble with negative caster in braking. The thing to remember nowadays is that this was the wrong way to make a spring unsymmetrical.

2. Unsymmetrical rear spring in traction, Figure 9.23

This represents correct use of an unsymmetrical spring.

$$\text{Weight transfer} = \frac{F_{XR}h}{\ell} \tag{9.109}$$

Rear spring deflection from this:

$$d_R = \frac{F_{XR}h}{K_R\ell} \tag{9.110}$$

Tilt due to weight transfer: $\theta_R = \dfrac{d_R}{R} = \dfrac{F_{XR}h}{K_R\ell R}$ $\tag{9.111}$

Tilt due to torque: $\theta_R = -\dfrac{F_{XR}H_R}{K_Rab}\left(\dfrac{L^2}{ab} - 3\right)$ $\tag{9.112}$

Total tilt of spring: $\theta_R = \dfrac{F_{XR}}{K_R}\left(\dfrac{h}{\ell R} - \dfrac{H_R}{ab}\left(\dfrac{L^2}{ab} - 3\right)\right)$ $\tag{9.113}$

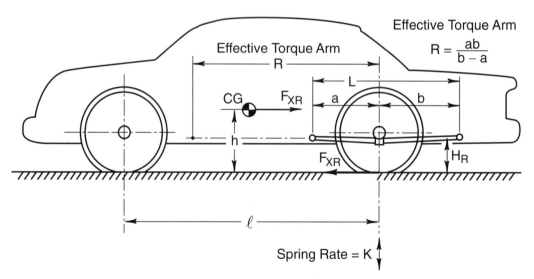

Figure 9.23 Unsymmetrical rear leaf spring, traction.

Total drop at rear:
$$d_R = \frac{F_{XR}}{K_R}\left(\frac{h}{\ell} - \frac{H_R}{R}\right)$$
(9.114)

Let $F_{XR} = 1000$ lb.
$K_R = 125$ lb./in.
$h/\ell = 0.225$ (for sprung mass)
$H_R = 11$ in.
$L = 62.5$ in.

Then $F_{XR}/K_R = 8$ in.

a.   Consider first a symmetrical spring

Deflection of spring: $d_R = \dfrac{F_{XR}h}{K_R\ell} = 8 \times 0.225 = 1.80$ in.
(9.115)

Wind-up stiffness: $\dfrac{T}{\theta_R} = \dfrac{K_R L^2}{4} = 122000$ lb.-in./rad.
(9.116)

Wind-up angle: $\theta_R = -\dfrac{F_{XR}H_R}{(T/\theta_R)} = -\dfrac{11000}{122000} = -0.0902$ rad. $= -5.17°$
(9.117)

b.   Consider an unsymmetrical spring, divided 40/60

Then a $= 25$ in., b $= 37.5$ in., L $= 62.5$ in.

and
$$R = \frac{ab}{b-a} = \frac{937.5}{12.5} = 75 \text{ in.}$$
(9.118)

Total deflection:

$$d_R = \frac{F_{XR}}{K_R}\left(\frac{h}{\ell} - \frac{H_R}{R}\right) = 8(0.225 - 0.1467) = 0.626 \text{ in.}$$
(9.119)

Wind-up stiffness:

$$\frac{T}{\theta_R} = \frac{K_R ab}{\left(L^2/ab\right) - 3} = \frac{125 \times 937.5}{\left(\dfrac{3906}{937.5}\right) - 3} = 100450 \frac{\text{lb.-in}}{\text{rad.}}$$
(9.120)

This is 82.4% of the symmetrical spring.

Wind-up angle:

$$\theta_R = \frac{F_{XR}}{K_R}\left(\frac{h}{\ell R} - \frac{H_R}{ab}\left(\frac{L^2}{ab} - 3\right)\right) = 8\left(\frac{0.225}{75} - \frac{11}{803.6}\right) \qquad (9.121)$$

$$\theta_R = \quad 0.024 \quad - \quad 0.1095 \text{ rad.}$$

$$\theta_R = \quad \underset{\text{(from transfer)}}{1.375°} \quad - \quad \underset{\text{(from torque)}}{6.27°} \quad = -4.895°$$

Although the wind-up stiffness has been reduced, the wind-up **angle** is less than with the symmetrical spring.

This is the angle of equilibrium. In other words we are not completely safe in accepting the 65% reduction in "squat," and the 6% reduction in equilibrium angle, because this had been obtained with an 18% reduction of wind-up stiffness, which **may** result in increased "stick-slip" effects between tire and road. This may increase brake-hop and power-hop tendency. Whether it does or not depends largely on damping in the suspension, and particularly on leaf-spring friction.

c.   **The third possibility is to cancel the power squat entirely**

This can be done simply by moving the spring 3 in. backward relative to the axle.

Then a = 22 in., b = 40.5 in.

and torque arm: $$R = \frac{ab}{b-a} = \frac{891}{18.5} = 48.2 \text{ in.} \qquad (9.122)$$

Total deflection:

$$d_R = \frac{F_{XR}}{K_R}\left(\frac{h}{\ell} - \frac{H_R}{R}\right) = 8(0.225 - 0.228) = -0.024 \text{ in.} \qquad (9.123)$$

Wind-up stiffness:

$$\frac{T}{\theta_R} = \frac{K_R ab}{(L^2/ab) - 3} = \frac{125 \times 891}{1.38} = 79800\frac{\text{lb.-in}}{\text{rad.}} \qquad (9.124)$$

This is 65% of the symmetrical spring.

Wind-up angle:

$$\theta_R = \frac{F_{XR}}{K_R}\left(\frac{h}{\ell R} - \frac{H_R}{ab}\left(\frac{L^2}{ab} - 3\right)\right) = 8\left(\frac{0.225}{48.2} - \frac{11}{645}\right) \tag{9.125}$$

$$\theta_R = \quad 0.037 \quad - \quad 0.1365 \text{ rad.}$$

$$\theta_R = \quad \underset{\text{(from transfer)}}{2.14°} \quad - \quad \underset{\text{(from torque)}}{7.82°} \quad = -5.68°$$

The power squat has been virtually canceled, but the decreased wind-up stiffness makes it probable that there will be brake- and power-hop.

It is intended to point out in above notes that unsymmetrical rear springs with the short end forward, while they are extremely effective in resisting power squat, are not necessarily desirable, since they lose wind-up stiffness very rapidly with increasing asymmetry.

9.9 Inclination of Leaf Springs

So far it has been assumed that the leaf springs are horizontally mounted. But this is seldom true. Generally rear springs are inclined downward toward the front to obtain roll understeer. From the viewpoint of power squat and brake dive this is wholly undesirable since it throws away a considerable portion of the resistance to power squat provided by the unsymmetrical rear springs.

For instance, consider first a symmetrical rear spring inclined as shown in Figure 9.24. There is a small stiffening effect on the spring due to its inclination, but we can neglect it.

Rate of spring: $\qquad K = \dfrac{W\cos\phi}{(z/\cos\phi)} = \dfrac{W}{z}\cos^2\phi \approx \dfrac{K_v}{1+\phi^2}$ $\qquad$ (9.126)

Note: In the above equations Olley says that

$$cos^2\phi \approx \frac{1}{1+\phi^2} \tag{9.127}$$

This has been shown by our associate Edward Kasprzak as follows, working from the trigonometric identity:

$$cos^2\phi = \frac{1+\cos 2\phi}{2} \tag{9.128}$$

Then $\qquad\qquad\qquad cos\,2\phi = \left(2cos^2\phi\right) - 1$ $\qquad\qquad$ (9.129)

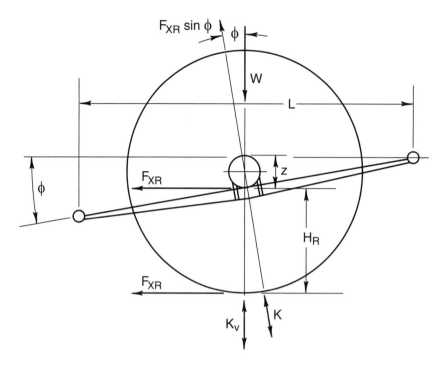

Figure 9.24 *Symmetrical rear leaf spring, inclined.*

The first two terms of the series representation for cosine are:

$$\cos\phi \approx 1 - \frac{\phi^2}{2} \tag{9.130}$$

So

$$\cos 2\phi \approx 1 - \frac{(2\phi)^2}{2} = 1 - 2\phi^2 \tag{9.131}$$

And, substituting from Equation 9.129 above,

$$\left(2\cos^2\phi\right) - 1 \approx 1 - 2\phi^2 \tag{9.132}$$

So,

$$\cos^2\phi \approx 1 - \phi^2 \tag{9.133}$$

But Olley says $\cos^2\phi = 1/\left(1 + \phi^2\right)$. *To show these are equivalent, set:*

$$1 - \phi^2 = \frac{1}{1 + \phi^2} \tag{9.134}$$

Then,
$$\left(1 - \phi^2\right)\left(1 + \phi^2\right) = 1 \qquad (9.135)$$

And,
$$1 - \phi^2 + \phi^2 - \phi^4 = 1 \qquad (9.136)$$

If ϕ^4 is considered negligible, $1 = 1$ and Olley's approximation is correct.

For example, if $\phi = 0.10$ (10% slope) then $K_v = 1.01K$, an increase of only 1% in the rate at the wheel.

But a traction force F_{XR} at the road represents a couple $F_{XR}H_R$ supplied by the axle shaft torque, plus a horizontal force F_{XR} at the spring clamp, one component of which is $F_{XR} \sin \phi$ (or $F_{XR}\phi$) upward on the spring. Thus deflection of spring under traction is now $\dfrac{F_{XR}}{K}\left(\dfrac{h}{\ell} + \phi\right)$ (refers to Figure 9.23).

In Case 2.a. above with 7.75% spring slope (approximately 4.5°) as actually used in the car under consideration [*Olley doesn't specify the car*], this becomes:

Deflection = $8 \times 0.3025 = $ **2.42** in. (instead of 1.80 in.; see Equatiion 9.115), an increase of 35% in power squat.

In Case 2.b. above:

Deflection = $8 \times (0.3025 - 0.1467) = $ **1.246** in. (a 100% increase).

In Case 2.c. above:

Deflection = $8 \times (0.3025 - 0.228) = $ **0.600** in. (where formerly there was no deflection).

It is interesting to note that $(H_R/R) - \phi$ is our old angle ϕ_F of Figure 9.9. And when $(H_R/R) = \phi$, Figure 9.25, the angle ϕ_R becomes zero, and all anti-squat action is lost. For example, in Case 2.b., if $\phi_R = 11/75 = 0.1467$ (approximately 8.5°) the effect of the unequal spring division is entirely gone.

This has a bearing on the question of tension shackles. For example, see Figure 9.26, which is roughly to scale for a 62.5 in. spring.

The use of the existing spring position AB is generally acceptable although it has sacrificed a good portion of the anti-squat effect of the unsymmetrical springs. But the use of a tension shackle as AC would lose all the anti-dive and anti-squat effects of the unequal spring division.

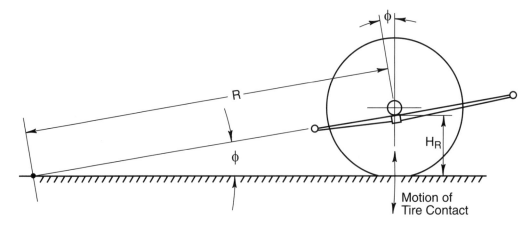

Figure 9.25 Inclined springs reduce anti-squat action.

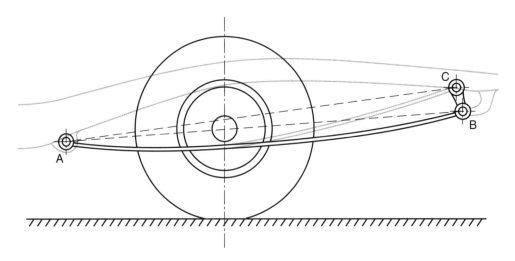

Figure 9.26 Tension vs. compression shackles.

9.10 Anti-Dive Front Wishbone Suspension

Figure 9.27 illustrates anti-dive with wishbone suspension.

- A is the upper kingpin ball. The upper wishbone pivot is inclined so that the upper ball moves in a plane inclined at angle α to the vertical.

- B is the lower kingpin ball. Since the lower wishbone pivot is horizontal this ball moves in a vertical plane BB_1.

- C is the wheel center on the vertical line AB.

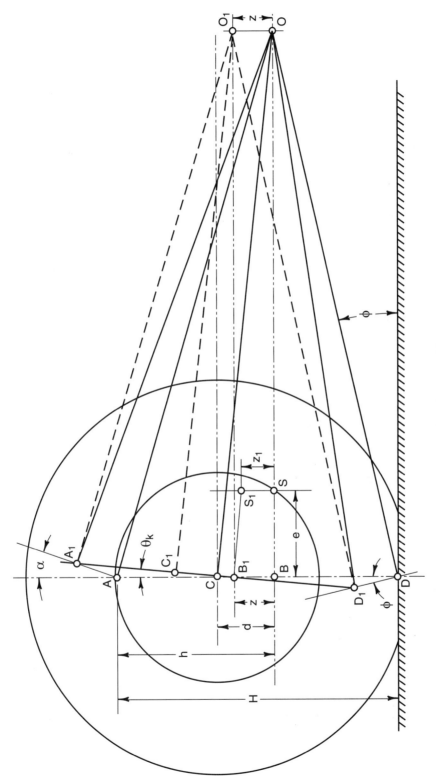

Figure 9.27 Anti-dive front wishbone suspension.

- D is the ground contact point. (Zero caster angle is assumed in design position.)

Since angle θ_k is always small we can assume that vertical displacement z is constant at all points, A, B, C, D, in the plane of the kingpin.

Also, we assume that for all angles, α, ϕ, θ_k, etc., the sine, tangent and angle in radians are approximately equal. Since B always moves vertically, the instantaneous center of rotation O moves upward with the displacement z of the lower ball, and the effective torque arm OB remains virtually constant. This means that the radius OD has a constant inclination ϕ to the horizontal, and that the motion of the ground contact point DD_1 is virtually a straight line.

The longitudinal motion of A is approximately $z\alpha$. Thus caster angle at displacement z:

$$\theta_k \approx \frac{z\alpha}{h} \qquad (9.137)$$

Movement of wheel center C is approximately d/h. Movement of ground contact point D is approximately $(H - h)z\alpha/h$.

Anti-dive angle: $\qquad\qquad \phi = \frac{H - h}{h}\alpha \qquad (9.138)$

The effectiveness of the anti-dive is the same at all standing heights.

A slight difficulty arises in connection with the steering. This has already been referred to in Section 7.4. If S is the steering third-arm ball which is assumed to lie in the horizontal plane of the lower wishbone, it will move almost vertically, parallel with the lower ball B. But its vertical travel will be:

$$z_1 \approx z - e\theta_k = z\left(1 - \frac{e\alpha}{h}\right) \approx z\left(1 - \frac{e}{OB}\right) \qquad (9.139)$$

It follows that the correct length of tie rod will be:

$$\left(\text{Wishbone radius}\right) \times \left(1 - \frac{e}{OB}\right)^2 \qquad (9.140)$$

Thus, for a rear-mounted steering linkage, the tie rods will need to be considerably shortened [*when compared with front-mounted steering linkage*].

9.11 Sudden Brake Application

All figuring on brake dive so far has assumed steady-state conditions. It has been pointed out that the lengths of torque arms or "effective torque arms" do not matter, and that the condition that affects anti-dive is the path of the tire contact and the angle ϕ which this makes with the vertical.

This is no longer true when we come to consider "panic braking," or sudden brake application. When this occurs we can theoretically consider that, for the fraction of a second needed to stop the rotation of the wheels, there is the possibility of applying to the brake backing plates the **maximum torque which is set by the strength of the driver's foot** and the design of the brake mechanism. And the brakes must be designed to support such high torques.

The duration of this high torque period is extremely short, and after the wheels have stopped, we have theoretically steady-state conditions with all wheels skidding.

This is an oversimplification, however. What actually occurs is that, due to elasticity and damping in the braking system, the brake application is by no means instantaneous even in a panic stop. The wheel rotation on a passenger car may probably have stopped before the maximum pressure has developed in the brake cylinders. However, the wheel stoppage occurs with a number of violent oscillations, both in the mechanical parts of the system and in the fluid lines, the maxima of which represent torques at least as great as those which would be produced by maximum fluid pressure.

It may be useful, as a rough estimate, to **assume** instantaneous application of all four brakes and hence find how quickly the wheels will stop and what may happen thereafter; refer to Figure 9.28.

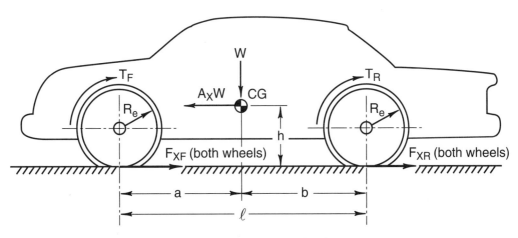

Figure 9.28 Transient braking.

Let: A_X = deceleration/g, before wheels stop turning (g)

R_e = rolling radius of wheels (ft.) [*now called "effective radius," based on roll-out or revs/mile*]

I_W = moment of inertia of one wheel and brake drum in slug-ft.^{2} (assumed equal on all wheels)

T_F = total maximum torque on both front brakes (lb.-ft.)

T_R = total maximum torque on both rear brakes (lb.-ft.)

μ = traction coefficient of tires

$\dot{\omega}_F$ = angular retardation, front wheels (rad./sec.^{2})

$\dot{\omega}_R$ = angular retardation, rear wheels (rad./sec.^{2})

V = vehicle speed (ft./sec.)

$time_F$ = time to stop front wheels (sec.)

$time_R$ = time to stop rear wheels (sec.)

Rotation speed of wheels:
$$\omega = \frac{V}{R_e} \text{ (rad./sec.)} \tag{9.141}$$

Then:
$$time_F = \frac{V}{R_e\,\dot{\omega}_F} \quad \text{and} \quad \dot{\omega}_F = \frac{T_F - F_{XF}\,R_e}{2I_W} \tag{9.142}$$

$$time_R = \frac{V}{R_e\,\dot{\omega}_R} \quad \text{and} \quad \dot{\omega}_R = \frac{T_R - F_{XR}\,R_e}{2I_W} \tag{9.143}$$

Also,
$$F_{XF} = \mu W\left(\frac{b}{\ell} + \frac{A_X h}{\ell}\right) \tag{9.144}$$

$$F_{XR} = \mu W\left(\frac{a}{\ell} - \frac{A_X h}{\ell}\right) \tag{9.145}$$

$$F_{XF} + F_{XR} = \mu W = A_X\left(W + \frac{4I_W g}{R_e^2}\right) \tag{9.146}$$

Or,
$$A_X = \mu\left(W \middle/ \left(W + \frac{4I_W g}{R_e^2}\right)\right) \tag{9.147}$$

Considering a simple case, let:

W = 4000 lb.

$a/\ell = b/\ell = 0.50$

$h/\ell = 0.20$

$I_W = 1.20$ slug-ft.^{2} (for front and rear wheels)

$R_e = 1.0$ ft.
$\mu = 1.0$ (dry road)
$V = 66$ ft./sec. (45 mph)

Let $T_F = 4200$ lb.-ft. (maximum torque, both front wheels)
$T_R = 3300$ lb.-ft. (maximum torque, both rear wheels)

This is a 56/44 brake distribution.

Then,
$$\frac{4I_W g}{R_e^2} = 155 \text{ lb.} \tag{9.148}$$

$$A_X = \frac{4000}{4155} = 0.96g \text{ (until the wheels stop)} \tag{9.149}$$

$$F_{XF} = 4000\big(0.5 + (0.96 \times 0.20)\big) = 2768 \text{ lb.} \tag{9.150}$$

$$F_{XR} = 4000\big(0.5 - (0.96 \times 0.20)\big) = 1232 \text{ lb.} \tag{9.151}$$

Moment retarding two front wheels:
$$T_F - F_{XF}R_e = 4200 - 2768 = 1432 \text{ lb.-ft.} \tag{9.152}$$

Moment retarding two rear wheels:
$$T_R - F_{XR}R_e = 3300 - 1232 = 2068 \text{ lb.-ft.} \tag{9.153}$$

Then,
$$\dot{\omega}_F = \frac{T_F - F_{XF}R_e}{2I_W} = \frac{1432}{2.4} = 597 \text{ rad./sec.}^2 \tag{9.154}$$

$$\dot{\omega}_R = \frac{T_R - F_{XR}R_e}{2I_W} = \frac{2068}{2.4} = 662 \text{ rad./sec.}^2 \tag{9.155}$$

Rotation speed of wheels:
$$\omega = \frac{V}{R_e} = \frac{66}{1} = 66 \text{ rad./sec. (630 rpm)} \tag{9.156}$$

Time to stop wheels:

Front:
$$\text{time}_F = \frac{66}{597} = \textbf{0.1105 sec.} \tag{9.157}$$

Rear: $$\text{time}_R = \frac{66}{862} = \textbf{0.0767} \text{ sec.} \tag{9.158}$$

Front wheels stop in 3.65 rad. = **0.58** of a turn.

Rear wheels stop in 2.53 rad. = **0.403** of a turn.

On a wet road, under the assumptions we have made, the torque on the brake backing plates is exactly the same [*as above*], but the wheels stop sooner because of the reduced frictional drag from the road.

Thus let $\mu = 0.50$

$$A_X = W \bigg/ \left(W + \frac{4I_W g}{R_e^2} \right) = 0.3 \times 0.96 = 0.288g \tag{9.159}$$

$$F_{XF} = 1200(0.5 + 0.0576) = 670 \text{ lb.} \tag{9.160}$$

$$F_{XR} = 1200(0.5 - 0.0576) = 530 \text{ lb.} \tag{9.161}$$

Moment on two front wheels:

$$T_F - F_{XF} R_e = 3530 \text{ lb.-ft.} \tag{9.162}$$

Moment on two rear wheels:

$$T_R - F_{XR} R_e = 2770 \text{ lb.-ft.} \tag{9.163}$$

Then, $$\dot{\omega}_F = \frac{3530}{2.4} = 1470 \text{ rad./sec.}^2 \tag{9.164}$$

$$\dot{\omega}_R = \frac{2770}{2.4} = 1155 \text{ rad./sec.}^2 \tag{9.165}$$

$$\text{time}_F = \frac{66}{1470} = \textbf{0.045} \text{ sec.} \tag{9.166}$$

$$\text{time}_R = \frac{66}{1155} = \textbf{0.057} \text{ sec.} \tag{9.167}$$

Front wheels stop in 1.485 rad. = **0.236** of a turn.

Rear wheels stop in 1.885 rad. = **0.30** of a turn.

In spite of the assumption of instantaneous application of maximum brake torque, which does not agree with experiment, the time to stop the wheels is of the same order as times found experimentally. Thus a rotary hammer blow of considerable magnitude is delivered to the brake backing plates. And the fact that the torques actually occurring show violent oscillations makes them the more troublesome.

It may be argued that the rotary inertia of the engine, flywheel, etc. should be multiplied by the square of the axle ratio and added to the inertia $2I_W$ of the two rear wheels. This would more than double the total moment of inertia to be brought to rest by the rear brakes, and thus would more than double the duration of the high torque period.

But experiments show that on the conventional passenger car this is not a true picture of what happens. Actually, the elasticity of the driveline is so great that the rear wheels stop turning well before the engine is stopped. The subsequent surge of torque from the engine inertia falls upon the stopped wheels, and undoubtedly accounts in great part for the violence of the torsional oscillations which occur after wheel stoppage.

The fact that pressure increases in the brake cylinder relatively slowly makes the time that the wheel takes to stop important. The greater the inertia and the longer the wheel keeps on turning, the higher the brake torque is likely to be.

It was stated at the beginning of this section that we were **not** concerned in this matter of sudden wheel stoppage, with the conventional "anti-dive" angles ϕ. On the other hand we **are** concerned with the amount of rotation of the backing plate which is associated with brake dive, or, in other words, with effective length of torque arms. When these sudden torsional shocks occur in the presence of a short torque arm, the wheel may be slammed down on the ground so hard as to lift one end of the car into the air, or on the contrary the wheel may be lifted off the ground temporarily. In either case the result is a brake-hop, which can be damaging both to the car and to the road.

The vertical momentum imparted to the car or to the wheel depends on the time-duration of the high-torque period. The duration of these torsional shocks is therefore important. And it is possible that in a "power-package" system, such as a rear engine or front drive car, in which the engine inertia is more rigidly connected with the driving wheels, brake-hop, when it occurs, may prove to be more severe, see Brake Hop, Section 6.8.

9.12 Summary

As with the lateral forces arising when a vehicle corners, the longitudinal forces associated with acceleration or deceleration of the vehicle during driving or braking also cause load transfer. Under braking, more of the weight of the vehicle is supported by the front tires, and the rear supports a larger portion under forward acceleration. The magnitude of this weight transfer is determined by the magnitude of longitudinal acceleration A_X and the height of the CG relative to the wheelbase, h/ℓ.

*Suspension geometry cannot influence the amount of load transferred. The suspension may be designed, however, to carry more or less of this load through the suspension arms—the rest being supported by the springs. These design features are known as "anti-dive" and "anti-squat." The result is that suspension design, while unable to change the amount of load transferred, **does** determine the amount of pitch the sprung mass experiences when driving/braking forces are applied.*

When designing leaf springs to have "anti" features, asymmetric and biased springs are often used. The magnitude of spring wind-up is an important factor in the design process. While the calculations for most of this chapter consider steady-state braking, Olley acknowledges panic braking situations in Section 9.11, where the dynamics of the entire braking system are noted. A further addition to the list of dynamic components would be the inclusion of tire lag and relaxation length in the system. These parameters, while known today (c. 2000), were not available to Olley at the time of his monographs.

*Maurice Olley, c. 1950. Photo credit Kettering/GMI Alumni Foundation,
Collection of Industrial History.*

CHAPTER 10

Leaf Springs–Combined Suspension Spring and Linkage

"The chief advantage of the leaf spring is that it can serve as suspension linkage. It was so used on light horse-drawn vehicles in which the springs were so long and light that they could adjust themselves to the axle motions without setting up undue stresses in themselves or their attachments … one other valuable feature of leaf springs is their internal damping. Even now the internal damping of rear springs is sufficient to absorb a great deal of vibration set up by the road, speed variations of the propeller shaft drive, and engine impulses."

Maurice Olley, October 15, 1958

10.1 Introduction

Olley's interests in springs and their application to the motorcar go back to his early days with Rolls-Royce. Years later, in 1944, he was a prominent member of the original SAE Spring Committee which produced the first Spring Design Manual and several revised editions of it. It is interesting to note that several of Olley's associates at General Motors were also on this original committee, notably Robert Schilling, H. O. Fuchs, Max Ruegg and J. W. Rosenkrands.

Mechanically, the Hotchkiss suspension (leaf spring located solid axle) is perhaps the simplest suspension. It is also one of the most complex to analyze, since the springs perform the dual functions of location and springing. In this chapter, Olley looks at both aspects of this system.

Suspension of a vehicle depends almost invariably on some form of link motion. In the Hotchkiss rear suspension, Figure 10.1 for example, a link motion is involved. Each leaf spring is equivalent to a central fixed link, BC, bolted to the axle, and two links AB and

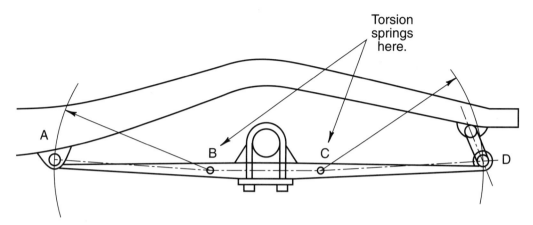

Figure 10.1 *Leaf spring—equivalent link model.*

CD, pivoted at B and C to the central block. If one imagines torsion springs of suitable angular rate at the pivots B and C, the resulting rate is almost exactly the same as that of the leaf spring.

Evidently it is important to know the **lengths** of the equivalent links AB and CD, which means estimating the curvature of the circular paths through A and D described by each spring eye as the spring is compressed and released, Figure 10.2.

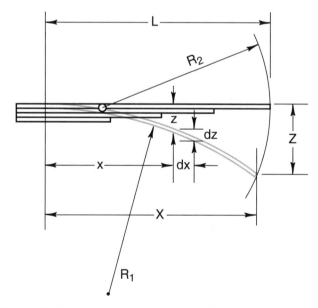

Figure 10.2 *Estimating the lengths of the equivalent links.*

To do this effectively we have to find an expression for R_2, the radius followed by the end of a cantilever spring when it is deflected. In almost all these problems we use the approximation:

$$X \approx \frac{z^2}{2R} \tag{10.1}$$

[*which was developed in Chapter 7 on Linkages*]. See Figure 10.3.

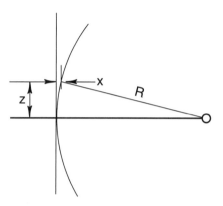

Figure 10.3 *Parabolic approximation to the circle.*

Hence, for the spring, we can say:

$$L - X = \int_0^X \frac{(dz)^2}{2dx} = \frac{1}{2}\int_0^X \left(\frac{dz}{dx}\right)^2 dx \tag{10.2}$$

But

$$L - X \approx \frac{Z^2}{2R_2} \tag{10.3}$$

So that

$$R_2 = \frac{Z^2}{\int_0^X \left(\frac{dz}{dx}\right)^2 dx} \tag{10.4}$$

This is the general statement which applies regardless of the type of spring bending which occurs.

10.2 Circular Bending

It is generally assumed in the case of a leaf spring that the leaf lengths are so proportioned that the spring halves bend uniformly throughout their length, to a radius R_1.

Then
$$z \approx \frac{x^2}{2R_1} \text{ and } Z \approx \frac{X^2}{2R_1} \tag{10.5}$$

or
$$z \approx \frac{x^2}{X^2}Z \tag{10.6}$$

Thus
$$\frac{dz}{dx} = \frac{2Zx}{X^2} \tag{10.7}$$

and
$$\left(\frac{dz}{dx}\right)^2 = \frac{4Z^2x^2}{X^4} \tag{10.8}$$

and
$$\int_0^X \left(\frac{dz}{dx}\right)^2 dx = \frac{4}{3}\frac{Z^2}{X} \tag{10.9}$$

Thus
$$R_2 = \frac{Z^2}{\int_0^X \left(\frac{dz}{dx}\right)^2 dx} = \frac{3}{4}X \tag{10.10}$$

As a matter of convenience we accept:

$$R_2 \approx \frac{3}{4}L \tag{10.11}$$

If the spring eye is offset, it can also be shown that the effective pivot center O (Figure 10.4) is set below the neutral axis of the main leaf by a distance equal to **half** the eye offset **e** above the neutral axis. Reverting to the leaf spring in Figure 10.1 it is thus seen that the radii AB and CD are each three-fourths of the length of the respective cantilever halves, and the centers B and C are offset below the neutral axis of the main leaf by half the eye offsets.

We have to estimate the length at the center of the spring put out of action by the center clamp [*approximately the region between B and C in Figure 10.1*]. For a metal clamp this is usually estimated as the distance between the **inside edges** of the clamp bolts. In a rubber faced clamp not more than an inch of the total spring length is clamped out of action.

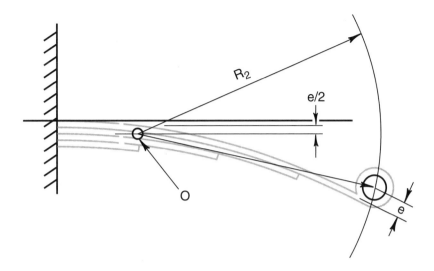

Figure 10.4 *Locating the effective pivot center.*

Considerable variation from the theoretical leaf spring, which bends in circular arcs, is now taking place. So it is useful to find out how much this sort of "faking" can affect the resulting "three-link" geometry of Figure 10.1.

Two extreme cases are the parallel cantilever and the constant-stress single leaf spring.

10.3 Parallel Cantilever

In Figure 10.5 [*the equation for the elastic curve is*],

$$\frac{d^2z}{dx^2} = \frac{W(X-x)}{EI} \tag{10.12}$$

$$\frac{dz}{dx} = \frac{W}{EI}\left(Xx - \frac{x^2}{2}\right) \tag{10.13}$$

$$z = \frac{W}{EI}\left(\frac{Xx^2}{2} - \frac{x^3}{6}\right) \tag{10.14}$$

where E is the Young's Modulus and I is the section moment of inertia.

At the end [*of the leaf spring*]: $\quad Z = \dfrac{W}{EI}\dfrac{X^3}{3}$ \hfill (10.15)

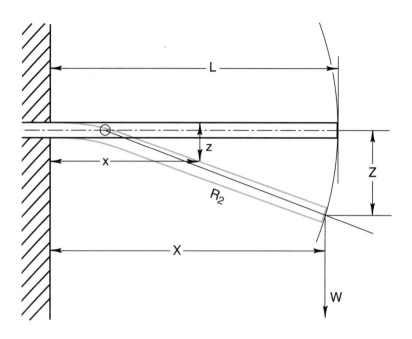

Figure 10.5 *Parallel cantilever analogy.*

or
$$W = \frac{3EIZ}{X^3} \qquad (10.16)$$

so
$$\frac{dz}{dx} = \frac{3Z}{X^3}\left(Xx - \frac{x^2}{2}\right) \qquad (10.17)$$

From this,
$$\int_0^X \left(\frac{dz}{dx}\right)^2 dx = \frac{6Z^2}{5X} \qquad (10.18)$$

or
$$R_2 = \frac{Z^2}{\left(\dfrac{6Z^2}{5X}\right)} = \frac{5}{6}X = 0.833X \approx 0.833L \qquad (10.19)$$

10.4 Theoretical Single Leaf

In Figure 10.6, the thickness varies as the square root of $L - x$. From this it can be shown that,

$$R_2 = \frac{2}{3}X \approx \frac{2}{3}L \qquad (10.20)$$

But in practice the end portion of the spring has considerable thickness and acts like a parallel cantilever. So that in practice:

$$R_2 \approx 0.70L \tag{10.21}$$

Supposing that L = 25 inches:

Leaf Spring Approximation:	R_2 (inches)	Difference
For a "perfect" spring leaf	18.75	—
For a parallel cantilever	20.83	+2.08 inch
For a practical single leaf	17.5	−1.25 inch

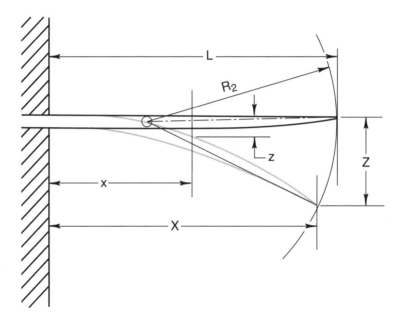

Figure 10.6 *Theoretical single leaf.*

It can be seen that there is some uncertainty about the position of the pivot centers in the "three-link equivalent." **But the figure of 0.75L adopted in the SAE Leaf Spring Manual[59] is a fair approximation**.

10.5 Figuring a Leaf Spring

The increasing use of leaf springs having few leaves and in which the leaf lengths are altered from the theoretical in such a way as to resist "traction squat" and brake dive,

[59] *SAE Spring Design Manual*, AE-11, Society of Automotive Engineers, Warrendale, Pa., 1990.

etc., makes obsolete the generally accepted equations for the cantilever rates which were based on assumed circular bending [*see Chapter 9 for more on squat and dive*].

The following method [*next section*] of figuring a leaf spring has been found to apply without significant error to modern [*c. 1960*] leaf springs.

Each cantilever half of the spring, in its clamped condition, is considered separately, and the cantilever rate at its end is ascertained. No assumptions are made as to circular bending and each spring half is dealt with as a series of parallel cantilevers.

It is first necessary to estimate the **effective length** of each leaf. In the case of a spring with inserts, the center of each insert may be taken to mark the effective length. In the case of a spring with tapered leaf points, with or without liners, the "center of bedding" appears to lie 1-1/2 inches to 1-3/4 inches from the end of each leaf. In the case of a spring with blunt, cropped ends the effective length is only about 1/2 inch less than the actual length.

10.6 Cantilever Spring

Consider, for example, a four-leaf spring with any leaf spacing, Figure 10.7.

ℓ_1, ℓ_2, ℓ_3 and ℓ_4 are "effective" lengths, as defined at the end of Section 10.5.

I_1 = combined moment of inertia of 4 leaves
I_2 = combined moment of inertia of 3 leaves
I_3 = combined moment of inertia of 2 leaves
I_4 = moment of inertia of main leaf only

z_1 is the deflection at the end due to bending of the four-leaf portion only.

In Figure 10.7 the leaves are shown as their "effective length" not their true length. The analysis treats each section of the spring, i.e., the four-leaf section, the three-leaf section, etc., as independent cantilevers. The deflection of each is added to get the total spring deflection.

Then, if θ is the slope of the spring leaves in the four-leaf portion at a distance x from the clamp,

$$\frac{d\theta}{dx} = \frac{\text{bending moment}}{EI_1} = \frac{W(L-x)}{EI_1} \tag{10.22}$$

$$\frac{dz_1}{dx} = \frac{d\theta}{dx}(L-x) = \frac{W}{EI_1}(L-x)^2 \tag{10.23}$$

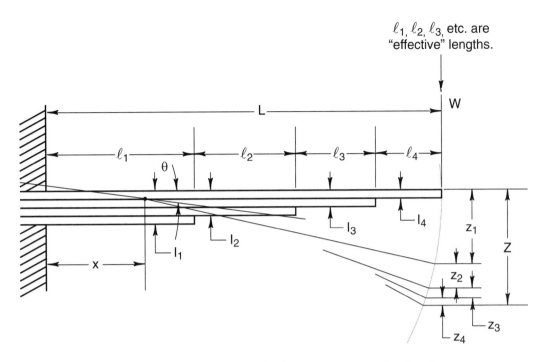

Figure 10.7 *General case of leaf spring, non-circular bending.*

So that
$$z_1 = \frac{W}{EI_1} \int_0^{\ell_1} \left(L^2 - 2Lx + x^2 \right) dx \tag{10.24}$$

or
$$z_1 = \frac{W\ell_1}{EI_1} \left(L^2 - L\ell_1 + \frac{\ell_1^2}{3} \right) \tag{10.25}$$

In the same way the contributions z_2, z_3, and z_4, of each of the other three sections to the total deflection Z, can be found. For example z_4 is evidently given by:

$$z_4 = \frac{W}{EI_4} \frac{\ell_4^3}{3} \tag{10.26}$$

And the cantilever rate of the spring is $K = \dfrac{W}{Z}$ \hfill (10.27)

10.7 Equal Leaves and Equal Spacing

To show the difficulty and departure from efficient design introduced by using a too small number of (parallel) leaves, it is useful to consider an assembly of equal leaves with equal spacing, Figure 10.8.

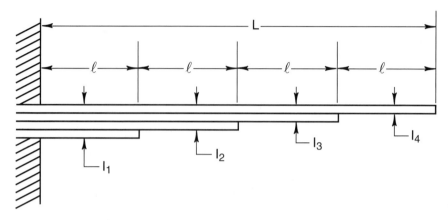

Figure 10.8 *Equal leaves with equal spacing.*

If there are n leaves, each step length, $\ell = L/n$:

$$I_2 = \frac{n-1}{n} I_1 \tag{10.28}$$

$$I_3 = \frac{n-2}{n} I_1 \text{, etc.} \tag{10.29}$$

Hence:

$$z_1 = \frac{WL^3}{EI_1}\left(\frac{1}{n} - \frac{1}{n^2} + \frac{1}{3n^3}\right) \tag{10.30}$$

$$z_2 = \frac{WL^3}{EI_1}\left(\frac{1}{n} - \frac{2}{n^2} + \frac{1}{3n^2(n-1)}\right) \tag{10.31}$$

$$z_3 = \frac{WL^3}{EI_1}\left(\frac{1}{n} - \frac{3}{n^2} + \frac{1}{3n^2(n-2)}\right) \tag{10.32}$$

$$z_n = \frac{WL^3}{EI_1} \times \frac{1}{3n^2} \tag{10.33}$$

Thus

$$Z = z_1 + z_2 + z_3 + \cdots + z_n \tag{10.34}$$

$$Z = \frac{WL^3}{EI_1}\left[1 - \frac{n(n+1)}{2n^2} + \frac{1}{3n^2}\left(1 + \frac{1}{2} + \frac{1}{3} + \cdots + \frac{1}{n-1} + \frac{1}{n}\right)\right] \tag{10.35}$$

or
$$Z = \frac{WL^3}{EI_1}\left[\frac{1}{2} - \frac{1}{2n} + \frac{1}{3n^2}\left(1 + \frac{1}{2} + \frac{1}{3} + \cdots + \frac{1}{n-1} + \frac{1}{n}\right)\right] \qquad (10.36)$$

Hence:

n	1	2	3	4	10	20	∞
$Z = \dfrac{WL^3}{EI_1} \times$	0.333	0.375	0.401	0.418	0.460	0.478	0.500

i.e., only a large number of leaves gives an approach to the flexibility of a theoretical spring with circular bending.

To check this statement, refer to Figure 5.2 in the 1990 version of the SAE *Spring Manual. In this figure the load rate for a cantilever spring designed for approximately circular bending is given as,*

$$K = \frac{2E\sum I}{L^3} \times SF \qquad (10.37)$$

where the "stiffening factor" SF is 1.0 for circular arc bending. Olley concludes that for "equal leaves and equal spacing," and for an **infinite number** *of leaves:*

$$\frac{Z}{W} = \frac{L^3}{EI} \times \frac{1}{2} \qquad (10.38)$$

Since $K = W/Z$*, this relationship compares exactly to that from the* SAE *Spring Manual for ideal circular bending. Note that the flexibility is the reciprocal of the spring rate.*

This is not so much an argument for a large number of leaves as a demonstration of the need for tapered leaf points.

10.8 Combined Spring Rate (with "Unbalanced" Springs)

It can readily be shown that the spring rate at the axle in Figure 10.9 is:

$$K = \frac{(a+b)^2}{\left(a^2/K_2\right) + \left(b^2/K_1\right)} = \frac{K_1 K_2 (a+b)^2}{K_1 a^2 + K_2 b^2} \qquad (10.39)$$

This relationship also appears in the section on Unconventional Springs in the Spring Manual.

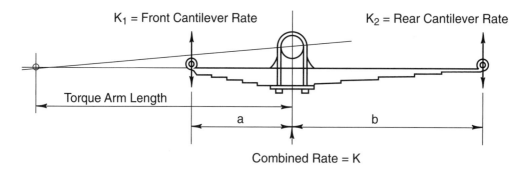

Figure 10.9 *Unbalanced spring.*

10.9 Effective Torque Arm

It is stated in the *Spring Manual* that the effective torque arm length, which is

$$\frac{1}{\text{Tilt per inch in radians}} \text{ is equal to } \frac{ab}{b-a}.$$ (10.40)

This is true only on the assumption of perfect circular bending. It does not apply to modern unbalanced springs [*reference Figure 9.16*]. The general expression, for all springs, is

Torque arm length (inches): $R = \dfrac{\dfrac{a^2}{K_2} + \dfrac{b^2}{K_1}}{\dfrac{a}{K_2} - \dfrac{b}{K_1}} = \dfrac{K_1 a^2 + K_2 b^2}{K_1 a - K_2 b}$ (10.41)

This relationship also appears in the Spring Manual.

Note: These two departures [*see Sections 10.7 and 10.9*] from theory, based on circular bending, become quite important in design and layout work.

10.10 Roll Rates

If one neglects the effect of tire deflection, Figure 10.10, the roll rate, K_ϕ, of a car on its axle is:

$$K_\phi = 2K\left(\frac{e}{2}\right)^2 = \frac{Ke^2}{2}$$ (10.42)

This is in lb.-in./rad.

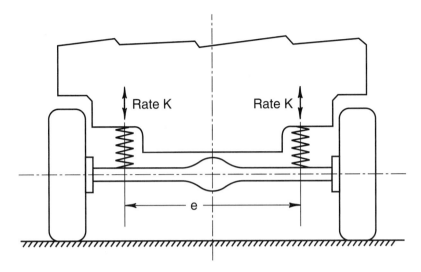

Figure 10.10 *Simplified roll rate calculation.*

To convert this to lb.-ft./deg.

$$K_\phi = \frac{Ke^2}{2 \times 12 \times 57.3} = \frac{Ke^2}{1375} \tag{10.43}$$

This is true when coil springs are used. But with leaf springs, even those which are symmetrically divided, an increase [*in roll rate*] of about 20 percent to 30 percent will occur, due to the complex lateral and torsional distortion of the leaf springs which takes place when the car rolls. This increase depends on spring dimensions (being less with longer springs) and on shackle and frame stiffness.

In addition to this there is a further increase in roll rate when unsymmetrical or unbalanced springs are used. And this increase depends on **the torsional stiffness of the axle itself**.

If we assume a torsionally rigid axle, then in roll the two ends of the leaf spring are forced to take equal deflections. Thus, referring to Section 10.8,

$$K_\phi = \frac{(K_1 + K_2)e^2}{1375} \tag{10.44}$$

The increase of $K_1 + K_2$ over K, the ride rate, can be considerable, even in the case of a "perfect" leaf spring, in which $K_1/K_2 = b^3/a^3$ when, for example, a is only half the length of b.

Thus, in this theoretically perfect spring,

If $$a = \lambda b \qquad (10.45)$$

Then [*reference the definition of K in Equation 10.39*],

$$\frac{K_1 + K_2}{K} = \frac{1}{\lambda} - 1 + \lambda \qquad (10.46)$$

and $$K_1 = \frac{K}{\lambda(1 + \lambda)} \qquad (10.47)$$

and $$K_2 = K_1\lambda^3 = \frac{K\lambda^2}{(1 + \lambda)} \qquad (10.48)$$

Suppose that $a = 0.5b$ and $K = 120$ lb./in.

Front cantilever rate: $$K_1 = \frac{120}{0.75} = 160 \text{ lb./in.} \qquad (10.49)$$

Rear cantilever rate: $$K_2 = \frac{120}{6} = 20 \text{ lb./in.} \qquad (10.50)$$

So, with a rigid axle, the spring rate in roll will be 180 lb./in., an increase of 50 percent over the ride rate.

There is a cost for this stabilizer effect. It is obtained by using the axle casing itself as a roll stabilizer, causing severe torsional stressing of the axle, as well as additional stressing of the leaf springs and frame fittings. Actually the theoretical equal deflections of the front and rear cantilevers in roll are never obtained, since considerable torsional deflection of the axle casing takes place.

10.11 Shackle Effects—Symmetrical and Unsymmetrical Springs

With Symmetrical Leaf Springs

Tension along a leaf spring produces its maximum effect in increasing the spring rate when the spring is flat. Thus, consider a symmetrical spring as Figure 10.11.

A tension **force** such as P adds an additional **rate** $2P/R$ to the spring rate in the flat position. Such a tension is produced by a shackle angle α as shown.

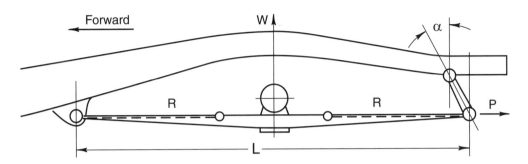

Figure 10.11 *Symmetrical leaf spring with shackle.*

If W is the load on the spring, tension force is

$$P = \frac{W}{2}\tan\alpha \qquad (10.51)$$

If arm R rotates through an angle β, the end of the spring is displaced, by R tan β. The additional vertical force at the end of the spring due to P (tension due to shackle) is P tan β. The additional rate of the spring is,

$$\frac{2P\tan\beta}{R\tan\beta} = \frac{2P}{R} = \frac{2}{R}\left(\frac{W}{2}\tan\alpha\right) = \frac{W\tan\alpha}{R} \qquad (10.52)$$

In the case of a "perfect" spring with circular bending R = 0.375L, so the additional rate when flat is $\frac{W\tan\alpha}{0.375L}$.

If   W = 1000 lb.
      α = 26.5° (tan α = 0.5)
      L = 60 in.

Then, added rate = $\frac{4000}{180}$ = 22.2 lb./in.

Evidently this is an important addition to a spring which may have a normal rate, when tested on rollers, of, say. 125 lb./in. The effective deflection based on wheel rate, which was supposed to be 8 inches, has become actually only 6.8 inches.

The shackle effect varies rapidly with spring deflection. For instance, as the spring deflects above the position shown in Figure 10.11, α decreases but the upward force W/2 increases. So the tension P at first increases and finally reverses, as the shackle swings past the vertical.

The effect on the rate is quite complicated, and is further confused by the fact that as the shackle swings forward in the sketch (Figure 10.11) the rear spring eye at first **drops**, further stiffening the suspension.

The general effect of the S-curves on rate is as shown in Figure 10.12. Sample curves for symmetrical springs are given in the *SAE Leaf Spring Manual* and are supplemented in later editions by a further discussion on unsymmetrical springs.

These S-curves of rate do not, in general, show up as any great departure from a straight line in the load deflection diagrams. They are to be distinguished from the S-shaped load deflection diagrams mentioned in Section 5.6 as being essential on an ultra-soft suspension.

The difficulty in measuring rate directly with our existing equipment is discussed below (Section 10.12).

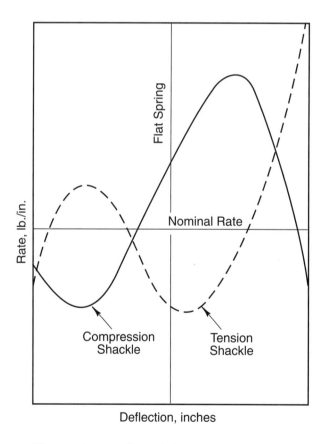

Figure 10.12 Effect of shackle angle on rate.

Shackle Effects, Unsymmetrical Springs

Considering a "perfect" spring:

$$\text{Tilt of spring } = \frac{b-a}{ab}d \qquad (10.53)$$

Front deflection: $\qquad d_1 = d\left(1 - \frac{b-a}{ab}a\right) = \frac{a}{b}d \qquad (10.54)$

Rear deflection: $\qquad d_2 = d\left(1 + \frac{b-a}{ab}b\right) = \frac{b}{a}d \qquad (10.55)$

Deflection at front pivot:

$$d_3 = d\left(1 - \frac{(b-a)}{ab}\frac{a}{4}\right) = \frac{d}{4}\left(3 + \frac{a}{b}\right) \qquad (10.56)$$

Deflection at rear pivot:

$$d_4 = d\left(1 + \frac{(b-a)}{ab}\frac{b}{4}\right) = \frac{d}{4}\left(3 + \frac{b}{a}\right) \qquad (10.57)$$

$$\text{Slope of } R_1 = \frac{d_3}{R_1} = \frac{d}{3a}\left(3 + \frac{a}{b}\right) = d\left(\frac{1}{a} + \frac{1}{3b}\right) \qquad (10.58)$$

$$\text{Slope of } R_2 = \frac{d_4}{R_2} = \frac{d}{3b}\left(3 + \frac{b}{a}\right) = d\left(\frac{1}{b} + \frac{1}{3a}\right) \qquad (10.59)$$

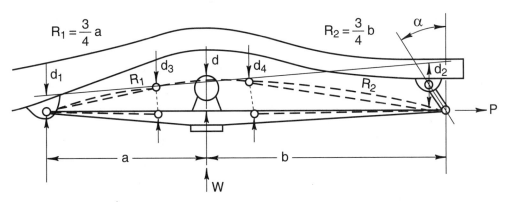

Figure 10.13 *Unsymmetrical leaf spring with shackle.*

If P = tension pull,

$$\text{Downward force} = Pd\left(\frac{1}{a} + \frac{1}{3b} + \frac{1}{b} + \frac{1}{3a}\right) = \frac{4}{3}Pd\left(\frac{1}{a} + \frac{1}{b}\right) = \frac{Pd(a+b)}{0.75ab} \qquad (10.60)$$

But $P = \dfrac{Wa}{a+b}\tan\alpha$ [*for this unsymmetrical spring*], so

$$\text{Downward force} = \frac{Wd\tan\alpha}{0.75b} \qquad (10.61)$$

$$\text{Added rate from shackle angle} = \frac{W\tan\alpha}{0.75b} \qquad (10.62)$$

Suppose a 60 inch spring as before, but divided 10 inches off center so that
    a = 20 inches
    b = 40 inches

And let
    W = 1000 lb.
    tan α = 0.5, as before.

$$\text{Then added rate} = \frac{1000 \times 0.5}{30} = 16.7 \text{ lb./in.} \qquad (10.63)$$

Unsymmetrical springs will be somewhat less affected by shackle angle, at normal design height.

10.12 Spring Testing

Methods of spring testing are not up to date [*c. 1960*].

Riding comfort depends on effective deflection, or $(\text{load})/(\text{rate})$ ratio. Yet we have no method in common use for measuring rate directly, and have to rely on a load deflection diagram, generally obtained under static conditions.

Effective rate readings were obtained over 30 years ago by recording resonant frequencies of a concentrated mass riding on an inverted leaf spring which was shackle-mounted, exactly as on the car. And these gave the first actual readings of rate change due to shackle angle, which are quoted in the *SAE Spring Manual*. Before this time it was common practice to regard the actual deflection of the springs from zero load to normal load as a measure of "wheel rate," paying no attention to the rate variations which actually occur.

Later came the use of spring test machines in which the inverted leaf spring is compressed with the eyes resting on roller carriages, the spring center being generally unclamped. Load deflection diagrams were obtained, and the old practice was to rap the leaves with a mallet to "loosen up" the static friction. Later, up-and-down readings were taken to provide a hysteresis loop, which gave some indication of internal Coulomb friction.

If such tests are made with extreme care and through a wide range, it is possible to establish the similarity of a leaf spring rate to the rate of a three-link mechanism with torsion springs at the two pivots, as already explained in Section 10.1. But the load deflection diagram so obtained is only a vague indication of the rate variations which occur when the spring is actually under the vehicle, clamped to an axle, with an inclined tension or compression shackle at one end, and probably with three rubber bushings [*acting as torsion springs at the pivots*] serving to increase the rate.

Inverted springs, shackle-mounted as on the car and with a rigid center clamp, can be tested on the conventional spring test machine, and give a closer approach to the truth. But the test is still static and only a load deflection diagram is obtained. The makers of spring test machines have never incorporated means for direct reading of rate. And even if they did, with the slow motion of these machines, the rate would be only static.

Rubber bushings contribute largely to the rate, especially in front suspensions, but, because of their creep, they do nothing toward carrying the load. Therefore their use requires softer and thus heavier and more costly load-carrying springs. Their great advantage is their complete lack of static or "Coulomb" friction, as well as lack of lubrication and [*positive contribution to*] noise isolation. Unfortunately the rate which they indicate in a low speed or static test is not even an approximation to their dynamic rate, which may be two or three times as great when the vehicle is in motion.

Leaf springs also may behave very differently when oscillating at normal ride frequencies. In some cases the static friction loop may almost disappear, while in others secondary oscillations may be set up by stick-slip motion between the leaves.

Modern suspension testing thus calls for pumping the vehicle up and down at something approaching ride frequency while the wheels, with or without tires, rest on load cells. Changes in wheel load and vertical motions are then recorded on oscilloscopes. And these readings can be (and preferably should be) electrically differentiated to also record **actual dynamic rates**.

10.13 Summary

Actual dynamic rates (with non-rolling tires) can now be measured quite easily with a four-post shaker rig. In the case of race cars with aerodynamic downforce a seven-post rig is used, the additional three jacks being used to simulate the downforce. Static, installed rates can be measured by constraining the vehicle on a kinematic and compliance rig. Even with these advances the rates measured, while approaching the actual rates seen by the car on the road, ignore the dynamics of the rolling tire.

Maurice Olley and his co-workers' notes on leaf spring design and measurement were used when the original version of the SAE Leaf Spring Manual *was written. The original manual is now (2000) incorporated into the* SAE Spring Manual *along with the other earlier books on coil and torsion bar springs.*

Slip Angle Sign Conventions

"Now I can be confused on a more sophisticated level."

Dr. William J. Rae
University at Buffalo

A.1 Introduction

Consider the tire/wheel shown in Figure A.1. This tire, traveling at velocity V, has been steered an amount δ from its initial straight-running condition. As a result an angle α exists, which, in turn, generates a lateral force F_y and an aligning torque M_z. (The angles are exaggerated for clarity.)

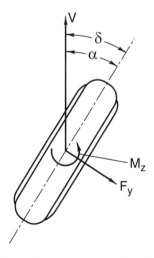

Figure A.1 *Tire/wheel immediately after it is steered.*

MRA Associate Edward Kasprzak wrote this appendix.

At small values of α, most of the tire print adheres to the road, while only small amounts of slippage may occur at the rear of the print. As α is increased, more and more of the rubber in the print slides relative to the road. The angle α, perhaps unfortunately, has been given the name of "slip angle" which does not properly describe small angle operation. Normal passenger vehicle operation occurs entirely in the small α range.

The sign convention used by Olley with respect to slip angles differs from the SAE standard[60] and needs clarification.

- As shown in Figure A.1, according to SAE convention: V is positive, δ is positive, F_y is positive, M_z is negative and **α is negative.**

- As shown in Figure A.1, according to the Olley convention: V is positive, δ is positive, F_y is positive, M_z is negative and **α is positive.**

The reasons behind these differing conventions are discussed below.

A.2 SAE Sign Convention

SAE's J670 series defines slip angle as the angle between the wheel's heading vector (based on the center plane of the wheel) and the wheel's velocity vector, projected in the ground plane.

SAE convention views the slip angle as the result of the wheel's forward velocity, u, and its lateral velocity, v. Slip angle is therefore referenced to the wheel heading vector. Applying basic trigonometry to Figure A.2 gives the relationship $\tan\alpha = v/u$.

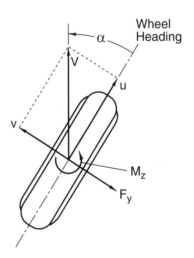

Figure A.2 *Tire/wheel immediately after it is steered, per SAE J670e.*

---

[60] Vehicle Dynamics Terminology, SAE J670e, Society of Automotive Engineers, 1976.

The slip angle, α, is given the same sign as the lateral velocity, v (assuming that u is positive). Thus, as drawn in Figure A.2, both v and α are **negative** and the tire is said to be "slipping" to the left. This generates a positive lateral force and a negative aligning torque (in the directions shown).

Using the SAE convention, typical lateral force and aligning torque curves (plotted against slip angle at constant normal load) appear as shown in Figure A.3.

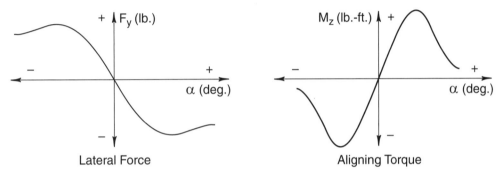

Figure A.3 *Tire data plotted with the SAE sign convention.*

Lateral force and slip angle have opposite signs. Thus the lateral force plot appears in the second and fourth quadrants, giving rise to negative cornering stiffness (C) values.

Informally, lateral force vs. slip angle curves are sometimes plotted in the first and third quadrants—ignoring the SAE sign convention. In practice, using (or even thinking about) data in the "wrong" quadrants is a continual source of confusion when working with tire data, equations and computer simulations written in the SAE axis system.

While SAE's definitions of slip angle and vehicle attitude angle, β, are consistent with each other, this similarity serves to reinforce the misconception that the tire is literally sliding sideways as a whole. It is true that both the vehicle CG and the **wheel center** have pure lateral velocity components. Within the tire contact patch, however, the print is not "slipping" laterally. Rather, due to the yawed-rolling condition of the tire, there is a region of adhesion to the road surface followed by a region of sliding in the aft section of the print. The use of the term "slip angle" makes it easy to overlook the presence of the region of adhesion.

A.3 Olley's Sign Convention

While Olley uses the same definition of slip angle as SAE—the angle between the wheel heading vector and the wheel velocity vector projected in the ground plane—his sign convention is opposite that of the SAE standard. The Olley sign convention is, instead, consistent with standard aircraft,[61] aircraft tire[62] and wind tunnel practice.

In aeronautical engineering, the yaw angle concept is in common use. Here, slip angle is referenced to the velocity vector. The wheel in Figure A.4 is shown yawed to the right of its velocity vector. This is a positive yaw and both the SAE and Olley sign conventions for steer angle agree that δ is positive. The Olley convention proceeds to recognize that tires normally operate in a "yawed-rolling" condition (not a "slipping" condition). Thus tendency to view α—the "slip angle"—as a yaw angle can be argued to follow naturally. As such, Figure A.4 shows a wheel/tire with **positive** yaw angle, α—the convention used by Olley.

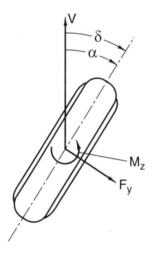

Figure A.4 *Tire/wheel immediately after it is steered, per Olley.*

This view of slip angle as a yaw angle causes typical lateral force and aligning moment curves to appear as in Figure A.5.

Lateral force and slip angle have the same signs. This conveniently places the lateral force and slip angle plot in the first and third quadrants. Cornering stiffness values are positive.

The aligning torque plot appears in the second and fourth quadrants. The slope at $\alpha = 0$ is negative, which is desirable when looking at the stability of a tire/wheel assembly. Small departures from $\alpha = 0$ cause the tire self-aligning torque to act as a restoring

---

[61] Vehicle Aerodynamics Terminology, SAE J1594, SAE Recommended Practice, Society of Automotive Engineers, June 1987.

[62] Horne, W. B., Stevenson, B. H., and Smiley R. F., "Low-Speed Yawed-Rolling and Some Other Elastic Characteristics of Two 56 inch Diameter, 24-Ply-Rating Aircraft Tires," NACA Tech Note No. 3235, 1954.

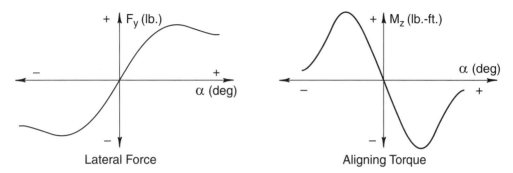

Figure A.5 *Tire data plotted with the Olley slip angle sign convention.*

moment, resisting yaw. While the physical effect exists (regardless of the sign convention chosen) it is Olley's convention that produces a negative slope in the plot at $\alpha = 0$. This **negative slope** is indicative of a non-divergent system (in the language of control theory).

A final justification for Olley's convention is the way tire testing machines generate tire slip angles. Nearly all machines create α by yawing the tire relative to the moving "roadway." Thus clockwise rotation of the wheel to produce a slip angle (positive yaw) results in positive lateral forces.

With Olley's notion of the slip angle as "yaw angle," a typical right hand turn would have positive steer angle, **positive** slip angles, positive vehicle yaw rate, positive vehicle attitude β (when above the tangent speed), positive lateral acceleration and positive tire lateral forces. This contrasts with the SAE convention in which negative slip angles exist in right hand turns, spoiling the uniformity of positive values.

Unfortunately, since the Olley slip angle sign convention is not the SAE convention, it differs from the bulk of literature published in the present day. While this is likely to cause some confusion, it is hoped this appendix will help clarify matters. Updating the figures and equations in Olley's original monographs to conform to SAE convention was considered but, in the spirit of following Olley's work as closely as possible, was not done.

A.4 Summary

SAE's slip angle sign convention is set forth in the J670 series and is based on the sign of the wheel center lateral velocity, **referenced to the wheel heading vector**. In a typical right hand turn slip angles are **negative** and lateral forces are positive.

Olley's sign convention is consistent with the aeronautical practice of working with yaw angles, **referenced to the tire velocity vector**. In a typical right hand turn the tire is yawed to the right of its velocity vector giving **positive** slip angles and resulting in positive lateral forces.

Olley's convention is preserved, unless otherwise noted, for use in this book.

Fiala/Radt Nondimensional Tire Representation

"A concurrence of several theories on combined lateral and longitu-dinal forces led to development of an approach with normalized resultant force as a function of a normalized resultant slip parameter. This function is universal in the sense that it is independent of load and applies equally well to pure slip angle (free rolling), pure trac-tion/braking (zero slip angle) or combinations thereof."

Dr. Hugo S. Radt
Milliken Research Associates, 1992

B.1 Introduction

Over a period of years, beginning in 1960, Dr. Hugo Radt developed a nondimensional scheme for treating tire data which is analogous to the aerodynamic coefficients used in presenting wind tunnel data. The next section develops the basic concept and the last section lists some of the advantages of this approach.

B.2 Derivation

The basic lateral force equation in nondimensional terms is,

$$\overline{F_Y} = \bar{\alpha} - \frac{1}{3}\bar{\alpha}|\bar{\alpha}| + \frac{1}{27}\bar{\alpha}^3 \tag{B.1}$$

Where $\qquad \bar{\alpha} = \dfrac{C\alpha}{F_{Y\,max}}$, the nondimensional slip angle, and

$$\overline{F_Y} = \frac{F_Y}{F_{Y\,max}}, \text{ the nondimensional lateral force.}$$

Substituting into Equation B.1 gives

$$\frac{F_Y}{F_{Y\,max}} = \frac{C\alpha}{F_{Y\,max}} - \frac{1}{3}\frac{C\alpha}{F_{Y\,max}}\left|\frac{C\alpha}{F_{Y\,max}}\right| + \frac{1}{27}\left(\frac{C\alpha}{F_{Y\,max}}\right)^3 \tag{B.2}$$

$$F_Y = C\alpha - \frac{1}{3}C\alpha\left|\frac{C\alpha}{F_{Y\,max}}\right| + \frac{1}{27}\frac{(C\alpha)^3}{(F_{Y\,max})^2} \tag{B.3}$$

$$F_Y = C\alpha\left(1 - \frac{1}{3}\left|\frac{C\alpha}{F_{Y\,max}}\right| + \frac{1}{27}\left(\frac{C\alpha}{F_{Y\,max}}\right)^2\right) \tag{B.4}$$

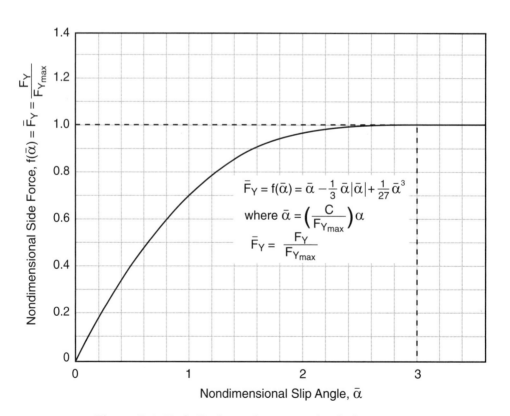

Figure B.1 *Fiala/Radt nondimensional side force curve.*

which is Equation 2.3. Equation B.1 is plotted on Figure B.1 for a typical bias-ply tire. When $\bar{\alpha} \geq 3$, $\bar{F}_Y = 1$ and $F_Y = F_{Y\,max}$. Also,

$$\bar{\alpha} = \frac{C\alpha}{F_{Y\,max}} = 3 \;\Rightarrow\; C\alpha = 3F_{Y\,max} \;\Rightarrow\; F_{Y\,max} = \frac{C\alpha}{3}$$

and Equation B.1 can be rewritten to correspond to Equation 2.4 and then to 2.5, etc.

When tire test data for a variety of loads are nondimensionalized and plotted, it will be found that all the data points fall on a single curve as shown in Figure B.2. Olley sensed the virtues of nondimensionalized tire data from the initial reference in 1960. Later developments are summarized in a more recent paper,[63] and book.[64]

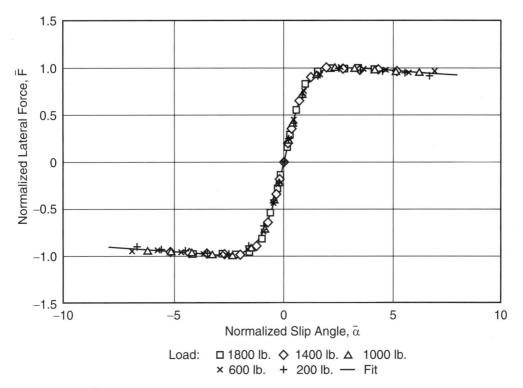

Figure B.2 $\bar{F}$ *vs.* $\bar{\alpha}$ *from typical tire test. Load points cover the full operating range.*

[63] Radt, Hugo S. and David A. Glemming, "Normalization of Tire Force and Moment Data," *Tire Science and Technology*, TSTCA, 11th Annual Meeting of the Tire Society, Akron, Ohio, March 1992.

[64] Milliken, W. F. and D. L. Milliken, *Race Car Vehicle Dynamics*, R-146, Society of Automotive Engineers, Warrendale, Pa., 1995, Chapter 14.

B.3 Advantages of Tire Nondimensionalization

- Greatly reduced test time and cost.
- Less wear and reduced need to test multiple samples of the same tire design (more accurate data).
- Nondimensionalized data improved when compared to raw test data via smoothing over different loads. Nondimensionalized data are mathematically consistent.
- Simple, accurate representation for use in vehicle simulation. Tire data are inserted once in dimensionless form in the vehicle model. Data is automatically reconstructed at different loads as needed.
- The friction coefficient can be changed from that at which the data was measured (without affecting cornering slopes).
- It is easy to "fit" the nondimensionalized free-rolling data, which is done once for all loads. The same fit coefficients work for nondimensionalized traction/braking data. "One fit fits all."
- Tire data nondimensionalization facilitates comparison of nonlinear tire behavior:
  - Between data and theory.
  - Across tires.
  - With respect to changes in the operating variables.

Technical Papers by Olley–Summaries and Reviews

"The attempt to insert new ideas laterally into an organization which permits only a vertical flow is impossible."

Maurice Olley

Olley wrote prodigiously throughout his life—letters, internal white papers, monographs, and longer technical papers, both published and unpublished. For example, he and his staff at the General Motors Proving Ground produced annual reports detailing their work. It is likely that these reports were drawn on heavily when, in his retirement, he produced the monographs that this book is based on. In this appendix we summarize some of his technical papers.

"Stable and Unstable Steering"

This white paper was written by Maurice Olley, May 23, 1934, when he was working for Cadillac at the General Motors Proving Ground.

*He discusses the problem of "stable and unstable steering" in the context of a small lateral disturbing force at the vehicle center of gravity, such as might be produced by a change in road camber. Using Goodyear tire data which had become available, he estimates the slip angle changes and resulting path curvature and disturbing force effects for various fore-and-aft load distributions and also examines cases in which the car turns toward or away from the disturbing force. He notes that when the car turns toward the disturbing force, "It behaves like the 'oversteering' that has been troubling us." **This may well be the first reference to the concept of oversteer and understeer.***

By carrying the analysis of this simple car further, he concludes that for the "oversteering" vehicle there is a "critical speed" at which the car will tend to go out of control unless the "front wheels are turned to correct it." **We believe that this is the first mention of the concept of "critical speed" in the literature***.*

The paper then continues with an examination of design factors which affect the critical speed, such as roll effects, Hotchkiss (rear axle) suspension, and independent front and/ or rear suspensions. For example, parallel independent front suspension raises the critical speed (when compared to an axle front suspension). He considers the possibility of a flexible steering linkage (steering compliance) as a way to raise the critical speed, though this may introduce other problems.

Thus in this brief note of 10 pages he presents a primer on the steady-state behavior of the automobile from the linear concept of oversteer and understeer to the divergent instability of the oversteer car.

Review of Four of Maurice Olley's Published Papers

In addition to the four monographs that this book is based on, Maurice Olley wrote a number of published technical papers. While we would have liked to include all four major papers in this book, they total well over 100 pages, with numerous figures, etc., so this was not feasible. Instead, we have included reviews of the papers, written in December 1968 and January 1969, by David W. Whitcomb at Cornell Aeronautical Laboratory. These reviews were part of an earlier attempt to publish Olley's work—this attempt failed for several reasons (see Origins and Objectives).

Maurice Olley wrote four technical papers which are regarded as "classics" in their fields. These publications are reviewed here in this section to show further the extent of Olley's interests and erudition.

"Independent Wheel Suspension—Its Whys and Wherefores"

This paper was presented at the Annual Meeting of the Society of Automotive Engineers, Detroit, January 1934. It was subsequently published in the SAE Transactions in March 1934.

The paper reports accomplishments of the past three years' research to improve the ride and handling of automobiles, and how independent suspension was developed to effect improvements. "Without these improvements, there would be no reason for the independent suspension," *says Olley.*

The initial phase of the program was to determine the various vibration modes of the car and find their frequency ranges and damping properties. A car seat was set up in the laboratory as a bounce table which could be oscillated at various frequencies and verti-

cal amplitudes. Human subjects were oscillated on this seat. Their opinions were used to establish riding comfort criteria in terms of frequency and amplitude.

Attention was paid to measuring the proper spring rates on the complete car. Attention is given to the positions of the pitch and bounce centers, and the significance of the k^2/ab ratio. Independent suspension is defined and its usefulness discussed. The k^2/ab car test rig is described and the test program outlined. Increased tire wear, for which IFS has been blamed, is explained and shown to exist in high performance maneuvers only.

Olley closes by saying, "Where do we go from here? If we live long enough, we shall find out."

"National Influences on American Passenger Car Design"

This paper was presented in February 1938 to The Institution of Automobile Engineers, in London. (This organization is now known as The Institution of Mechanical Engineers, Automobile Division). The paper was published in the XXXII Volume of the Proceedings, Session 1937–1938, IAE. Olley was awarded the Institute's Crompton Medal for this paper.

The original editor (IAE) is quoted as follows: "A few months ago when the author (Olley) got worried about the title of this paper, he was advised that the title did not matter: everybody knew he would talk about independent suspension because that was the only thing he knew anything about."

Highly incensed at this attitude, Olley has written a paper in which independent suspension is barely mentioned.

The subject naturally divides itself under two headings: first of all the national influences, then the resulting design. National influences can do two things, (1) create a need, and (2) provide a means for satisfying it.

Olley begins with some thoughts on the history of transportation in the United States.

"The early citizens could make things work; they were engine drivers rather than craftsmen, they could develop a mechanism for every need. The first 50 years are a history of water transport. The rivers and the Great Lakes led them up to the plains. The challenge of the plains led to the wagon trains—a mass development of individual transportation, which foretells and explains the 25 million motor cars in the States today. The early railroads were steel threads spiked down on the countryside. Strung along these threads were the settlements, innocent of roads and dependent upon the railway for everything. They lacked, however, some means of transportation to go between their homes and the railroad depot. Soon, large carriage and wagon builders, like Studebakers, were mass-producing vehicles long before the automobile arrived. The first automobiles were horseless buggies, but also at their price were poor man's transportation. Henry Ford is credited with replacing the horseless buggy with the Model T, the car which really motorized the earth. Next came the development of mass production techniques. Early Americans were effective 'hack-saw' mechanics, but later immigration brought the craftsmen. This mixture of skills led to the production line turning out thousands of vehicles all mechanically identical. Initially, there were no roads, but as the number of cars and owners increased, roads were built to suit the present needs, and were not designed for any other purpose. As roads were built and improved, vehicles were changed to take advantage.

The driving habits of the American motorist has its effect on car design. He is going to use his car to go to some definite place for a specific reason. He expects to be comfortable, hence, the popularity of closed cars.

Relative to English cars, the American product is distinguished by its uniformity of engine size, weight, wheelbase and means for accommodation provided for passengers and luggage. They will weigh between 2700 and 4000 pounds, and cost about one shilling per pound, of which the manufacturer gets about 8d [*8 pence*].

The role of mass suppliers to the industry has an important influence on car design. They represent a number of very efficient suppliers who are constantly hammering on the doors of the industry with new ideas, new variations, accepted components at lower cost, or of higher efficiency, or of greater life. The supply business is highly competitive, and results in a good product. Thus, the final car design depends upon a great number of people all acting under the supervision of the chief engineer, whose life cannot be regarded as a happy one. He must also live in at least four years at once, to obtain enough lead time to lay down plans for the 1940 car while coping with teething problems of the 1938. More often than not, the junior engineers are the men who really start the new designs. They test them and prove their validity before going to the drawing office.

Lines of development can be shown by the addition, subtraction, or rearrangements of features and components. Additions: bumpers, automatic choke, independent front suspension, hypoid gear rear axles, heating and ventilating, etc. Subtractions: magnetos, free wheeling, starting handles, oil, paints, etc. Rearrangements: spare wheel inside, batteries in engine compartment, wheel diameters have decreased, tire sections have increased.

The modern driver pays the engine the supreme compliment of ignoring its existence. The engine is usually arranged to be inaccessible to discourage tinkering."

So much for vehicle design. Olley next describes the performance of the vehicle of his day in several ways: performance in terms of speed, acceleration, braking and grade abilities. Other measures of performance have to do with ride, rolling, handling, and motions of the unsprung mass. Although it is possible to think of these attributes separately, they are all together simultaneously in the vehicle.

The ride performance is discussed in terms of front and rear spring rates, and the inertial factor k^2/ab. Tables and charts are given for suspension rates, including tire rates, for various American cars of the 1936–37 era. For good ride, the front suspension rate must be lower than the rear, and the k^2/ab ratio should be between 0.75 and 1.00. American cars generally have softer springs than others, a situation resulting from: relatively few winding roads, lower driver control inputs, feminine passengers seeking comfort, generally larger cars and the problem of pitch-resonance. Graphs are included showing vehicle response in pitch acceleration due to road waves of various lengths at varying car speeds, for both soft and stiff suspensions.

The roll performance of cars is discussed in terms of the roll angle developed by the sprung mass when cornering at constant lateral acceleration. Typical values are 4-1/2 to 6-1/4 degrees at 0.40g.

Performance is discussed in terms of vehicle handling, pointing out the importance of tire behavior, primarily the effect of slip angle and load. The concepts of "understeer," "neutral steer" and "oversteer" are introduced and the effect of speed on vehicle response is shown graphically. The skid pad test technique is explained and typical test data given. Reaction of the roll couple and tire aligning torque are discussed in terms of handling.

Performance also includes the movements of the unsprung masses. These are wheel hop, parallel hop, axle tramp, lateral and shimmy shake—these are discussed in terms of chassis rigidity.

"Road Manners of the Modern Car"[65]

This paper was presented at the annual meeting of the Institution of Automotive Engineers (later to become The Institution of Mechanical Engineers, Automobile Division) in London, and was published in the Journal of the IAE, Vol. 51, 1946–47.

This paper may be best described as a "state of the art" review and evaluation of both analytical and experimental research pertaining to vehicle stability and handling. Major topics include: vehicle configuration, tire performance, suspension dynamics, steering and stability and skid pad testing.

The content of the paper may be best presented by enumerating the topic headings and sub-headings in the paper:

Introduction
Stylism

---

[65] Reprinted with Olley's original sketches in *Proceedings of the 2000 SAE Automotive Dynamics & Stability Conference*, P-354, Society of Automotive Engineers, Warrendale, Pa., May 2000, pp. v–xl.

Driving Habits
Tires
    Conformability
    Life
    Noise
    Cornering Power
    Cornering Force Against Slip Angle
    Cornering Power Against Load
    Aligning Torque
    Camber Thrust
    Traction and Braking
Wheel Hop
Shimmy
Rear Axle Suspension
Cross Shake
The Vehicle
    Vehicle Steering
    Wind Yaw
    Weight Distribution
    Factors for Under Steer
    Roll Steer Effects
    Ackermann vs. Actual Steering
    Rear Steering Car
    Roll Steering of the Rear Axle
    Further Notes on Under Steer
The Skid Pad
Front Drive Cars
Transient Conditions
Flexibility and Friction in the Steering Mechanism
Friction in Suspensions (Apparent Backlash)
Distribution of the Overturning Couple
Scrub and Tire Wear
Conclusions

"Progress in Passenger Cars"

Published in the SAE Journal, February 1955, this paper was written to summarize the developments in passenger car design over the preceding 50 years to commemorate the 50th anniversary of the Society of Automotive Engineers.

Olley divides automobile development into four stages:

Stage 1 Courageous Pioneering

"The pioneer designs were logical but not practical. They were essentially carriages with the platform space devoted to passengers and the mechanism tucked decently out of sight. This was unpractical only because the mechanism was unreliable, and the car spent most of its life dismantled to get at its innards."

Stage 2 The Machine Flexes Its Muscles

"The reign of the chassis engineers. The vehicle was practical but illogical. The car developed into a road locomotive with the passengers merely catching a ride on the rear end. When closed cars became the 'standard,' their appearance was so unsightly and reluctant looking as to lead to..."

Stage 3 The Stylist Rules the Automotive Roost

"... the age of the stylists. This is essentially a return to the logical. The platform area is reclaimed by the passengers. The car is designed to move through the air and look as though it wanted to do so. The mechanism is again tucked out of sight. This is now practical because the mechanism is reliable. The impact of this modern design is international in scope."

Stage 4 The Future

"The coming fourth stage may be more dramatic in character or less so. The pressures which have developed in Stage 3 and the great variety of means for meeting them, may make for radical changes. The fourth stage will be less the work of any one dominant group. It must be a joint effort of a large number of groups and will have to be handled tactfully and in slow stages. In general, we can be sure that the appearance factor will continue to lead, and the mechanism to adjust itself to the shape of the vehicle."

Olley presents charts showing trends in vehicle design during the period 1925–1955. Variables include: average engine displacement—little change; horsepower per cu. in. displacement—strong increase; compression ratios—steady increase; gross installed horsepower—initial increase to 1934, little change to 1948, then increase; shipping weight—little change, average 3250 lb.; average overall height—steady decrease from 75 to 63 inches.

Problems that have arisen due to current designs: load on the rear tires has been reduced, has resulted in loss of traction; increased need for power steering to reduce driver control forces; directional stability problems especially at high speeds.

Maurice Olley in Denver, Colorado, 1955.
Photo credit Rolls-Royce Heritage Trust.

Olley Correspondence

"An engineering organization which works in complete harmony is making no progress."

Maurice Olley

Introduction by Bill Milliken

Maurice Olley and I first met in 1952 at the General Motors Proving Ground in a meeting inspired by a curiosity about car handling, which I had experienced as an amateur competitor in early post-war races at Watkins Glen and elsewhere. As we described our current research in aircraft dynamics at the Cornell Aeronautical Laboratory (CAL), Olley became enthusiastic about applying transient analysis techniques developed for aircraft to the time-dependent behavior of automobiles—a continuation of his own pioneering work in car behavior. The upshot of the meeting was the initiation of the long-range research program in automobile stability and control at CAL, sponsored by General Motors.

From the beginning a natural rapport existed between us based upon the passionate interest we shared in understanding vehicle handling. Olley's career had evolved from his exposure as a child to the earliest automobiles, later from his work at Rolls Royce with steering problems of shimmy and tramp, and finally from his years at Cadillac during the introduction of the independent front suspension and the development of the basic concepts of car control and stability. My interests in aircraft handling began with the flight of my homemade machine (in 1932) which had "Dutch Roll" instability, rudder over-balance and insufficient elevator control! Subsequent education and employment were concerned with analysis and flight test of aircraft for stability and control. At CAL I had initiated an advanced research program in aircraft dynamics.

Thus began a friendship and communication that continued for some 20 years until Olley's death in 1972. In addition to numerous visits and personal contacts we kept in touch by phone and literally hundreds of letters. Olley was a phenomenal letter writer—a master of the King's English with his own graphic form of expression. He carried on an immense correspondence with key figures in the industry; his views were seldom colloquial and he had an inexhaustible memory for technical detail and automotive history.

We had plenty to write about. At Cornell in our flight and (later) vehicle dynamics departments, we were at the leading edge of aircraft and automotive dynamics research, pioneering equations of motion, frequency response techniques, variable stability vehicles, a six-component on-road tire tester and a host of other analytical and experimental tools. Maurice followed all of these activities with great interest and an ability to absorb new concepts and place them in the context of car design. At the same time he contributed immensely to the orientation of our research in relation to long-term automotive trends.

Looking back, I can see that it was a period of great creativity for all of those involved at GM and CAL. To give the reader some idea of the breadth and depth of Olley's thinking, we have abstracted from his letters his views on a variety of automotive subjects as follows:

Maurice Olley on "Review of Cornell IME Papers,"[66] letter of July 27, 1956 from Detroit, Michigan

Personally I don't believe the most important development will be along the lines of "gadgetry," but rather by doing "those things which are requisite and necessary as well for the body as for the soul." For example—increasing yaw damping by some form of non-spin differential, and by aerodynamic improvements of a not too unsightly type, and perhaps most by avoiding excessive nose-heavy weight distribution or other contributions to excessive understeer. I would repeat the summary which I read over the phone:

1. Differential equations of motion have been written on an assumption of linearity which represents with sufficient accuracy the actual motions of a test car under "fixed control" conditions. Therefore it becomes possible to solve such car handling problems realistically on an analog computer.

2. A single step or ramp excitation and its response, obtained by test, can be harmonically analyzed to represent the response of the vehicle to sinusoidal excitations of any frequency. High frequency excitations offer a promising means for determining the lag in response of tires.

3. Much more complete and generalized dynamic characteristics of tires are urgently required. Preliminary information has been obtained by a new method of flat-road testing. But much more remains to be done, and, because of the large number of variations, it seems essential that tire makers should cooperate in this form of testing. Results under drastic traction and braking are particularly lacking.

---

[66] "Research in Automobile Stability and Control and in Tire Performance," presented at The Inst. of Mech. Engineers, London, November 1956, based on the General Motors sponsored research at Cornell Aeronautical Laboratories 1953–56.

4. In general the directional stability of all vehicles whether "understeer" or "oversteer," decreases with increasing speed, due to a decrease in yaw-damping. This is true without regard to aerodynamic effects which, in general, on present passenger cars, have the same tendency.

5. Excessive directional stability, in the lack of adequate yaw damping, may become undesirable in the presence of external disturbances, from road irregularities, or relative wind. This parallels experience with aircraft and ships. It leaves open the question of how much and what sort of directional stability to provide.

6. An immediate next step is the solution of "free-control" problems.

Maurice Olley on "Drivers," letter of December 22, 1957 from Lexington, Massachusetts

[I] am as sure as you are that the "missing link" in studies of handling is lack of understanding of the driver. I recall riding from Atlantic City to the Philadelphia Airport after an SAE meeting in a 1936 (I think) Cadillac seven-passenger limousine which was grossly overloaded in the body and in the overhung trunk. By sighting along the road from the rear seat you could see that it was oversteering excessively, yet there was no feeling of lateral uncertainty within the car, because the driver was good, and was used to it, and was well braced in his seat.

I know other drivers ([I] am sorry that Norma is one of them) who, even in a stable car, give the passengers a sensation of instability. Partly this is due to not bracing themselves in the seat. And it is particularly a fault of American cars because there are no bucket seats or even "bucketed" seat backs. Then I think it is also due to applying too great a turning velocity to the steering wheel, which is equivalent to rate of change of lateral acceleration, or lateral jerk. Too great velocity of the steering wheel may also be due to lack of self-confidence, or to a subconscious impression on the part of the individual that his reaction time is slow, which induces a tendency to hurry his movements of the steering wheel. I notice for example that N steers vastly more steadily after the first 50 miles.

One could cite the cases of delivery vans, often grossly overloaded and so prone to oversteer that one's first impression in trying to drive them is that they are completely unsafe above 40 mph. Yet the young drivers take them all over the place at 70 mph, and are seldom involved in accidents.

Maurice Olley on "Sports Cars," letter of March 28, 1958, from San Mateo, California

Sports Cars—after months in California I hate the very name of the damn things. Every silly young punk with a broken down heap thinks that by pulling the innards out of the muffler and putting a trumpet mouth on the exhaust outlet, he has produced a sports car.

I recognize that the genuine sports car enthusiasts have an ideal, and think that it's high time they defined it. Because if they did it might stop our manufacturers from making circus floats, and get them making more rational automobiles.

Perhaps what they are trying to do is to simplify and to speed up the action of the "control loop" on which the handling of the car depends, and to promote the importance of the driver himself, as the most essential link in the circuit.

When this is done the driver gets the same satisfaction from it as from handling a precision instrument. Possibly the finest example of this precision is the handling of a good motorcycle, which almost anticipates the rider's intentions.

You have produced this precision in aircraft by the use of "black boxes." I suggest that it is highly desirable to achieve similar precision in automobiles, but without the use of black boxes, as on your 2.7 Ferrari. There can be little question that, if we did this, we should reduce accidents, especially if at the same time we reduced the size of passenger cars, and improved road vision.

As part of this movement we need a shift mechanism (whatever the transmission) which feels like a gun lock, and not like a wire fence. Since the shift lever first went up on the steering column this mechanism has gotten worse and worse (and has cost more and more).

Maurice Olley on "Crash Safety," letter of October 28, 1958 from San Mateo, California

I know that in my last letter I had made some good resolutions and promised a more constructive approach and less sarcasm. But honestly some of these "safety" programs make my gorge rise.

The American people have now reached the stage where, except on farms, practically all manual labor has been transferred to machinery. It now appears to be the ambition of some of these "futurists" to do the same with all mental effort also.

Thus we build our ground vehicles as padded cells on wheels, so that our gilded youth, whether drunk or sober, can hurl itself around the countryside without taking any damage to themselves. And, as an explanation, we say that this is done on airplanes, ignoring the fact that airplanes have to run on roads where the waves are sometimes enormous and generally invisible. Craziest of all, we propose to make our vehicles "safe," by a multiplication of "black box" servo mechanisms each of which is highly complex and potentially unreliable.

And we ignore the fact that our civilization has now become so complex that the one thing it cannot do is to "suffer fools gladly," which is the true explanation behind our auto accident records. Instead of designing these incredibly costly and incredibly silly "safety cars," we should do better to spread the gospel of traffic safety. "Stay alert—Stay alive!

Crash Research

Much of this work on safety in car design leaves me cold. The waste of life in automobile crashes is true enough, but my understanding is that while head-on collisions at speed are the most spectacular they are not numerically the most important cause of fatalities.

Plain damn foolishness, lack of judgement and lack of experience, particularly in young people, and most particularly in young men, is largely responsible. Outrageous conditions in streets and highways, and totally inadequate examinations for driving licenses, also contribute. And car design particularly contrived to flatter and inflate the ego of a fool is probably the principal contribution of the automobile industry to the accident total.

Mounting the driver centrally and well forward, in glorious isolation, and making all his passengers face backward (why limit it to the rear passengers only?) is an obvious way of increasing at least the passenger's chances of survival, but after all an automobile is supposed to be an interesting and agreeable way of traveling in company (just consider the mental condition of the rearward facing passengers, sitting there and wondering where the fool is going next?). This whole business of strapping oneself by waist and shoulders into a vehicular projectile is contrary to the whole spirit of the thing. If anything will bring the automobile into disrepute—this will.

Side bumpers are good. We used to have them in the form of running boards, sometimes with bundles and leather baggage and even spare wheels, strapped to them. I wouldn't be here otherwise, having caromed off some palm trees at the side of a Route Nationale in France in 1913, thanks to this fortunate side cushion.

Steering Wheel

It is undoubtedly true that in head-on crashes the driver is frequently punctured by the steering wheel. In lesser collisions, however, the fact that he is braced against the steering wheel saves him, and it is his passengers and particularly his rear passengers who suffer. (I have experienced this condition, too.)

The steering post mounted on the forward part of the frame, and aimed through the body straight at the driver's chest is the real offender, not the wheel itself. And there really isn't a reason why it should be there. The steering wheel could just as well be mounted on the instrument panel and connected to the steering box on the frame by a light propeller shaft or other means. And this is actually done on some trucks. (Incidentally it saves assembly time and reduces vibration and noise in the body.)

Early cars steered with tillers. The best of these was the Lanchester with a forward-facing tiller like the tiller of a boat, which, with the addition of a couple of pounds of lead in the handle grip, gave the very first example of the natural stability of positive centrifugal caster. (The second was the Chevrolet Dubonnet.) But a bicycle handlebar, supplemented by a "black box" servo mechanism, as a contribution to safety, strikes me as ludicrous.

Undistorted Vision for the Driver

I doubt whether any accident has been caused by distorted vision due to windshield glass. Reflections in the windshield perhaps, obscured windshields undoubtedly, distorted vision due to alcohol, certainly, but not refraction distortion in the glass.

Bucket Seats

I would consider [*bucket seats*] obvious as the only sensible seats to put in a motor car. In the early cars they were almost universal. Progress in seats has been steadily backward. The pretense (little more) of producing a three-place bench seat in which the center passenger rolls against his neighbors, and is exceedingly uncomfortable because of the shaft tunnel, has never seemed to me anything to boast about. The best rear seats ever put into an automobile were undoubtedly the bucket seats in the old "Roi des Belges" touring cars of about 1910. These were two comfortable leather armchairs, with padded arms and head rests, facing forward and inward at 45 degrees, thus allowing the rear passengers to brace themselves against all the car motions and to converse with each other and the forward passengers, without any need for seat belts or other "straitjacket" combinations.

Improved instrument panel is good—but keep it simple. Another thing seldom considered is that the handbrake should be placed centrally or at least within easy reach of the right hand passenger, and so should the ignition switch. This is so obvious that it needs no elaboration—yet it is seldom done!

Automobile Crash Protection

The notion of making the inside of every car into a sort of huge cocoon for the protection of the occupants in case of a crash is all very well. But what about the other fellow, who may be an unarmored pedestrian, for example?

An ounce of prevention is better than a pound of cure, and the self-taught drivers of today who have never studied how to drive, beyond perhaps passing a police test, are "accident-prone" from the time they start driving to the time when, if they are lucky, they learn how by bitter experience.

The roads are full of evidence in the form of tire marks and broken guard rails that too many drivers are no judges of speed on curves and that on long grades they run themselves into brake-fade conditions by sheer ignorance. Education and stricter examinations before issuing licenses, and licensing only persons of adequate age and intelligence, would do much more good than any amount of fancy car design.

The Air Force has to face cases where crashes will occur even with highly trained personnel. Car drivers cannot always avoid them, but could do a much better job at this than they are doing. I am not sure that we don't baby them too much. These multitudes of stop signs and stop lights, which sometimes almost paralyze our traffic, are just lifting the responsibility that the driver constantly has, of thinking out his problems and doing something sensible about them.

Maurice Olley on "Seats and Fatigue," letter of October 28, 1958 from San Mateo, California

Apparently the authors [*at GM*] have not been informed about the "ischial tuberosities," the lumps of gristle below the ham-bones provided by a kindly Nature to permit comfortable **squatting**. Until recently (anthropologically speaking) only kings sat in chairs. The rest of the world squatted. And probably most of the 2000 million squat today. They can and do squat indefinitely, for years if need be, without fatigue because Nature has provided for it.

Western man has sat in chairs so long he has forgotten how to squat. But nature hasn't caught up with him, and sitting in chairs therefore is at best an exhausting business.

What is the best we can do? Sit upright for one thing, not half recline as our modern cars too often force us to do. Put the major support near the tuberosities, which few of our seats do. Avoid too-soft cushions that "smother" the blood vessels in our legs, and particularly avoid high contact pressure at the back of the thighs, which gradually paralyze the leg motions on which we depend for safety.

Another matter not covered and seldom considered is that, although bucket seats are good, they must be big enough and free enough not to restrict changes of position. There must be room to fidget!

It used to be thought that maximum car width should be at the shoulders. Now it is realized that freedom at the feet, the knees, and the buttocks is essential to prevent fatigue. Our modern cars with their "tumble-home" would be fine for this if only the floors were flat and if the doors were not so excessively thick.

Present seat cushions appear to be designed to attract customers on the showroom floor. Experienced drivers (particularly truck drivers) prefer harder seats and even springless seats for comfort on long journeys.

Maurice Olley on "Brakes," letter of October 28, 1958 from San Mateo, California

On your question of October 22 re brakes, the really interesting thing is that, within the limits imposed by the variable nature of any friction coefficient, the theories of Stepney Acres published by the IAE and on which my notes elaborate, do actually work, as shown by the GM Research tests. So one is justified in applying his theories to our existing designs. These show that our existing Bendix Duo-servo brake design has a brake factor vs. coefficient which is of an exponential type and in most cases the brake factor jumps to infinity, i.e., the brake locks, at a coefficient of a little over 0.70. The Research tests show that a "damp" drum with most brake linings will show on the square inch test a coefficient very close to 1.0. This has nothing to do with rust in the drum, as was at one time thought, but is a function of the high shear strength of mono-molecular fluid films, as referred to by F.P. Bowden. ([*This is*] the same reason that a windshield wiper consumes about double the "dry-glass" power, when the glass has still a thin film of moisture.)

But some linings, those of porous or granular texture, do not promote the formation of thin moisture films, and seldom show more than 0.50 coefficient on a damp drum. Sintered metallic linings are amongst these. Also some of the non-metallic linings, at least when new. So such linings can be used in Duo-servo brakes without morning grab.

For the smaller cars also the modified Duo-servo which has slidable cam faces instead of the fixed pivot can postpone grab to a higher coefficient.

Now, there's an entirely different way of obtaining self-energization. This is essentially the method of the Rolls-Royce mechanical servo brake, and it has also been used experimentally by Moraine on a rear disk brake. This is to use a non-energized primary or master brake to apply by its drag-motion a non-energized secondary or slave brake. This can be done on a disc brake in various ways, one of the simplest of which I designed for Chevrolet. (Don't suppose it was ever built.)

I played around with the same principle for drum brakes, but did not produce a working design. The characteristic of this principle is that the brake drag versus coefficient is **linear**, so there is no possibility of locking, even with much higher self-energizing factors than we use today. In other words, we could forget "power brakes."

Unfinished business on this program is that we don't know the relative merits of drum brakes, conventional disc brakes with contracting "caliper" shoes, or "reversed" disc brakes (which are really brakes with U section drums and expanding shoes).

The first relies in heat dissipation after conduction through the drum, so does the third. The second allows the air to wipe the heat off the face on which it is generated. Actually, however, none of them dissipate heat anything like fast enough to cope with a high speed stop and they rely on mass of metal in the drum to absorb the heat and dissipate it later. So we get to consider **how much of the total weight in the brake is heated by direct**

friction? And we find, surprisingly enough, that our present drum brake designs are far ahead of any disc brake in this respect. But that, when we use metallic linings with high conductivity, we run a serious risk of overheating and distorting the shoes and retracting springs.

That's about all I know. If you want a guess I should say that:

> Reduction of size and weight of cars in the future will reduce the urgency of the braking problem (you seldom hear of brake failure even today except on trucks).

> The drum brake with inward extension of drum and aluminum drums is almost bound to come. Aluminum drums will probably be [*made of*] an alloy which requires no metal lining, and the friction linings will be non-metallic.

> The Duo-servo design will continue, with automatic adjustment, reduced self-energizing, and linings reasonably free from "morning grab."

Maurice Olley on the "Pneumatic Tire," letter of January 5, 1959 from Pasadena, California

I think the pneumatic tire has always fascinated me, even as a boy when it was only seen on bicycles. At the turn of the century it was so unsatisfactory that the air was full of attempts to replace it. And these were revived around 1940. They were all completely unsuccessful.

It's a supreme example of the fact that worthwhile ideas frequently come from cross-breeding. It could never have been invented by an engineer, but had to come from a general practitioner, and an Irishman at that! And from the days of Dr. Dunlop 'til now no one has really understood how it works.

(Another example of crossbreeding is Major Hoke and the quantity production of Johanssen gauge blocks in WWI. He wasn't an engineer but an optical mechanic. He used to say that if engineers had got into the optical business, and if one broke a spectacle lens, it would require a quarter million dollars worth of machinery and three months to get a replacement, and then the first three replacements would be wrong!)

If you were seeing a tire casing built for the first time, I think the first idea would be the extraordinary ingenuity both of the conception and the method of construction, and the second would be that this is not 20th century manufacturing at all. It has the artistry of glassblowing, or of making wooden cart wheels or wooden casks, and belongs rather in the late 18th century. In its way it is literally a form of shoemaking. And it is also a bit like baking a pie! The pie has a very smooth crust, but Heaven alone knows what has happened to the filling. On general principles, it seems most improbable that any such construction could run smoothly on the road.

I may not be sound on my history, but I think that Palmer, when he produced the first "cord" tires in the nineteen-tens, had in mind to mechanize tire construction and to machine wind the cords as one would machine wind a generator. These were "radial cord" tires I understand (i.e., zero bias angle) and R.D. Evans at Goodyear reproduced them experimentally some thirty years ago, and showed that they were marvelous at enveloping obstacles, and completely lacking in any sense of direction!

But, although I'm again uncertain of my facts, I understand that Michelin in the X tire, has revived the radial cords, and by combining them with a flexible metal rim of circumferential wires, has produced what Watson Ford of U.S. Rubber describes as a flexible wheel, rather than a pneumatic tire (and 60% to 80% increase of mileage life).

Now it would be very interesting to know—whether the Michelin X tire does in fact use a more mechanized and less "manual" type of construction. And whether the Michelin X tire is freer from thumps and roughness than the conventional.

I know the tire industry has been longing for years to get the manual labor and manual inaccuracy out of their tire construction. But I wonder whether the time hasn't come for some "crossbreeding," say, from the weaving industry, or the garment-makers, or even from the package machinery industry? And I'm extremely curious about the Michelin people and their ideas. During my time with Chevrolet I met some of their engineers, and, while they play their cards very close to their chest, I have the impression that Michelin has originated at least 75% of the worthwhile advances in tire making in the last half-century. The "Pilote" tire before WWII was a basic advance that the American industry has been slow to follow. And I think the Michelin X is a similar advance and is winning its way just as slowly.

Yes, it would be very interesting to know more about Michelin X and to know how the tire companies are tackling the need for greater accuracy in their shoemaking.

Maurice Olley on "Smog," letter of January 10, 1959 from Pasadena, California

Now for some weeks I have been interested almost exclusively in "smog." And, if you see the L.A. newspapers you'll realize that millions of people in this area are concerned with almost nothing else. I have been trying to alert friends in Detroit on this subject, and have them realize that in the L.A. area at least, and ultimately in most large cities, a clean exhaust is the No. 1 requirement.

Now there is a bill in Sacramento that California (with the exception of certain counties that feel themselves sufficiently well ventilated to waive the requirement) will require by 1961 that all motor vehicles shall be fitted with an **effective** and **approved** smog preventer, or pay a special tax of 7% of the rated value of the car. This bill is announced as a move to get Detroit to wake up and do something. Here's a parallel to the headlight crisis of 1937/8, but this time the Big Three have been asleep at the switch and have let the problem get away from them and into the hands of the politicians.

Ford has a vanadium pentoxide catalytic afterburner muffler which should be in the hands of the Los Angeles APCD (Air Pollution Control District) just about today, for testing under traffic conditions. GM appears to have done an ostrich act on the whole thing, burying its head in a mass of denials that automobile exhausts ever could or ever have been responsible for smog. And Harry Williams of the Automobile Manufacturers Association put his foot in it at the Surgeon General's Conference in Washington last November, by making what was probably the silliest address delivered by an adult in the 20th century, in which he impugned the credibility of the Federal Government, the State of California, the medical profession, and the general car-driving public and succeeded in making the very name of Detroit stink to high heaven.

So now the politicians will be committing the industry to an "antiseptic" program rather than an "aseptic" one. The traffic analysis in L.A. shows that in the emission of unburned hydrocarbons:

Idling causes	5%
Cruising causes	25%
Acceleration causes	25%
Deceleration causes	45%

So that 45% of the trouble could be stopped by simply fitting a freewheel! (Perhaps 40% rather.)

Another evident fact is that even for cars as heavy as we are now building, our engines are twice as big as they need to be. Compare for example the '59 Pontiac with the Mercedes 300 (389 cu. in. vs. 183 cu. in.).

Then the carburetors are straight-gutted downdrafts with four or even six throats for an 8-cylinder engine, and with accelerating pumps that are small toilet flushes. The twisted crank V8 engine, which we use in this country rather than the old mirror-symmetric flat-crank V8, has such a mixed up firing order that the avoidance of blow-back on some cylinders is almost impossible. So the uniform working of all eight cylinders is at best very difficult. On the other hand the old straight 8 and flat crank V8, and vertical 4 cylinder are essentially better than the line 6.

What happens seems to be at least partly understood. Hydrocarbon vapors and nitrogen oxides (mostly NO) are emitted from the exhaust together, the former depending on engine design and the latter on combustion temperature. The mixture lies for hours under blazing sunlight in our stagnant atmosphere (stagnant because of a prevalent temperature inversion above 2000 feet) generally drifting very slowly NE from the coast. At about 5 o'clock in the afternoon and generally somewhere between Pasadena and San Bernardino the mixture gets really ripe and can reach nearly 1ppm of ozone. 2ppm of ozone will kill mice except that they can develop immunity by taking short preliminary doses (but lose their immunity with one dose of alcohol!). But 2ppm does not seem to embarrass humans. So they **think** that it is intermediate compounds in the irradiation process which cause eye irritation, headaches, and the general symptoms of tear gas.

And the source of the initial mixture is now known to be automobile exhaust to at least 80%. There is also evaporation from float chambers and gas tanks, and vapor spillage from filler spouts in gas stations. These can be very serious, but only in 100°F weather.

So, after 60 years of building motor cars, the whole basic design of the prime mover is under severe criticism. Fuel injection [*mechanical*] as inspected so far by APCD has shown uniformly worse results under all four running conditions. The 2-stroke engines are uniformly bad. The truck diesels are terrible when they smoke at all. APCD is studying European diesels which seem cleaner. (Possibly because they only get about 0.20 hp per cu. in.). The fair-haired boy is the small gas turbine which, in samples seen, has an almost "pure" exhaust.

The fault of the proposed legislation is that it takes no account of engine size, or displacement per mile, and evidently a large engine which never really works at city speeds of 30–55 mph is liable to be a much worse smog producer than a small engine which is working hard to earn its keep. I feel the industry has been caught in a de-panted position. With the exception of Nash and of Knudson at Pontiac who has made an economy job of his big engine and can show 20 mpg.

My theoretical smog-proof car would be an "electro-motive" car, basically an electric, but with a charging set under the hood which would run when it was needed at a governed constant speed full throttle, so with all conditions favoring a clean exhaust. I wish General Electric would build one, or else GM down at Lagrange. I think it would be fun for a lazy old so-and-so like me to drive!

The only "clean breathing" car Linville has seen so far is an old White steamer belonging to Edgar Bergen. This is almost 100% pure.

Maurice Olley on "Summarizing," letter of January 13, 1959 from Pasadena, California

At intervals for several weeks I have been trying to read and digest the Cornell report on tire thump. But I've had to lay it aside, because I cannot understand what it says. For dumb heads like me I wish summary reports could be prepared of not more than two pages, saying in simple words what a given report really means.

I think of the preacher's sermon:

> "First I tell 'em what I'm gonna tell 'em
> Then I tell 'em.
> Then I tell 'em what I told 'em
> And then I give 'em hell."

And I think of the 19th century gentleman who apologized for writing such a long letter, because he'd not had time to compose a short one!

I think that, given the perspective of a little time interval, most new findings, in automobile matters at least, can be expressed in few words. Kettering was good at this. [*I*] am sorry to sound critical.

Maurice Olley on "General Vehicle Design," letter of February 15, 1959 from San Mateo, California

As an introduction to overall vehicle design, there is the matter of how many feet the animal should have. One trouble is, our ideas have loosened up so immensely in the last few years. For example one could cover:

1. Two wheelers—the side by side double two-wheeler—in terms of steering, handling and ride.
2. Three wheelers
   a. One wheel in front—oversteer when braking on turns and overturning.
   b. Two wheels in front—understeer, braking stability, tire wear at rear.
3. Four wheelers
   a. Narrow rear tread (2 passenger Isetta)—problem similar to b. above.
   b. Wide rear tread—reduced effect of rear roll couple, hence understeer tendency, but how to reconcile this with the three wheeler with single leading wheel, which oversteers? Needs study.
   c. Imagine a four wheeler with parallel independent suspension both ends and no roll stability at all. Is this the same as the double two-wheeler? Can it be handled as a bicycle? dunno. But it would be fun to find out.
4. While we're about it, we might consider the five (5)-wheeler. This is a common 4-wheel ark type vehicle, with a tricycle substituted for the front axle. One of the early steam cars of the 1830s was built this way. This is an extremely interesting vehicle.
   a. It doesn't have independent suspension, but has only one pivot-mounted wheel. It cannot shimmy. (It can have a "nose-wheel wobble" of course, but this is a mere castering-wobble, an entirely different thing and easily suppressed with a touch of pivot friction.)
   b. It has the simplest form of power steering.
   c. In a crosswind it has the same inherent stability as positive centrifugal caster (Chevrolet Dubonnet).
5. So we get to the 6-wheeler, or 3-row suspension. All 3 rows can be separately sprung, in which case the pitch stability is reduced by one-third compared with suspension at the ends only.
   a. Or the rear two rows can be bogied. In this case we have to watch the drive to the [*bogie*] front and rear wheel pair very carefully. If the wheels rotate with the bogie when the bogie pitches we're going to have the rear tires digging in and the fronts lifting on forward drive. If the wheels stay without rotation relative to ground when the bogie pitches, we're o.k.

b. The greater the number of independent rows of suspension the less the pitch stability. With an infinite number of rows we get the effect of a plank floating in water which has 1/3 the pitch stability of suspension at the two ends only. (This is the major fault of tank suspension, and the reason they "fall on their noses" every so often when driving cross-country. Fault too of the Packard compensated suspension and the Citroen 2CV in both of which a portion of the pitch stability was deliberately destroyed.)

c. Then, the steering of 6-wheelers, or 3-row suspension. Experience shows that steering of the front pair only, if the two rear pairs are close-spaced, or steering at proportionate angles of the front and middle pairs, are practices essential to safety. Reversed steering of the rear pair, generally with considerable delay action, has been used for minimum turning circles, but has always proved dangerous. (In the case of a "hook & ladder" truck, independent rear steering, with trained handlers, seems safest.)

d. Then comes the tractor-trailer combination, which is similar to the tricycle front-axle, above, except that it's a "front drive." How to deal with the ride or handling of these I don't know. Janeway and Bill Le Fevre of Freightliners Inc. in Portland, Oregon, have been struggling with the ride, the height of the virtual center of the "5th wheel" linkage on the tractor, etc. And I understood that Bill Milliken at Cornell Laboratory was going to train an IBM machine to handle the steering problem! The miracle is that they steer at all with the brakes on. (So what about the proposed virtues of the tricycle front axle? I don't know!)

Weight Distribution

I suppose we really need more information to determine how nearly we can assume that the skid point is 0.80 of the load on the tire at all loads. It seems to depend a bit on speed, since "static" tests show a coefficient > 1.0, but road tests on dry roads agree on about 0.80.

1. 34/66 Weight Distribution—if we assume that (height of CG/wheelbase) = about 0.20, then a static weight distribution of 34/66, will give a weight distribution under maximum forward braking of 50/50. If the **brake** distribution is 50/50, this looks like giving optimum braking condition. Under lighter braking, say deceleration/g = 0.4, the weight distribution will be 42/58, and, if the road is wet, for example, the front wheels will start to slide first, which is as it should be. On the other hand, if the driver is a damn fool and locks his wheels on a wet road, he will end up rear end to.

Maximum traction on a dry road represents a weight distribution of 18/82, which should entirely prevent squealing the rear tires (however, the front end lifts about half the spring deflection in acceleration).

The handling problem isn't so simple. In 1956 CAL has shown that typical American cars have the neutral steer point about 3% of the wheelbase back of the CG. This gives more understeer than CAL engineers think we should have, and they are inclined to favor neutral steer, i.e., NSP on the CG. If we could get tires of which the "cornering stiffness" (i.e., cornering force/slip angle) were strictly proportional to load and if we then held the wheels upright, we should then always get neutral steer, whatever the weight distribution, and whatever the roll couple distribution. [*CAL later changed this rather extreme position.*]

Truck tires have cornering stiffness much more nearly proportional to load than conventional passenger car tires, probably because they need to be more adequate for the load carried. Probably Michelin X tires are more nearly in the category of truck tires. However this may be, it is evident that, to get success with any car with weight distribution of the order of 34/66, it is essential to use tires which will give a close approach to neutral steer. Our present considerable understeer condition will be a thing of the past.

The understeer of parallel independent front suspension is probably essential. Swing axle at the rear does not have the extra cornering qualities it was once believed to have, but is at least tolerable. So much for the rear engine car.

2. 50/50 Weight Distribution—practically all the early passenger cars (prior to 1930) had weight distribution running normally between 50/50 and 45/55. Of course with rear brakes only, this was not enough on the rear for safe braking. At max deceleration, weight distribution on a 50/50 car would be 66/34. With brake distribution of 60/40 the rear wheels would skid first. But at 0.4g deceleration and weight distribution of 58/42, as on a wet road, the front wheels would skid first. With all wheels locked the vehicle was "neutral" [*see Chapter 9*].

3. 55/45 Weight Distribution—under maximum deceleration weight distribution is 71/29. Lift of the rear end is almost half the spring deflection and anti-lift geometry to be effective requires an angle of motion of the tire contact spot which is scarcely acceptable [*requires a steep side view swing arm angle*]. At 0.4g deceleration, weight distribution is 63/37 and with 60/40 brake distribution, rear wheels will skid. We know we get by with this sort of weight distribution on modern cars, but it is far from ideal. The one virtue is that when all four wheels come adrift the car runs straight. (Whether this is really a virtue I can't say. Roy Brown of Firestone, from his experience with youthful racing and flying, used to say the only safe thing to do in the face of an accident was to swerve. If you swerved you might roll, but if you hit head-on you hadn't a chance.)

4. 65/35 Front Drive—maximum deceleration weight distribution 81/19, the car almost summersaults. Lift of rear end is 50% of spring deflection or more and cannot be compensated by anti-lift geometry. It's scarcely worth fitting rear brakes since all they'll do is skid the rear wheels. Maximum acceleration weight distribution is about 50/50, adequate to prevent slipping front tires with reasonable engine power. The complaint in maneuvering is the rear end going out of control when braking on wet downgrades.

Roll Rate Distribution

It would be desirable to have zero roll **rate** at one end of the vehicle. Then **static** torsional distortion of the car structure would be impossible. A swing axle or ordinary axle with a high roll center, can have very little roll rate and still distribute the roll couple [*total roll moment*] adequately to the rear tires. The Packard or 2CV [*Citroën*] suspensions put less roll couple into the car structure. In the Packard, with the rear supplementary torsion rods removed, the combined front and rear suspension has little or no torsional resistance.

Roll Couple Distribution

Roll couple distribution must be proportioned to the weight carried by each pair of wheels, and to the tread. We can't have the "inside" wheels lifting off the road. The importance of roll couple distribution decreases as tires are produced with cornering stiffness more nearly proportional to load. But it doesn't cease while wheel **cambers** change. Camber thrust is proportional to load. And too much roll couple on a swing axle, for example, will take load off the inside wheel with its positive camber which is trying to understeer, and put load on the outside wheel which (with the lifting that occurs) is also getting a positive camber, and tending to oversteer.

With conventional short and long arm IFS the positive camber of the outside wheel is decreased, and the negative camber of the inside wheel is increased by the linkage. Increasing the front roll couple carried by the pair of wheels would therefore **decrease** the total camber thrust tending to understeer. On earlier tires, because of the characteristic curve of cornering stiffness vs. load, the couple would tend to decrease the combined cornering stiffness of the pair, thus tending toward understeer. So the camber thrust and cornering effects were in opposition.

However with Michelin X tires, for example, we might expect a decreased actual understeer with an increased front stabilizer.

Probably the thing that really matters most in the distribution of roll couple at the front is that increased roll couple puts increased load on the outside front wheel and increases aligning torque and "feel." (I don't know. This whole business needs some younger minds, free from prejudice and above all free from the accursed fascination of "black box" instrumentation, to do our experimentation of the 1930s all over again with modern tires.)

Tires

I was writing Bill Milliken the other day about his work at CAL on tire thump. What a wonderful thing a pneumatic tire is, and yet how completely "unmechanical"! It could have only been invented by a general practitioner, and an Irishman at that. To this day, no one really understands how it works. And the way it is built is just sheer shoemaking.

The wonder is not that the thing thumps, but that it is ever possible to run it against a road under a heavy load at say 1300 rpm, without the whole affair disintegrating.

I was asking Milliken whether anyone in their outfit knows how a Michelin X tire is built. Because I suspect that they have done what Palmer was aiming at in the original Palmer cord tires, namely to actually "machine build" a tire, without the laying on of hands.

I can't help thinking that we still know far too little about the tires on which our lives depend. We have some of the fundamentals of cornering stiffness, and aligning torque (or pneumatic trail) as affected by slip angle, load, inflation, rim width, cord angle, etc. And we have representative figures on camber thrust and camber aligning torque, as affected by camber angle, load, inflation, etc. But we have not gotten used to considering the camber thrust and camber aligning torque as a "pneumatic lead" of the camber thrust point. And we have failed to get any clear idea how these four quantities are affected by tractive forces or braking forces up to the limit of slip. Obviously we must get this information if we are ever to really understand handling.

But we can never hope to rest on our oars because the tires don't stay put. For example the best modern construction apparently gives a variation of perhaps +/-20% in tire characteristics between individual tires after running in. And the pneumatic trail of a tire may **double** in 1000 miles running, from new condition.

Then a new variation like the Michelin X, or new construction methods which may make our present efforts look like the work of village cobblers, will come along, and the whole job has to be done over again. Then again all our "dynamic" figures on tires are really "static" figures. Similar constant-state tests on airfoils in wind tunnels used to be considered adequate, but now are known to be misleading. So, what we really need are tire dynamic results, cornering force, pneumatic trail, camber thrust, and camber thrust lead, under rapidly changing conditions of angle. Because we know there is a lag.

Another thing we haven't considered sufficiently is the characteristics of truck tires and their effect on the handling of trucks. Cornell Lab has got us thinking in terms of "yaw damping", which decreases with increasing speed. But dual rear wheels must increase yaw damping and dual rear axles (unsteered) must increase yaw damping considerably.

Suspension

On suspensions I am not prepared to say that we have reached the point of diminishing returns, but the comparatively cool reception of things like the Packard suspension, or the DS19 [*Citroën*] ultra-soft suspension, seem to show that, by and large, suspension of American cars is regarded as satisfactory. Noise and shakes are more disturbing to the passengers than the basic ride motions of the vehicle.

This is certainly not true of trucks, where a fundamental change in suspension is long overdue. Air suspension on large trucks seems inevitable (as on buses) because they mostly already have a compressed air system, and because the frequency remains constant at all loads.

Air suspension on passenger cars seems unnecessary. The load doesn't vary enough. Leveling a torsion rod suspension seems easier. If we want "zero ride rate" with a torsion rod, we can get it easily with a toggle. And the additional weight of spring steel in the toggle is less than 12.5%.

There's another possibility. I just heard from Paul Taylor (Taylor Devices Inc., North Tonawanda, N.Y.) that he is about to send his first set of combined liquid springs and shock absorbers for passenger car suspension to Joseph Lucas in Birmingham, England. This is a thing we can't afford to ignore, particularly for trucks, where the immense energy storage of these extremely small units is really important. He is already deep in the aircraft and missile field, as well as press-tools and machine tools.

Maurice Olley—Comments on a report outlining a "Proposed Investigation of Handling Characteristics of Passenger Cars," letter of March 15, 1959 from San Mateo, California

Now for critical appraisal—

Any "Study of Handling Properties of Passenger Vehicles" should most certainly include an investigation of the neutral steer point [*NSP*]. (See Lind Walker[67] paper in "Automobile Engineer" and [*numerous*] Cornell Lab reports.)

The NSP can be deduced by analysis of skid pad test charts. But it would seem to me high time that the GMPG[68] had developed a direct method of finding the NSP along the lines suggested by Lind Walker.

Lind Walker points out that actually NSP is not a "point," but a transverse plane through the vehicle inclined rearwardly upward, because the roll of the vehicle normally promotes understeer. However, any conscientious work at GMPG to develop a measuring practice should soon establish whether to determine the NSP at ground level, at the height of the roll axis, or at height of CG.

CAL has shown that a "static margin" of .03, i.e., NSP 3% of the wheelbase back of the (total) CG represents about typical American passenger car understeer. (And in their opinion this is too much for safety at high speeds since it tends to directional oscillation. However, that's a matter of opinion, and I think requires a lot of confirmation.)

---

[67] Walker, G. E. L., 1950, *Automobile Engineer*, Vol. 40, Nos. 530, 533, pp. 281, 370, "Directional Stability, A Study of Factors Involved in Private Car Design."

[68] GMPG = General Motors Proving Ground

To summarize, therefore, I think that, since GM seems determined to scrap the skid pad test (though many European makers still use it), they should be prepared to substitute the Lind Walker test, which has the advantage of being done on the straightaway.

Now, taking the nine items of the subject report, I'd like to comment on them individually.

Driving Appraisal

A number of items enter into the actual handling, which are not mentioned in the report. For example:

> Tire pressures and the cornering stiffness of the tires used, at the loads and inflations used.
>
> Body shape and movement of the center of wind pressure with change in the angle of attack and yaw.
>
> Steering ratio, steering friction, and moment of inertia of the steering wheel.
>
> Elasticity of the steering wheel.
>
> Characteristics of power steering, when used.
>
> Hysteresis of the suspension in roll.
>
> Distribution of the engine driving torque on front and rear wheels (different in LH and RH turns).

Ride and Roll Rates

As I recall the ride and roll rates quoted and charted by the GMPG are really compound characteristics including, as I think they always do, the tire deflections. This has to be whittled out[69] by figuring before the PG rates can be compared with theoretical (or even actual) suspension rates.

And don't forget that, in any **independent** suspension, the ride rate for one wheel, multiplied by the square of the tread, divided by 1375, **must** equal to the actual roll rate. If it doesn't there's something wrong with the measurements. The distribution of the roll **rates** and the distribution of the roll **couples**, are entirely different. In fact for the sake of minimizing frame distortion, it might be desirable in some cars to use a high rear roll center with a **zero** roll rate at the rear.

Camber, Caster and Toe Change

These PG charts of camber, caster, and toe change are also not directly comparable with actual suspension geometries, since these also contain tire deflections.

---

[69] See, for example, Chapter 16 of Milliken, W. F. and D. L. Milliken, *Race Car Vehicle Dynamics*, R-146, Society of Automotive Engineers, Warrendale, Pa., 1995.

Weight Distribution and CG

The GMPG double-swing method for getting the vertical plane moment of inertia, and the height of CG, is about as good as one can get. But what is obtained is the k^2 of the entire car about the CG of the entire car. The k^2/ab, which is significant for ride, is the k^2 of the sprung mass about the CG of the sprung mass, divided by the $a \times b$ of the sprung mass. This is quite different, and in most cases is less than the k^2/ab ratios listed by the GMPG. It has to be figured by elementary deduction from the PG figures.

When dealing with small cars the PG method is probably less accurate. The weight of the swings and the extreme height of the 15-foot swing, make the significant figures for the car appear as minor variations in the equations.

Personally I prefer getting the height of CG by lifting either end of the car and weighing on the four horizontal scales, and by then getting the moment of inertia by swinging from an overhead pivot by four light cables to the wheels. I understand that the PG applies a correction for the mass of air enclosed in the car.

Horizontal k^2/ab Ratio

The horizontal moment of inertia is significant only in periods of transition. In contrast the terms "oversteer" and "understeer" refer to steady-state conditions such as are obtained on the skid pad, and are in fact determined by a negative or positive "static margin."

The significance of a horizontal $k^2/ab > 1$ is that in the initiation of a turn the lateral deflection of the rear tires is negative, so that the rear tires are "flipped" or "staggered" when starting a turn.

In the case of an understeering car at high speed the directional oscillations, so clearly demonstrated by CAL,[70] are certainly slower in frequency and more violent when horizontal k^2/ab is > 1. In other words an adequate wheelbase is essential to handling stability. The lateral stiffness of the rear suspension must affect the directional frequency also, since lateral flexibility must have a similar effect to shortening the wheelbase or increasing horizontal k^2/ab.

Lateral Rate of Rear Suspension

(See note above.) The effect of lateral flexibility in effectively shortening the wheelbase has probably been neglected in the past.

---

[70] "Research in Automobile Stability and Control and in Tire Performance," presented at The Inst. of Mech. Engineers, London, November 1956, based on the General Motors sponsored research at Cornell Aeronautical Laboratories 1953–56.

Also of significance is the direction of "yaw" of the rear axle when deflected laterally, and this should be ascertained. If the center of yaw is ahead of the axle, as with a torque tube, the position of the neutral steer point is affected in the direction of oversteer. The tendency toward axle tramp is also affected significantly.

Some flexibility in lateral control of the rear wheels is generally found to be essential, however, to reduce lateral shocks and "harshness" in the ride.

Timing Response

My objection to the test method is that a quarter turn of the steering wheel is **not** a standardized impulse. The impulse will vary with the steering ratio, the flexibility of the steering, the steering backlash, the power steering characteristics and the length of the wheelbase.

Another objection is that the readings of the accelerometers at either end will not distinguish between lateral acceleration and roll angle [*because of gravity component*].

I have no constructive suggestions except that I think the GMPG staff should develop a modernized version of the old "checkerboard test." I know this has been debated, and think it high time that it should he done.

Roll Centers

I completely disagree with the method proposed and think that its use will only create confusion.

Roll axes were obtained accurately and well by Schameharn's tests at the PG around 1935/6, using a long-focus camera and vertical lines at either end of the vehicle. I have used a simpler method at Vauxhall, with a transit to replace the camera.

In both cases the tires were overinflated "dead hard" [*perhaps 60 psi*] to eliminate appreciable tire deflection. And in both cases rolling moments were produced by vertical loads.

When lateral pull is used a whole flock of extraneous deflections are introduced, for example:

> Lateral deflections of suspensions.
>
> Lateral deflections of tires.
>
> Vertical deflections of tires, which are increased by lateral distortion.
>
> In the case of a swing axle, vertical lift of the rear of sprung mass. This lift is not a linear effect, but increases rapidly as the lateral pull at the CG increases.

I wish we could put across the idea that the **roll axis is a more or less idealized geometrical conception which is significant chiefly in determining the distribution of the roll couple on the tires, and the direction in which the vehicle faces when it rolls**. Ideally the roll axis determines the plane along which the vehicle can sustain lateral forces **without** rolling (disregarding tire deflections).

Roll Steer Characteristics

Using dial indicators for the angles is correct. Using lateral pulls is not. To obtain the roll steer angles it is necessary to mount the tires on free-sliding turntables, and for this the roll of the car must be produced by vertical loading.

A steering effect due to lateral loads in the absence of rolling can occur, and several methods are available and have been used (by Chevrolet R&D, for example) for measuring this "lateral distortion steer."

Note: Roll Rates

The **roll** rate without tires is equal to (ride rate) $\times$ (tread)^2/1375, in the absence of a stabilizer. In fact testing with and without a stabilizer is the way in which the effective roll rate due to stabilizer is ascertained. However, in the case of a swing axle the actual **ride** rate, which can be ascertained only by allowing the tire treads to move freely sideways, is somewhat less than (roll rate) $\times$ 1375/(tread)^2, because of the tread change which occurs in ride but of which there is very little in roll.

If T_o is the rate of a torsion [*spring in*] roll in lb.-in./rad., the ride rate dW/dz is $\left(T_o - Wh\right)/R^2$, where h is the effective wheel radius, which is approximately the radius to the tire base.

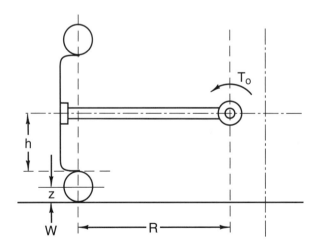

Figure D.1 *Swing axle ride rate.*

Selection of Test Vehicles

I don't anticipate any considerable difference in geometry between Chevrolet, Ford and Plymouth. But the two swing axle jobs, Light Chevrolet [*the Corvair*], and 190 Mercedes will call for some careful handling. Avoiding side loads to obtain the true swing axle geometry has been referred to above.

The single-joint swing axle of the Mercedes is not truly an independent suspension since the engine torque falls on the rear tires, and, on a skid pad test at least, would be expected to show differences in geometry between RH and LH turns, such as occur with conventional rear axles.

With equal cornering ability ("cornering stiffness") in front and rear wheel pairs and lacking any roll steer effects a car with 40/60 weight distribution will have a 5% negative static margin and will definitely oversteer. It depends on the use of tires with cornering stiffness proportional to load (either by tire size, rim width, inflation differences, or tire construction) to offset this effect.

And parallel independent front suspension helps to put it over toward the understeer side, though the roll should be little by reason of the rearward CG and the high roll axis at the rear.

With all the precautions I should expect this car to vary between neutral and a very slight oversteer margin. I think this is its great interest, since with the light steering and with a fast steering ratio I think it will be found to handle excellently. Although the CAL tests cannot be considered conclusive yet, I think it will be found that a light and carefully controlled oversteer margin, combined with light, fast, and sensitive steering, will produce a better handling car than our present vehicles with their slow and rubbery steering and exaggerated understeer.

Cartoons

Maurice Olley was a close personal friend of Frank Winchell, who replaced Olley as head of Chevrolet Research and Development when Olley retired. In later years, Olley entrusted Winchell with some of his personal effects, such as ancestral material. On Winchell's recent death (2001), Winchell's daughters transferred this material to Bill Milliken. This included the four "automotive sketches" reproduced here, done during the period when Olley was chief engineer of Rolls-Royce of America, Springfield, Massachusetts.

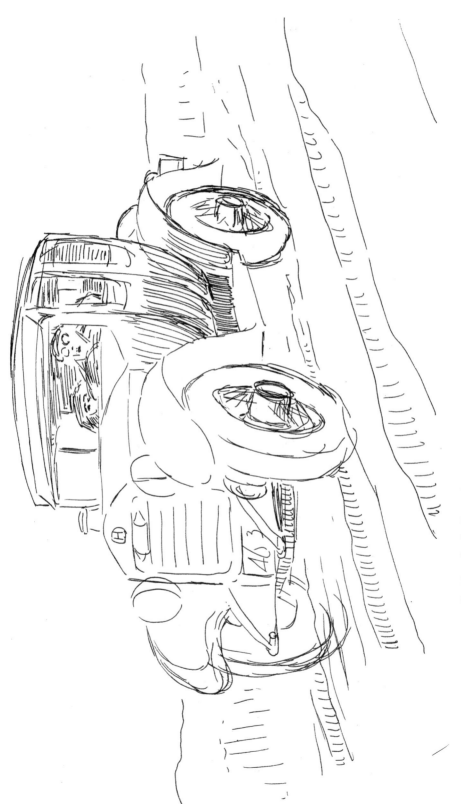

To Hartford. First long run with 30 × 5 tires. Katalysed Head & Swing Shutter. February 25, 1923.

To Brookfield. Sunday, April 23, 1921.

The Bus. February 25, 1923.

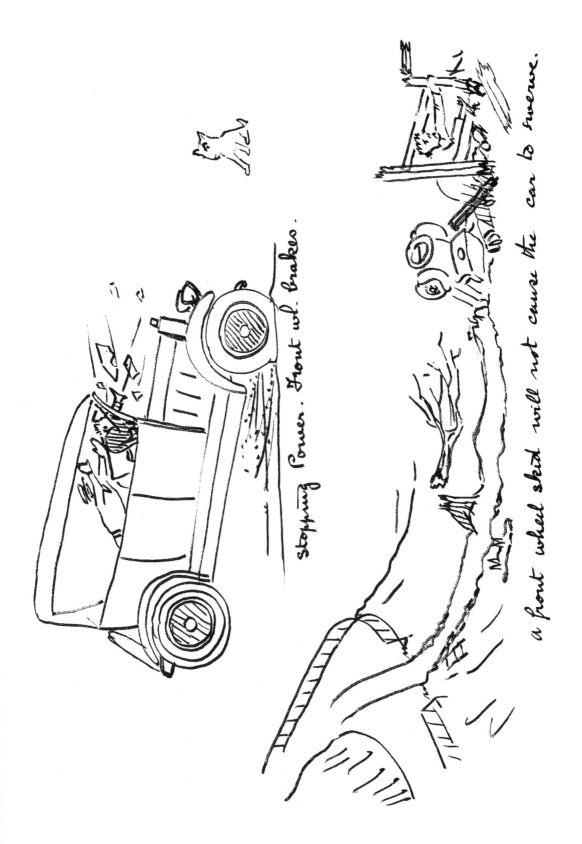

Balloon Tires and Front Wheel Suspension

"The automobile today, instead of the loose assemblage of parts and mechanisms of fifty-odd years ago, is a very complex and closely integrated piece of machinery."

Alfred P. Sloan, Jr.
My Years with General Motors, **1963**

From the beginning, the problem of supplying a smoother and softer ride has been one of the most complex in automotive engineering. Since a car went much faster than a horse-drawn vehicle, it communicated the irregularities in the road surface to the passengers with greater intensity. The internal combustion engine added its own source of discomfort in the form of vibration. Consequently, improvements in the cushioning of the driver and passengers were necessary, and this need increased as cars became speedier.

One basic approach to this problem was through the tires. Early motorcars had used solid rubber or vented solid rubber tires. These were soon replaced by inflated tires, but in this early stage neither the rubber nor the construction was good enough, and interminable tire-changing was a sad necessity on any extended trip.

By the early twenties the rubber companies had learned a good deal about construction methods, chemistry, rubber curing, and selection of materials. Tires were much better, and engineers began to consider the possibility of low-pressure tires, which would create a softer and more resilient air cushion under the wheels. Many problems had to be met,

This appendix is an excerpt from *My Years With General Motors*, by Alfred P. Sloan, Jr., Doubleday & Company, Inc., New York, 1963. This section is from Chapter 12, "The Evolution of the Automobile."

particularly in connection with steering and ride. The engineers had to deal with front-end instability, scuffing of the treads, squeals on turns, driving under fast braking conditions, and a particular condition known as wheel tramp, caused by a slight imbalance of the rotating mass of tire and wheel. These phenomena did not show up as major problems until car owners began to take long road trips at high speeds.

During this development of modern, low-pressure tires, General Motors engineers made important contributions because of our many miles of test road work under varying conditions. The General Technical Committee from the start maintained close contact with the tire industry, cooperating in standardization of sizes, and in the establishment of the best types, treads, and sections. Our recommendations, based on our research, have been incorporated year after year in better and safer tires.

The second basic approach to the improvement of the ride, and one of greater engineering complexity, was by way of the suspension—the attachment of the wheels to the chassis.

In one of my early trips abroad, my attention was called to an engineering development used in the production of European cars: the independent springing of the front wheels. Up to that time, independent springing had not been used in production cars in the United States. The use of this principle, of course, would add considerably to the comfort of the ride.

In France I came in contact with an engineer named André Dubonnet, who had given considerable study to the matter and had taken out a patent on one form of independent springing. I brought him back to this country and put him in contact with our engineers.

Quite independently, Lawrence P. Fisher, then general manager of our Cadillac Division, had engaged a former Rolls-Royce engineer, Maurice Olley, who also was interested in working on the problem of ride. Mr. Olley recorded his recollections of the development of independent suspension in a letter he has written for me. I will continue the story in his words:

> [*Olley's letter below is reproduced exactly from Sloan's book including the comments in square brackets.*]

> You have asked for my recollections of independent suspension on General Motors cars.... You'll have to excuse the very personal atmosphere of the following notes, which may give the impression that independent suspension was a one-man show. It was very far from that, and owes a great deal to Henry Crane, Ernest Seaholm [chief engineer of Cadillac], Charles Kettering and a number of Cadillac and Buick engineers; also to the tolerance and constant support of L.P. Fisher, who accused the writer at that time of being the first man in GM to spend a quarter of a million dollars in building two experimental cars!

You will recall that I came from Rolls-Royce to Cadillac in November of 1930. Frankly I was surprised to find Rolls-Royce so popular. A Rolls-Royce car had just completed a phenomenal test at the new GM Proving Grounds, and had been torn down for inspection....

At Rolls-Royce, for the past several years, we had been engaged in a concentrated drive on riding quality. The British factory had become intrigued by this work because of the fact that cars which were considered acceptable on British roads, were far from acceptable when exported, even to the improved roads of the United States. And we were beginning to realize that this was not because ... American roads were worse, but because the waves in them were a different shape.

A great deal of work had been done at Rolls Royce along the lines of swinging cars from overhead pivots to measure their moments of inertia ... measuring the stiffness of chassis frames and coachwork ... and measuring the suspension rates of the springs as installed on the actual car. The British factory had also developed one of the first practical ride meters, which consisted simply in measuring how much water was lost from an open-topped container in a measured mile at various speeds.

Some of this practice had been carried over to Cadillac in 1930, and soon we also were swinging cars, measuring installed spring rates, etc. We also built ourselves a "bump rig," along the Rolls-Royce lines (the first in Detroit) and used it to produce a synthetic ride on a stationary car.

Early in 1932 we built the "k^2 rig" ... consisting of a complete seven-passenger limousine, on which it was possible, by moving weights, to produce any desired changes in relative deflection of front and rear springs and in the moment of inertia of the vehicle. No instrumentation was used on this to measure ride. With the assistance of Henry Crane, to check up on our efforts, we simply asked ourselves under which conditions we got the best ride.

This was the best method because we did not know then, and do not know today, what a good ride is, but we could make so many fundamental changes in ride on this vehicle in a single day's running, that our impressions remained fresh, and direct comparison was possible.

It was at this stage, early in 1932, that we began to feel the urge toward independent suspension. The k^2 rig was telling us, in no uncertain terms, that a flat ride which was an entirely new experience, was possible if we used front springs which were softer than the rear. But you will recall that all attempts to use extremely soft front springs with the conventional front axle fell down badly, because of shimmy ... and a general lack of stability in handling....

The next step after the k^2 rig therefore consisted in building two experimental Cadillac cars.... these had two different independent front suspensions.... [One of these was that developed by Mr. Dubonnet; the other, the "wishbone" type, we had developed.] An independent rear suspension was also used, as we had in mind that, as soon as possible, we should also get rid of the conventional rear axle (a change which in my own opinion is now several years overdue).

On these cars which were ridden by many of the Corporation engineers, it was evident that we had something very special in the way of improved ride and handling. We also ran into our usual share of troubles. The chief of these was the steering, which, especially on the wishbone suspension, was not free from shimmy.

We had to redesign the steering mechanism several times....

Finally, by March of 1933, we were ready for a full-dress demonstration. Early in March the General Technical Committee met at the Cadillac Engineering Building to ride our two experimental cars, and a Buick car without independent front suspension, but with an I.V. [infinitely variable] transmission....

I recall that [you] and Mr. Grant were riding one of the [wishbone type] cars, when Ernest Seaholm and I, in one of the accompanying cars, pulled up alongside [you] at the traffic light in River Rouge. We could see [you] smiling widely at Dick Grant [vice president of sales] in the rear seat, and moving the flat of [your] hand up and down [and] horizontally. Within two miles from the Cadillac plant the flat ride had sold itself.

After the run to Monroe and back on the three cars, the Committee sat at the Cadillac plant, and Seaholm and I, in the background, awaited the verdict, with the pious hope that Cadillac would be granted a clear year's run on the new suspension, ahead of the other divisions.

O. E. Hunt [vice president of engineering], I recall, led off by asking Mr. Grant what he thought of the new automatic transmission.

You will recall that in March of 1933 there was not a bank open in the United States, and anyone who owned a farm was thankful that at least he could eat. Under these circumstances Dick Grant's reaction was not surprising. He turned down the [automatic] transmission, and the hundred dollar cost that went with it, as something that a Buick buyer could very well do without. "But," said he, "if I could have a ride like you've shown us, for a matter of fifteen bucks, I'd find the money somehow."

Dutch Bower [chief engineer] at Buick had already put in his claim for the new front suspension, and the Oldsmobile and Pontiac engineers also seemed determined that they would show it in New York next November.

Then finally Bill Knudsen [the general manager of Chevrolet] declared in words of one syllable that Chevrolet [was] not going to be left out. O. E. Hunt tried to persuade him that there were not enough centerless grinding machines available in the United States to grind the wire for the coil springs for Chevrolet. But Knudsen was adamant, saying that the machine tool industry had been in a bad way for years, but they were going to be —— busy for the next year at least. And Chevrolet actually made the New York Show in November with their 1934 model on the Dubonnet suspension. Pontiac also inherited this suspension from Chevrolet, while the three other divisions adopted the wishbone suspension.

This meeting stays in my mind because it was such a tremendous demonstration of American enterprise in action. In the face of the conditions then existing, the millions of expenditure to which the Corporation was committing itself argued a type of courage which was new in my experience. I still remember Ket's statement, "It seems to me we can't afford *not* to do it."

We thus introduced simultaneously two different types of independent front wheel suspension. However, after some further improvements on the wishbone type, it became apparent that it was cheaper and easier to manufacture and more trouble-free in operation, and soon all our lines of cars adopted it.

Sense of Direction

"Bicycles hovered like moths in the head lamps."

Maurice Olley
On early motoring in England

Let's imagine ourselves back in 1900 and in Britain. Lots of sentimental nonsense is written about 1900 simply because it's getting to be a long time ago. The fact is (in a dignified Victorian way) hell was popping.

The South African war was on—Britain was torn between Imperialists and pro-Boers. Labor was becoming noisy, demanding "the 3-8's." Lloyd George had the reputation of another Welshman, Aneurin Bevan, today considered a traitor or a dangerous radical, dodging mobs in Manchester. Fifteen years later he saved Britain—as surely as Winston Churchill 25 years after that. And, like Churchill, was thrown out for his pains.

Britain was pushed off Free Trade by the fear of "unfavorable" trade balance. Income tax was threatening to reach 5%. Changing "hatreds." Closer to home: Cigarette lighters replacing matches. Soft collars. Creases in pants. End of century of "exploitation" (looting) of whole world, through agency of reciprocating steam engine.

One thing one can say for 1900—we did not raise our children in the atmosphere of suppressed horror and anxiety that afflicts the world today. We seem to have had the impression (quite erroneously, of course) that most of the world was comfortably well off.

But the ancestral peace of the countryside was being disturbed by "these newfangled motor cars."

Olley's notes for an informal talk given at a General Motors Institute Faculty and Staff Meeting, Flint, Michigan, May 22, 1957.

Let's go back even further.

Up to 1840 Britain had been ahead of the world in building and operating steam coach lines. But lacking rubber tires, these had knocked the roads to pieces, and had been killed by increasing turnpike tolls. (Chas. Goodyear insisted on being born 50 years too late to save us from railroads.)

After 1840 any "road locomotive" had to have a man walking ahead carrying a red flag—about as ingenious a way of killing a budding industry as I know of. Railroad interests were the pressure group that did it.

But by 1896 jealousy of French and German progress in automobiles had forced a change in the law. A universal speed limit of 20 mph was substituted. Twenty mph is still applied to trucks weighing more than 3 long tons, by special request of the truck drivers themselves, since by driving at 40 mph they can thus crowd more tea-breaks into a day's work.

By 1900 cars were being registered and drivers licensed by the hundreds on the strict understanding that all taxation and license receipts were to be applied to road maintenance. In 1900 policemen were already leaping out of hedges, eager to collect fines, and the cold war between the citizen and "The Law," hitherto a prerogative of the "lower classes," was now spreading to all classes of society, who have enjoyed it ever since.

In 1900 I was 11 years old, being raised in North Wales right at the side of the Holyhead Road, part of the road system built in the 18th century for the mail coaches, largely on foundations left by the Romans 1500 years before. (The "standard gauge" also is a legacy of the Romans.) Before 1900 these magnificent roads were regarded as outstanding examples of human folly. The Manifest Destiny of 1900 was the God-given right of every modern man to travel everywhere by steam train at one penny per mile (3rd class), or two pence (1st class). Except for a few bicycles and an occasional farm wagon, the entire road system lay white and silent, memorials to a dead past.

But now the roads were coming to life again! A thumping noise and jingling of driving chains down the road, and small boys would leap to doors and windows to see one of the new motor cars dash past, and to breathe the heady aroma of lamp oil which it left in its wake. The cars were chiefly French, with a few German. Practically no American. I had seen no more than a dozen American cars before coming to this country in 1917. Prejudice against American cars—prejudice against all American machinery—it looked "too cheap," applied to electrical machinery, machine tools, printing machines, bicycles, lawn mowers—they were designed to run for ten years, not for a century.

British car building started in 1900, about 20 years late. British bicycles already were exported all over the world (they still are) and naturally the motorcycle industry grew out of it. So the motorcycle had the lead over the car industry and with few exceptions has shown more ingenuity and originality ever since, and today has enormous export trade.

"Real" motor cars came more slowly in Britain. There was a mental block in the choice between steam, electric and "petrol" for motive power. Respectable and accredited engineers (with a reputation to lose) were all in favor of steam—because of loyalty to the past, and because steam was self-starting, free from gear shifting, free from electrical gadgets which, in the days when mica or hard rubber were the only insulators, habitually disliked a wet climate and, above all, steam was **silent**. Serpollet in France and White & Locomobile in this country were already building successful steam cars which held all the speed records. Second favorite was the electric. This was the only car a lady could drive and still remain a lady.

Petrol cars generally were voted "least likely to succeed." No responsible engineer could condone lighting a fire **inside** a machined cylinder, using piston as crosshead, or getting one power stroke out of four. Or building engines that had to be wound up like a child's toy, and then exploded and broke your wrist. Or driving through gears which had to be thrown together edgewise while the car was running. In view of the prejudice, it is remarkable that no successful steam cars were built in Britain. Steam coaches were. Probably new motor car builders were young men, without much money, who listened to their elders and betters, but then played it safe by copying French designs (which is exactly what Royce did).

No one approaching the age of discretion soon after the turn of the century could fail to take interest in new transportation. For one thing, the effect of the railroads was clearly disastrous. They had clotted the population in congested cities, while beautiful countryside lay all around almost deserted. British public with its total disregard for incidental discomforts of climate, took to motorcycles like ducks to water (and do so still). The automobile was more of a problem, involving two fundamental difficulties—first, getting several people to agree on where they wanted to go, and then there was the greater expense which, on British salaries, was a real drawback.

But in spite of aroused interest, I was not apprenticed into the automobile trade. A relative recommended machine tools, on the principle that you cannot go far wrong learning to make things, and that designing anything without this knowledge was impossible. So 1908–1912 was spent in Birmingham on machine tools and tool design, but always with one eye on the automobile and the other on the USA.

What cars were like—

Two ancestries—the plebeian and the aristocratic, the small and the large, the grown-up bicycle and the horseless town-carriage. No enclosure of any sort. No windshield. Leather upholstery, to shed rain. Tiller or wheel on the right, for some reason as left-hand road rule, or having the lady on the left to leave the sword arm free. Leaf springs. Mixed pride, fear, and extreme discomfort. Fear of the inevitable. Tires, ignition, chain breakage, carburetion (by lamp wicks), lamp failure (kerosene or acetylene). Excitement and danger of starting. Restless idling. Ensuing calm when under way.

The "upper classes" still used horses. They regarded automobiles with amused tolerance as one of the dirty habits of adolescents.

1912. To Rolls Royce as a tool designer. Amazing experience. An automobile for wealthy, and therefore respectable, people. Designed for perfection only—regardless of cost. Quiet, extremely reliable, and almost comfortable (at low speeds).

1913. Royce in the South of France. If Rolls Royce car had been interesting, encounter with Royce was dazzling. The fountainhead of perfectionism. **Tooling machining of connecting rods** (circular fillers no good), grinding of camshafts, tapping of steering nuts. (Five-year contract with Royce for 3 months each year in USA).

1914. Isotta-Fraschini has front wheel brakes. Objections. Interference with steering—shimmy. First self-starters. Air and electric. Testing first non-metallic brake linings. Projected trip to USA via Stuttgart.

1914–18. World War I. First interruption. Aircraft engines—**Rolls-Royce perfectionism pays off**. Adventures of the Eagle.

1915. Reduction gears. German comments. Torsional damper led to Atlantic flight of Alcock and Brown in 1918.

1917–18. The USA at last. Liberty engine. (Day of Pentecost.)

1920–30. Rolls Royce in America. "Domestic" vs. "Imported." A peculiar national characteristic. Volkswagen almost made same mistake.

November 1930. Detroit. Cars looked black and ungainly. "Styling" in its infancy. New experience in **democratic chassis engineering**.

1933. Fundamentals of ride. Moment of inertia of sprung mass. IFS. Nature of shimmy known since 1925. Study of tire dynamics (Goodyear 1931). With IFS front springs could be softened without shimmy.

1937. England again. An education in passenger car fundamentals. Chiefly, question of **size**, "scale" and spring deflection. Small cars did not need so much spring deflection (shorter seesaw). Making small cars low enough to look decent and still contain human beings. Hence frameless construction (inevitable here also). Developing an integral body frame on the torsion and bending rig.

1939. World War II. Second interruption. Return to Rolls-Royce Ltd., work on leave of absence. Merlin engine five times as powerful as Eagle. How the IC engine had grown up from the automobile engine of 1900! Turbocharger. Rolls-Royce installation engineer says, "When we put in turbocharger we shall leave the engine out." Questions of whether to change details to American standards. Wright Field says "No!" Tanks, tracklayers, and tank engines.

1945. Britain again (another step in education). Crippled, colorless, lacking paint, food, clothing, hosiery, coal—lacking everything but courage, a sense of humor, and some of the best fish in the world. Working in drawing offices at 32°F (winter '46/'47). Overcoats and suits with too many pockets or pockets on the wrong side. Had forgotten how to make garden forks, wooden casks, cart wheels.

Ruled dictatorially by a Labor gout who "managed" everything from chicken runs to national meat purchasing, and exasperated everyone in the process. Would turn a man off his farm after generations of ownership if his methods were old-fashioned. Sold electrical gadgets without coal or power to supply them. Raised pigs and then had them all killed. Built "garden cities" on vital farmland. But did some things excellently. Infant feeding, and national health insurance.

"Export or starve." 75% passenger cars. 60% trucks. Hence a worldwide viewpoint, with test results from Australia, South Africa, the Sahara, the Middle East, the dust of India, mud of the Tropics. Britain, Germany, France, Italy have now set the automobile standards of the world. America excluded from this movement by the "dollar barrier"— as impenetrable as the "iron curtain." Our cars—once, in the days of the Model T the standard of the world—are now scarcely taken seriously outside North America.

After half a century of engineering it is interesting to look back and wonder how much of the tumult and shouting has been worthwhile. For instance, the first stages of making expensive cars for the rich seemed a bit pointless. But it paid off in World War I.

The vagaries of the automobile industry during the last 50 years has been as good as a circus. Two distinct eras, each marked by the development of a logical design to the point of absurdity.

The first, now called the "classical" era, marked by supremacy of the chassis engineers, who took a defective mechanism and made it into an impressive-looking road locomotive which was silent, reliable, supremely accessible, and a joy **to a mechanical engineer**. Rather less than a joy to the public. Yearly models were the last thing they were looking for. Some models remained fundamentally unchanged for 15 or 20 years. The proud trademark and badge of ownership was the radiator. By the time the hood and cowl occupied half the wheelbase length, **and a car without this feature was unsaleable** whether it had a large engine or not, the chassis engineers were reaching their point of absurdity. They failed to take account of the human beings who paid for the car. These unfortunates were crowded into a tight little box perched above and behind the rear wheels. In side view the whole contraption appeared to be falling over backward. These also were the days of the drivers' schools, devoted to the elaborate care and feeding of their particular chassis. And of the large and complex instruction book which assumed that the owner or driver would devote the rest of his life to attendance on this particular car. (**But** working on one's own car increases intimacy and therefore loyalty.)

Now we appear to be nearing the end of a second era—the Age of the Stylists. One admired these young radicals, when in 1930 they started to clear up the mess left by the chassis engineers. They were aided by two things—the car hoist which gave access to the chassis from below, and independent suspension which cleared the way for the **forward and downward movement of the whole car on its wheels**. This has been their main theme during the whole of their reign.

Unfortunately, as with so many human activities, this movement also has been carried to the point of absurdity. The great increase in overall length and width, with masses of chrome plated "art work" stuck on either end, and without any corresponding increase in wheelbase, has converted our cars into Toonerville Trolleys, with poor results on handling. Worst of all, from the point of view of sales, the personalities of the various makes have been lost by loss of the distinctive radiator. Like being married to a woman who has to have her face lifted and hair re-colored every year. The roofs have been depressed 1/2 inch per year for 30 years, with too little regard for human dimensions and the directions in which humans can be bent with comfort and dignity. Entrance to American, as in European, cars is now a matter of "putting them on." Entrance to the front seat with the present windshield pillars demands an attitude appropriate to the backhouse rather than the living room. A comparatively small area of the car can be sat in, but the trunk now becomes more and more like the body of a pickup truck. The congestion of mechanical parts up forward becomes worse and worse, and the engine, far from being accessible, can barely be seen. And the paddle-box up forward, with the shaft tunnel in the rear, now virtually divides the car in two down the middle so that the middle passengers ride it like a bicycle.

Where do we go from here?

A crisis in engineering comparable with nothing since 1900 when we had three sources of power and two distinct types of vehicle, the true motor car and the cycle car. Today we have three possible engines and two vehicle types, large and small, American and European. All the world outside North America is being conditioned to accept the small car. Europe is designing cars to suit cities, rather than rebuilding cities to suit cars.

By 1980—200 million people in USA, 88 million automobiles (1 for 2½), 84 billion gallons of fuel per year.

Materials. Raising hardness and raising stresses. Peening. Getting rid of cast iron in favor of light alloys (are in the midst of this). But cast crankshafts in "improved" iron, call it "nodular" or "inoculated," or what have you? Modulus above 28 million. Get rid of nickel, copper, tin, lead, etc. Use the non-metallics as in Germany. Frameless construction—of course, whatever material, aluminum or steel sheet. Plastics in frameless appear doubtful. Plastics make a good panel but a poor post.

Where to put engine?

(1) **Front engine - rear drive**. Cuts car in two. But good for truck and station wagon.

(2) **Front engine - front drive**. Long hood. Passengers shoved into rear end again. Front tires too busy. Hooking on turns. Expensive.

(3) **Rear engine - rear drive. Means turning car around and driving it backward**. Who would notice? Reduced head resistance. Better traction and braking. Inexpensive. Collision risks? Baggage space. Roof racks.

Alternative power. Caris' SAE paper of last March [*c. 1956*] is most instructive. New engines show little promise for passenger cars, except will get piston engine designers really waked up to developing piston engine to limit of its capacity, for producing maximum power from minimum space at lowest cost (outboard motors). Ability of some of the turbine engines to divide themselves in two is overrated. Means instead of messing up only one end of car will mess up both ends. To get rid of shaft tunnel at cost of an obstructed hood **and** obstructed trunk is a poor exchange.

What **size** of piston engine? Assuming we can get the weight down from 4000 to 3000 pounds, then 250 peak horsepower can accelerate at the limit of traction of the rear tires on a dry road, up to 60 mph. Does this seem reasonable? Not good for tires, and to **maintain** even 80 mph takes only about 50 horsepower. Considering fuel costs, probably 50–100 horsepower with transmissions that don't need manual shifting will be considered enough for most cars. But real performers will need 250 cubic inch engines giving a horsepower per cubic inch.

Transmissions. Europeans showing some clutchless transmissions which do pretty well without excessive power loss.

Suspension. Air springing certain, with leveling and big reductions in spring rate.

Steering. Hydraulic.

Brakes. Disc—on wheels.

Conclusion: Automobile now 70 years old, since the first gas-buggy pioneers. Not quite as set in its ways as the railroads were 70 years ago, but equally sure of itself as the one ultimate form of general transportation. The railroads ignored the fact that they could never carry anyone or anything **all the way**. When passengers left the trains, the railroads washed their hands of them (the airlines are showing better sense).

But in its way, the automobile trade is also doing an ostrich act. It ignores the fact that "rocketing away in a rocket to the joys of the open road" has been a fantastic dream for 30 years past. The open road is either an endless chain or a plugged pipeline.

Parking in downtown areas has become an expensive luxury or an impossibility. The automobile requires as much parking space as its owner does office space to earn his living.

USA sets out to build more roads, and wider streets, destroying valuable acreage in the process. But smaller, poorer and perhaps wiser countries, like Britain, Belgium, Holland, cannot afford to give up more valuable farmland to unproductive concrete. They want to know why a single individual should be entitled to take up 120 square feet of road space and parking space to get himself to work.

Legal actions of all sorts have hamstrung the railroads and the legal actions of many sorts may equally hamstring the automobile. It seems that we should pay more attention to the relation between its actual useful carrying capacity and the space it occupies on the road. For one thing, the passengers might sit a little more upright rather than lying on their backs, and why trail around that enormous trunk when it is so seldom used?

What to teach? The automobile in some form or another, probably reduced in size from its present dropsical condition, will be with us for a long time. So, what to teach the rising generation about it?

(1)   That we don't really know how to build motor cars.

(2)   That engineering is not a science, but an art supported by the sciences.

As an illustration: How many times have we been annoyed when a man who obviously does not understand what he is doing, yet turns out designs which work, frequently better than our own? Simply because, without accurate knowledge, he yet has a "feeling" for his job. Example:

a.   O. E. Hunt and the Allison connecting rod.
b.   Royce's accurate description of detonation in 1913! Twenty-seven years before first pictures were taken.

(3)   That we know less about what goes on in and under a motorcar than we did 25 years ago. We used to be able to run without floorboards, fenders and hoods and actually **see** what was happening. For 25 years we have been forced to speculate or use instruments. Development of new test methods and instrumentation is in its infancy.

(4)   The automobile has been the product of some reasonably intelligent mechanics and practical engineers, and has corresponding qualities and defects.

(5)   It is up to the rising generation to detect what has been wrong with our ideas. They must avoid the two extremes of making the thing a road locomotive as we did in our heyday, or making it an overgrown opportunity for vulgar display, as is done today.

(6)   As an efficient container it must have a powerplant of minimum size and weight, for the performance required, and must be economical to operate. The days of 12–15 mpg cannot go on forever.

(7)   The application of the sciences to engineering techniques must help and not hinder them. Otherwise the mechanics will take the job away from the scientists and do it themselves, just as they did in 1905 when young mechanics took the gas-buggy away from the accredited engineers and made it work.

(8)   Must avoid the ultra-scientific idea that we can improve only what we can **measure**. We do not use 2-cycle engines because they stink. But we cannot measure smell. We have improved appearance and ride, but cannot measure them.

(9)   What to do with new instrumentation techniques?

    a.   Reduce noise.
    b.   Investigate dynamics of ride and handling.
    c.   Understand the pneumatic tire, manufacture it consistently, and predict its performance.
    d.   Reduce wind resistance without increasing instability.
    e.   Perhaps understand a little more of the production processes.
    f.   Understand friction and lubrication about which we know practically nothing.
    g.   Most important is "synthetic instrumentation." The use of analogs, so we no longer just find what **has** happened, but predict what **will** happen when we make changes.

(10)   Prediction of future trends is dangerous ground because engineering is an **art**.

Who would have predicted even ten years ago that a monstrous model of two discolored cornflakes outside the Styling Section at the Tech Center would today be considered artistic rather than purely absurd? The only predictable thing about the automobile industry, like the Michigan weather, will be its infinite variety.

Development of the Flat Ride

"I think the solution is that for a flat ride at, say, 40 mph, you use a front end much softer than the rear, for a flat ride at 100 mph you use almost equal front and rear deflections."

Maurice Olley, July 16, 1959

It all started with the Rolls-Royce chassis dynamometer. Since about 1911 all Rolls-Royce car chassis had been tested for power, carburetor adjustments, etc. by setting the rear wheels on a pair of steel drums or rolls, of four-foot diameter mounted on a common axle, the power being absorbed by a suitable dynamometer.

It was found desirable also to arrange a pair of rolls to be driven by a car engine and transmission, for fatigue testing of suspension parts, frames, steering linkage, etc. For this work, cams of suitable rounded shapes, having lifts of two inches or so, were bolted to the rolls. Driving the rolls by the car engine was preferable to an electric motor drive because the engine of the period was fitted with a centrifugal governor, and capable of accurate speed adjustments, whereas sensitive speed regulation of electric motors had not yet arrived. This was the original "bump rig." This fatigue testing was a low-frequency cycle, about 100 cpm [*cycles per minute*].

"Low speed wobble," a rather lazy flapping of the front wheels at about 250 cpm had always been common, occurring most frequently at about 12–15 mph. It could be cured simply by adding a little kingpin friction by means of a plain thrust washer on each kingpin. Its only effect was a slight discomfort as the front of the car oscillated laterally. In later vehicles more violent forms of this same oscillation have been encountered, occurring at higher frequencies and at speeds over 50 mph. So the modern name is "caster wobble." In caster wobble there is little "tramping" of the axle.

Olley's hand-printed original of this paper, written Nov. 29–Dec. 6, 1967, is in the MRA library. The three figures were scanned from the original and retouched slightly, primarily to remove stray marks.

With the coming of front wheel brakes and balloon tires in the twenties, the much more disturbing "shimmy" appeared. On a smooth road with front wheels carefully balanced, the car might be traveling at 60 or 70 mph. Suddenly, for no apparent reason (perhaps a small dip or pothole passing under one front wheel), the steering wheel would be wrenched out of the driver's hands, and would start oscillating violently, while each front wheel would leap along the road in giant ten foot jumps. The front axle would be tramping at 550–600 cpm, each front wheel jumping three inches into the air. Attempting to hold the steering wheel tight would increase the oscillation. So would applying the foot brake. The handbrake [*rear only*] was the only safe way of restoring order.

And shimmy was destructive. It could break Pitman arms, and cause fantastic tire wear patterns. After a shimmy one could walk back along the road and see alternate scallop markings of burnt rubber, with curling crumbs of rubber, all along the track of the car.

There were all sorts of "explanations" of the shimmy cycle. W.A. Robotham of Rolls-Royce, around 1925, set himself to examine shimmy on the bump rig using **smooth** drums, but an unbalance in both front wheels, and examining the sequences of the self-induced shimmy vibration with a homemade stroboscope. As, due to small differences in tire diameter, the two unbalance weights crept toward "opposition," the front axle would suddenly leap into the shimmy cycle.

This would build up to a maximum, and then, as the weights worked toward a parallel position, the shimmy would die out. If the shimmy were especially violent it could hold the weights in opposition and continue indefinitely.

The cycle was always that the downward moving wheel contacted the road **toed-in** (as much as ten degrees). The road contact swerved the wheel out through as much as twenty degrees very rapidly, causing a gyroscopic torque due to the forced precession of **both** wheels. And this torque lifted the down wheel, and slammed its opposite number down on the road in the toed-in position, which continued and built up the cycle.

Wetting even just one roll would stop the shimmy instantly. Removing the tie rod between the wheels made it impossible to excite shimmy. Instead there occurred various forms of mild caster wobble. Increasing the caster angle, increasing toe-in of the wheels, deflating tires to lengthen the contact with the roll, softening front springs, etc., were all unfavorable.

Softening the steering linkage, with spring ends on the links was favorable. So particularly was the "shimmy shackle." Lightening the front wheels, brake drums and tires (reducing their polar moments) was very favorable.

Friction in the kingpins, so successful with caster wobble, was completely inadequate to deal with shimmy. (Strangely enough, on modern front axles there seems no evidence of shimmy, except in cases of gross neglect. Reduced wheel inertia? Reduced caster? Increased damping in power steering? I don't know.)

The use of the bump rig to solve the problems of shimmy, was brought by me to Detroit in 1930, and a bump rig was set up in the Cadillac experimental shop. A whole program of resonance testing was started, using small exciter cams on the rolls, or plain rolls with a "flying-wedge" between tire and roll to start an oscillation which might be self-exciting. Oscillations of the unsprung masses were studied, and presently, using parallel cam settings, we were examining the excitation of the basic riding frequencies of pitch and bounce.

We were learning something about road bumps. The **length** of the cams was almost as important as the **height**. The shape of the cams was not very important provided they were moderately rounded at either end. The frequency of excitation was all-important, and in general so was the wheel speed, i.e., with two cams per roll the excitation was much greater than with four cams.

By applying the appropriate frequency at the front wheels we could produce wheel hop at about 600 cpm, or a pitching of the sprung mass at 90 to 110 cpm. Or with alternately spaced cams, we could produce severe tramp and "wheelfight" at 550–600 cpm.

In all types of wheel hop there was a marked difference in amplitude between speeding up and slowing down. At increasing frequency the hop seemed reluctant to start and then came in suddenly. At decreasing frequency the hop could continue to increase down to quite low frequencies, which explained the violent "brake hop" which sometimes occurred when slowing down on washboard gravel. The excitation of pitch on the bump rig was remarkable in giving a passenger in the rear seat most of the sensations of a thoroughly uncomfortable ride. In other words the typical car of the period, with stiff front and soft rear springs, was excellently suited to disturb the rear passengers by oscillations in pitch. And these were present to a certain extent on almost all road surfaces, and were sometimes combined with the slower bounce oscillations in such a phasing as to give the rear passengers a "kick" like an ejector seat on a plane. Hence driver's advice to rear passengers, "If you're thrown through the top, don't come back, it makes two holes!"

The rear wheels could be similarly excited on the bump rig by parallel or alternate cam settings, exciting bounce of the sprung mass or hopping of the unsprung, according to the frequency.

Rear unsprung had the same "bouncing ball" tendency to persist and increase down to low frequencies at decreasing roll speeds. But rear axle hop has several bad habits of its own. Even when excited by parallel cam settings, rear axles had a persistent tendency to tramp. In certain conditions this would take the form of one wheel riding almost smoothly while the opposite wheel was tramping violently. This was a combination of parallel hop and tramping and could be studied at leisure on the bump rig.

A De Dion axle, or removing the differential assembly from the standard rear axle vastly reduces the tramping frequency. This isn't because of reducing the unsprung mass. It's due to increasing the $k^2/(\text{track})^2$ ratio of the axle. A similar quietening tendency can be produced on the standard rear axle by **adding** weights outside the wheel hubs.

On alternate cam settings the standard axle tramps vigorously, but differences in response are very marked when the roll steer characteristics of the rear suspension are altered. Roll understeer has a strong tendency to increase axle-tramp, and a small roll oversteer setting can produce wonderful reductions in tramp and consequent improvements in ride and handling.

In the 1920s there was much study of the papers of H.S. Rowell and James Guest[71] on the oscillations of the sprung mass. They had pointed out the influence on the ride of the k^2/ab ratio of the sprung mass and of the front and rear spring deflections on the frequencies of pitch and bounce, and on the position of the oscillation centers about which these motions occurred. Also that the only way "pure" simple-harmonic-motion **pitch** motion could be produced was by excitation at the **bounce** center, and vice versa.

A simple spring suspended model confirmed everything they said. And by exciting either end of the car by cams under the front or rear wheels, on the bump rig at the appropriate frequencies, we found we could produce such close approximations to pure pitch or bounce that we could establish the two oscillation centers by observation and measurement. (We had previously swung the car on wire cables from the line-shafting to obtain the radius of gyration of the sprung mass.)

The results of observing and riding the cars on the bump rig were disquieting to say the least.

Since the earliest days of the industry nearly all cars had been sprung stiffly up front, under the engine, and softly at the rear under the passengers. Superficially this seemed reasonable. But what struck us first about it was the possibility of a severe kick at the rear seat due to the simultaneous occurrence of pitch and bounce thus—

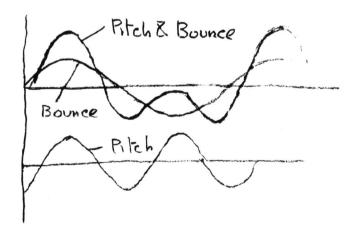

---

[71] See Chapter 5, page 304.

We knew from experience that a motion rather like this did occur at the rear seat.

The thing we had missed was that the excitation at front and rear did not occur simultaneously. The actual case was more like this—

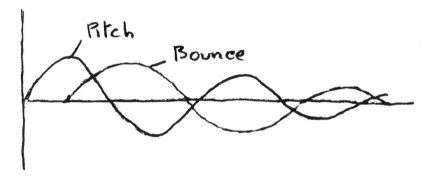

—with the angle of crossing of the two wave lines representing the severity of the pitch.

By arranging the suspension with the lower frequency in front, this motion could be changed to—

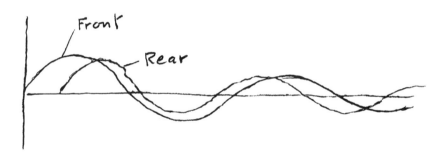

—a much closer approach to a "flat" ride.

Rowell in his paper[71] had emphasized the importance of the k^2/ab ratio on riding quality. With $k^2/ab = 1.0$ the oscillation centers are in the planes of the front and rear axles. Consequently a pitching motion occurring at the front does not tend to develop into a mixed bounce and pitch. And similarly a bounce at the rear tends to remain there as a simple harmonic motion.

Rowell pointed out that it was possible to build a car and suspension which would have only one natural frequency, so that all riding motions would be truly simple harmonic. To do this would require the sprung mass to have k^2/ab equal to 1.0, **and** equal spring deflections front and rear.

The Cadillac "k^2 rig" of 1931 was built to test the Rowell theories (and anything else we could find) actually on the roads. The car was a Cadillac 12-cylinder, seven-passenger limousine of the period, fitted with front and rear outriggers and 720 pounds in 60 pound weights, which could be stored in the car or distributed on the outriggers at will. The car was sprung so that with all weights in the car, or equally distributed on the outriggers the spring deflection was equal front and rear. As I recall we started with about 4-1/2 inch deflection and later resprung it for 6 inch deflection. With a k^2/ab of 1.0 this would give a frequency of 77 cpm.

The k^2/ab ratio of the standard model of the period was about .70. And the car with its outriggers empty and all weights inside was about the same. But with the weights all on outriggers the k^2/ab, as I recall, was about 1.10. So we had an opportunity to explore Rowell's single frequency idea of $k^2/ab = 1$ and equal deflections.

The surprise was that, under these supposedly ideal conditions, the ride was universally condemned as being unsatisfactory. A car sprung this way has no fixed oscillation centers, so the ride has no "pattern." It appeared to us therefore that a "good ride" was not a negative quality, not just an absence of certain vertical and angular accelerations. A good ride was rather something one could **enjoy**. More like the "good action" of a horse.

By filling the front outriggers with all the weights it would take and leaving the others behind we obtained a front spring deflection some 30% greater than the rear, and, at the same time had a k^2/ab of about .80. This gave us a ride which, for those days, was a revelation, on all types of road.

On the bump rig excitation of the front wheels now gave us a slow bounce frequency about an oscillation center several feet back of the rear bumper. And excitation of the rear wheels produced a pitch frequency with its oscillation center at about the front toe board. The sequence was like the last of the previous sketches and gave the impression of a "flat ride."

With the conventional leaf spring front axle there were objections to softening the front springs. First, the springs permitted by the overall car design were too short to permit softening without encountering excessive stresses. Then the windup of such short springs when braking led to even greater stresses, to reversal of the caster angle, to great errors in steering geometry, to unmanageable brake swerve. Finally, the lateral separation of the front springs was only about half the wheel track, so that their "roll rate" was only about a quarter of what it would have been if the spring rate had been applied in the plane of the wheels, as is done in an independent suspension. This low front roll rate led to an almost complete lack of "feel" at the steering wheel. Also the disproportionate roll couple carried by the rear tires caused oversteer on hard turns.

These objections were not insuperable. Roll stabilizers could restore the roll-rate, and several devices could be used to get accurate steering geometry. But probably the final argument was that it was desired to move the entire sprung mass of the car some 30 inches forward on its wheelbase, thus bringing the rear passengers forward of the rear wheels, permitting three-place rear seats, with a wider body, extinguishing the running boards, and allowing a permanent rear trunk as part of the body. This meant that the plane of the front wheels was about halfway along the length of the engine, so there was no room for a front axle and tie rod, with their necessary bump clearance, below the engine. Hence the change to independent front suspension.

So much for the front end. But the rear end also needed attention. The conventional "Hotchkiss" rear end of the 1930 era had a poor reputation for handling. This was because the two soft rear springs generally had positive camber and upturned eyes, giving a geometry causing roll oversteer at the rear. By lowering the front end of the rear springs, and in some cases by changing to a downturned front eye, the rear axle geometry could be changed to roll understeer.

Cars were arranged so that these geometry changes could be made swiftly on the road. And it was apparent that the change to understeer made an enormous improvement in road-feel at the steering wheel and in handling. It was also apparent that this change was strictly limited by the fact that understeer geometry increased axle tramp both in riding and particularly in braking. Also, this new geometry increased "harshness" in the ride due to the rear wheel center moving forward as it moved upward. As already stated the tramping tendency could be mastered by changing to a De Dion axle. But there were objections to the increased cost of the De Dion, the four additional universal joints, etc.

The three original Cadillac experimental cars of 1933 had parallel independent suspensions front and rear. Two forms of front suspension were used, the "wishbone" (Mercedes) type and the Dubonnet. Each had advantages, but the first type was lighter and less expensive and had better structural strength. The parallel independent rear suspension had a delightful ride, but there were problems in tire wear and in handling.

Further Notes on the Three Experimental Cadillacs.

It had been demonstrated on the k^2 rig that there was no appreciable difference in ride (when the springing conditions were right) between a k^2/ab ratio of .80 and 1.0. On the experimental cars the best combination for a flat ride appeared to be a front deflection of eight inches and rear of six inches. But because so much riding is done with only two passengers it is usual on larger American cars to go softer than this with front deflection of ten inches and rear of eight and a half to nine inches at full load.

$$\text{Deflection noted is } \frac{\text{Sprung load per wheel}(\text{lb.})}{\text{Rate}(\text{springs only})\text{ at this load}(\text{lb.}/\text{in.})}$$

Under these conditions the conventional leaf spring front axle could not be used and IFS was the most practical solution. And it was appreciated at once that there was an extra bonus in IFS, since the "rolling" of the front wheel planes on turns provided increased understeer.

It was found that evaluation of ride under artificial or specialized conditions of road excitation was futile. Even proving ground "ride roads" didn't work out. The best way was to take a group of four or five for a considerable trip on the open road, concrete, blacktop and gravel, and to change riding positions frequently. On the k^2 rig many changes were made on the road in relative spring deflections and in moment of inertia. When a strong preference developed for riding in the rear seat and letting somebody else drive, we were beginning to gain success!

Since the 1930s, cars have lengthened but wheelbases have shortened, so that nowadays the wheelbase is only about 5/8ths of the overall car length. Consequently the k^2/ab ratio even on the larger cars is close to 1.0. On smaller models this ratio tends to be even higher. Since the car has to contain humans, scaling down of the vehicle in strict proportion is not practical. The smaller models have to be "dumpier" in shape, and the height of the CG from the ground remains about the same in all models. One result is that, for a given pitch stability in braking, the smaller has to have less spring deflection. And, because of the constant CG height this reduced deflection cannot be in strict proportion to the wheelbase but more nearly as the square of the wheelbase, meaning that the ride **frequencies** tend to vary inversely with the wheelbase. The larger car therefore tends to ride better not because of its weight, but because of its size.

Vans

On delivery vans of the present popular type there has been a return to the leaf spring front axle. The riding quality can be acceptable without the use of very soft front springs because the k^2/ab of the sprung mass approaches 1.30, which slows down the pitch frequency. Also there is always considerable weight on the front springs, so that these are stiff enough (and long enough) to avoid severe brake wind-up. Lightly loaded rear springs, with big variation in rear load present a problem and there is a danger of brake somersaults at light loads.

Unsprung Masses

A low unsprung mass is not necessarily an advantage. A higher frequency wheel hop is more uncomfortable and more difficult to control. The unsprung mass serves as a useful barrier between the innumerable small impulses received by the tire and the sprung mass of the car. However, the unsprung mass does become significant in, say, the case of the rear of an unladen flat-bed truck, where the unsprung mass of the axle may be at least equal to the sprung mass riding on it.

IFS succeeds, not by reducing unsprung mass, but by providing only one form and one frequency of wheel hop, and by removing any significant coupling of this with camber change and gyroscopic reaction.

Tramp of the conventional rear axle is mostly due to the mass of the differential carrier at the axle center. It is increased by an "understeer" geometry in the axle control linkage, i.e., by making the axle "face left" when the car rolls to the right, and vice versa. The De Dion axle is one solution. Any form of IRS is another, but has one difficulty, namely about double the roll rate of a conventional rear axle with the usual spring separation. A car with IRS is liable to carry too much of the total overturning couple in cornering on the rear tires.

Shock Absorbers

Double acting arm type shock absorbers were just coming into use in the 1930s. Previously hydraulic shock absorbers had been mostly designed to "snub" the rebound only. Delco Products was introducing in 1930 the Rolls-Royce type of horizontal cylinder double acting shock absorber with end-to-end discharge. In the "wishbone" type of IFS this design was adapted to use as the upper arm of the suspension, with a manual control from the driver's seat. We were able to confirm the contention of Delco Products engineers that the least damping was the best damping. Any damping interferes to some extent with the natural ride action of the car. Any elasticity in the damping interferes with the control, particularly of the higher frequencies such as wheel hop.

The direct acting ("flit-gun" type) shock absorbers in the early stages showed their superiority in controlling wheel hop by regularly blowing up after a few minutes on the bump rig. They have since been enormously improved. But still they are a separate device which "fights" the suspension movements in both directions, bump and rebound.

It is evidently much better in principle to incorporate the damping in the suspension, actually compressing the spring or its equivalent through the pressure in the damping fluid, as in the Citroën DS or the BMC Hydrolastic suspensions.

Index

About the Authors

Doug Milliken grew up in the heady atmosphere of basic vehicle stability and control research at CAL/Calspan, first in the flight hangar and later with ground vehicle activity. During the same period he attended numerous motor races including time in the pits and garage with the Formula One teams at Watkins Glen and work with a Trans-Am race team (2.5 liter). He received a B.S. from Massachusetts Institute of Technology in 1977 and joined Milliken Research Associates (MRA) shortly thereafter. Projects at MRA include mechanical design and fabrication of prototypes and instrumentation; and test and development work including planning, design, driving and data analysis. He has experience with a wide range of vehicles including bicycles, record-breaking streamlined human powered vehicles, motorcycles, production and race cars, active control cars, automotive simulators and trucks of various sizes. He currently manages the vehicle dynamics and analysis activity at MRA.

Bill Milliken studied mechanical engineering at the University of Maine, and received a B.S. in mathematics/aeronautical engineering from Massachusetts Institute of Technology in 1934. He also took private pilot training at the Boeing School of Aeronautics. He was successively employed at MIT, Chance Vought, Vought-Sikorsky, Boeing Aircraft, Avion/Northrup, Curtiss-Wright, and CAL/Calspan—20 years in aircraft stability and control/flight tests, including pioneering work in stability augmentation and variable stability. Since then he has been involved with automotive stability and control, first at CAL/Calspan and then at Milliken Research Associates, Inc. (MRA), the company he founded in 1976 to continue this work. He designed, built and crashed his own airplane and has competed in more than 100 post-war road races and hill climbs.

Comments and corrections can be sent to the authors in care of their corporate website, http://www.millikenresearch.com.